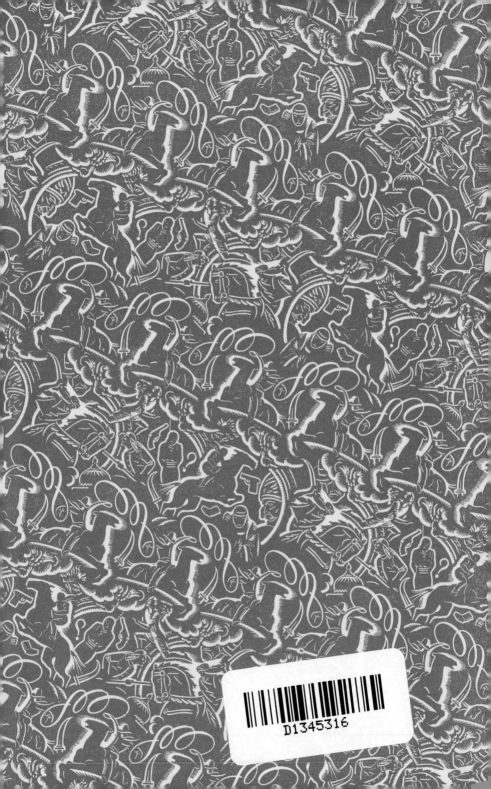

FIFTY TRUE STORIES
STRANGER THAN
FICTION

In bounded the lions.

See p. 450.

FIFTY
TRUE STORIES

STRANGER THAN FICTION

ODHAMS PRESS LTD.
LONG ACRE, LONDON, W.C.2

Copyright 1936

G 1136
Printed in Great Britain

CONTENTS

8   CONTENTS

ILLUSTRATIONS

ACKNOWLEDGMENTS

The Editor wishes to express his thanks for permission to include in this volume stories by the following authors :

TREVOR ALLEN, *Romance in the Underworld* : to George Newnes Ltd.

RT. HON. WINSTON CHURCHILL, *My Escape from the Boers* (from *My Early Life*) : to the Author and Thornton Butterworth Ltd.

SIR HUGH CLIFFORD, *The Death March of Kûlop Sûmbing* (from *Blackwood's Magazine*) : to Lady Clifford and William Blackwood & Sons Ltd.

A. C. COLLODON, *Thrills on a Windjammer* : to Sampson, Low, Marston & Co. Ltd.

ROGER COURTNEY, *The Forest of Illusion* (from *Claws of Africa*) : to the Author and George G. Harrap & Co. Ltd.

ALEC DIXON, *Dope in Chinatown* (from *Singapore Patrol*) : to the Author and George G. Harrap & Co. Ltd.

BOB DYKER, *The Red Indians' Dance of Death* and *Saving a Worthless Life* : to Sampson, Low, Marston & Co. Ltd.

PERCEVAL GIBBON, *The Trader of Last Notch* (from *Blackwood's Magazine*) : to the Author.

ASHLEY GIBSON & H. F. FENN, *The Hunting of Ngagi* (from *Blackwood's Magazine*) : to the Authors and William Blackwood & Sons Ltd.

AMIR HABIBULLAH, *The Man who Snatched a Throne* : to Sampson, Low, Marston & Co. Ltd.

SIR HENRY RIDER HAGGARD, *Major Wilson's Last Fight* (from *The Red True Story Book*) : to Longmans Green & Co. Ltd.

H. K. HALES, *A Race for a Bride* : to Sampson, Low, Marston & Co. Ltd.

JO HALLAM, *Illegal Cargo*, *The " Greaser " Meets his Match* and *A Narrow Escape from Death* : to Sampson, Low, Marston & Co. Ltd.

LEONARD HANDLEY, *Tanoy, Prince of Poachers* : to Macmillan & Co. Ltd.

MAJOR a.d. FRANZ MASKE, *The Whirl of Fate* (from *On the Run*) : to Capt. H. C. Armstrong and Rich & Cowan Ltd.

WILLIAM G. JOHNSON, *He Laughed at Death* (from *Everyman at War*) : to the Author and J. M. Dent & Sons Ltd.

MRS. BELLOC LOWNDES, *Where Platonic Love May Lead a Man* : to the Author.

WESTON MARTYR, *Facing Death on the Georges Shoals* (from *Tales of Hazard*) : to the Author and John Lane, The Bodley Head Ltd.

DOUGLAS McHARDIE, *Trading in Death* : to Sampson, Low, Marston & Co. Ltd.

R. McKINLEY, *The End of the Baron* : to Falcon Books.

JAMES MILLIGAN, *Lynch Law in the West, Dead Men Tell no Tales* and *On the Spot* : to Sampson, Low, Marston & Co. Ltd.

AXEL MUNTHE, *The Plague at Naples* (from *the Story of San Michele*) : to the Author and John Murray.

CAPT. RAGNAR NYBERG, *The Mystery of the " Ear," Mysteries in the South Sea Islands* and *The Severed Hand* : to Hurst and Blackett Ltd.

" TIGER " O'REILLY, *Ambush* and *The Den of Death* : to Sampson, Low, Marston & Co. Ltd.

DARE du BOIS PHILLIPS, *The Secrets of the Cards* : to John Lane, The Bodley Head Ltd. *The Crossing of the Casitas Pass* and *The Death Valley—The Gates of Hell* : to Sampson, Low, Marston & Co. Ltd.

PETULENGRO, *Michael Collins Gambles with Death, Log of a Hell Ship* and *The Passing of Arthur* : to Sampson, Low, Marston & Co. Ltd.

" POUSSE CAILLOUX," *Retaliation* (from *Blackwood's Magazine*) : to the Author and William Blackwood & Sons Ltd.

P. L. RICHARD, *The Prince of Escapers* (from *On the Run*) : to Capt. H. C. Armstrong and Rich & Cowan Ltd.

" LORD " GEORGE SANGER, *The Circus People Take Revenge* and *The Lions are Loose !* (from *Seventy Years a Showman*) : to J. M. Dent & Sons Ltd.

EX-SUPERINTENDENT PERCY SAVAGE, *How the German Spy Organisation was Smashed* : to Hutchinson & Co. Ltd.

" SELIM," *White Man's Ground* (from *Blackwood's Magazine*) : to the Author and William Blackwood & Sons Ltd.

" SHALIMAR," *The Timber Drogher* (from *Blackwood's Magazine*) : to the Author and William Blackwood & Sons Ltd.

" SINBAD," *A Modern Treasure Hunt* (from *A Modern Sinbad*) : to the Author and George G. Harrap & Co. Ltd.

FRED WALKER, *The Luck of an Earthquake* (from *Destination Unknown*) : to the Author and George G. Harrap & Co. Ltd.

P. C. WREN, *Twenty-Four Hours in the Foreign Legion* (from *Tales of Hazard*) : to the Author and John Lane, The Bodley Head Ltd.

EX-LEGIONNAIRE 1384, *The Death of Me-Too* : to Sampson, Low, Marston & Co. Ltd.

TWENTY-FOUR HOURS IN THE FOREIGN LEGION

By
P. C. WREN

I WENT to the *Bureau de Recrutement* in the Rue St. Dominique for enlistment in the Legion, and, to be quite fair and honest, I fully admit that the recruiting officer there made no secret of the fact that he thought I was a fool. I thought it was very decent of him. He didn't actually try to deter me from joining ; but he mentioned casually that the Foreign Legion was rather the Spiritual Home of the labourer, the long-service professional soldier, and the man who had really roughed it in earnest. He added that he would be very glad to enlist me, in view of my inches and enthusiasm, but I must go away and sleep on it, think it over in the light of what he had said, and return next day if I were still of the same foolish mind.

I returned. I was vetted *bon pour le service* by the Medical Corps doctor, and enlisted. I had contracted to serve France for five years in any part of her colonial possessions for the sum of a halfpenny a day, without deductions or income tax.

Purely in the spirit of romance and make-believe—for I was not fleeing from Justice—I took a name that was not my own. Most légionnaires do this. A few, because they are fugitive criminals and the vast majority for the same reason that small boys wear black masks or feather head-dresses when playing robbers or Red Indians.

I travelled that night to Fort St. Jean at Marseilles, the bureau depôt and clearing-house of the XIX Army Corps, which is the Army of Africa. Here, it is true, I found dirt, discomfort, fatigues, nasty menial, manual labour, and somewhat rough contemptuous treatment ; but what did these things matter ? My barracks was a moated medieval castle, within sight of Monte Cristo's Chateau d'If, and my companions were wearing the most romantic and attractive uniforms in the world !

15

Every branch and service of the French Army was represented, and if the noise were reminiscent of a parrot house, so
were the colourfulness and the exotic sights and sounds.
There were spahis, in incredibly gorgeous dress, Zouaves,
Turcos, Tirailleurs, Chasseurs d'Afrique, Colonial Infantry,
Gunners, Sappers and Légionnaires : and undoubtedly the
parrots could swear—as well as eat, drink and flutter gay
plumage.

I was thrilled, and couldn't see or hear enough of these
men who brought a breath of so strange and different a life
from across the sea—men who had marched and served and
fought in such strange places—men from Africa ! And I
thought of a Latin tag from schoolboy days : " There's
always something new from Africa."

I made no friends among the recruits on our way to join
the Legion. Frankly, I didn't like the look of them. Nor
did I gather that they particularly liked the look of me. They
were mostly unshaven, unwashed, collarless men, rather
rough, rather dirty, and with ways that differed widely from
those to which I had been accustomed. They were entirely
foreign to me in speech and habits, and some of them reminded
me of the sea-captain's terse official report on the manners and
customs of the Cannibal Islanders : " Manners none and
customs nasty ! "

After a few days at Fort St. Jean we were shipped across
to Oran in Algeria, and taken thence by train eighty miles
inland, to Sidi bel Abbès, the depôt of the 1st Battalion.

Here things were different. We had our uniforms now,
and uniform was a great leveller. We were all soon shaved
and clean and shining bright. Every one understood French,
which was the *lingua franca*, and one quickly found one's own
level, and companions of one's own sort and kind. That is
one of the marvels of the Legion. Every nation is represented :
and not only every class, but every sort and kind, every rank
and trade and profession. I was most enthusiastic, and derived
endless interest from observing my comrades—the most
incredibly mixed assemblage of men on the face of the earth.
They included not only people of all nations of Europe, but
even Chinese, Japanese, Arabs and assorted Africans.

I was glad when I completed a selection of representatives
of all five continents by meeting an Australian and more than
one American.

.   .   .   .   .   .

I have to tell you about one particular day of glorious

life in the Legion, and will first describe some of the men of my own *escouade*, my comrades of the day in question.

First of all, there was Pierre. You would have liked Pierre —one of the merriest souls I ever met. Nothing could damp his joyous cheerfulness, except wine, and that in sufficient quantity to quench him altogether. Pierre only ceased to be amusing when he could speak no more. Only at one stage of his long and happy journeys from sobriety to speechlessness was he ever a bore, and that was the moment—the inevitable moment—when he would tell you all about his murder. I am afraid the story must have been true, for he always told it in the same way and never varied a detail. And nothing could stop him.

"And to think how kind I always was to her," he would expostulate. "I hardly ever beat her when she didn't deserve it. She always had plenty to eat—when there was plenty ; and she frequently tasted wine—when I was asleep. . . . Why, I actually married the woman. And what did she do when my back was turned—and my stomach was being badly turned—while I was doing six months in The Box for borrowing money from a bourgeois, without telling him, one night, in the Place Pigalle ? She went off with Tou-Tou-Boil-the-Cat, the lieutenant of our band. Fact. She did. She won't again though. I went after her when I came out.

"'Your heart's in the right place, my love,' I said. 'It's your head that leads you astray.' Then I cut it off. *Oui, Monsieur*. I, Pierre Pompom held her up by her hair with my right hand—so—and cut her head off. . . . *Psstt !* Yes. With this very knife."

And at this point Pierre would produce a knife from the back of his belt.

Yes, I believe Pierre was a murderer. But he was a very nice one to meet, and only made these *faux pas*—or talked about them—when not quite himself. I never met a braver man in my life. He was true as steel, a splendid comrade, and faithful unto death.

In curious contrast to him was Müller, a German—an aristocrat, an ex-officer and a typical Junker. He was as self-controlled and unemotional as Pierre was vivacious and flamboyant.

"Hans Müller," he called himself (though he was certainly *von* and *zu* and probably *Graf* or *Baron*, and possibly Hohenzollern or Hohenlohe). He was a man who simply hated to laugh with joy, or swear with rage, or to express

F.T.S.   B any emotion whatsoever. His exceedingly handsome face, with its cold blue eyes, high-bridged nose, golden moustache, hard mouth and fine chin, was a face that never changed—never smiled or frowned. And this wasn't by any means because he was stupid, stolid or phlegmatic : not a bit of it. He was an extremely clever man—musical, widely read, highly cultured, travelled, and, in the best sense of the word, a gentleman. I knew nothing of his life, but only of his death. Why he joined the Legion I don't know. But there was certainly a woman in his story. For in a quiet voice and with an expressionless face, he would speak most bitterly of women. And it was his intention to remain in the Foreign Legion until he died.

There was Ramon Diego, a very tough Spaniard from the Pyrénées, smuggler or smuggler's muleteer, known as " The Devil." And he *was* a devil—to fight, though unfortunately he would only fight with a knife. As he explained, it was the weapon he had been taught to use in childhood, and since then he had used no other. He was a big, dark, saturnine, smouldering sort of volcano, always about to erupt. Much respected by those who didn't care for knife fighting.

I was very fond of Ramon, a simple forthright soul.

Then there was " Ivan the Terrible "—six foot seven : I am not sure it wasn't six foot eight—weight unknown, as he always broke the machine. He had been a subaltern of the famous Preobrazhenski Regiment of the Imperial Guard (alas ! no more, I fear), and made no secret of how he came to the Legion. He went on leave, and followed a lady, of whose appearance he approved, the length of the Siberian Railway from Port Arthur to St. Petersburg, thence to Paris, on to Marseilles and across to Algiers.

There the dream had ended, probably with Ivan's money. And finding the French Legion nearer than his Russian Regiment, and probably much more likely to extend a welcome, Ivan had turned in with them, instead of going back. He was a great lad, with a heart of gold, a tongue of silver, a hand of iron, and a front of brass.

Torvaldsen the Dane was another fine fellow : so clean-looking and clean-living. A seeker of adventure.

Cortlandt, the Dutchman, unlike nearly all Dutchmen, was a bad lot, though he had had a lot to make him bad. And once he was up against a sergeant, his stubborn Dutch spirit kept him there. He used to drink a vile rice-spirit called *tchum-tchum*, which was, I suppose, the nearest thing he could get to *Schnapps*, and when he had had a drink or two of this poison, he would seek me out and remind me that the Dutch once sailed up the Medway. I invariably replied : " Never mind, Fatty. Nobody noticed them." And he would go away and think this over, with the help of more *tchum-tchum*, until he fell asleep.

What makes the particular day I am going to tell you about an outstanding one for me, is the fact that on it I lost these friends of mine, and though I hadn't known them long I missed them badly ; also because I got an interesting little souvenir scar on my head and an interesting little souvenir dagger which now decorates my study wall, having failed to decorate my stomach.

We were on the march, and in a hurry. We slept where we dined, and we dined where we fell down, after marching the whole of a terrible day, over sand. Although I had done some gruelling marches during training days and after, I thought of the warning of the recruiting officer in Paris. There *was*, as he had ironically said, " lots of sand ; blue sky ; no rain ; no snow ; no fog ; sunshine—sunshine all the time." Camels (glimpsed far off—with scouts on them), mirages, palms and oases (in the mirages), I thought not only of the recruiting officer, but of Coleridge's *Ancient Mariner* and his bitter complaint. You may know the verse beginning :

> " *And all in a hot and copper sky*
> *The bloody sun at noon*
> *Stood right above . . .*"

the whole beastly show. And at 4 a.m. next morning the buglers blew reveille, and this particular, slightly hazardous day in the Legion began.

I rolled over and dressed—by putting on my *képi*. I then slipped on my equipment, and was ready. I was particularly ready for my share of the contents of the pail brought from the company cooking-fire by Ivan the Terrible. It was hot, liquid, sweet, and had an unmistakable flavour of coffee. I dipped out a mugful of this heartening brew, and produced the remainder of my breakfast from my haversack. If I remember rightly, it was a hard, dry biscuit and some soft, wet macaroni.

We fell in by sections, each section in three ranks, so that when we got the order to right-turn and march, we marched

in threes, and not in columns of fours as the British Army does.
One long march is very like another, but this was more so than
most, by reason of the record length, the record heat, the
soft looseness of sand, and the fact that we were marching,
by compass, across sand-dunes, and were perpetually climbing
up one side and down the other, instead of marching on the
flat.

We were literally crossing an uncharted ocean—of sand ;
and its billows were as regular, numerous and monotonous
as those of any of the great ocean wastes of waters. However,
we realised that it was necessary to avoid the usual road or
caravan route, for we were hastening to the relif of a suddenly
beleaguered fort ; and the Arabs would no doubt be on the
watch for us on the road. We were a surprise-packet, posted
to arrive when and where least expected.

Nor did we march as the British soldier does under a
tropical sun, in pith helmets, half-sleeved open-necked shirts,
shorts and puttees. We wore cloth caps with a peak in front
and a white or khaki curtain hanging round the neck behind ;
thick, long, heavy overcoats buttoned right up to the throat ;
baggy trousers tucked into leggings ; thick heavy boots and
no socks. We were pretty well loaded, too, with long rifles,
long bayonets in steel sheaths, very big water-bottles, two
hundred rounds of ammunition, stuffed *musettes* or knapsacks,
containing spare kit, laden haversacks, canteens, and spare
pairs of boots. But besides these things each man had some
such extra load as part of a tent, firewood, or a cooking
vessel ; so that the top of the load on one's back rose as high
as the top of one's head—or higher, and bumped against it.
It took me a long time to get used to this.

No. We weren't a bit smart to look at, and there was no
march-discipline. We didn't march. We shuffled, shambled,
staggered, tottered, strolled, rolled, bowled and pitched along
any how. The one thing we didn't do was to straggle. The
pace was set and the pace kept and the slogan was " *Marchez
ou crevez !* " (" March or die "), for if you didn't march you
would most certainly die—of thirst and starvation if you were
lucky, or of Arabs if you weren't.

At the end of each hour the whistle blew and the little
column halted for " the cigarette-space," just time to smoke a
cigarette. In theory it was ten minutes in each hour.

During one longer halt, the cooks prepared a meal of a
sort of stew.

In time the strain began to tell, and it was just about when people were beginning to grumble that I realised that the recruiting officer had been premature in his sarcastic praises of desert life as regards the absence of fog. For, to the appalling heat and electrical atmospheric conditions, fog was added. A beastly oppressive choking fog—of dust, that diminished the circle of our horizon and rendered the almost unbearable conditions of marching even more unbearable.

" Sand storm," said the less experienced soldiers, but the old, long-service men growled that a sand storm wasn't a sand storm while you could see and breathe and march and weren't buried alive—or dead. This was nothing but a little dust !

It was truly awful anyway, and I plodded along, bent nearly double, not caring what particular name they gave it.

There was one thing to be thankful for, however. We were off the soft, shifting sand-dunes, and now marching across a level plain of hard, sand-covered ground. Between us and the sky was a veil of dust through which the sun did not so much shine as loom like a great ball of brass in the hot and coppery sky. And from time to time, great blinding clouds of sand enveloped us.

. . . . . .

I suppose it was owing to these conditions that the Arabs caught us as they did.

We had out a " point " and flankers, of course, but presumably the flankers were ridden down when plodding along, bent double, seeing nothing but the ground, and not caring if it snowed Arabs.

They seemed to come down the wind like the dust itself. There were a few shots, a whistle, one or two orders, and thanks to Legion drill and Legion discipline, the Arab charge was met in the right way, and just in time.

My own *escouade* was unlucky in happening to be opposite to the thickest part of the Arab line, and, in spite of the number of men and horses that our fire brought down, the remainder charged home with lance and sword, and long gun fired at short range from the hip—with a weird and wild war-cry of " *Lah illa il Allah ! Allahu Akbar !* " It sounded rather like a pack of jackals.

Just behind me the excellent Sergeant Krantz, a cool veteran, shouted his orders.

" Steady, now, steady ! Aim low. Shoot at the horses ! Aim low ! " until suddenly, for the best of reasons, he stopped.

I don't really remember very much of this particular

scrap. But I do remember the incredulity and the thrill at finding that I was actually taking part in a real good old-fashioned fight ; just the sort of thing one had read about.

" This is what I came for," I said to myself. " The genuine thing ! What splendid luck ! A real fight with real Arabs in a real desert ! It doesn't seem real."

But it was, and we got what is known to the vulgar as a " bellyful." Since the first shots and shouts it was only a matter of seconds, I suppose, when, with an earth-shaking thunder of hoofs, the leaders of the charge were upon us.

Suddenly I realised that a big bearded man in flowing, fluttering, dirty-white garments, with a nasty long lance was coming straight at me—me personally. I fired at him point-blank, and apparently missed him. Also his spear missed me, due to the fact that Pierre shot either him or his horse.

Quite unwounded, I was knocked head over heels, either by this horse or another, and got to my feet as an Arab, who had reined up, or whose horse had been wounded, made a cut at me with a sword. More by luck than judgment I parried the cut, the sword striking the curved cross-hilt of my bayonet. As I drew my rifle back to lunge, the Arab whirled up his sword and cut again ; and either my bayonet went in under his ribs below his raised sword-arm just before the blow fell, or else Ivan shot him from behind, just in time. Anyhow, the sword-cut which should have split my skull, only gave me a cut on the head.

As I staggered back, a bit dazed, a man on the ground grabbed my leg, tripped me up, and slashed at me with a dagger. He meant well—but was presumably a bit shaken by the fall that had sent his lance, rifle or gun flying from his hand—and only struck my cartridge pouch.

After an intimate minute with him I got the dagger.

Once more I rose to my feet and saw that the Arabs were in full flight—not in defeat, but according to their tip-and-run plan.

" Salvo " or rather " Volley fire " continued while they were in sight. It was not until the " Cease fire ! " sounded that I realised what this little fight had cost me personally.

Pierre was dead. The front of his coat was sodden with blood. Hans Müller was dead, with a hideous spear-wound in his throat. Ivan was dead, and, ironically in the case of so tigerishly brave a man, had his wound in his back. Torvaldsen was dead ; demonstrating in death what we had known

After an intimate minute with him I got the dagger.

of him in life—that he had a brain. Cortlandt, though not dead, was unconscious and dying, kicked on the head by a horse. Ramon was all right, and showed me the body of an Arab whom he had killed. The bayonet in Ramon's empty rifle had been bent double, and whipping out his knife, Ramon had done the Arab's business.

Kneeling beside this man, Ramon patted his face in a friendly manner.

" *A carne de lobo, diente de perra*," he grinned, as he felt the point of his knife. " For the flesh of a wolf, the tooth of a dog."

There was undoubtedly a good deal of the Arab in Ramon, for the Moors owned his part of Spain for five hundred years.

. . . . . .

I think that, for a little while at least, this violent interlude in our montony of misery did us good.

And after a brief rest, and the somewhat sketchy burial of our dead, we marched on again, talking of our miraculous escapes and wonderful deeds, until the heat and choking dust defeated us.

. . . . . .

At sunset the scorching wind dropped and the fog of dust slowly turned to a mere mist. When we could go no farther we camped for the night, or rather for a small part of it on a sandy plateau, scratching out a hasty square of trenches in the sand, posting sentries, and then just falling down and sleeping where we fell ; many too weary even to eat.

. . . . . .

My own personal cup was not yet quite full, as I was chosen for guard, and had to do two hours sentry-go forthwith.

Long before dawn we marched again, and when we reached the Fort it was to learn that its attackers had raised the siege and departed, probably at receiving news of the approach of the main body of the relieving force.

It was probably a tribe belonging to the besieging force, who, on their way home to bed, had encountered us.

So ended, very tamely, a nevertheless sufficiently strenuous twenty-four hours in the Legion—strenuous, but not, in the eyes of survivors of the Great War, particularly hazardous.

MY ESCAPE FROM THE BOERS

By
THE RT. HON. WINSTON CHURCHILL

In 1899 Mr. Winston Churchill was Press Correspondent to the " Morning Post " for the Boer War. On November 5th he and two companies of English soldiers were ambushed in an armoured train. Largely due to Mr. Churchill, the engine and forty wounded men escaped from the ambush, but he and the others were captured.

DURING the first three weeks of my captivity, although I was a party to all plans of revolt or escape, I was engaged in arguing with the Boer Authorities that they should release me as a Press Correspondent. They replied that I had forfeited my non-combatant status by the part I had taken in the armoured-train fight. I contended that I had not fired a shot and had been taken unarmed. This was strictly true. But the Natal newspapers had been captured by the Boers. These contained glowing accounts of my activities, and attributed the escape of the engine and the wounded entirely to me. General Joubert therefore intimated that even if I had not fired a shot myself, I had injured the Boer operations by freeing the engine, and that I must therefore be treated as a prisoner-of-war. As soon as I learned of this decision, in the first week of December, I resolved to escape.

I shall transcribe what I wrote at the time where I cannot improve upon it.

" The State Model Schools stood in the midst of a quadrangle, and were surrounded on two sides by an iron grille and on two by a corrugated-iron fence about ten feet high. These boundaries offered little obstacle to any one who possessed the activity of youth, but the fact that they were guarded on the inside by sentries, fifty yards apart, armed with rifle and revolver, made them a well-nigh insuperable barrier. No walls are so hard to pierce as living walls.

" After anxious reflection and continual watching, it was

discovered by several of the prisoners that when the sentries along the eastern side walked about on their beats they were at certain moments unable to see the top of a few yards of the wall near the small circular lavatory office which can be seen on the plan. The electric lights in the middle of the quadrangle brilliantly lighted the whole place, but the eastern wall was in shadow. The first thing was therefore to pass the two sentries near the office. It was necessary to hit off the exact moment when both their backs should be turned together. After the wall was scaled we should be in the garden of the villa next door. There the plan came to an end. Everything after this was vague and uncertain. How to get out of the garden, how to pass unnoticed through the streets, how to evade the patrols that surrounded the town, and above all how to cover the two hundred and eighty miles to the Portuguese frontier, were questions which would arise at a later stage."

" Together with Captain Haldane and Lieutenant Brockie I made an abortive attempt, not pushed with any decision, on December 11. There was no difficulty in getting into the circular office. But to climb out of it over the wall was a hazard of the sharpest character. Any one doing so must at the moment he was on the top of the wall be plainly visible to the sentries fifteen yards away, if they were in the right place and happened to look ! Whether the sentries would challenge or fire depended entirely upon their individual dispositions, and no one could tell what they would do. Nevertheless I was determined that nothing should stop my taking the plunge the next day. As the 12th wore away my fears crystallised more and more into desperation. In the evening, after my two friends had made an attempt, but had not found the moment propitious, I strolled across the quadrangle and secreted myself in the circular office. Through an aperture in the metal casing of which it was built I watched the sentries. For some time they remained stolid and obstructive. Then all of a sudden one turned and walked up to his comrade, and they began to talk. Their backs were turned.

" Now or never ! I stood on a ledge, seized the top of the wall with my hands, and drew myself up. Twice I let myself down again in sickly hesitation, and then with a third resolve scrambled up and over. My waistcoat got entangled with the ornamental metal-work on the top. I had to pause for an appreciable moment to extricate myself. In this posture I had one parting glimpse of the sentries still talking with their backs turned fifteen yards away. One of them was lighting his cigarette, and I remember the glow on the inside of his hands as a distinct impression which my mind recorded. Then I lowered myself lightly down into the adjoining garden and crouched among the shrubs. I was free ! The first step had been taken, and it was irrevocable. It now remained to await the arrival of my comrades. The bushes in the garden gave a good deal of cover, and in the moonlight their shadows fell dark on the ground. I lay here

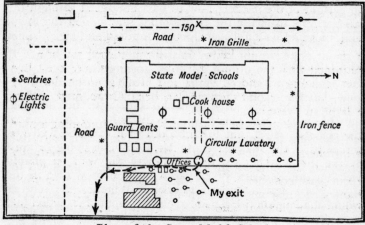

Plan of the State Model Schools.

for an hour in great impatience and anxiety. People were continually moving about in the garden, and once a man came and apparently looked straight at me only a few yards away. Where were the others ? Why did they not make the attempt ?

" Suddenly I heard a voice from within the quadrangle say, quite loud, ' All up.' I crawled back to the wall. Two officers were walking up and down inside, jabbering Latin words, laughing and talking all manner of nonsense—amid which I caught my name. I risked a cough. One of the officers immediately began to chatter alone. The other said, slowly and clearly, ' They cannot get out. The sentry suspects. It's all up. Can you get back again ? ' But now all my fears fell from me at once. To go back was impossible.

I could not hope to climb the wall unnoticed. There was no helpful ledge on the outside. Fate pointed onwards. Besides, I said to myself, ' Of course, I shall be recaptured, but I will at least have a run for my money.' I said to the officers, ' I shall go on alone.'

" Now I was in the right mood for these undertakings— failure being almost certain, no odds against success affected me. All risks were less than the certainty. A glance at the plan will show that the gate which led into the road was only a few yards from another sentry. I said to myself, ' *Toujours de l'audace*,' put my hat on my head, strode into the middle of the garden, walked past the windows of the house without any attempt at concealment, and so went through the gate and turned to the left. I passed the sentry at less than five yards. Most of them knew me by sight. Whether he looked at me or not I do not know, for I never turned my head. I restrained with the utmost difficulty an impulse to run. But after walking a hundred yards and hearing no challenge, I knew that the second obstacle had been surmounted. I was at large in Pretoria.

" I walked on leisurely through the night, humming a tune and choosing the middle of the road. The streets were full of burghers, but they paid no attention to me. Gradually I reached the suburbs, and on a little bridge I sat down to reflect and consider. I was in the heart of the enemy's country. I knew no one to whom I could apply for succour. Nearly three hundred miles stretched between me and Delagoa Bay. My escape must be known at dawn. Pursuit would be immediate. Yet all exits were barred. The town was picketed, the country was patrolled, the trains were searched, the line was guarded. I wore a civilian brown flannel suit. I had seventy-five pounds in my pocket and four slabs of chocolate, but the compass and the map which might have guided me, the opium tablets and meat lozenges which should have sustained me, were in my friends' pockets in the State Model Schools. Worst of all, I could not speak a word of Dutch or Kaffir, and how was I to get food or direction ?

" But when hope had departed, fear had gone as well. I formed a plan. I would find the Delagoa Bay Railway. Without map or compass, I must follow that in spite of the pickets. I looked at the stars. Orion shone brightly. Scarcely a year before he had guided me when lost in the desert to the banks of the Nile. He had given me water. Now he should lead to freedom. I could not endure the want of either.

"After walking south for half a mile I struck the railway.
Was it the line to Delagoa Bay or the Pietersburg branch?
If it were the former, it should run east. But, so far as I
could see, this line ran northwards. Still, it might be only
winding its way out among the hills. I resolved to follow
it. The night was delicious. A cool breeze fanned my face,
and a wild feeling of exhilaration took hold of me. At any
rate, I was free, if only for an hour. That was something.
The fascination of the adventure grew. Unless the stars in
their courses fought for me, I could not escape. Where, then,
was the need of caution? I marched briskly along the line.
Here and there the lights of a picket fire gleamed. Every
bridge had its watchers. But I passed them all, making very
short *détours* at the dangerous places, and really taking
scarcely any precautions. Perhaps that was the reason I
succeeded.

"As I walked I extended my plan. I could not march
three hundred miles to the frontier. I would board a train
in motion and hide under the seats, on the roof, on the
couplings—anywhere. I thought of Paul Bultitude's escape
from school in *Vice Versa*. I saw myself emerging from under
the seat, and bribing or persuading some fat first-class
passenger to help me. What train should I take? The first,
of course. After walking for two hours I perceived the signal
lights of a station. I left the line, and circling round it, hid
in the ditch by the track about two hundred yards beyond
the platform. I argued that the train would stop at the
station and that it would not have got up too much speed by
the time it reached me. An hour passed. I began to grow
impatient. Suddenly I heard the whistle and the approaching
rattle. Then the great yellow headlights of the engine flashed
into view. The train waited five minutes at the station, and
started again with much noise and steaming. I crouched by
the track. I rehearsed the act in my mind. I must wait until
the engine had passed, otherwise I should be seen. Then I
must make a dash for the carriages.

"The train started slowly, but gathered speed sooner than
I had expected. The flaring lights drew swiftly near. The
rattle became a roar. The dark mass hung for a second
above me. The engine-driver silhouetted against his furnace
glow, the black profile of the engine, the clouds of steam
rushed past. Then I hurled myself on the trucks, clutched
at something, missed, clutched again, missed again, grasped
some sort of hand-hold, was swung off my feet—my toes

bumping on the line, and with a struggle seated myself on the couplings of the fifth truck from the front of the train. It was a goods train, and the trucks were full of sacks, soft sacks covered with coal-dust. They were in fact bags filled with empty coal bags going back to their colliery. I crawled on top and burrowed in among them. In five minutes I was completely buried. The sacks were warm and comfortable. Perhaps the engine-driver had seen me rush up to the train and would give the alarm at the next station ; on the other hand, perhaps not. Where was the train going to ? Where would it be unloaded ? Would it be searched ? Was it on the Delagoa Bay line ? What should I do in the morning ? Ah, never mind that. Sufficient for the night was the luck thereof. Fresh plans for fresh contingencies. I resolved to sleep, nor can I imagine a more pleasing lullaby than the clatter of the train that carries an escaping prisoner at twenty miles an hour away from the enemy's capital.

" How long I slept I do not know, but I woke up suddenly with all feelings of exhilaration gone, and only the consciousness of oppressive difficulties heavy on me. I must leave the train before daybreak, so that I could drink at a pool and find some hiding-place while it was still dark. I would not run the risk of being unloaded with the coal bags. Another night I would board another train. I crawled from my cosy hiding-place among the sacks and sat again on the couplings. The train was running at a fair speed, but I felt it was time to leave it. I took hold of the iron handle at the back of the truck, pulled strongly with my left hand, and sprang. My feet struck the ground in two gigantic strides, and the next instant I was sprawling in the ditch considerably shaken but unhurt. The train, my faithful ally of the night, hurried on its journey.

" It was still dark. I was in the middle of a wide valley, surrounded by low hills, and carpeted with high grass drenched in dew. I searched for water in the nearest gully, and soon found a clear pool. I was very thirsty, but long after I had quenched my thrist I continued to drink, that I might have sufficient for the whole day.

" Presently the dawn began to break, and the sky to the east grew yellow and red, slashed across with heavy black clouds. I saw with relief that the railway ran steadily towards the sunrise. I had taken the right line, after all.

" Having drunk my fill, I set out for the hills, among which I hoped to find some hiding-place, and as it became broad daylight I entered a small grove of trees which grew on the side of a deep ravine. Here I resolved to wait till dusk. I had one consolation : no one in the world knew where I was —I did not know myself. It was now four o'clock. Fourteen hours lay between me and the night. My impatience to proceed while I was still strong doubled their length. At first it was terribly cold, but by degrees the sun gained power, and by ten o'clock the heat was oppressive. My sole companion was a gigantic vulture, who manifested an extravagant interest in my condition, and made hideous and ominous gurglings from time to time. From my lofty position I commanded a view of the whole valley. A little tin-roofed town lay three miles to the westward. Scattered farmsteads, each with a clump of trees, relieved the monotony of the undulating ground. At the foot of the hill stood a Kaffir kraal, and the figures of its inhabitants dotted the patches of cultivation or surrounded the droves of goats and cows which fed on the pasture. . . . During the day I ate one slab of chocolate, which, with the heat, produced a violent thirst. The pool was hardly half a mile away, but I dared not leave the shelter of the little wood, for I could see the figures of white men riding or walking occasionally across the valley, and once a Boer came and fired two shots at birds close to my hiding-place. But no one discovered me.

" The elation and the excitement of the previous night had burnt away, and a chilling reaction followed. I was very hungry, for I had had no dinner before starting, and chocolate though it sustains does not satisfy. I had scarcely slept, but yet my heart beat so fiercely and I was so nervous and perplexed about the future that I could not rest. I thought of all the chances that lay against me ; I dreaded and detested more than words can express the prospect of being caught and dragged back to Pretoria. I found no comfort in any of the philosophical ideas which some men parade in their hours of ease and strength and safety. They seemed only fair-weather friends. I realised with awful force that no exercise of my own feeble wit and strength could save me from my enemies, and that without the assistance of that High Power which interferes in the eternal sequence of causes and effects more often than we are always prone to admit, I could never succeed. I prayed long and earnestly for help and guidance. My prayer, as it seems to me, was swiftly and wonderfully answered."

I wrote these lines many years ago while the impression
of the adventure was strong upon me. Then I could tell no
more. To have done so would have compromised the liberty
and perhaps the lives of those who had helped me. For many
years these reasons have disappeared. The time has come
when I can relate the events which followed, and which
changed my nearly hopeless position into one of superior
advantage.

During the day I had watched the railway with attention.
I saw two or three trains pass along it each way. I argued
that the same number would pass at night. I resolved to
board one of these. I thought I could improve on my procedure of the previous evening. I had observed how slowly
the trains, particularly long goods trains, climbed some of the
steep gradients. Sometimes they were hardly going at a
foot pace. It would probably be easy to choose a point
where the line was not only on an up grade but also on a
curve. Thus I could board some truck on the convex side of
the train when both the engine and the guard's van were
bent away, and when consequently neither the engine-driver
nor the guard would see me. This plan seemed to me in every
respect sound. I saw myself leaving the train again before
dawn, having been carried forward another sixty or seventy
miles during the night. That would be scarcely one hundred
and fifty miles from the frontier. And why should not the
process be repeated ? Where was the flaw ? I could not see
it. With three long bounds on three successive nights I could
be in Portuguese territory. Meanwhile I still had two or
three slabs of chocolate and a pocketful of crumbled biscuit—
enough, that is to say, to keep body and soul together at a
pinch without running the awful risk of recapture entailed
by accosting a single human being. In this mood I watched
with increasing impatience the arrival of darkness.

The long day reached its close at last. The western clouds
flushed into fire ; the shadows of the hills stretched out across
the valley ; a ponderous Boer wagon with its long team
crawled slowly along the track towards the township, the
Kaffirs collected their herds and drew them round their kraal :
the daylight died, and soon it was quite dark. Then, and not
until then, I set forth. I hurried to the railway line, scrambling
along through the boulders and high grass and pausing on my
way to drink at a stream of sweet cold water. I made my way
to the place where I had seen the trains crawling so slowly
up the slope, and soon found a point where the curve of the

F.T.S.   C track fulfilled all the conditions of my plan. Here, behind a little bush, I sat down and waited hopefully. An hour passed ; two hours passed ; three hours—and yet no train. Six hours had now elapsed since the last, whose time I had carefully noted, had gone by. Surely one was due. Another hour slipped away. Still no train ! My plan began to crumble and my hopes to ooze out of me. After all, was it not quite possible that no trains ran on this part of the line during the dark hours ? This was in fact the case, and I might well have continued to wait in vain till daylight. However, between twelve and one in the morning I lost patience and started along the track, resolved to cover at any rate ten or fifteen miles of my journey. I did not make much progress. Every bridge was guarded by armed men ; every few miles were huts. At intervals there were stations with tin-roofed villages clustered around them. All the veldt was bathed in the bright rays of the full moon, and to avoid these dangerous places I had to make wide circuits and even to creep along the ground. Leaving the railroad I fell into bogs and swamps, brushed through high grass dripping with dew, and waded across the streams over which the bridges carried the railway. I was soon drenched to the waist. I had been able to take very little exercise during my month's imprisonment, and I was quickly tired with walking and with want of food and sleep. Presently I approached a station. It was a mere platform in the veldt, with two or three buildings and huts around it. But laid up on the sidings, obviously for the night, were three long goods trains. Evidently the flow of traffic over the railway was uneven. These three trains, motionless in the moonlight, confirmed my fears that traffic was not maintained by night on this part of the line. Where, then, was my plan which in the afternoon had looked so fine and sure ?

It now occurred to me that I might board one of these stationary trains immediately, and hiding amid its freight be carried forward during the next day—and night too, if all were well. On the other hand, where were they going to ? Where would they stop ? Where would they be unloaded ? Once I entered a wagon my lot would be cast. I might find myself ignominiously unloaded and recaptured at Witbank or Middelburg, or at any station in the long two hundred miles which separated me from the frontier. It was necessary at all costs before taking such a step to find out where these trains were going. To do this I must penetrate the station, examine the labels on the trucks or on the merchandise, and see if I could extract any certain guidance from them. I crept up to the platform and got between two of the long trains on the siding. I was proceeding to examine the markings on the trucks when loud voices rapidly approaching on the outside of the trains filled me with fear. Several Kaffirs were laughing and shouting in their unmodulated tones, and I heard, as I thought, a European voice arguing or ordering. At anyrate, it was enough for me. I retreated between the two trains to the extreme end of the siding, and slipped stealthily but rapidly into the grass of the illimitable plain.

There was nothing for it but to plod on but in an increasingly purposeless and hopeless manner. I felt very miserable when I looked around and saw here and there the lights of houses and thought of the warmth and comfort within them, but knew that they meant only danger to me. Far off on the moonlit horizon there presently began to shine the row of six or eight big lights which marked either Witbank or Middelburg station. Out in the darkness to my left gleamed two or three fires. I was sure they were not the lights of houses, but how far off they were or what they were I could not be certain. The idea formed in my mind that they were the fires of a Kaffir kraal. Then I began to think that the best use I could make of my remaining strength would be to go to these Kaffirs. I had heard that they hated the Boers and were friendly to the British. At anyrate, they would probably not arrest me. They might give me food and a dry corner to sleep in. Although I could not speak a word of their language, yet I thought perhaps they might understand the value of a British bank-note. They might even be induced to help me. A guide, a pony—but, above all, rest, warmth, and food—such were the promptings which dominated my mind. So I set out towards the fires.

I must have walked a mile or so in this resolve before a realisation of its weakness and imprudence took possession of me. Then I turned back again to the railway line and retraced my steps perhaps half the distance. Then I stopped and sat down, completely baffled, destitute of any idea what to do or where to turn. Suddenly without the slightest reason all my doubts disappeared. It was certainly by no process of logic that they were dispelled. I just felt quite clear that I would go to the Kaffir kraal. I had sometimes in former years held a " Planchette " pencil and written while others had touched my wrist or hand. I acted in exactly the same unconscious or subconscious manner now.

I walked on rapidly towards the fires, which I had in the first instance thought were not more than a couple of miles from the railway line. I soon found they were much farther away than that. After about an hour or an hour and a half they still seemed almost as far off as ever. But I persevered, and presently between two and three o'clock in the morning I perceived that they were not the fires of a Kaffir kraal. The angular outline of buildings began to draw out against them, and soon I saw that I was approaching a group of houses around the mouth of a coal-mine. The wheel which worked the winding gear was plainly visible, and I could see that the fires which had led me so far were from the furnaces of the engines. Hard by, surrounded by one or two slighter structures, stood a small but substantial stone house two storeys high.

I halted in the wilderness to survey this scene and to revolve my action. It was still possible to turn back. But in that direction I saw nothing but the prospect of further futile wanderings terminated by hunger, fever, discovery, or surrender. On the other hand, here in front was a chance. I had heard it said before I escaped that in the mining district of Witbank and Middelburg there were a certain number of English residents who had been suffered to remain in the country in order to keep the mines working. Had I been led to one of these ? What did this house which frowned dark and inscrutable upon me contain ? A Briton or a Boer ; a friend or a foe ? Nor did this exhaust the possibilities. I had my seventy-five pounds in English notes in my pocket. If I revealed my identity, I thought that I could give reasonable assurance of a thousand. I might find some indifferent neutral-minded person who out of good nature or for a large sum of money would aid me in my bitter and desperate need. Certainly I would try to make what bargain I could now— now while I still had the strength to plead my cause and perhaps to extricate myself if the results were adverse. Still the odds were heavy against me, and it was with faltering and reluctant steps that I walked out of the shimmering gloom of the veldt into the light of the furnace fires, advanced towards the silent house, and struck with my fist upon the door.

There was a pause. Then I knocked again. And almost immediately a light sprang up above and an upper window opened.

" *Wer ist da ?* " cried a man's voice.

I felt the shock of disappointment and consternation to my fingers.

" I want help ; I have had an accident," I replied.

Some muttering followed. Then I heard steps descending the stairs, the bolt of the door was drawn, the lock was turned. It was opened abruptly, and in the darkness of the passage a tall man hastily attired, with a pale face and dark moustache, stood before me.

" What do you want ? " he said, this time in English.

I had now to think of something to say. I wanted above all to get into parley with this man, to get matters in such a state that instead of raising an alarm and summoning others he would discuss things quietly.

" I am a burgher," I began. " I have had an accident. I was going to join my commando at Komati Poort. I have fallen off the train. We were skylarking. I have been unconscious for hours. I think I have dislocated my shoulder."

It is astonishing how one thinks of these things. This story leapt out as if I had learnt it by heart. Yet I had not the slightest idea what I was going to say or what the next sentence would be.

The stranger regarded me intently, and after some hesitation said at length, " Well, come in." He retreated a little into the darkness of the passage, threw open a door on one side of it, and pointed with his left hand into a dark room. I walked past him and entered, wondering if it was to be my prison. He followed, struck a light, lit a lamp, and set it on the table at the far side of which I stood. I was in a small room, evidently a dining-room and office in one. I noticed besides the large table, a roll desk, two or three chairs, and one of those machines for making soda-water, consisting of two glass globes set one above the other and encased in thin wire-netting. On his end of the table my host had laid a revolver, which he had hitherto presumably been holding in his right hand.

" I think I'd like to know a little more about this railway accident of yours," he said, after a considerable pause.

" I think," I replied, " I had better tell you the truth."

" I think you had," he said slowly.

So I took the plunge and threw all I had upon the board.

" I am Winston Churchill, War Correspondent of the *Morning Post*. I escaped last night from Pretoria. I am making my way to the frontier." (Making my way!) " I have plenty of money. Will you help me?"

There was another long pause. My companion rose from the table slowly and locked the door. After this act, which struck me as unpromising, and was certainly ambiguous, he advanced upon me and suddenly held out his hand.

" Thank God you have come here ! It is the only house for twenty miles where you would not have been handed over. But we are all British here, and we will see you through."

It is easier to recall across the gulf of years the spasm of relief which swept over me, than it is to describe it. A moment before I had thought myself trapped ; and now friends, food, resources, aid, were all at my disposal. I felt like a drowning man pulled out of the water and informed he has won the Derby !

THE PLAGUE AT NAPLES

By
AXEL MUNTHE

When a fearful cholera plague broke out at Naples Dr. Axel Munthe was visiting Lapland. On hearing the news Dr. Munthe dashed at once to the assistance of the city.

IF anybody would care to know about my stay in Naples, he must look it up in " Letters from a Mourning City " if he can get hold of a copy, which is not probable, for the little book is long ago out of print and forgotten. I have just been reading myself with considerable interest these " Letters from Naples " as they were called in the Swedish original. I could not write such a book to-day to save my life. There is plenty of boyish boisterousness in these letters, there is also plenty of self-consciousness, not to say conceit. I was evidently rather pleased with myself for having rushed from Lapland to Naples at the moment when everybody else had left it. There is a good deal of swaggering how I went about night and day in the infected poor quarters, covered with lice, feeding on rotten fruit, sleeping in a filthy locanda. All this is quite true, I have nothing to retract, my description of Naples in cholera time is exact as I saw it with the eyes of an enthusiast.

But the description of myself is far less exact. I had the cheek to put in writing that I was not afraid of the cholera, not afraid of Death. I told a lie. I was horribly afraid of both from the first till the last. I described in the first letter how, half-faint from the stench of carbolic acid in the empty train, I stepped out on the deserted Piazza late in the evening, how I passed in the streets long convoys of carts and omnibuses filled with corpses on the way to the cholera cemetery, how I spent the whole night amongst the dying in the wretched fondaci of the slums. But there is no description of how a couple of hours after my arrival I was back once more in the station eagerly inquiring for the first train for Rome, for Calabria, for the Abruzzi, for anywhere, the farther the better,

only to get out of this hell. Had there been a train there
would have been no " Letters from a Mourning City." As it
was, there was no train till noon the next day, the com-
munications with the infected city having been almost cut
off. There was nothing to do but to have a swim at Santa
Lucia at sunrise and to return to the slums with a cool head
but still trembling with fear. In the afternoon my offer to
serve on the staff of the cholera hospital of Santa Maddalena
was accepted. Two days later I vanished from the hospital
having discovered that the right place for me was not among
the dying in the hospital, but among the dying in the slums.

How much easier it would have been for them and for me,
thought I, if only their agony was not so long, so terrible !
There they were lying for hours, for days in stadium algidum,
cold as corpses, with wide-open eyes and wide-open mouths, to
all appearances dead and yet still alive. Did they feel
anything, did they understand anything ? So much the
better for the few who could still swallow the teaspoonful
of laudanum one of the volunteers of the Croce Bianca
rushed in to pour into their mouths. It might at least finish
them off before the soldiers and the half-drunk beccamorti
came at night to throw them all in a heap in the immense
pit on the Camposanto dei Colerosi. How many were
thrown there alive ? Hundreds, I should say. They all
looked exactly alike, I myself was often unable to say if they
were dead or alive. There was no time to lose, there were
dozens of them in every slum, the orders were strict, they all
had to be buried in the night.

As the epidemic approached its climax I had no longer
any reason for complaining that their agony was so long.
Soon they began to fall down in the streets as if struck by
lightning, to be picked up by the police and driven to the
cholera hospital to die there a few hours later. The cabby
who drove me in the morning in tearing spirits to the convict
prison of Granatello, near Portici and was to take me back
to Naples, was lying dead in his cab when I came to look for
him in the evening. Nobody wanted to have anything to do
with him in Portici, nobody wanted to help me to get him
out of the cab. I had to climb on to the box and drive him
back to Naples myself. Nobody wanted to have anything
to do with him there either, it ended by my having to drive
him to the cholera cemetery before I could get rid of him.

Often when I returned in the evening to the locanda, I
was so tired that I threw myself on the bed as I was, without

On the filthy floor of the cave sat half a dozen enormous rats.

undressing, without even washing myself. What was the good of washing in this filthy water, what was the good of disinfecting myself when everybody and everything around me was infected, the food I ate, the water I drank, the bed I slept in, the very air I breathed ! Often I was too frightened to go to bed, too frightened to be alone. I had to rush out into the street again, to spend the remainder of the night in one of the churches. Santa Maria del Carmine was my favourite night-quarter, the best sleep I have ever had I have had on a bench in the left-side aisle of that old church. There were plenty of churches to sleep in when I dared not go home. All the hundreds of churches and chapels of Naples were open the whole night, ablaze with votive candles and thronged with people. All their hundreds of Madonnas and saints were hard at work night and day to visit the dying in their respective quarters. Woe to them if they ventured to appear in the quarter of one of their rivals ! Even the venerable Madonna della Colera who had saved the city in the terrible epidemic of 1834, had been hissed a few days before at Bianchi Nuovi.

But it was not only of the cholera I was afraid. I was also terrified from first to last of the rats. They seemed just as much at home in the fondaci, bassi and sotterranei of the slums as the wretched human beings who lived and died there. To be just, they were on the whole inoffensive and well-behaved rats, at least with the living, attending to their business of scavengers, handed over to them alone since the time of the Romans, the only members of the community who were sure to get their fill. They were as tame as cats and almost as big. Once I came upon an old woman, nothing but skin and bones, almost naked, lying on a rotten straw-mattress in a semi-dark sort of grotto. I was told she was the " vavama," the grandmother. She was paralysed and totally blind, she had been lying there for years. On the filthy floor of the cave sat, on their haunches, half a dozen enormous rats in a circle round their unmentionable morning meal. They looked quite placidly at me, without moving an inch. The old woman stretched out her skeleton arm and screamed in a hoarse voice : " pane ! pane ! "

But when the sanitary commission started on its vain attempt to disinfect the sewers, the situation changed, my fear grew into terror. Millions of rats who had been living unmolested in the sewers since the time of the Romans, invaded the lower part of the town. Intoxicated by the sulphur fumes and the carbolic acid, they rushed about the slums like mad dogs. They did not look like any rats I had ever seen before, they were quite bald with extraordinarily long red tails, fierce blood-shot eyes and pointed black teeth as long as the teeth of a ferret. If you hit them with your stick, they would turn round and hang on to the stick like a bulldog. Never in my life have I been so afraid of any animal as I was of these mad rats, for I am sure they were mad. The whole Basso Porto quarter was in terror. Over one hundred severely bitten men, women and children were taken to the Pellegrini hospital the very first day of the invasion. Several small children were literally eaten up. I shall never forget a night in a fondaco in Vicolo della Duchessa. The room, the cave is the better word, was almost dark, only lit up by the little oil-lamp before the Madonna. The father had been dead for two days but the body was still lying there under a heap of rags, the family having succeeded in hiding him from the police in search of the dead to be taken to the cemetery, a common practice in the slums. I was sitting on the floor by the side of the daughter, beating off the rats with my stick. She was already quite cold, she was still conscious. I could hear the whole time the rats crunching at the body of the father. At last it made me so nervous that I had to put him upright in the corner like a grandfather clock. Soon the rats began again eating ravenously his feet and legs. I could not stand it any longer. Faint with fear I rushed away.

The Farmacia di San Gennaro was also a favourite haunt of mine when I was afraid to be alone. It was open night and day. Don Bartolo was always on his legs concocting his various mixtures and miraculous remedies from his row of seventeenth-century Faenza jars with Latin inscriptions of drugs, mostly unknown to me. A couple of large glass bottles with snakes and a fœtus in alcohol adorned the sideboard. By the shrine of San Gennaro, the patron saint of Naples, burned the sacred lamp and among the cobwebs in the ceiling hung an embalmed cat with two heads. The speciality of the Farmacia was Don Bartolo's famous anti-cholerical mixture, labelled with a picture of San Gennaro on one side and a skull on the other with the words " Morte alla coléra " underneath. Its composition was a family secret handed down from father to son ever since the epidemic of 1834 when, in collaboration with San Gennaro, it had saved the city. Another speciality of the Farmacia was a mysterious bottle

labelled with a heart pierced by Cupid's arrow, a filtro
d'amore. Its composition also was a family secret, it was much
in demand, I understood. Don Bartolo's clients seemed
chiefly drawn from the many convents and churches round his
street. There were always a couple of priests, monks or frati
sitting on the chairs before the counter in animated discussion
about the events of the day, the last miracles performed
by this or that saint, and the efficacy of the various Madonnas,
La Madonna del Carmine, la Madonna dell'Aiuto, la
Madonna della Buona Morte, la Madonna della Coléra,
l'Addolorata, la Madonna Egiziaca. Seldom, very seldom,
I heard the name of God mentioned, the name of His Son
never. I once ventured to express my surprise to a shabby
old Frate who was a particular friend of mine over this
omission of Christ in their discussions. The old Frate made
no secret of his private opinion that Christ owed his reputation
solely to His having the Madonna for His Mother. As far as
he knew, Christ had never saved anybody from the cholera.
His Blessed Mother had cried her eyes out for Him. What had
He done for Her in return? "Woman," He said, "what
have I to do with Thee?"

"Percio ha finito male, that's why He came to a bad
end."

As Saturday approached the names of the various saints
and Madonnas dropped more and more from the conversation. On Friday night the Farmacia was full of people
gesticulating wildly in animated discussion about their chances
for the Banco di Lotto of to-morrow.

Trentaquattro, sessantanove, quarantatre, diciasette!
Don Antonio had dreamt his aunt had died suddenly
and left him five thousand lire, sudden death—49, money
—70! Don Onorato had consulted the hunchback in Via
Forcella, he was sure of his terno—9, 39, 20! Don Bartolo's
cat had had seven kittens in the night—numbers 7, 16, 64!
Don Dionisio had just read in the 'Pungolo' that a camor-
rista had stabbed a barber at Immacolatella. Barber—21,
knife—41! Don Pasquale had got his numbers from the
custodian of the cemetery who had heard them distinctly
from a grave—il morto che parla—48!

It was at the Farmacia di San Gennaro I first made the
acquaintance of Doctor Villari. I had been told by Don
Bartolo that he had come to Naples two years ago as an
assistant to old Doctor Rispù, the well-known doctor of all the
convents and congregations in the quarter, who at his death

had handed over his large practice to his young assistant. I was always glad to meet my colleague, I took a great liking to him from the very first. He was a singularly handsome man with nice, quiet manners, very unlike the ordinary type of Neapolitan. He came from the Abruzzi. It was through him I first heard of the convent of the Sepolte Vive, the grim old building in the corner of the street with its small Gothic windows and huge massive iron gates, sombre and silent like a grave. Was it true that the nuns entered through these gates wrapped in the shroud of the dead and laid in a coffin, and that they could never get out as long as they were alive?

Yes, it was quite true, the nuns had no communication with the outer world. He himself during his rare professional visits to the convent was preceded by an old nun ringing a bell to warn the nuns to shut themselves up in their cells.

Was it true what I heard from Padre Anselmo, their confessor, that the cloister garden was full of antique marbles?

Yes, he had noticed lots of fragments lying about, he had been told that the convent stood on the ruins of a Greek temple.

My colleague seemed to like to talk to me, he said he had no friends in Naples, like all his countrymen he hated and despised the Neapolitans. What he had witnessed since the outbreak of the cholera made him loathe them more than ever. It was difficult not to believe that it was the punishment of God that had fallen on their rotten city. Sodom and Gomorrah were nothing compared to Naples. Did I not see what was going on in the poor quarters, in the streets, in the infected houses, even in the churches while they were praying to one saint and cursing another? A frenzy of lust was sweeping all over Naples, immorality and vice everywhere in the very face of Death. Assaults on women had become so frequent that no decent woman dared to leave her house.

He did not seem to be afraid of the cholera, he said he felt quite safe under the protection of the Madonna. How I envied him his faith! He showed me the two medallions his wife had hung round his neck the day the cholera broke out, one was a Madonna del Carmine, the other was Santa Lucia, the patron saint of his wife, his wife's name was Lucia. She had worn the little medallion ever since she was a child. I said I knew Santa Lucia well, I knew she was the patron saint of the eyes. I had often wished to light a candle before her shrine, I who had lived for years in fear of losing my sight. He said he would tell his wife to remember me in her

prayers to Santa Lucia, who had lost her own eyes but had
restored the light to so many others. He told me that from
the moment he left his house in the morning his wife was
sitting by the window looking out for his return. She had
nobody but him in the world, she had married him against
the wish of her parents, he had wanted to send her away
from the infected city but she had refused to leave him.
I asked him if he was not afraid of death. He said not for
himself but for the sake of his wife. If only death from
cholera was not so hideous ! Better to be taken at once to
the cemetery than to be seen by eyes that loved you !

" I am sure you will be all right," I said, " you have at
least somebody who prays for you, I have nobody."

A shadow passed over his handsome face.

" Promise me if . . ."

" Don't let us talk about death," I interrupted him with
a shudder.

The little Osteria dell' Allegria behind Piazza Mercato
was a favourite resting-place of mine. The food was abominable but the wine was excellent, six sous the litre, I had plenty
of it. I often spent half of the night there when I dared not
go home. Cesare, the night-waiter, soon became a great
friend of mine. After the third case of cholera in my locanda
it ended by my moving into an empty room in the house he
lived in. My new quarters were as dirty as the locanda, but
Cesare was right, it was much better to be " in compagnia."
His wife was dead, but Mariuccia, his daughter, was alive,
very much so. She believed she was fifteen, but she was
already in full bloom, black-eyed and red-lipped, she looked
like the little Venus of the Capitol Museum. She washed my
linen, cooked my macaroni, and made up my bed when she
did not forget it. She had never seen a forestiere before. She
was always coming into my room with a bunch of grapes, a
slice of water-melon or a plate of figs. When she had nothing
else to offer me she took the red rose from her black curls
and handed it to me with her enchanting smile of a siren and
a sparkling question in her eyes, whether I would not like to
have her red lips as well ? The whole day she was singing from
the kitchen in her strong, shrill voice :

" Amore ! Amore ! "

In the night I heard her tossing about in her bed on the
other side of the partition wall. She said she could not go to
sleep, she said she was afraid to be alone at night, she was
afraid to dormire sola. Was I not afraid to dormire solo ?

"Dormite, signorino?" she whispered from her bed.

No, I did not sleep, I was wide awake, I did not like to dormire solo more than she did.

What new fear was making my heart beat so tumultuously and making the blood rush through my veins with fever speed? Why, when sitting half-asleep in the side aisle of Santa Maria del Carmine, had I not noticed before all these beautiful girls in their black mantillas kneeling on the marble floor by my side and smiling at me on the sly in the midst of their prayers and incantations? How could I have passed every day for weeks in front of the fruttivendola in the street corner without stopping to chat with Nannina, her beautiful daughter, with the same colour on her cheeks as the peaches she was selling? Why had I not discovered before that the fioraia in Piazza Mercato had the same enchanting smile as Botticelli's Primavera? How could I have spent so many evenings in the Osteria dell' Allegria unaware that it was not the vino di Gragnano but the sparkle in Carmela's eyes that went to my head? How was it possible that I had only heard the groans of the dying and the tolling of the church bells when from every street sounded laughter and love-songs, when under every portico stood a girl whispering to her amoroso?

"O Mari', O Mari', quanto sonno ho perso pez te.
Fammi dormire
Abbracciato un poco con te,"
sang a youth under Mariuccia's window.

"O Carmé! O Carmé!" sang another outside the Osteria.
"Vorrei baciare i tuoi capelli neri,"
rang out from Piazza Mercato.
"Vorrei baciare i tuoi capelli neri,"
echoed in my ears as I lay in my bed listening to the respiration of Mariuccia asleep on the other side of the partition wall.

What had happened to me? Was I bewitched by a strega? Had one of those girls poured some drops of Don Bartolo's filtro d'amore in my wine? What had happened to all these people around me? Were they all drunk with the new wine or had they gone mad with lust in the very face of death?

Morto la coléra, evviva la gioia!

I was sitting at my usual table in the Osteria half-asleep before my bottle of wine. It was already past midnight, I thought I had better wait where I was, to return home with Cesare when he had finished his job. A boy ran up to my table and handed me a piece of paper.

" Come," was scribbled on the paper in almost illegible letters.

Five minutes later we stopped before the huge iron gates of the convent of the Sepolte Vive. I was let in by an old nun who preceded me across the cloister garden ringing a bell. We passed along an immense, deserted corridor, another nun held up a lantern to my face and opened the door to a dimly-lit room. Doctor Villari was lying on a mattress on the floor. I hardly recognised him at first. Padre Anselmo was just giving him the Last Sacraments. He was already in stadium algidum, his body was quite cold but I could see by his eyes that he was still conscious. I looked at his face with a shudder, it was not my friend I looked at, it was Death, terrible, repulsive Death. He raised his hands several times pointing at me, his ghastly face twitching under a desperate effort to speak. From his grimacing lips came distinctly the word : " specchio ! " A nun brought after some delay a little mirror, I held it before his half-closed eyes. He shook his head several times, it was the last sign of life he gave, an hour later the heart stood still.

The cart stood before the gate to take away the bodies of the two nuns who had died during the day. I knew it rested with me whether he he was to be taken away at the same time or left where he was till the next evening. They would have believed me had I said he was still alive, he looked exactly the same as when I had come. I said nothing. Two hours later his body was thrown with hundreds of other bodies in the common grave in the cholera cemetery. I had under-stood why he had raised his hand and pointed at me and why he had shaken his head when I had held the mirror before his eyes. He did not want his wife to see what he had seen in the mirror, and he wanted me to go and tell her when all was over.

As I stood before his house I saw the white face of a woman, almost a child, in the window. She reeled back with terror in her eyes as I opened the door.

" You are the foreign doctor he has told me so much about, he has not come back, I have been standing in the window the whole night. Where is he ? "

She threw a shawl over her shoulders and rushed to the door.

" Take me to him at once, I must see him at once ! "

I held her back, I said I must speak to her first. I told her he had been taken ill in the convent of the Sepolte Vive, the whole place was infected, she could not go there, she must think of the child she was going to give birth to.

"Help me downstairs, help me downstairs! I must go to him at once, why don't you help me?" she sobbed.

Suddenly she gave a piercing scream and sank down on the chair on the point of fainting.

"It is not true, he is not dead, why don't you speak, you are a liar, he cannot be dead without my seeing him."

She sprang to the door once more.

"I must see him, I must see him!"

Once more I held her back.

"You cannot see him, he is no longer there, he is . . ."

She sprang at me like a wounded animal.

"You had no right to have him taken away before I had seen him," she screamed, mad with rage. "He was the light of my eyes, you have taken the light from my eyes! You are a liar, a murderer! Holy Lucia, take the light from his eyes as he has taken the light from my eyes! Sting out his eyes as you stung out your own eyes!"

An old woman rushed into the room and sprang at me with uplifted hands as if she wanted to scratch my face.

"Holy Lucia, take the sight away from him! Blind him!" she screamed at the top of her voice.

"Potess' essere ciecato, potess' essere ciecato," she was still shouting from the landing as I reeled down the stairs.

The terrible curse, the most terrible that ever could have been hurled against me, was ringing in my ears the whole night. I dared not go home, I was afraid of the dark. I spent the remainder of the night in Santa Maria del Carmine, I thought the day would never come.

When I staggered into the Farmacia di San Gennaro in the morning for my usual pick-me-up, another of Don Bartolo's specialities of extraordinary efficacy, Padre Anselmo had just left a message for me to come to the convent at once.

The whole convent was in commotion, there had been three fresh cases of cholera. Padre Anselmo told me that after a long conversation between the Abbess and himself, it had been decided to ask me to replace my dead colleague, no other doctor being available. Panic-stricken nuns were running to and fro through the corridors, others were praying and singing incantations in the chapel. The three nuns were lying on their straw mattresses in their cells. One of them died in the evening. In the morning, the old nun who had been assisting me was struck down in her turn. She was replaced by a young nun I had already noticed during my first visit, indeed it was difficult not to notice her, for she was very young and strikingly beautiful. She never said a word to me. She did not even answer when I asked her what was her name, but I found out from Padre Anselmo that she was Suora Ursula. Later in the day I asked to speak to the Abbess and was taken by Suora Ursula to her cell. The old Abbess looked at me with her cold, penetrating eyes, severe and scrutinising as those of a judge. Her face was rigid and lifeless as if cut in marble, her thin lips looked as if they had had never parted in a smile. I told her the whole convent was infected, the sanitary conditions were appalling, the water in the garden well was polluted, the whole place must be evacuated or they would all die of cholera.

She answered it was impossible, it was against the rules of their order, no nun, once inside their convent, had ever left it alive. They all had to remain where they were, they were in the hands of the Madonna and of San Gennaro.

Except for a rapid visit to the Farmacia for a steadily increased dose of Don Bartolo's miraculous pick-me-up, I never left the convent for several unforgettable days of terror. I had to tell Padre Anselmo I must have some wine, and soon I had plenty of it, probably too much. Sleep I had next to none, I did not seem to need any sleep. I do not even believe I could have slept had I had the chance, fear and innumerable cups of black coffee had roused my whole mental machinery into an extraordinary state of excitement which took away all fatigue. My only relaxation was when I could steal into the cloister garden where I sat smoking endless cigarettes on the old marble bench under the cypresses. Fragments of antique marbles were lying all over the garden, even the well-head was made out of what had once been a cippo, a Roman altar. It is now in the courtyard of San Michele. At my very feet lay a mutilated fawn of rosso antico, and half-hidden amongst the cypresses stood a little Eros still erect on his column of African marble. A couple of times I had found Suora Ursula sitting on the bench, she said she had come out for a breath of fresh air or she would faint from the stench all over the building. Once she brought me a cup of coffee and stood in front of me waiting for the cup while I drank my coffee as slowly as possible to make her stand there a little longer. It seemed to me as if she had become a little less shy, as if she did not mind that I was so slow in handing back my empty cup to her. It seemed a rest to my tired eyes to look at her.

It soon became a joy, for she was very beautiful. Did she understand why my eyes said to her but my lips dared not say, that I was young and she was fair? There were moments when I almost thought she did.

I asked her why she had come here to bury her young life in the grave of the Sepolte Vive. Did she not know that outside this place of terror and death the world was as beautiful as before, that life was full of joy and not only of sorrow!

"Do you know who is this boy?" I said, pointing to the little Eros under the cypresses.

She thought it was an angelo.

No, it is a god, the greatest of all gods and perhaps the oldest of all gods. He ruled over Olympus and he still rules over our world to-day.

"Your convent stands on the ruins of an antique temple, its very walls had crumbled to dust, destroyed by time and man. This little boy alone has remained where he stood with the quiver of arrows in his hand, ready to raise his bow. He is indestructible because he is immortal. The ancients called him Eros, he is the god of Love."

As I spoke the blasphemous word the bell from the chapel called the nuns to their evening prayer. She crossed herself and hurried out of the garden.

A moment later another nun came rushing to take me to the Abbess, she had fainted in the chapel, they had just carried her to her cell. The Abbess looked at me with her terrible eyes. She raised her hand and pointed to the Crucifix on the wall, they brought her the Last Sacraments. She never rallied, she never spoke, the action of the heart grew weaker and weaker, she was sinking rapidly. She lay there the whole day, the Crucifix on her breast, her rosary in her hands, her eyes closed, her body slowly growing cold. Once or twice I thought I heard a faint beating of the heart, soon I heard nothing. I looked at the rigid, cruel face of the old Abbess which even death had not been able to soften. It was almost a relief to me that her eyes were closed for ever, there was something in those eyes that had frightened me. I looked at the young nun by my side.

"I cannot stay here any longer," I said, "I have not slept since I came here, my head is swimming, I am not myself, I do not know what I am doing, I am afraid of myself, I am afraid of you, I am afraid of . . ."

I had not time to finish the word, she had not time to draw back, my arms had closed round her, I felt the tumultuous beating of her heart against my heart.

" Pietà ! " she murmured.

Suddenly she pointed towards the bed and sprang out of the room with a cry of terror. The eyes of the old Abbess were looking straight at me, wide-open, terrible, menacing. I bent over her, I thought I heard a faint fluttering of the heart. Was she dead or alive ? Could those terrible eyes see, had they seen ? Would those lips ever speak again ? I dared not look at those eyes, I pulled the sheet over her face and sprang from the cell, from the Sepolte Vive, never to return there any more.

THE
CIRCUS PEOPLE TAKE REVENGE

By
"LORD" GEORGE SANGER

At this time (about 1840) the author had just reached his 'teens and travelled from fair to fair in his showman-father's caravan.

FROM place to place we went with our little show, and at length found ourselves at Lansdown, near Bath, for the big cattle, sheep, and pleasure fair that then used to be held annually on 10th August at the hill village, which is some two miles from the old city.

It was here that I saw an example of the rough justice that the showmen occasionally meted out to their enemies and tormentors, who in those days were legion. Such things could not happen now, for we live in better times, the arm of the law is longer, and life and property have safeguards that in those days were not dreamt of. Men then had to protect themselves and their belongings as best they could, and often to right their own wrongs as I saw the showmen do at Lansdown fair.

Though it was the resort of all the rank and fashion in the land, who came to seek health from the famous waters, and was the home as now of a multitude of wealthy, stately, and dignified personages, who dwelt beneath the shadow of its ancient cathedral, Bath had at that time a very unenviable reputation as regarded its lower classes. I have, by the way, noticed that most cathedral cities—and in Britain I have visited them all—show remarkable contrasts in regard to their populations. At the top you have all that is best in the way of piety and learning, all that is enviable in the way of ease and dignity. At the bottom you will find dirt, degradation, misery, and evil of the most appalling kinds. Why this should be I cannot say, but I have certainly observed it. Anyhow, Bath at this period had in its slums what was considered to be the most brutish and criminal mob in England, and for

these people Lansdown fair was, as they put it, " their night
out."

Though it lasted but one day, the fair was always a big
one, occupying a great space on a broad hill-side. On this
booths, shows, and refreshment tents of all descriptions were
erected to form an enormous ring, in the centre of which were
the droves of sheep, cattle, and horses that formed the staple
of the fair to which the country-folk flocked from all the
district round.

On this occasion the gathering was a very great one. All
the best-known showmen in the country were there, money
was plentiful, and throughout the day we did exceedingly
well. As dusk came on the regular business people—the
farmers, graziers, and others who had been dealing in the
horses, cattle, farm produce, and such-like—left the fair to
the pleasure-seekers. The drinking booths, gingerbread stalls,
and shows began to twinkle with lights. Twinkle is the only
word that fits the illumination of fairs in those days.

Recollect it was before the time of the naphtha lamps. We
had only candles, the commonest of dips and rushlights, for
inside work and these kept numbers of people busy the night
long doing nothing else but snuffing them. Outside the booths
hung flares—horrible, odorous things, consisting of three
prongs set in a shallow iron or tin dish. Rags were rolled up
and put into these prongs, then round about were packed
lumps of rough tallow, that melted and kept the rag-wick
supplied with fat after it was lit. These flares were slung up
with three chains to the booth poles, and their spluttering
smoky flame was our chief illuminant. Think of it, you who
only know the brilliance of gas and electricity, and you may
be able to realise something of the disadvantages that night
brought to those old-time showmen.

As night advanced the character of the fair crowd gradually
changed. It grew rougher and rougher. Fights were frequent.
Oaths and screams were mingled with coarse songs from the
drinking and dancing booths, which were filled with a motley
throng. Business at our peep-show and with our roundabout
became slacker and slacker, till at last, about ten o'clock,
father gave the word to close up. Even as he did so a terrible
row broke out amongst the booths nearest the Bath road, and
very soon we got the news that the Bath roughs were out in
force, bent on mischief.

How we toiled and hurried to make our belongings as safe
as possible ! Everything that could be broken or stolen was

hastily packed in or under the living-wagon, and made secure with chains and bolts. At last we finished, and then with every light out so as not to attract attention, we sat and listened to the turmoil that was now raging all round us.

The roughs were led by a red-headed virago, a dreadful giantess of a woman, known as " Carroty Kate." She was an awful creature, strong as a navvy, a big brutal animal, caring nothing for magistrates or gaol, and had long been the terror of every respectable person in Bath and its neighbourhood. With the majority of her followers, she hailed from Bull Paunch Alley, the lowest slum in the cathedral city, where no policeman ever dared to penetrate, and innumerable horrors were committed nightly.

Half-stripped, with her red hair flying wildly behind her, she incited the gang of ruffians with her to wreck the fair. The drinking booths were the first to suffer. The mob took possession of them, half-killed some of the unfortunate owners, and then set to work to drink themselves into a state of frenzy even more acute than before. The scenes that followed are almost indescribable. Not content with drinking all they could, the ruffians turned on the taps, staved in barrels, smashed up bottles, and let the liquor run to waste. Then they started to wreck the booths. Canvas was torn to shreds, platforms were smashed up and made bonfires of, wagons were battered and overturned, show-fronts that had cost some of their poor owners small fortunes were battered to fragments. Everywhere was riot, ruin, and destruction.

The few police that were about were utterly helpless, and the show-folk had to protect themselves as best they could, some of them making a very manful fight against overpowering numbers. Assistance, it was said, had been sent for by the authorities, but if that was so it did not arrive until the mischief was complete. We children and poor mother were in a state of fear that can well be imagined. Father had told us to get ready to run away up the hill-side and lie down on the grass if the mob came towards our caravan, so that we might escape injury. For himself, he had no fear ; he put an extra handful of slugs into the old blunderbuss, meaning to have at least one good shot at the wreckers if they touched the bit of property that was his living.

But the ruffians did not touch us. The mischief was confined chiefly to the lower end of the fair, where everything was practically destroyed, and more than one poor traveller brought close to ruin. As dawn broke the riot died down,

and the drunken mob, glutted with the wanton destruction
of the belongings of poor people who had never done them
any harm, began to straggle, shouting, swearing and singing,
back towards Bath.

Then, by ones and twos, the showmen came together, pale
with anger, some of them bruised and bleeding from the fray,
and all resolved on vengeance. They had marked one or two
of the ringleaders of the riot, and meant to give them a taste
of showmen's law. The scene is before me now as I saw it
when I stood with my brother William, still pale with fear,
but full of childish curiosity, on the steps of our caravan, in
the dawnlight, and watched some thirty stalwart showmen,
my father amongst them, armed with stout cudgels, mount
the hastily collected wagon horses, and, bare-backed, ride
after the retreating mob.

Presently the riders returned, dragging with them as
prisoners about a dozen men and the terrible woman " Carroty
Kate," with their hands tied behind them. They who had
been the bold leaders of the attack on the booths now shook
with fear, as the drink evaporated, and they found themselves
in the hands of the men they had so wantonly injured.

All the show-folk, young and old, turned out to see the
punishment of the rioters, which was carried out with a
precision and thoroughness that deeply impressed me. First
of all, the woman was securely fastened to the wheel of a
heavy wagon, and was left cursing us as we followed the male
prisoners down the hill. At the foot there was a deep, wide
pond, and there the punishment commenced.

With long tent ropes the showmen linked the wreckers
together by their bound hands. Then a stout rope was thrown
across the pond and fastened to the living chain, some twenty
stalwart showmen holding the line on the farther bank. On
the near side father quickly attached another line to the
prisoners, which was similarly manned by showmen.

All was now ready, and an old van-dweller stepped out
and told our prisoners that as it was no use looking to the law
to revenge the injuries they had caused the showmen the latter
were going to give them a lesson that should be a lasting one.
His address was very brief and emphatic, and when it was
finished he threw up his hand and shouted " Go ! "

In a moment the prisoners were dragged into the pond.
Right across the showmen pulled them with hearty good will.
Then back again they were lugged, spluttering and howling
for mercy. No notice was taken of their cries, but backwards

and forwards through the muddy water they were pulled until no breath was left in their bodies. One or two, indeed, were so still that some of the showmen cried out in alarm that they were drowned.

"No fear," shouted my father, in tones that I can hear even yet. "That sort doesn't die from drowning. Fetch 'em out!"

Out they were dragged and laid on the grass for a few minutes, "to drain," as some one remarked, then they were brought to their feet and forced once more towards the wagons on the hill-side. I shall never forget the picture they presented as, dripping wet, with ghastly faces, and literally quaking with fear, they were driven onwards by the showmen, and the crowd that followed behind jeered and taunted them. One of the fellows turned, and said : "Are you a-going to kill us? Ain't you done enough to us?"

"Not half enough," was the reply. Thereupon the fellow set up a shout of "Murder! Murder!" "Shut it!" said one of the showmen roughly ; "save your breath for the next scene. You'll want it then!" So we came up again to the wagons.

One of the latter had extra large wheels, and very quickly two of the prisoners had their clothes torn off them to the waists, and were triced up each to a wheel with arms and legs stretched out. Then four muscular showmen, smocks and vests off, shirt-sleeves rolled up, and carrying new whalebone riding-whips, took their places by the bound men.

"What is it to be?" asked one of the men, as he drew his whip through his fingers and balanced it. "Two dozen!" said my father, who had been addressed. "Make it three dozen! Make it three dozen for all my beautiful chaney ornaments they smashed, the vagabones!" shrieked an old woman, whose caravan had been wrecked. "Very well, mother," said father curtly, "three dozen it shall be ; three dozen for every man jack of 'em. Lay on, boys!"

There was a sudden swish and flash as the whips curled in the air, then two such yells as I had never heard before from human throats. They seemed to paralyse me, and I could not turn my eyes from the scene, though it frightened me. Swish! swish! went the merciless whips, rising and falling regularly, the yells of the suffering wretches, echoed by the other prisoners in anticipation of their own turn, being punctuated by the sound of some one counting the strokes.

At last " thirty-six " was called. Then the two fellows, with their backs purple-striped and bleeding, were cast loose, their wet rags of clothes were thrown at them, and they were told to " Hook it, sharp ! " They needed no second bidding, and scurried, staggering, moaning, and cursing, down the hill-side to the road. " Thank yer stars ye've got off as light as 'ee 'ave ! " shouted an old man as they went. " Next time you tries such tricks we'll 'ang 'ee ! D'ye hear me ? We'll 'ang 'ee, sure ! "

Six times this scene was repeated, and when the last of the men had disappeared, with smarting back and oath-laden tongue, down the hill, the woman's turn came.

" Carroty Kate " flung many foul words at us as she was unfastened from the wagon wheel and dragged forward, but her face was white—ay, I can see it in my mind even now, after all these years—chalky white, against the tousled mass of red hair that framed it, and she was evidently badly frightened.

" What are you going to do to me ? " she raved.

" Give you a lesson same as the men," replied one of the showmen. He was proprietor of a little waxwork booth, I recollect, and his property had suffered badly in the roughs' onslaught. " We're not a-going to drag 'ee through the pond," he continued, " bad as you wants washin', nor use the horse-whip to 'ee, but you're a-goin' to be made to smart all the same." And she *was* made to smart.

Some penny canes were brought out, such as were sold in the fair, the virago was forced over a trestle, and two strong young women administered a sound thrashing.

She screamed and swore horribly, and writhed about, so that the half-dozen stout show-women who were holding her had a difficult task. But the young women flogged on till they were tired, and then the red-haired wretch was allowed to limp away, cursing us as she went in the most dreadful fashion.

Some others of the fair-wrecking mob also got punished, though not by the showmen. They fell in with a party of police near Bath, and a desperate fight ensued, the officers using the heavy staves with deadly effect on the drink-soddened rioters. Many of the latter, besides being badly mauled, were arrested, and several were transported for breaking the king's peace. I heard in after years, though we knew nothing of it at the time, that one man who maimed a policeman with an iron bar, so that the poor fellow was crippled for life, was sentenced to death, and executed, for " wounding, with intent to kill."

At any rate, an amazing amount of mischief was wrought by the Bath roughs on that occasion at Lansdown fair, and the night of awful fear they caused us, with the rough justice their leaders met at the hands of my father and his companions, are things that burned into my memory, to remain with every detail fresh and vivid through the whole of my life.

Such scenes are impossible in England now, and for that fact no one is more sincerely thankful than myself. At the same time, looking back upon them, I cannot but feel that the showmen were justified in taking the law into their own hands, and in dealing with those old-time hooligans as they did.

I remember my mother saying as we left Lansdown on that memorable August day for another fair : " Oh, James ! It was a terrible beating those Bath people got. I shall never forget it."

" They'll remember it longer than you will, my lass, I'll warrant," was father's reply. " Those chaps wanted a lesson written in for 'em so as to keep it in their memories. There's nothing a rough is so careless about as the skin of other people, nothing he is so careful about as his own. Touch his skin and you touch his conscience, and there's no other way of doing it."

Such were my father's sentiments in regard to dealing with that worst of all brutes, the human one, and I have heard him express them many a time. I still appreciate their wisdom, though I have lived on into a softer age in which the ordering of corporal punishment even for the most violent robber would arouse a storm of indignation. But it is not for the showman to moralise.

MAJOR WILSON'S LAST FIGHT

By
SIR HENRY RIDER HAGGARD

"They were men whose fathers were men"

To make it clear how Major Wilson and his companions came to die on the banks of the Shangani on December 4, 1893, it will be necessary, very briefly, to sketch the events which led to the war between the English settlers in Mashonaland in South Africa and the Matabele tribe, an offshoot of the Zulu race.

In October 1889, at the instance of Mr. Cecil Rhodes and others interested, the Chartered Company of British South Africa was incorporated, with the sanction of Her Majesty's Government.

In 1890 Mashonaland was occupied, a vast and fetile territory nominally under the rule of Lobengula, king of the Matabele, which had been ceded by him to the representatives of the Company in return for certain valuable considerations. It is, however, an easier task for savage kings to sign concessions than to ensure that such concessions will be respected by their subjects, especially when those subjects are warriors by nature, tradition, and practice, as in the present case, and organised into regiments, kept from year to year in perfect efficiency and readiness for attack. Whatever may have been Lobengula's private wishes and opinions, it soon became evident that the gathering of the white men upon their borders, and in a country which they claimed by right of conquest if they did not occupy it, was most distasteful to the more warlike sections of the Matabele.

Mashonaland takes its name from the Mashona tribes who inhabit it, a peaceful and, speaking by comparison, an industrious race, whom, ever since they first settled in the neighbourhood, it had been the custom of the subjects of Lobengula and of his predecessor, Mosilikatze, " the lion," to attack with every cruelty conceivable, raiding their cattle, slaughtering their men, and sweeping their maidens and young children into captivity. Terrified, half exterminated indeed, as they were by these constant and unprovoked onslaughts, the Mashonas welcomed with delight the occupation of their country by white men, and thankfully placed themselves under the protection of the Chartered Company.

The Matebele regiments, however, took a different view of the question, for now their favourite sport was gone : they could no longer practise rapine and murder, at least in this direction, whenever the spirit moved them. Presently the force of habit overcame their fear of the white men and their respect for treaties, and towards the end of 1891 the chief Lomaghondi, who lived under the protection of the Company, was killed by them. Thereupon Dr. Jameson, the Administrator of Mashonaland, remonstrated with Lobengula, who expressed regret, saying that the incident had happened by mistake.

This repudiation notwithstanding, an impi, or armed body of savages, again crossed the border in 1892, and raided in the Victoria district. Encouraged by the success of these proceedings, in July, 1893, Lobengula sent a picked company to harry in the neighbourhood of Victoria itself, writing to Dr. Jameson that he made no excuse for so doing, claiming as he did the right to raid when, where, and whom he choose. The "indunas," or captains, in command of this force were instructed not to kill white men, but to fall particularly upon those tribes who were in their employ. On July 9, 1893, and the following days came the climax, for then the impi began to slaughter every Mashona whom they could find. Many of these unfortunates were butchered in the presence of their masters, who were bidden to "stand upon one side as the time of the white men had not yet come."

Seeing that it was necessary to take action, Dr. Jameson summoned the head indunas of the impi, and ordered them to cross the border within an hour or to suffer the consequences of their disobedience. The majority obeyed, and those who defied him were attacked by Captain Lendy and a small force while in the act of raiding a kraal, some of them being killed and the rest driven away.

From this moment war became inevitable, for the question lay between the breaking of the power of Lobengula and the evacuation of Mashonaland. Into the details of that war it is not proposed to enter ; they are outside the scope of this narrative. It is enough to say that it was one of the most brilliant and successful ever carried out by Englishmen. The odds against the little force of a thousand or twelve hundred white men who invaded Matabeleland were almost overwhelming, and when it is remembered that the Imperial troops did not succeed in their contest against Cetywayo, the Zulu king, until nearly as many soldiers were massed in the country as there were abled-bodied Zulus left to oppose them, the brilliancy of the achievement of these colonists led by a civilian, Dr. Jameson, can be estimated. The Matabele were beaten in two pitched battles : that of the Shangani on October 25, and that of the Imbemzi on November 1. They fought bravely, even with desperation, but their valour was broken by the skill and the cool courage of the white man. Those terrible engines of war, the Maxim guns and the Hotchkiss shells, contributed largely to our success on these occasions. The Matabele, brave as they were, could not face the incessant fire of the Maxims, and as to the Hotchkiss they developed a curious superstition. Seeing that men fell dead in all directions after the explosion of a shell, they came to believe that as it burst out of each missile numbers of tiny and invisible imps ran forth carrying death and destruction to the white men's foes, and thus it happened that to their minds moral terrors were added to the physical dangers of warfare. So strong was this belief among them, indeed, that whenever a shell struck they would turn and fire at it in the hope that thus they might destroy the " live devils " who dwelt within it.

After these battles Lobengula, having first set fire to it, fled from his chief place, Buluwayo, which was occupied by the white men within a month of the commencement of the campaign.

In reply to a letter sent to him by Dr. Jameson, demanding his surrender and guaranteeing his safety, Lobengula wrote that he " would come in."

The promised period of two days' grace having gone by, however, and there being no sign of his appearance, a force was despatched from Buluwayo to follow and capture him. This force, which was under the leadership of Major Patrick W. Forbes, consisted of ninety men of the Salisbury Column, with Captains Heany and Spreckley and a mule Maxim gun under Lieutenant Biscoe, R.N. ; sixty men of the Victoria Column commanded by Major Wilson, with a horse Maxim under Captain Lendy ; sixty men of the Tuli Column, and ninety men of the Bechuanaland Border Police, commanded by Captain Raaf, C.M.G., accompanied by two horse Maxims and a mule seven-pounder, commanded by Captain Tancred.

The column, which started on or about November 14, took

with it food for three days only, carried by natives, and a hundred rounds of ammunition per man. After several days' journeying northward the patrol reached the Bubye River, where dissensions arose between Captain Raaf and Major Forbes, the former being of opinion, rightly enough as the issue showed, that the mission was too dangerous to be pursued by a small body of men without supplies of food, and having no reserve of ammunition and no means of carrying the wounded. The upshot was that Major Forbes decided to return but was prevented from doing so by a letter received from Dr. Jameson, stating that he was sending forward a reinforcement of dismounted men under Captain Napier, with food, ammunition, and wagons, also sixteen mounted men under Captain Borrow. The force then proceeded to a deserted Mission Station known as Shiloh. On November 25 the column, three hundred strong and carrying with it three-quarter rations for twelve days, took up the king's wagon spoor about one mile from Shiloh, and followed it through much discomfort, caused by the constant rain and the lack of roads, till on December 3 a point was reached on the Shangani River, N.N.W. of Shiloh and distant from it about eighty miles.

On November 29, however, Major Forbes, finding that he could make small progress with the wagons, sent them away, and proceeded with the best mounted men and two Maxims only, so that the actual force which reached the Shangani on the 3rd consisted of about one hundred and sixty men and a couple of machine guns.

At this time the information in possession of the leaders of the column was to the effect that the king was just in front of them across the river, accompanied only by a few of his followers. Under these circumstances Major Forbes instructed Major Wilson and eighteen men to go forward and recon-noitre along Lobengula's spoor ; the understanding seeming to have been that the party was to return by sundown, but that if it did not return it was, if necessary, to be supported by the whole column. With this patrol went Mr. Burnham, the American scout, one of the three surviving white men who were eye-witnesses of that eventful night's work, which ended so tragically at dawn.

What followed is best told as he narrated it by word of mouth to the compiler of this true story, and to a reporter of the *Westminster Gazette*, the editor of which paper has courte-ously given permission for the reproduction of the interview,

Indeed, it would be difficult to tell it so well in words other than Mr. Burnham's own.

"In the afternoon of December 3," says Mr. Burnham, "I was scouting ahead of the column with Colenbrander, when in a strip of bush we lit on two Matabele boys driving some cattle, one of whom was caught and brought in. He was a plucky boy, and when threatened he just looked us sullenly in the face. He turned out to be a sort of grandson or grand-nephew of Lobengula himself. He said the King's camp was just ahead, and the King himself near, with very few men, and these sick, and that he wanted to give himself up. He represented that the King had been back to this place that very day to get help because his wagons were stuck in a bog. The column pushed on through the strip of bush, and there, near by, was the King's camp—quite deserted. We searched the huts, and in one lay a Maholi slave-boy, fast asleep. (The Maholis are the slaves of the Matabele.) We pulled him out, and were questioning him, when the other boy, the sulky Matabele, caught his eye, and gave him a ferocious look, shouting across to him to take care what he told.

"The slave-boy agreed with the others that the King had only left this camp the day before; but as it was getting dark, Major Forbes decided to reconnoitre before going on with the column. I learnt of the decision to send forward Major Wilson and fifteen men on the best horses when I got my orders to accompany them, and, along with Bayne, to do their scouting. My horse was exhausted with the work he had already done; I told Major Forbes, and he at once gave me his. It was a young horse, rather skittish, but strong and fairly fresh by comparison.

"Ingram, my fellow-scout, remained with the column, and so got some hours' rest; thanks to which he was able not only to do his part of tracking for the twenty men afterwards sent on to us through the bush at night, but also, when he and I got through after the smash, to do the long and dangerous ride down country to Buluwayo with the despatches—a ride on which he was accompanied by Lynch.

"So we set off along the wagon track, while the main body of the column went into laager.

"Close to the river the track turned and led down stream along the west bank. Two miles down was a drift" (they call a fordable dip a drift in South Africa), "and here the track crossed the Shangani. We splashed through, and the first thing we scouts knew on the other side was that we were riding into the middle of a lot of Matabele among some scherms, or temporary shelters. There were men, and some women and children. The men were armed. We put a bold face on it, and gave out the usual announcement that we did not want to kill anybody, but must have the King. The natives seemed surprised and undecided ; presently, as Major Wilson and the rest of the patrol joined us, one of them volunteered to come along with us and guide us to the King. He was only just ahead, the man said. How many men were with him ? we asked. The man put up his little finger— dividing it up, so. Five fingers mean an impi ; part of the little finger, like that, should mean fifty to one hundred men. Wilson said to me, " Go on ahead, taking that man beside your saddle ; cover him, fire if necessary, but don't you let him slip.'

" So we started off again at a trot, for the light was failing, the man running beside my horse, and I keeping a sharp eye on him. The track led through some thick bush. We passed several scherms. Five miles from the river we came to a long narrow vlei (a vlei is a shallow valley, generally with water in it), which lay across our path. It was now getting quite dark. Coming out of the bush on the near edge of the vlei, before going down into it, I saw fires lit, and scherms and figures showing dark against the fires right along the opposite edge of the vlei. We skirted the vlei to our left, got round the end of it, and at once rode through a lot of scherms containing hundreds of people. As we went, Captain Napier shouted the message about the King wherever there was a big group of people. We passed scherm after scherm, and still more Matabele, more fires, and on we rode. Instead of the natives having been scattering from the King, they had been gathering. But it was too late to turn. We were hard upon our prize, and it was understood among the Wilson patrol that they were going to bring the King in if man could do it. The natives were astonished : they thought the whole column was on them ; men jumped up, and ran hither and thither, rifle in hand. We went on without stopping, and as we passed more and more men came running after us. Some of them were crowding on the rearmost men, so Wilson told off three fellows to ' keep those niggers back.' They turned, and kept the people in check. At last, nearly at the other end of the vlei, having passed five sets of scherms, we came upon what seemed to be the King's wagons, standing in a kind of enclosure, with a saddled white horse tethered by it. Just before this, in the crowd and hurry, my man slipped away, and I had to report to Wilson that I had lost him. Of course it would not have done to fire. One shot would have been the match in the powder magazine. We had ridden into the middle of the Matabele nation.

" At this enclosure we halted and sang out again, making a special appeal to the King and those about him. No answer came. All was silence. A few drops of rain fell. Then it lightened, and by the flashes we could just see men getting ready to fire on us, and Napier shouted to Wilson, ' Major, they are about to attack.' I at the same time saw them closing in on us rapidly from the right. The next thing to this fifth scherm was some thick bush ; the order was given to get into that, and in a moment we were out of sight there. One minute after hearing us shout, the natives with the wagons must have been unable to see a sign of us. Just then it came on to rain heavily ; the sky, already cloudy, got black as ink ; the night fell so dark that you could not see your hand before you.

" We could not stay the night where we were, for we were so close that they would hear our horses' bits. So it was decided to work down into the vlei, creep along to the other edge of it to the end we first came round, farthest from the King's camp, and there spend the night. This, like all the other moves, was taken after consultation with the officers, several of whom were experienced Kaffir campaigners. It was rough going ; we were unable to see our way, now splashing through the little dongas that ran down into the belly of the vlei, now working round them, through bush and soft bottoms. At the far end, in a clump of thick bush, we dismounted, and Wilson sent off Captain Napier, with a man of his called Robinson, and the Victoria scout, Bayne, to go back along the wagon-track to the column, report how things stood, and bring the column on, with the Maxims, as sharp as possible. Wilson told Captain Napier to tell Forbes if the bush bothered the Maxim carriages to abandon them and put the guns on horses, but to bring the Maxims without fail. We all understood—and we thought the message was this— that if we were caught there at dawn without the Maxims we were done for. On the other hand was the chance of capturing the King and ending the campaign at a stroke.

" The spot we had selected to stop in until the arrival of Forbes was a clump of heavy bush not far from the King's spoor—and yet so far from the Kaffir camps that they could not hear us if we kept quiet. We dismounted, and on counting it was found that three of the men were missing. They were Hofmeyer, Bradburn and Colquhoun. Somewhere in winding through the bush from the King's wagons to our present position these men were lost. Not a difficult thing, for we only spoke in whispers, and, save for the occasional click of a horse's hoof, we could pass within ten feet of each other and not be aware of it.

" Wilson came to me and said, ' Burnham, can you follow back along the vlei where we've just come ? ' I doubted it very much as it was black and raining ; I had no coat, having been sent after the patrol immediately I came in from firing the King's huts, and although it was December, or midsummer south of the line, the rain chilled my fingers. Wilson said, ' Come, I must have those men back.' I told him I should need some one to lead my horse so as to feel the tracks made in the ground by our horses. He replied, ' I will go with you. I want to see how you American fellows work.'

" Wilson was no bad hand at tracking himself, and I was put on my mettle at once. We began, and I was flurried at first, and I did not seem to get on to it somehow ; but in a few minutes I picked up the spoor and hung to it.

" So we started off together, Wilson and I, in the dark. It was hard work, for one could see nothing, one had to feel for the traces with one's fingers. Creeping along, at last we stood close to the wagons, where the patrol had first retreated into the bush.

" ' If we only had the force here now,' said Wilson, ' we would soon finish.'

" But there was still no sign of the three men, so there was nothing for it but to shout. Retreating into the vlei in front of the King's camp, we stood calling and cooeying for them, long and low at first, then louder. Of course there was a great stir along the lines of the native scherms, for they did not know what to make of it. We heard afterwards that the natives were greatly alarmed as the white men seemed to be everywhere at once, and the indunas went about quieting the men, and saying, ' Do you think the white men are on you, children ? Don't you know a wolf's howl when you hear it ? '

" After calling for a bit, we heard an answering call away down the vlei, and the darkness favouring us, the lost men soon came up and we arrived at the clump of bushes where the patrol was stationed. We all lay down in the mud to rest, for we were tired out. It had left off raining, but it was a miserable night, and the hungry horses had been under saddle, some of them twenty hours, and were quite done.

" So we waited for the column.

" During the night we could hear natives moving across into the bush which lay between us and the river. We heard the branches as they pushed through. After a while Wilson asked me if I could go a little way around our position and find out what the Kaffirs were doing. I always think he heard something, but he did not say so. I slipped out and on our right heard the swirl of boughs and the splash of feet. Circling round for a little time I came on more Kaffirs. I got so close to them I could touch them as they passed, but it was impossible to say how many there were, it was so dark. This I reported to Wilson. Raising his head on his hand he asked me a few questions, and made the remark that if the column failed to come up before daylight, ' we are in a hard hole,' and told me to go out on the King's spoor and watch for Forbes, so that by no possibility should he pass us in the darkness. It was now, I should judge, 1 a.m. on the 4th of December.

" I went, and for a long, long time I heard only the dropping of the rain from the leaves and now and then a dog barking in the scherms, but at last, just as it got grey in the east, I heard a noise, and placing my ear close to the ground, made it out to be the tramp of horses. I ran back to Wilson and said, ' The column is here.'

" We all led our horses out to the King's spoor. I saw the form of a man tracking. It was Ingram. I gave him a low whistle ; he came up, and behind him rode—not the column, not the Maxims, but just twenty men under Captain Borrow. It was a terrible moment—' *If* we were caught there at dawn ' —and already it was getting lighter every minute.

" One of us asked, ' Where is the column ? ' to which the reply was, ' You see all there are of us.' We answered, ' Then you are only so many more men to die.'

" Wilson went aside with Borrow, and there was earnest talk for a few moments. Presently all the officers' horses' heads were together ; and Captain Judd said in my hearing, ' Well, this is the end.' And Kurten said quite quietly, ' We shall never get out of this.'

" Then Wilson put it to the officers whether we should try and break through the impis which were now forming up between us and the river, or whether we would go for the King and sell our lives in trying to get hold of him. The final decision was for this latter.

" So we set off and walked along the vlei back to the King's wagons. It was quite light now and they saw us from the scherms all the way, but they just looked at us and we at them, and so we went along. We walked because the horses hadn't a canter in them, and there was no hurry anyway.

" At the wagons we halted and shouted out again about not wanting to kill any one. There was a pause, and then came shouts and a volley. Afterwards it was said that somebody answered, ' If you don't want to kill, we do.' My horse jumped away to the right at the volley, and took me almost into the arms of some natives who came running from that side. A big induna blazed at me, missed me, and then fumbled at his belt for another cartridge. It was not a proper bandolier he had on, and I saw him trying to pluck out the cartridge instead of easing it up from below with his finger. As I got my horse steady and threw my rifle down to cover him, he suddenly let the cartridge be and lifted an assegai. Waiting to make sure of my aim, just as his arm was poised I fired and hit him in the chest ; he dropped. All happened in a moment. Then we retreated. Seeing two horses down, Wilson shouted to somebody to cut off the saddle pockets which carried extra ammunition. Ingram picked up one of the dismounted men behind him, Captain Fitzgerald the other. The most ammunition any one had, by the way, was a hundred and ten rounds. There was some very stiff fighting for a few minutes, the natives having the best of the position ; indeed they might have wiped us out but for their stupid habit of firing on the run, as they charged. Wilson ordered us to retire down the vlei ; some hundred yards farther on we came to an ant-heap and took our second position on that, and held it for some time. Wilson jumped on the top of the ant-heap and shouted—' Every man pick his nigger.' There was no random firing, I would be covering a man when he dropped to somebody's rifle, and I had to choose another.

" Now *we* had the best of the position. The Matabele came on furiously down the open. Soon we were firing at two hundred yards and less ; and the turned-up shields began to lie pretty thick over the ground. It got too hot for them ; they broke and took cover in the bush. We fired about twenty rounds per man at this ant-heap. Then the position was flanked by heavy reinforcements from among the timbers ; several more horses were knocked out and we had to quit. We retreated in close order into the bush on the opposite side of the vlei—the other side from the scherms. We went slowly on account of the disabled men and horses.

" There was a lull, and Wilson rode up to me and asked if I thought I could rush through to the main column. A scout on a good horse might succeed, of couse, where the patrol as a whole would not stand a chance. It was a forlorn hope, but I thought it was only a question of here or there, and I said I'd try, asking for a man to be sent with me. A man called Gooding said he was willing to come, and I picked Ingram also because we had been through many adventures together, and I thought we might as well see this last one through together.

" So we started, and we had not gone five hundred yards when we came upon the horn of an impi closing in from the river. We saw the leading men, and they saw us and fired. As they did so I swerved my horse sharp to the left, and shouting to the others, ' Now for it ! ' we thrust the horses through the bush at their best pace. A bullet whizzed past my eye, and leaves, cut by the firing, pattered down on us ; but as usual the natives fired too high.

" So we rode along, seeing men, and being fired at continually, but outstripping the enemy. The peculiar chant of an advancing impi, like a long, monotonous baying or growling, was loud in our ears, together with the noise they make drumming on their hide shields with the assegai—you must hear an army making those sounds to realise them. As soon as we got where the bush was thinner, we shook off the niggers who were pressing us, and, coming to a bit of hard ground, we turned on our tracks and hid in some thick bush. We did this more than once and stood quiet, listening to the noise they made beating about for us on all sides. Of course we knew that scores of them must have run gradually back upon the river to cut us off, so we doubled and waited, getting so near again to the patrol that once during the firing which we heard thickening back there, the spent bullets pattered around us. Those waiting moments were bad. We heard firing soon from the other side of the river too, and didn't know but that the column was being wiped out as well as the patrol.

" At last, after no end of doubling and hiding and riding in a triple loop, and making use of every device known to a scout for destroying a spoor—it took us about three hours and a half to cover as many miles—we reached the river, and found it a yellow flood two hundred yards broad. In the way African rivers have, the stream, four feet across last night, had risen from the rain. We did not think our horses could swim it, utterly tired as they now were ; but we were just playing the game through, so we decided to try. With their heads and ours barely above the water, swimming and drifting, we got across and crawled out on the other side. Then, for the first time, I remember, the idea struck me that we might come through it after all, and with that the desire of life came passionately back upon me.

"We topped the bank, and there, five hundred yards in front to the left, stood several hundred Matabele ! They stared at us in utter surprise, wondering, I suppose, if we were the advance guard of some entirely new reinforcement. In desperation we walked our horses quietly along in front of them, paying no attention to them. We had gone some distance like this, and nobody followed behind, till at last one man took a shot at us ; and with that a lot more of them began to blaze away. Almost at the same moment Ingram caught sight of horses only four or five hundred yards distant ; so the column still existed—and there it was. We took the last gallop out of our horses then, and—well, in a few minutes I was falling out of the saddle, and saying to Forbes : ' It's all over ; we are the last of that party ! ' Forbes only said, ' Well, tell nobody else till we are through with our own fight,' and next minute we were just firing away along with the others, helping to beat off the attack on the column."

Here Mr. Burnham's narrative ends.

What happened to Wilson and his gallant companions, and the exact manner of their end after Burnham and his two comrades left them, is known only through the reports of natives who took part in the fight. This, however, is certain: since the immortal company of Greeks died at Thermopylæ, few, if any, such stands have been made in the face of in-evitable death. They knew what the issue must be ; for them there was no possibility of escape ; the sun shone upon them for the last time, and for the last time the air of heaven blew upon their brows. Around them, thousand upon thousand, were massed their relentless foes, the bush echoed with war-cries, and from behind every tree and stone a ceaseless fire was poured upon their circle. But these four-and-thirty men never wavered, never showed a sign of fear. Taking shelter behind the boles of trees, or the bodies of their dead horses, they answered the fire shot for shot, coolly, with perfect aim, without haste or hurry.

The bush around told this tale of them in after days, for

There he stood silent and solitary.

the bark of every tree was scored with bullets, showing that wherever an enemy had exposed his head there a ball had been sent to seek him. Also there was another testimony— that of the bones of the dead Matabele, the majority of whom had clearly fallen shot through the brain. The natives themselves state that for every white man who died upon that day, there perished at least ten of their own people, picked off, be it remembered, singly as they chanced to expose them- selves. Nor did the enemy waste life needlessly, for their general ordered up the King's elephant hunters, trained shots, every one of them, to compete with the white man's fire.

For two long hours or more that fight went on. Now and again a man was killed, and now and again a man was wounded, but the wounded still continued to load the rifles that they could not fire, handing them to those of their companions who were as yet unhurt. At some period during the fray, so say the Matabele, the white men began to " sing." What is meant by the singing we can never know, but probably they cheered aloud after repelling a rush of the enemy. At length their fire grew faint and infrequent, till by degrees it flickered away, for men were lacking to handle the rifles. One was left, however, who stood alone and erect in the ring of the dead, no longer attempting to defend himself, either because he was weak with wounds, or because his ammuni- tion was exhausted. There he stood silent and solitary, presenting one of the most pathetic yet splendid sights told of in the generation that he adorned. There was no more firing now, but the natives stole out of their cover and came up to the man quietly, peering at him half afraid. Then one of them lifted his assegai and drove it through his breast. Still he did not fall ; so the soldier drew out the spear and, retreating a few yards, he hurled it at him, transfixing him. Now, very slowly, making no sound, the white man sank forward upon his face, and so lay still.

There seems to be little doubt but that this man was none other than Major Allan Wilson, the commander of the patrol. Native reports of his stature and appearance suggest this, but there is a stronger piece of evidence. The Matabele told Mr. Burnham who repeated it to the present writer, that this man wore a hat of a certain shape and size, fastened up at the side in a peculiar fashion ; a hat similar to that which Mr. Burnham wore himself. Now, these hats were of American make, and Major Wilson was the only man in that party who possessed one of them, for Mr. Burnham himself had looped it up for him in the American style, if indeed he had not presented it to him.

The tragedy seemed to be finished, but it was not so, for as the natives stood and stared at the fallen white men, from among the dead a man rose, to all appearances unharmed, holding in each hand a revolver, or a " little Maxim " as they described it. Having gained his feet he walked slowly and apparently aimlessly away towards an ant-heap that stood at some distance. At the sight the natives began to fire again, scores, and even hundreds, of shots being aimed at him, but, as it chanced, none of them struck him. Seeing that he remained untouched amidst this hail of lead, they cried out that he was " tagati," or magic-guarded, but the indunas ordered them to continue their fire. They did so, and a bullet passing through his hips, the Englishman fell down paralysed. Then finding that he could not turn they ran round him and stabbed him, and he died firing with either hand back over his shoulders at the slaughterers behind him.

So perished the last of the Wilson patrol. He seems to have been Alexander Hay Robertson—at least Mr. Burnham believes that it was he, and for this reason. Robertson, he says, was the only man of the party who had grey hair, and at a little distance from the other skeletons was found a skull to which grey hair still adhered.

It is the custom among savages of the Zulu and kindred races, for reasons of superstition, to rip open and mutilate the bodies of enemies killed in war, but on this occasion the Matabele general, having surveyed the dead, issued an order : " Let them be," he said ; " they were men who died like men, men whose fathers were men."

No finer epitaph could be composed in memory of Wilson and his comrades. In truth the fame of this death of theirs has spread far and wide throughout the native races of Southern Africa, and Englishmen everywhere reap the benefit of its glory. They also who lie low, they reap the benefit of it, for their story is immortal, and it will be told hundreds of years hence when it matters no more to them whether they died by shot and steel on the banks of the Shangani, or elsewhere in age and sickness. At least through the fatal storm of war they have attained to peace and honour, and there within the circle of the ruins of Zimbabwe they sleep their sleep, envied of some and revered by all. Surely it is no small thing to have attained to such a death, and England may be proud of her sons who won it.

FACING DEATH ON THE GEORGES SHOALS

By
WESTON MARTYR

I HAPPEN to have spent a good part of my life sailing little boats about the big seas. It is a game that appeals to me, and I can say in general it is not the hazardous business most landsmen appear to think it. The last voyage I made, for instance, was in a cutter (a small one-masted sailing yacht), from Falmouth to New York and back to Plymouth, via the Bermudas ; a double crossing of the Atlantic. The outward passage lasted fifty days, and it took only twenty-eight days to sail home again. That whole business was a matter of less than ten thousand miles, a few gales of wind, and all the meat aboard going bad in the middle of the Atlantic. Nothing much to make a song about, and a mere picnic compared with the shorter voyage I propose to tell of now.

This voyage was from a small harbour on the east coast of Nova Scotia to Vineyard Haven in Martha's Vineyard, Massachusetts, in all only some three hundred-odd miles —not a long passage, you see, and I hoped, with luck, to make it within four days. The time was the first week in March, which is really rather too early in the year to go sailing about those seas in a little boat ; because in March in Nova Scotia it is still winter, when gales of wind are far too apt to occur, and where sometimes a blizzard—a freezing, killing hurricane—sweeps down out of the Arctic to devastate that part of the world.

However, I was in a hurry—which is usually a mistake. The boat in which I sailed was a thirty-foot schooner—that is, she had two masts and four fore-and-aft sails, and if you will pace out ten paces on your carpet, you will see how long, or short, she was. Three good paces will show you her greatest breadth, and if you are over five feet six inches tall you would certainly bump your head on the deck beams every time you tried to stand upright in the cabin.

Which thought gives me an idea. I think it will make this story more realistic if *you*, in imagination, make this voyage

77

with me. Step aboard, Shipmate ! Come below—and shut
the cabin hatch after you, for it is perishing cold on deck.
If you will sail with me to Vineyard Haven we should have
a good time. You can take the starboard bunk. The mattress
smells slightly of iodine because it is stuffed with dried sea-
weed. It sends you to sleep. When you lie down on that you
have *got* to sleep. And here are half a dozen Hudson Bay
three-point blankets. If they do not keep you warm nothing
will. Forward here is the galley, with a big coal stove ; for
I like to keep things below as warm, dry and comfortable as
I can. Aft of the cabin there is this forty gallon tank of
fresh water, and enough food and stores for the two of us for
three weeks.

Will you come ? Do not be apprehensive at the smallness
of the boat. She is small, but she is good. She is strong and
well built ; and I have sailed about the high seas in many
worse boats than this during the last thirty years and never
come to much harm yet—touch wood. The truth is, any small
boat, be she well built and properly handled, is as safe during
bad weather at sea as any big luxury liner. This is a fact,
which has been proved repeatedly.

I could give you a number of instances, but one will do.
In 1901 John Voss sailed all the way around this world in the
thirty-eight foot dug-out canoe " Tilikum." He sailed over
49,000 miles, rode out in perfect safety twenty-two major
gales and enjoyed himself thoroughly—all that, mark you,
in a dug-out canoe. In comparison our boat is a fine big ship,
and our voyage is only 300 miles. So there is not a thing to
be scared of.

If you are a lady, so much the better, because I remember
one of the very best shipmates I ever sailed with was a girl.
She pulled her weight all the time—even if it was only eight
stone. But she made every ounce count. She stood her watch
on deck, turn and turn about with me, every four hours,
fine or blow. She did her half of the work of the ship ; and
there was no nonsense about her not turning out on deck in
bad weather, nor of her doing all the housemaid work or the
cooking just because she was a woman. No ! We shared the
job. And, anyway, I was a darned sight better cook than she
was. And I know of three cases where women have lasted
out long small-boat voyages better than their men. Will you
come ? Good ! We sail at day-break to-morrow, so I advise
you to follow my example and turn in now for an all-night
sleep. We may not get another chance.

We sleep—and you awake at dawn to sniff with appreciation two of the most divine incenses known to man—I allude
to the smells of hot coffee and fried bacon. We enjoy our
early breakfast and then we go on deck, and while you are
heaving up the anchor I set the sails.

Within five minutes we are gliding out of the little harbour
before a light land breeze that smells deliciously as the pine
forests ashore begin to warm up in the sun. In an hour we
are six miles out at sea, well clear of the coast—a line of low
cliffs, topped with pine woods and fringed with reefs and
detached rocks, against which the great swells, rolling in from
the North Atlantic, break in thunder and a wild white turmoil
of foam.

It is a bad coast to be caught on, so we set a course to pass
ten miles clear of Cape Sable, the most south-easterly point
of Nova Scotia and now distant from us twenty-five miles.

I regret to see that you are looking rather apprehensively
at those swells. They are rolling in majestically from seaward
and they must have been caused by a heavy gale of wind out
there. But they are not breaking here. Their tops are round
and smooth, and all they do to our small boat is to lift her up
for twenty feet or so and let her down again into the trough.
Well, what of it? it is as safe as a switchback, and much
more pleasant. So long as the crests do not break there is
nothing to worry about. The swells themselves, I assure you,
cannot hurt us.

Consider, for your comfort, that it is not the actual water
in the waves that comes charging at us, it is only the form,
the *shape* of the waves that move. And how can a mere shape
hurt us?

So—be bold! If you wait until we lift on the top of a
swell you will just be able to see a white lighthouse on a little
island. That is Cape Sable. And it is eight bells—noon.
Here! Take the wheel. Steer west by south. It is easy and
you will soon get the hang of it. Keep that point on the
compass card opposite the black line on the compass case.
That is our course for Nantucket. We have got 250 miles
to go before we get there—say two days more, before we sight
land again. So, till then, we have got nothing to worry about.
We cannot hit anything if we try—except the Georges Shoals.
But they lie a good fifteen miles to the south of our course,
thank Heaven.

We do not want to hit *them*. They are sand shoals, but
you cannot see them because they are submerged. They lie

out in deep water, one hundred miles from Nantucket. There
is less than ten feet of water over them in places, and in fine,
calm weather we could probably sail right across them without coming to much harm, perhaps, if only we dared to take
the risk. But in bad weather the Georges is a terrible place.
The seas break everywhere on the shallower patches and any
vessel caught there in a gale of wind could not last ten seconds.
So I am glad we pass fifteen miles off the beastly place.

Now we will have our lunch and then I will have a nap
till 4 p.m. All you have to do in the meantime is to steer a
straight course and call me if the wind changes or if you do
not like the look of the weather.

Wake me at four o'clock, when I'll take charge till eight.
Then you'll be on watch again till midnight. We'll stand
watch and watch. Four hours on and four off. It breaks
one's sleep, but you'll soon get used to it.

Thus we carry on, through the afternoon and the night.
You find that your watch on deck from eight to midnight
passes quickly. You have acquired confidence in yourself
and in the boat by this time. You can steer a straight course
now with one hand on the wheel and one eye on the compass.
In fact, you begin to fancy yourself as a sailor. And as for the
boat, she has not as much as taken a drop of spray on deck,
in spite of the big swell ; and the cheeky, buoyant way she
rises as the great hills of water overtake her shows you she
thinks nothing of them at all. The wind is fair, a good whole
sail breeze and between the clouds the stars are showing. All
round you it is pitch-black darkness, and you feel very much
alone and a little awed as you think of your situation—far
out at sea, in the night, in a boat so small that you have but
to stretch out your hand to touch the face of the mighty
deep. But the tiny light shining on the compass is a comfort
to you—and you laugh to yourself when you look in through
the cabin hatch and see me down there, fast asleep and snoring
hard. At midnight you wake me, and I relieve you at the
wheel. You go below and lay yourself down—and in an instant you are fast asleep.

You awake, amazed, to a world of sound and fury. You
start up in your bunk and the violent motion of the boat
nearly pitches you out headlong. You hear wind whistling
in the rigging, the angry roar of breaking waters and the great
crash of a sea hitting the planking within six inches of your

head. You hear a faint shout, and struggling to the cabin hatch you slide it open.

Immediately the noise is multiplied tremendously and, for a moment, you are daunted. Then you look outside and a shower of spray strikes you in the face. It hurts. It is as though some one had thrown a handful of gravel at you. You see me braced at the wheel, with cascades of water running from my oilskins. Behind me rears a grey-green hill of water, hoary with foam and spindrift, bearing a roaring angry crest. Then the hill of water vanishes as the stern of the boat flings up to a sky all sinister greens and evil copper, blotches with purple-black cloud. Down goes the stern, revealing another great wave baring its teeth at us—and when you realise from my urgent gestures that I want you to come on deck and steer, you are—dismayed. But only for the moment. By the time you reach the wheel you are wet to the skin and the wind seems striving to tear your hair and clothes off you. I cry in your ear :

" Steer her dead before the wind ; " and such is the power of the wind that to you my shout seems to come from a great distance.

You steer. It is hard work to steer. The wheel kicks viciously, and tries to tear the spokes from your hands. But you steer. It takes most of your strength and all of your mind to keep the boat running before the wind. As each sea roars up behind her she struggles to turn round and face the thing. But you check her each time. You know if one of those waves catches her broadside on that it will sweep right over her and wash us and everything on deck away. You keep the boat running before the seas. You steer with all your might and all your faculties. And presently you become aware of a struggle—a fight going on inside you.

It is me, battling with a berserk sail. I am trying to stow the main, the biggest sail in the boat. I drag it slowly down the mast, a flapping, slashing maniac of a sail. A child can stow it in an ordinary wind—but *now* ! It is a savage thing, and dangerous. But at last it is down and lashed and double-lashed to the boom.

For minutes I sit on the deck, clasping the mast, panting, catching my breath, licking my wounds. Then I crawl, slowly and fearfully forward, flat on my belly like a snake, and tackle the two head sails. The instant I start to lower the jib the canvas gives two savage flaps that shake the whole boat, and then the sail disintegrates in whipping threads

and tatters. The fore staysail comes down easily enough ;
but it takes an hour of wary, weary effort to double reef the
foresail. An hour and nearly all my strength ; but I have
enough left when the job is done, to crawl to the wheel,
bring the boat's head round to the wind and heave her to.

We watch her anxiously for some minutes. Under her
one small triangle of sail she now faces the seas, lifts herself
over them as they come rushing at her, gives way before them
when they threaten to come crashing down upon her deck.
She does well. She is all right. Hove-to like this she can look
after herself for a while, so we lash the wheel, then crawl
down into the cabin—played out, done to a turn, with no more
strength left in us.

According to the clock it is 10 a.m.—three hours since
you came on deck ! It seems like ten minutes. And the fire
is out. And the cabin floor is a foot deep in ashes, stores,
blankets and *water* ! Heaven help us, we've sprung a leak !
For a little we gaze at each other in consternation.

To spring a leak at sea is bad enough at any time ; but
in our present circumstances it is a calamity. However,
calamity or not, we have to tackle it, and, played out as we
are, we must pump. So we pump—a back-breaking job, and
after a while the pump refuses to work. The suction is choked
by the ashes washed out of the stove. As we can't pump
we must bail with buckets, which is harder work even than
pumping and gives less results. But we bail for our lives.
And presently, when we begin to feel we might as well drown
quietly as go on any more with that heartbreaking, hopeless
labour, we notice there is not quite so much water in the boat
as before.

We are gaining on the leak. In time we bail the boat nearly
dry and suspect that there is no leak after all. And when it
becomes clear that most of the water must have come in
through the cabin hatch, which some one forgot to shut, a
great weight is lifted from our minds, and we become almost
cheerful—but not for long.

It is hard to be cheerful when everything, including yourself is sopping wet in a temperature only just above freezing.
Our bailing has made us sweat—one does not perspire in
such circumstances, one sweats good and plenty. So very
soon we are shuddering in the bitter cold and our teeth
chatter. I try to light the stove. It is a long job, because somehow or other in my struggle with the sails I have managed to
sprain one thumb and tear the nail off the other ; also the

kindlings are wet, and most of the matches. However, some paraffin poured into the stove does the trick in the end, and in the strong draught the flames go roaring up the stove-pipe.

The heat is heavenly and we huddle close to the stove. But not for long. We can feel that things are not going well with the boat. The whistling of the wind has changed to howlings. The vibration of the rigging makes the whole boat shake and every time she rises to the top of a sea the wind knocks her flat, in spite of the tiny area of sail she is carrying. And now she cannot rise soon enough to all the seas. They begin to break aboard, and down in the cabin the sound of them as they crash on the deck is frightening. The boat is being overpowered.

Every minute the weather is getting worse, and soon she will be overwhelmed, unless we help her. We must relieve her by stowing the reefed foresail and putting out a sea-anchor. This is a daunting thought. Down in the cabin we have to hold on hard and brace ourselves even to remain seated on the floor, so who can be expected to go out on the open deck and fight with sails and ropes in the face of all that fury of the wind and sea ? It isn't fair ! It seems futile to make the effort, absurd. Better to drown quietly in the cabin than be swept off the deck to die struggling in all that uproar and brutal violence out there.

Then we look at each other—and feel guilty and ashamed of our unspoken thought. We crawl aft and drag out from a locker, with groans and curses, the sea-anchor and its coil of thick rope. We gingerly open the cabin hatch, and gasp and slam it shut again against the torrent of icy water that instantly bursts in—against the roar and fury of the gale—against all those things that terrify us out there. We hesitate. We tremble in each nerve and muscle and fetch deep shivering sighs. And then, thank heavens, our desperation, or something, suddenly makes us angry. Cursing, we fling open the hatch and scramble out. On deck the wind takes our breath away. We bow our heads and gasp and hang on like grim death.

And then I scramble madly forward along the deck with the end of the anchor rope. Out there I feel like a soldier who climbs from the comparative shelter of a trench, out into the bareness, the noise and the violence of a no-man's-land filled with bullets and bursting shells. I am desperately afraid and desperately anxious to get the job over and done. I dare not look at the seas. Every ten seconds I hear the roar of one coming and clamp my legs and arms around anything solid I can reach.

A giant plunges me beneath Niagara, holds me down, shakes me viciously, tries to wrench me from my hold—and in between whiles I find myself frantically bending on the anchor rope to the bow bitts.

At last it is done and I make violent motions at you and you understand the time has come for you to put the sea-anchor over the side. I see you wrestling with the thing in the wind. It is a bag of the stoutest canvas, eight feet long with its mouth held open by a steel ring. Into the water it goes and I watch you almost follow it, without so much as one quicker beat of my heart. You were nearly lurched overboard, but narrow escapes have long ago become part of our natural order of things. *I* can't help you. The vital thing is, what effect will the sea-anchor have?

It sinks and I see the boat carried down wind of it between the scend of two enormous seas. Then the anchor rope tautens with a wrench and jerk and swings the boat's bow to wind and sea. It is doing its job, by heavens—and by that same token I had better finish mine. With the boat held head on to the sea it is now less difficult to work on deck. I lower away the foresail in frantic haste and the canvas comes down, slatting and thundering in the rush of that mighty wind. I subdue the mad sail with ropes, and, throwing caution to the winds, dive for the cabin.

You have dived, too, and together we poke our heads out of the hatch, watching with anxiety how the boat will now behave. And she does well. With her bow held up to the seas by her sea-anchor she takes less water on deck, and under her bare poles she is no longer knocked down by the wind every time she climbs a sea.

But heavens above! how she rolls and pitches. She flings herself thirty feet up the face of each sea, pitchpoles over the crest and falls another thirty feet into the valley beyond. And she rolls, rolls, rolls—through one hundred degrees and more, every two seconds. It sickens us to watch her. It seems as if she soon must shake herself to pieces, shake her masts right out.

We notice for the first time that it is and has been snowing heavily. The snow and spray are beginning to freeze to the rigging. We shut the hatch and jam ourselves between the berths on the cabin floor. Even there we are flung about unless we hold on hard. But the stove is still alight—which is lucky, for we understand now it is not an ordinary gale we have been caught in ; it is that terror of those seas, a blizzard. And without the stove it would freeze us to death to-night.

We are wet through, bruised all over and exhausted. We lie down on the floor. The wind howls like a pack of wolves, screams like a maniac, booms like great guns. Sea after sea hits us with a rending crash and the motion is unbelievable, terrific. And we lie there, hour after hour, trying to stop ourselves from being rolled about, craving, yearning for quietness, some rest, some peace, knowing those things to be all equally impossible.

But in the night we both nearly attain peace—almost, but not quite. And if we had, our rest would have been for ever. For the wind affects the draught of the stove and the fumes, instead of going up the pipe, are blown back into the cabin, where we have shut tight every opening to keep out the water and the freezing cold.

After we seem to have been lying there for years in misery, I begin to notice a nasty taste of sulphur in my mouth, but I ignore it for a delicious feeling of numbness has come over me and I think, I hope, I pray that at last I am actually going to sleep. To sleep ! To sleep ! If only you would stop breathing so noisily, so stertorously. You sound, confound you, like some one choking in a fit.

And then, suddenly, I understand. I reach the hatch somehow and open it and fall half outside in a faint. And when I come to I am stupid and nearly frozen, but I have enough sense left and enough strength to drag you half out of the hatch, too. When we come to our senses we put out the fire—and lose the warmth, our last comfort. We wrap ourselves up in the wet blankets and some spare sails—and suffer—for fifteen ghastly hours, wherein the bitter cold is to bear than the fear of death which also never leaves us.

Suddenly, in the middle of the next day, something comes through to me from the pandemonium outside—a change in the noise, in the motion—the sensation of something impending is so strong that this all but frozen corpse springs up alert, intense, listening. Through the noise of the wind comes the sound of the furious waters ; but the seas are roaring no longer—they are crashing all round us, and the boat, instead of being flung from hollow to crest is being stamped on, savaged, kicked aside. I open the hatch and look outside

—and my heart stops beating. For the water is green no longer. It is brown! And our decks are covered with sand! This is the end. We have been driven into shallow water. We're done for. We're on the Georges Shoals!

Man is a queer creature. Before the prospect of pain and suffering he is very apt to squeal and give up. But face him with almost certain and apparently inescapable death, and as likely as not he will put up a good fight for his life. I have noticed this peculiar psychological reaction frequently, especially during the War.

And it is so with us now. We are in water so shallow that the sand on the bottom is being churned up by the waves. And down wind, dead to leeward of us, and no more than a quarter of a mile off is a shallower patch still. We can see that by the breakers. The waves are having a sort of savage dog-fight there. The spot is chaos, awful to look at—and we are drifting right down on it fast. It is better to do something than just sit and wait to be killed.

Without any consultation, one of us saws through the sea-anchor rope with a knife, while the other hoists the foresail half up. We don't believe that any boat can possibly sail in such a wind and sea and we certainly cannot sail into the wind and away from those terrific breakers. But we may, by some miracle, skirt them—if we try. And presently we find we are doing, actually, that very thing! The miracle is happening! The breakers are slowly passing to one side. They are desperately close—but they are passing. They *have* passed. Well done, good boat.

But we do no congratulate ourselves. We have now sailed right amongst the shoals. At the moment we are in a less shallow part, but on each side of us, and ahead—and astern, too, now—are more and more shoal patches, with the breakers roaring over them in a way that is frightful to see. We must simply try to keep in the deeper channels and thread our way through the maze ahead if we can. It seems absurd to try it. But it's all we can do. It's thousands to one against us; but we've dodged one bank already—and we may again.

So we carry on; a forlorn hope indeed, driven on by the gale behind, watching the breakers ahead, turning now half right, now half left, side-stepping disaster by yards, dodging destruction by feet, missing death by inches, waiting as we fall into the hollow of each and every wave for the shock of our keel striking the bottom and our boat being instantaneously shattered to splinters.

Time does not exist under such conditions of hazard and mental strain ; but we know it took us four hours to cross the shoals. And the dark was falling when the face of the waters changed from brown to green and told us we had escaped from that Valley of the Shadow.

THE TRADER OF LAST NOTCH

By
PERCEVAL GIBBON

IN Manicaland summer wears the livery of the tropics. At the foot of the hills north of Macequece every yard of earth is vocal with life and the bush is brave with colour. Where the earth shows it is red, as though a wound bled. The mimosas have not yet come to flower, but amid their delicate green the long thorns, straight or curved like claws, gleam with the flash of silver. Palms poise aloft, brilliant and delicate and underfoot flowers are abroad. The flame-blossom blazes in scarlet. The sangdieu burns in sullen vermilion. Insects fill the world with the noise of their business—spiders, butterflies and centipedes, ants, beetles and flies, and mysterious entities that crawl nameless underfoot. A pea-hen shrieks in the grass and a kite whistles aloft. A remote speck in the sky denotes a watchful vulture, alert for any mishap to the citizens of the woods, and a crash of twigs may mean anything from a buck to a rhinoceros. There is a hectic on the face of nature.

The trader of Last Notch went homewards to his store through such a maze of urgent life, and panted in the heat. He had been out to shoot guinea-fowl, had shot none and expended all his cartridges, and his gun, glinting in the strong light as he walked, was heavy to his shoulder and hot to his hand. His mood was one of patient protest, for the sun found him an easy prey and he had yet some miles to go. Where another man would have said, "Damn the heat," and done with it, John Mills, the trader, tasted the word on his lips, forbore to slip it, and counted it to himself for virtue. He set a large value on restraint, which, in view of his strength and resolute daring, was perhaps not wholly false. He was a large man, more noticeable for a sturdy solidity of proportion than for height, and his strong face was won to pleasantness by a brown beard, which he wore "navy fash." His store, five big huts above the kloof known as Last Notch, was at the heart of a large Kafir population ; and the natives, agriculturists by convention and warriors between whiles, patronised him very liberally. The Englishman and Portuguese of the country held him in favour, and he enjoyed that esteem which a strong quiet man, who has proved himself to have reserves of violence. commonly wins from turbulent neighbours.

He was trying for a short-cut home, and purposed to wade the Revue River wherever he should strike it. Over the low bush about him he could see his hills yet a couple of hours off, and he sighed for thirst and extreme discomfort. No one, he knew, lived thereabouts—no one, at least, who was likely to have whisky at hand, though, for the matter of that, he would have welcomed a hut and a draught of Kafir *itywala*. His surprise was the greater, then, when there appeared from the growth beside his path as white a man as himself, a tall, somewhat ragged figure—but rags tell no news at all in Manicaland—who wore a large black moustache and smiled affably on him.

He noted that the stranger was a fine figure of a man, tall and slim, with clear dark eyes and tanned face, and he saw, too, that he wore a heavy Webley on his right hip. The newcomer continued to smile as Mills scanned him over, and waited for the trader to speak first.

" Hullo ! " said Mills at length.

" 'Ullo ! " replied the stranger, smiling still. He had a capital smile, and Mills was captivated into smiling in sympathy.

" Who may you be ? " he asked agreeably ; " didn't expect to meet no white men about here. Where's your boys ? "

The tall man waved his hand vaguely in the direction of the coast, as though to imply that he had carriers somewhere in that part of the world.

" Yais," he said pleasantly. " An' you are Jone Mills, eh ? "

" That's me," said Mills promptly, lowering the butt of his gun to the ground and resting both hands on the muzzle. The stranger started slightly, but did not cease to smile.

" I don't seem to know you," pondered Mills. " I can't fix you at all."

" Ah, but you will. Le' me see. Was it Beira, eh ? "

Mills shook his head decidedly. " I never was in Beira," he said.

" Not Beira ? " queried the stranger. " Oh, but surelee. No ? Well, Mandega's, per'aps ? "

"Mandega's? Yes, I was there for a bit. I had a block of claims on the ditch, next to old Jimmy Ryan's."

"Ah, yais," said the tall man eagerly. "I know 'im. An' there you shoot the Intendente, not? That was ver' fine. I see you coom down all quiet, an' shoot 'im in the 'ead. It was done ver' nice, eh?"

Mills face darkened. "He was robbin' me, the swine," he answered. "He'd been robbin' me for six months. But that's nobody's business but mine, and anyhow I didn't shoot him in the head. It was in the chest. An' now, who the blazes are you?"

"You do' know me?" smiled the stranger; "but I know you. Oh, ver' well. I see you ver' often. You see? My name is Jacques."

"Jack what?" demanded Mills.

"Not Jack—Jacques. Tha' 's all. All the people call me Frenchy, eh? You don' remember?"

"No," said Mills thoughtfully; "but then I seen a good many chaps, and I'd be like to forget some o' them. You doin' anything round here?"

The man who called himself Jacques held up a finger. "Ah, you wan' to know, eh? Well, I don' tell you. I fin' anything, I don't tell all the people; I don't blow the gaff. I sit still, eh? I lie low, eh? I keep 'im all for me, eh? You see?"

"Well, of course," agreed Mills; "struck a pocket, I suppose. I shouldn't have thought you'd have found much here. But then, of course, you're not going to give your game away. Where's your camp? I could do with a drink."

"Back there," said the Frenchman, pointing in the direction whence Mills had come. "'Bout five miles. You don't want to come, eh? Too far, eh?"

"Yes, I reckon it's too far," replied Mills. "I'm not more than four miles from my own *kia* now. You goin' on?"

"Yais," agreed the Frenchman, "I go a leetle bit. Not too far, eh?"

They moved on through the bush. Mills shifted his gun from shoulder to shoulder, and suffered still from heat and sweat. His taller companion went more easily, striding along as Mills thought, glancing at him, "like a fox." The warmth appeared not to distress him in the least.

"By Jove," exclaimed the trader. "You're the build of man for this blooming country. You travel as if you was born to it. Don't the heat trouble you at all?"

" Oh, no," answered the Frenchman carelessly. " You see, I come from a 'ot country. In France it is ver' often 'ot. But you don't like it, eh ? "

" No," said the trader with emphasis. " I was after pea-hen, or you wouldn't see me out this time o' the day. English chaps can't stand it."

" Eh ? "

" English chaps can't stand it, I said," repeated Mills. " They mos'ly lie up till its cooler."

" Ah, yais."

They were now nearing the river. A steam rose over the bushes and spiralled into the air, and the hum of water going slowly was audible. A few minutes of walking brought them to its banks. The stream flowed greasily and dark, some forty yards wide, but in the middle it forked about a spit of sand not more than ten paces broad. It was a very Lethe of a river, running oilily and with a slumberous sound, and its reputation for crocodiles was vile.

Mills sat down and began to pull off his boots.

"As well here as anywhere," he said. " I'll try it, anyhow."

" I go back now," said the Frenchman. " Some day I come up an' see you, eh ? You like that ? "

" Come along any time," replied Mills cheerfully as he slung his boots across his shoulders. " You don't think that island's a quicksand, eh ? "

The Frenchman turned and stared at it. " I do' know," he answered. " Per'aps. You goin' to try, eh ? "

" Yes, I'll have a shot at it. You can mos'ly trust yourself on 'em if you walk light an' quick. But we'll see."

The Frenchman watched him as he waded out. The black water reached no higher than his knees, but the ground was soft underfoot, and he floundered anxiously.

" It sucks at you," he called. " It's all greasy."

He moved on and came to the sand island.

" It's better here," he called. " It'll be all right now."

The Frenchman jumped to his feet.

" Look out ! " he shouted, gesticulating violently. " You go down ; walk off 'im ! "

Mills glanced down and saw that the creeping sand had him knee-deep. He dragged his right foot forth and plunged forward, but with the action his left leg sank to the crutch, and he only kept his balance with a violent effort.

The Frenchman danced on the bank. " Throw you' gun down," he shouted. " Throw you' boots down. You' in to the waist now. Push yo'self back to the water. Push hard."

He wrung his hands together with excitement.

Mills threw down his rifle and the sand swallowed it at once. He turned his head to the man at the bank.

"It's no good, chum," he said quietly. "I reckon you better take a shot at me with that revolver."

The sand was in his armpits. The Frenchman ceased to jump and wring his hands, and smiled at him oddly. Mills, in the midst of his trouble, felt an odd sense of outraged propriety. The smile, he reflected, was ill-timed—and he was sinking deeper.

"What you grinning at?" he gasped. "Shoot, can't you?"

"I coom pull you out," said the Frenchman, fumbling at the buckle of his belt, and he forthwith stepped into the water.

He waded swiftly to within five feet of the sinking man and flung him the end of the belt. Mills failed to catch it, and the Frenchman shifted his feet cautiously and flung again.

"Now," he shouted as the trader gripped it, "catch 'old tight," and he started to drag him bodily forwards.

"Careful," cried Mills; "you're sinking!"

The Frenchman stepped free hastily and strained on the belt again. Mills endeavoured to kick with his entombed legs, and called a warning as his rescuer sunk in the sands. Thus they wrestled, and at length Mills found his head in the water and his body free.

He rose, and they waded to the bank.

"Of all the quicksands *I* ever saw," said the trader slowly, as he sat down and gazed at the place that had so nearly been his grave, "that one's the worst."

"'Orrid," agreed the Frenchman, smiling amicably. "You was ver' near buried, eh?"

"Yes," said the trader thoughtfully. "I suppose any one 'ud say you saved my life, Frenchy?"

"Yes," replied the other.

"Exactly," said Mills. "Well, there's my hand for you, Frenchy. You done me a good turn. I'll do as much for you one of these days."

"Eh?" said the Frenchman as he shook hands.

"You've got a nasty habit of saying 'Eh?'" retorted the trader. "I said I'd do as much for you one of these days. Comprenny?"

" Oh, yais," smiled the Frenchman. " I think you will. Tha's all right."

" Well," said Mills, " I wish you'd come up and see me at my *kia*. Sure you can't come now ? "

" Yais, I coom now," answered the other.

Mills stared. " 'Fraid you can't trust me to go alone, are you ? " he queried. " 'Cause, if so——"

" Tha's all right," interrupted the Frenchman. " I coom now."

" Right you are," said Mills heartily. " Come along then ! "

They strode off in the direction of the drift, Mills going thoughtfully, with an occasional glance at his companion. The Frenchman smiled perpetually, and once he laughed out.

" What's the joke ? " demanded the trader.

" I think I do a good piece of business to-day," replied the Frenchman.

" H'm, yes," continued Mills suspiciously.

It was a longish uphill walk to the trader's store and the night fell while they were yet on the way. With the darkness there came a breeze, cool and refreshing ; the sky filled with sharp points of light and the bush woke with a new life. The crackle of their boots on the stiff grass as they walked sent live things scattering to left and right, and once a night-adder hissed malevolently at the Frenchman's heel. They talked little as they went, but Mills noticed that now and again his companion appeared to check a laugh. He experienced a feeling of vague indignation against the man who had saved his life ; he was selfish in not sharing his point of view and the thoughts which amused him. At times reserve can be the most selfish thing imaginable, and one might as well be reticent on a desert island as in Manicaland. Moreover, despite the tolerant manners of the country, Mills was conscious of something unexplained in his companion— something which engendered a suspicion on general grounds.

The circle of big dome-shaped huts which constituted the store of Last Notch came into view against a sky of dull velvet as they breasted the last rise. The indescribable homely smell of a fire greeted the nostrils with the force of a spoken welcome. They could hear the gabble of the Kafirs at their supper and the noise of their shrill empty laughter.

" That's home," said Mills, breaking a long silence.

" Yais," murmured the Frenchman ; " 'ome, eh ? Yais. Ver' naice."

"You may say what you like," continued the trader aggressively. "Home is something. Though ever so 'umble, ye know, there's no place like home."

"Tha's all right," assented the other gaily. "I know a man name' Albert Smith, an' 'e sing that in the jail at Beira. Sing all the night till I stop 'im with a broom. Yais."

Mills grunted, and they entered the *skoff kia*—the largest of the huts, sacred to the uses of a dining-room. It contained two canvas chairs, a camp table, a variety of boxes to sit upon, and some picture-paper illustrations on the mud wall. A candle in a bottle illuminated it, and a bird in the thatch overhead twittered volubly at their presence. Some tattered books lay in the corner.

They washed in the open air, sluicing themselves from buckets, and dressed again in clean dungarees in another hut.

"*Skoff* [food] 'll be ready by now," said Mills ; "but I think a gargle's the first thing. You'll have whisky, or gin ? "

The Frenchman pronounced for whisky, and took it neat. Mills stared.

"If I took off a dose like that," he observed, "I should be as drunk as an owl. You know how to shift it ! "

"Eh ? "

"Gimme patience," prayed the trader. "You bleat like a yowe. I said you can take it, the drink. Savvy ? *Wena poosa meningi sterrik.* Have some more ? "

"Oh, yais," smiled the guest. "Ver' good w'isky, eh ? "

He tossed off another four fingers of the liquor and they sat down to their meal. The food was such as most tables in Manicaland offered. Everything was tinned, and the *menu* ran the gamut of edibles from roast capon (cold) to *pâté de foie gras* in a pot. When they had finished Mills passed over his tobacco and sat back. He watched the other light up and blow a white cloud, and then spoke.

"Look here, Frenchy," he said, looking at him steadily ; "I don't quite cotton to you, and I think it proper you should say a bit more than you have said."

"Eh ? " queried the other, smiling.

Mills glowered, but restrained himself. "I want to know who you are, and I guess I mean to know too, so out with it ! "

"Ah, yais," replied the Frenchman, and removed his pipe from his mouth. He trimmed the bowl fastidiously with his thumb, smiling the while. Of a sudden he looked up and the smile was gone. He gave Mills back a look as purposeful as his own.

" I'm the man that save you in the river," he said meaningly.

" Well," began the trader hotly, but stopped. " That's true," he answered thoughtfully, as though speaking to himself. " Yes, that's true. You've got me, Frenchy."

" Yais," went on the Frenchman, leaning forward across the table, and speaking with an emphasis that was like an insult. " You sink there in the sand. I stop and save you. I stop, you see, although the men from Macequece coom after me and want to kill me. But I don' run away ; I don' say to you, ' I can' stop. You go down ; you die.' I don' say that. I stop. I save you. An' now you say to me, ' Frenchy, 'oo the 'ell are you ? ' Yais."

Mills shrugged protestingly. The appeal was to the core of his nature ; the demand was one he could not dishonour.

" I didn't say just that," he urged. " But what are the chaps from Macequece after you for ? "

" Tha's all right," replied the Frenchman with a wave of his hand. " You say, ' Frenchy, I don't like you. Dam' you, Frenchy ! ' Ver' well. The men coom, you give me to them. They shoot me. Tha's all right ; yais."

He replaced his pipe and commenced again to smoke with an expression of weary indifference.

" I'm not that sort," said Mills. " I'm open to admit I didn't quite take to you—at first. I can't say fairer than that. But tell me what you done to rile the chaps. Did you kill a bloke, or what ? "

" Jone Mills," said the Frenchman ; " Jone Mills shoot the Intendente at Mandega's. Kill 'im dead. Dead as pork. They don' chase Jone Mills. They don' wan' to shoot Jone Mills. No. Frenchy—po' ol' Frenchy—'e shoot a man in Macequece. Shoot 'im dead. Dead as pork. *Then* they all coom after 'im. Wan' to shoot 'im. An' po' ol' Frenchy, 'e stop to pull Jone Mills out of the river. 'E save Jone Mills. Jone squeak an' say, ' Shoot me quick befo' I choke.' But Frenchy stop an' pull 'im out. Yais. An' then they shoot Frenchy. Yais ! " He blew a huge volume of smoke and lay back serenely.

" Look 'ere, Frenchy," cried Mills, stretching his hand across the table, " I'm in this. They won't catch you here, old son. Savvy ? There's my hand for you."

" Eh ? "

" There's my hand, I'm tellin' you. Shake hands, old son. You may be a hard case, but you *did* save my life, and it's up to me to see you through. We'll be able to call quits then."

The Frenchman rose with a serious face, and the two shook hands over the candle. The Frenchman held Mills's hand a moment longer.

" I know you," he said. " You do' kno' me. I trust you, Jone. I know yo' a good man."

He sat back again, and Mills turned matters over. In that rough community no man would own himself devoid of gratitude. " I'll do as much for you," was the common acknowledgment of a favour. It appeared to Mills that his new acquaintance might be a precious scoundrel, but that point was not at present in issue, and there remained a debt to be satisfied before he could raise that point. The knowledge that Frenchy had shot a man did not trouble him in the least, so long as the accompanying circumstances and the motive were in accordance with the simple standards of Manicaland. Here came in the doubt, engendered by nothing more concrete or citable than a trifle of mystery in the man's manner, and some undefined quality that disagreed with the trader. He glanced over to him ; the Frenchman was glowing rings of smoke and smiling at them. There was nothing in his face but innocent and boyish amusement.

" Gad, you're a cool hand ! " exclaimed Mills. " How d'you reckon we better work it ? "

" I do' know," replied the other indifferently.

" You don't, eh ? Well, d'you think they'll follow you all night ? "

" I don' think," said the Frenchman, with confidence and a swelling of his chest ; " I don' think they wan' to meet me in the night. Not ver' naice, eh ? Leetle dangerous."

" H'm. You've got a bit of an opinion of yerself, anyhow. If that's all right, it'll be time enough to clear by daylight. Did you bolt just as you are—no niggers, no *skoff*, no anything ? "

" No time," was the answer. " So I coom out without everything. Just like this."

" I can get you a couple of niggers," mused Mills, " an' you'll want a gun. Then, with *skoff* for a fortnight, you ought to be up at the Mazoe before they find your spoor. What do you think ? "

" I think i's ver' naice," smiled the other.

" Then we'll *hamba lala* " (go to sleep), said Mills, rising. " I don't know how you feel, but I'm just done up."

A bed was soon fixed for the Frenchman, who retired with

a light-hearted "goo'-night." Mills, keeping full in view his guest's awkward position and the necessity for packing him off at daylight, determined not to sleep. He went out of the kraal and listened to the night. It spoke with a thousand voices —the great factory of days and nights was in full swing ; but he caught no sound of human approach, and returned to the huts to prepare his guest's kit for the departure. He found and partially cleaned an old rifle, and unpacked a generous donation of cartridges. Meal for the carriers, blankets and tinned meats for the Frenchman, were all at hand. Candles, a lantern, matches, gin, a pannikin, a pair of pots, and so on, soon completed the outfit. Packing is generally an interesting operation, and Mills was an expert in it. He forgot most of his perplexity and ill-ease as he adjusted the bundles and measured the commodities. He had the whole of the gear spread out on the floor of the *skoff kia* when a voice accosted him.

"You needn't bother no more, Jack," it said softly.

A man tiptoed in. He was short and lightly built, and carried a sporting rifle in his hand. His reddish moustache was draggled with dew and his clothes were soaked in it. He looked at Mills with gleeful blue eyes.

"Where's Frenchy ? " he asked softly.

Mills laboured to express surprise. "What're you talkin' about ? " he demanded loudly.

"Don't shout, blast yer ! " whispered the other vehemently. "We saw yer go up 'ere together, Jack, and nobody ain't gone away since. There's five of us, Jack, and we want that swine—we want 'im bad."

"What for ? " asked Mills desperately, without lowering his voice.

The other made an impatient gesture for silence, but his words were arrested by a clamour in the yard. There were shouts and curses and the sound of blows.

"We've got 'im, Charley," shouted some one triumphantly.

The smaller man rushed out, and Mills followed swiftly. There was a blackness of moving forms in the open and some one struck a match. The man called Charley stepped forward. Mills saw the face and hand of a man standing upright, brilliantly illuminated by the flame of the match ; and on the ground three men, who knelt on and about a prostrate figure. One was busy with some cord. In the background stood Mills's Kafirs. The match burned down to the holder's fingers and he dropped it.

F.T.S.   G

" Well, Dave," said Mills, " what's the meanin' o' this game o' yours—comin' to a man's *kia* in the middle o' the night and ropin' his mate out o' bed ? "

The man who had lit the match laughed. " That you, Jack ? " he said. " Well, you wouldn't be so ready to call this bloke ' mate ' if you knew what he'd been up to."

" The—swine ! " commented Charley.

" Get a lantern," commanded Mills to the Kafirs. " What d'you mean ? " he asked of the tall man.

" He shot a *woman* ! " said Dave. The tone was eloquent of the speaker's rage and disgust.

Mills stared open-mouthed. " A *woman* ! " he gasped.

" A woman," replied Dave. " Shot her, as bold as the devil, *on* the street, *in* the daytime, and did a bolt for the bush. Every man that could put foot to the ground is out after him."

A Kafir arrived then with the lantern Mills had designed for the Frenchman, and by its light he was able to see the faces of the men. They were all known to him. The man who was cording the prisoner's arms had seen his daring work at Mandega's. He knelt on the prostrate form as he worked, and the Frenchman's face showed like a waxen mask on the ground. Blood was running from a deep cut on his cheek.

" I save yo' life, Jone," he gasped.

" Shut up ! " snapped one of the men, and struck him on the mouth.

" Here," protested Mills ; " go slow, can't you ! There's no call to bang him about."

They stared at him with astonishment. " Why, man," exclaimed Charley, " didn't we tell you he shot a woman ? "

" What's that he said about savin' your life ? " demanded Dave.

" He did," explained Mills. He told them the story, and they listened without sympathy.

" It was a bloomin' plucky thing to do," concluded the trader. " I'd ha' bin dead by now but for him, and I owe 'im one for it."

" Oh, nobody's sayin' he isn't plucky," said the man who had been tying the Frenchman's arms as he rose to his feet. " He's the dare-devillest swine alive, but he's done with it now."

Dave came round and clapped Mills on the shoulder.

" It's worked you a bit soft, old man," he said. " Why,

hang it all, you wouldn't have us let him go after shooting a woman, would you ? "

" Oh ! stow it," broke in one of the others. " If it wasn't that 'e's got to go back to Macequece to be shot, I'd blow his head off now."

" I'm not asking you to let him go," cried Mills. " But give the bloke a chance, give 'im a run for it. Why, I wouldn't kill a dog so ; it's awful—an'—an'—he saved my life, chaps, he saved my life."

" But he shot a woman," said Charley.

That closed the case—the man had committed the ultimate crime. Nothing could avail him now. He shot a woman—he must suffer.

" Jone," moaned the Frenchman—the cords were eating into his flesh ; " Jone, I saved yo' life."

" Why couldn't you tell me ? " cried Mills passionately ; " why couldn't you trust me ? I could ha' got you away."

" That'll do," interrupted Dave, thrusting Mills aside. " We'll trouble you for a drink and a bite, old boy, an' then we'll start back."

Mills led the way to the *skoff kia* in silence. There was food and drink still on the table, and the men sat down to it at once. The Frenchman lay in the middle of the kraal, bound ; his captors' weapons lay at their feet. He was as effectually a prisoner as if their five barrels were covering him. Mills stood moodily watching the men eat, his brain drumming on the anguished problem of the Frenchman's life or death without effort or volition on his part.

" Got any more *poosa*, old boy ? " asked Dave, setting down the whisky bottle empty.

" Yes," said Mills thoughtfully. " Plenty." He shouted for a boy, and one came running.

" Go to the store-hut," ordered Mills slowly, " and bring a bottle of whisky." He spoke the " kitchen-Kafir " that every one in Manicaland understands.

" Yes, baas," said the native.

" But first," said Mills, still speaking slowly and quietly, " take a knife and cut loose the man on the ground. *Quick !* " The last word was a shout.

Dave sprang to his feet and stood motionless. The others were arrested in the action of rising or reaching for their weapons. From the wall beside him Mills had reached a revolver and held them covered. The barrel moved over them, presenting its black threatful mouth to one after the other. It moved in jerks, but not without purpose. It held them all subject, and the first movement doomed.

"Jack!" cried Dave.

"Shut up!" commanded Mills. "Don't move now. For God's sake don't move. I'll shoot the first one that does."

"He shot a woman," they protested.

"He saved my life," said Mills. "Are you all right, Frenchy?"

"Yais," came the answer, and with it the ghost of a laugh.

Mills did not look round, and the steady remorseless barrel still sailed to and fro across the faces of the men in the hut.

"Clear out, then," he shouted. "I'll only give you five minutes. You shot a woman. And, Frenchy——"

"Yais, Jone."

"This makes us quits, see?"

"Ver' good, Jone. Good-bye."

"Good-bye, Frenchy."

Dave ripped out a curse and shifted slightly. The barrel sprang round to him and he froze into stillness.

"Don't do that again, Davy," warned Mills.

"You'll catch it hot for this," snarled one of them.

"Very like," replied the trader.

He counted a liberal five minutes by guess. He dared not look away from his men. At last he spoke.

"It was up to me, boys," he said, with a sigh. "I couldn't do no less. If it 'ad been a man 'e shot I'd ha' kept you here all day. But I've done enough, I reckon, seein' it was a woman."

He dropped the revolver to the ground.

"Now!" he said.

They sat round and stared at him. For a full minute no one spoke. Mills gave them back their eyes gloomily, leaning with folded arms against the wall. Then Dave drew a long breath, a very sigh.

"Well, Jack," he said, shaking his head, "I didn't think it of you—I didn't, indeed. A skunk like that! a woman-shooter, and a Frenchman!! You didn't use to be like this."

"We're quits now, him and me," answered Mills. "He saved my life, and I'm satisfied. So if you've got anything to say—or do—then get it over."

Charley burst out at this in a fuss of anger. "You ought to be shot," he shouted. "That's all you're fit for."

"Charley's right," growled one of the others.

"Oh, cut it off," cried Dave impatiently; "we're not

The barrel moved over them, presenting its black threatful mouth.

going to shoot Jack. But I guess we won't say we've lost the Frenchman yet."

He lowered his brows and turned his eyes on Mills.

"You an' him's quits, Jack," he said. "What do you think about it?"

Mills looked up slowly, like a man newly awaked from a dream.

"You might get a shot at him from the path," he answered musingly. "That is, if he's keeping north. I'll show you the place." •

"You don't think we'd have a chance of catching him?"

"Not a ghost," replied the trader decisively. "Once you get into the kloof, he's lost. All you can do is wait till he breaks cover down below an' try a long shot. By God!" he cried with sudden energy, "I'll try a lick at him myself. We're quits now, the—the woman-shooter!"

He snatched a rifle and led the way, the others tumbling after him. Some hundred yards beyond the kraal the footpath dipped abruptly towards the valley, and at an angle of it there was to be gained a clear view of the bush beneath, where it surged at the foot of the hill and ran down the kloof; at the lower part of the kloof it ceased, and the ground was bare red earth for a space of some thousand yards. Mills sat down on a stone. Dave squatted beside him and the others grouped themselves on adjacent boulders.

The sun was well into the sky by now—it was about six o'clock in the morning. The air was of diamond, and the chill of the night had already passed. The men glued their eyes on the bare patch and waited.

"Funny game you played up there," whispered Dave to the trader.

Mills nodded without speaking.

"I'm not blaming you," continued the other, "I reckon I understand, old boy. But are you goin' to shoot at him?"

"I am that," was the reply.

"Well, I hope you get him," said Dave. "The chaps'll forget the other business then. They didn't like it, you know —nobody would."

"It's not because I care for them or what they think," began Mills.

"I know it's not," interrupted Dave. "You know all the ranges, I suppose?"

"Nine hundred yards to that black spot," said Mills.

" The spot's a bit of a hole in the ground. Twelve hundred to the big boulder."

He rose off the stone he was sitting on and lay down on the path, belly-under, and ran up the back-sight of his weapon with care. Flinging back the bolt, he blew into the chamber and thrust a cartridge in ; tested the air with a wet finger and wriggled the butt home into his shoulder. Dave watched him in silence ; Mills was, he knew, a good shot, and he was now preparing, with all the little tricks and graces of the rifle-range, to pull trigger on the man he had risked— nay, almost thrown away—his life to save from the consequences of an unspeakable crime.

"Ah ! " breathed Mills, with an artist's luxurious satisfaction.

Down the valley a figure had broken from the bush and was plainly to be seen against the red ground. The men on the hill flopped down and prepared to shoot.

" Don't fire," Dave warned the others. He was watching Mills. The trader's face bore no signs of his recent mental struggle. It carried no expression whatever save one of cool interest, just touched with a craftsman's confidence. His barrel was steady as his head. The little figure below was moving over the rough ground towards the black spot. They could see its legs working grotesquely, like a mechanical toy.

" So," murmured Mills. " Now just a *little* farther. So ! " He fired.

There was no leap into the air, no tragic bound and sprawling tumble. The little figure in the valley fell where it was and never moved.

Mills jerked open his breech.

" I'll bet that took him in the spine," he said.

THE DEATH-MARCH OF KÛLOP SÛMBING

By

SIR HUGH CLIFFORD, K.C.M.G.

" From age to age a glowing page
    Their names must win in story,
The men who wrought and dared and fought
    To make a nation's glory.
Half men, half gods, they feared no odds,
    And made our England's name
Echo and roll from pole to pole,
    A widening din of fame !

But had their ways, for all their days,
    Been set in lands apart,
Straitened and pent, with ne'er a vent
    For mighty brain and heart,
These very men, perhaps, might then
    Have joined the nameless throng
Who wage red war against the Law,
    But win no name in song."
               —*The Song of the Lost Heroes.*

HE was an ill fellow to look at—so men who knew him tell me—large of limb and very powerfully built. His face was broad and ugly, and a peculiarly sinister expression was imparted to it by a hare-lip, which left his gums exposed. It was to this latter embellishment that he owed at once his vicious temper and the name by which he was known. It is not difficult to understand why : for women did not love to look upon the gash in his lip, and his nickname of *Sûmbing* —which means " The Chipped One "—reminded him of his calamity whenever he heard it.

He was a native of Pêrak, and he made his way into Pahang through the untrodden Sâkai country. That is practically all that is known concerning his origin. The name of the district in which Kûlop Sûmbing had his home represented nothing to the natives of the Jĕlai Valley, and now no man knows from what part of Pêrak this adventurer came. The manner of his coming, however, excited the admiration, and impressed itself upon the imaginations, of the people of Pahang—who love pluck almost as much as they hate toil : so the tale of his doings is still told, though these things happened nearly a score of years ago.

Kûlop Sûmbing probably held a sufficiently cynical opinion as to the nature of his countrywomen, who are among the most venal of their sex. He knew that no girl could love him for the sake of his marred unsightly face, but that many would bestow their favours upon him if his money-bags were well lined. Therefore he determined to grow rich with as little delay as possible, and to this end he looked about for some one whom he might plunder. For this purpose Pêrak was played out. The law of the white men could not be bribed by a successful robber, so he turned his eyes across the border to Pahang, which bore an evil reputation, as a land in which ill things were done with impunity, while the doer throve exceedingly.

He had a love of adventure, was absolutely fearless and was, moreover, a good man with his hands. In common with most Malays the Central Gaol, and the rigid discipline of prison life, had few attractions for him ; and as he did not share with the majority of his race their instinctive dread of travelling alone in the jungle, he decided on making a lone-hand raid into the Sâkai country, which lies between Pêrak and Pahang. Here he would be safe from the grip of the white man's hand, and well removed from the sight of the Government's eyes, as the Malays name our somnolent policemen, and much wealth would come to the ready hand that knew full well how to seize it. He, of course, felt absolutely no twinges of conscience, for you must not look for principle in the men of the race to which Kûlop Sûmbing belonged. A Malay is honest and law-abiding just so long as it suits his convenience to be so, and not more than sixty seconds longer. Virtue in the abstract does not fire him with any particular enthusiasm, but a love of right-doing may occasionally be galvanised into a sort of paralytic life in his breast, if a haunting fear of the consequences of crime are kept very clearly before his eyes. So Kûlop kicked the dust of law-restrained Pêrak from his bare brown soles, and set out for the Sâkai country and the remote interior of Pahang, where the law of God was not and no law of man held true.

He carried with him all the rice that he could bear upon

his shoulders, two dollars in silver, a little tobacco, a handsome *kris*, and a long spear with a broad and shining blade. His supplies were to last him till the first Sâkai camps were reached, and after that his food, he told himself, would " rest at the tip of his dagger." He did not really propose to begin his operations until the mountains, which fence the Pêrak boundary, had been crossed, so was content to allow the first Sâkai villages to pass unpillaged. He impressed some of the naked, frightened aborigines as bearers, he levied such supplies of food as he needed, and the Sâkai, who were glad to be rid of him so cheaply, handed him on from village to village with the greatest alacrity. The base of the jungle-covered mountains of the interior was reached at the end of a fortnight, and Kûlop and his Sâkai began to drag themselves up the steep ascent by means of roots, trailing creepers and slender saplings.

Upon a certain day they reached the summit of a nameless mountain and threw themselves down panting for breath upon the round bare drumming-ground of an argus pheasant. On the crest of almost every hill and hog's back in the interior these drumming-grounds are found, bare and smooth as a threshing-floor, save for the thin litter of dead twigs with which they are strewn by the birds. Sometimes, if you keep very still, you may hear the cocks strutting and dancing, and thumping the hard earth, but no man amongst us had ever seen the pheasants going through their performance. At night-time their full-throated yell rings across the valleys, waking a thousand echoes, and the cry is taken up and thrown backwards and forwards by a host of pheasants, each answering from his own hill. Judging by the frequency of their cry, they must be among the most common of all jungle birds, yet so deftly do they hide themselves that they are but rarely seen, and the beauties of their plumage—at once more delicate and more brilliant than that of the peacock—and the wonders of the countless violet eyes with which their feathers are set, are only known to us because these birds are so frequently trapped by the Malays.

Where Kûlop and his Sâkai lay the trees were thinned out. The last two hundred feet of the ascent had been a severe climb, and the ridge, which formed the summit, stood clear of the tree-tops which grew half-way up the slope. As he lay panting, Kûlop Sûmbing gazed down for the first time upon the eastern slope of the Peninsula, the

theatre in which ere long he proposed to play a very daring
part. At his feet were tree-tops of every shade of green,
from the tender, brilliant colour which we associate with
young corn, to the deep dull hue which is almost black.
They fell away beneath him in a broad slope of living
vegetation, the contour of each individual tree, and the grey,
white or black lines which marked their trunks or branches,
growing less and less distinct, until the jungle covering the
plain was a blurred wash of colour that had more of blue
than green in it. Here and there, very far away, the sunlight
fell in a dazzling flash upon something which glistened like
the mirror of a heliograph, and this, Kûlop knew, was the
broad reaches of a river. The jungle hid all traces of human
habitation, and no sign of life was visible, save only a solitary
kite " sailing with supreme dominion through the azure
depth of air," and the slight uneasy swaying of some of the
taller trees, as a faint breeze swept gently over the forest.
Here, in the mountains, the air was damp and chilly, and a
cold wind was blowing, while the sun appeared to have lost
half its power. In the plain below, however, the land lay
steaming and sweltering beneath the fierce perpendicular
rays, while the heat-haze danced restlessly above the forest.

During the next day or two Kûlop Sûmbing and his
Pêrak Sâkai made their way down the eastern slope of the
mountains and through the silent forests, which are given
over to game, and to the equally wild jungle-folk, who fly
at the approach of any human beings, precisely as do the
beasts which share with them their home.

Kûlop and his people passed several deserted camps
belonging to these wild Sâkai, but the instinct of the savages
tells them unerringly that strangers are at hand, and never
once were any of these folk caught sight of by the travellers.

These people live a nomadic life, roaming hither and
thither through the forest in quest of fresh feeding-grounds
when the old ones are temporarily exhausted. They have
no knowledge of planting, and they live chiefly upon yams
and roots, sour jungle fruits, and the fish which they catch
in cunningly devised basket-work traps. These things are
known to such of us as have journeyed through their country,
for their tracks tell their story up to this point. We know,
too, that they camp in rude shelters of leaves propped
crazily on untrimmed uprights, and that they obtain wood
knives from the tamer tribesmen in exchange for the long
reeds of which the inner casing of the Sâkai blow-pipes is

made. But even when they barter thus, they never willingly meet other human beings, their wares being deposited in certain well-known places in the jungle, where they are replaced by other articles which the wild folk remove when no man is watching. A few survivors of the captives made by the tamer Sâkai on various slave-raiding expeditions may be found in some of the Malay villages in Pahang, but of the life of these people in their wild forest state no man knows anything.

Kûlop Sûmbing, of course, took very little interest in them, for they possess no property, and nothing was therefore to be gained by harrying them. So he pushed on through the wild Sâkai country until the upper waters of the Bĕtok, the principal tributary of the Jĕlai, was reached.

Bamboos were felled, a raft was constructed, and then Kûlop Sûmbing dismissed his Sâkai and began his descent of the unknown river, which led he knew not where, alone, save for his weapons, but full of confidence in his ability to pillage this undiscovered country single-handed.

When you come to think of it, there was something bordering upon the heroic in the action of this unscrupulous man with the marred face, who glided gently down the river on this wild, lone-hand raid. The land was strange to him ; the river, for all he knew, might be beset with impassable rapids and unknown dangers of every kind ; his object was robbery on a large scale, and a plunderer is not likely to meet with much love from those whom he despoils. He was going to certain enmity, one might say to almost certain death, yet he poled his raft down the stream with deft punts and gazed calmly ahead of him with a complete absence of fear.

Under happier circumstances Kûlop of the Hare-lip might surely have won rank among those brave men whose names still ring through the centuries as heroes, whose courage has won for them a lasting niche in human history.

It was at noon upon the second day that Kûlop sighted a large camp of the tamer Sâkai in a clearing on the right bank of the Bĕtok. The sight of a Malay, coming from such an unusual quarter, filled the jungle people with superstitious dread, and in a few minutes every man, woman and child had fled screaming to the forest.

Kûlop went through the ten or fifteen squalid huts which stood in the clearing, and an occasional grunt attested that he was well satisfied with the stores of valuable gĕtah lying stowed away in the sheds. He calculated that there

could not be less than seven *pîkul*, and that would mean $600
in cash—a small fortune for any Malay. But then a difficulty
presented itself. How was this precious sum to be carried
down-stream into Pahang? His raft would hold about one
pîkul—he knew that the Sâkai would not interfere with him
if he chose to remove that amount and to leave the rest. But
the sight of the remaining six *pîkul* was too much for him.
He could not find it in his heart to abandon it, and he
began to feel angry with the Sâkai, who, he almost persuaded
himself, were defrauding him of his just rights.

He rolled his quid of betel-nut and sat down to await
the return of the Sâkai, and as he thought of the injury
they were like to do him if they refused to aid in the removal
of the rest of the *gĕtah*, his heart waxed very hot within him.

Presently two frightened brown faces, scarred with
blue tattoo-marks on cheek and forehead, and surmounted
by a frowzy mop of sun-bleached hair, rose stealthily above
the level of the flooring near the door and peeped at him
with shy, terrified eyes.

Kûlop turned his face towards them, and the bobbing
heads disappeared with surprising alacrity.

" Come hither ! " cried Kûlop.

The heads reappeared once more, and in a few brief
words Kûlop bade them go call their fellows.

The Sâkai sidled off into the jungle, and presently a
crowd of squalid aborigines came from out the shelter
of the trees and underwood and stood looking at Kûlop
curiously, with light feet gingerly treading the ground,
every muscle braced for a swift dart into cover at the first
alarm of danger.

" Who among ye is the chief? " asked Kûlop.

" Thy servant is the chief," replied an aged Sâkai.

He stood forward as he spoke, trembling a little as he
glanced timidly at the Malay, who sat cross-legged in the
doorway of the hut. His straggling mop of hair was almost
white, and his skin was dry and creased and wrinkled. He
was naked, as were all his people, save for a slender loin-clout
of bark-cloth, and his thin flanks and buttocks were white
with the warm wood-ashes in which he had been lying when
Kûlop's arrival interrupted his midday snooze.

" Bid these, thy children, build me eight bamboo rafts,
strong and firm, at the foot of yonder rapid," said Kûlop.
" And mark ye, be not slow, for I love not indolence."

" It can be done," said the Sâkai headman submissively.

"That is well," returned Kûlop. "See thou to it with speed, for I am a man prone to wrath."

The Sâkai fell to work, and by nightfall the eight new rafts were completed, and while the jungle-folk toiled, Kûlop of the Hare-lip, who had declared that he loved not indolence, lay upon his back on the floor of the chief's hut and roared a love-song in a harsh, discordant voice to the lady whose heart the wealth he sought so eagerly, and now began to see within his grasp, would enable him to subdue.

Kûlop slept that night in the Sâkai hut among the restless jungle-folk. The air was chilly up here in the foothills, and the fire, which the Sâkai never willingly let die, smoked and smouldered in the middle of the floor. Half a dozen long logs, all pointing to a common centre like the spokes of a broken wheel, met at the point where the fire burned red in the darkness, and between these boughs in the warm grey ashes lay men, women and children sprawling in every conceivable attitude into which their naked brown limbs could twist themselves. Ever and anon they would rise up and tend the fire. Then they would sit round the newly-kindled blaze and talk in the jerky monosyllabic jargon of the aborigines. The pungent smoke of the wood enshrouded them as with a garment, and their eyes waxed red and watery, but they heeded it not, for as their old saw has it, "Fire-smoke is the blanket of the Sâkai."

And Kûlop of the Hare-lip slept the sleep of the just.

The dawn broke greyly, for a mist hung low over the forest, white as driven snow and cold and clammy as the forehead of a corpse. The naked Sâkai peeped shiveringly from the doorways of their huts, and then went shuddering back to the grateful warmth of the fire and the frowzy atmosphere within.

Kûlop alone made his way down to the river-bank and there performed his morning ablutions with scrupulous care—for whatever laws of God and man a Malay may disregard, he never forgets the virtue of personal cleanliness, which, in an Oriental, is even more immediately important to his neighbours than all the godliness in the world. A Malay would as soon think of foregoing his morning tub as he would of fasting when food was to be had in plenty, and the days of Ramathân had sped.

When his ablutions were completed, Kûlop climbed the steep bank once more, and, standing outside the chief's hut, called the Sâkai from their lairs, bidding them hearken to his words. They stood or squatted before him in the white mist, through which the sun, just peeping above the jungle, was beginning to send long slanting rays of dazzling white light.

They were cold and miserable—this little crowd of naked men—and they shivered and scratched their bodies restlessly. The trilling of the thrushes and the chorus raised by other birds came to their ears through the still air mingled with the whooping and barking of the anthropoid apes ; but the morning song has small power to cheer those who, like the Sâkai, are very sensitive to cold, and it is during the chilly waking hour that men's courage and vitality are usually at the lowest ebb.

" Listen to me, ye Sâkai ! " began Kûlop, in a loud and angry voice, and at the word those of his hearers who stood erect squatted humbly with their fellows, and the shivering of cold was increased by the trembling of fear. If there is one thing the jungle-folk dislike more than another it is to be called " Sâkai " to their faces, and the term is never used to them by the Malays unless the speaker wishes to bully them. The word really means a slave, but by the aborigines it is regarded as the most offensive epithet in the Malay vocabulary. In their own tongue they speak of themselves as Sĕn-oi, which means a " man," as opposed to Gob, a foreigner—for even the Sâkai has some vestiges of pride if you know where to look for it, and to his mind the people of his race are alone entitled to be called " men." When speaking Malay they allude to themselves as Ôrang Bûkit—men of the hills ; Ôrang Ûtan—jungle-folk ; or Oran Dalam—the folk who dwell within the forests. They delight to be spoken of as räayat—peasants, or as räayat râja—subjects of the king ; and the Malays, who delight in nicely graded distinctions of speech in speaking to men of various ranks and classes, habitually use these terms when addressing Sâkai, in order that the hearts of the jungle-folk may be warmed within them. When therefore the objectionable name " Sâkai " is used to the forest-dwellers, the latter know that mischief and trouble are afoot, and since they are as timid as other wild creatures, a deadly fear falls upon them at the word.

" Listen, ye accursed Sâkai ! " cried Kûlop of the Hare-lip, waving his spear above his head. " Mark well my words, for I hear the warm earth calling to the coffin planks in which your carcasses shall be presently if ye fail to do my behests.

Go, gather up the *gĕtah* that lies within your dwellings and bring it hither speedily, lest a worse thing befall ye ! "

The Sâkai rose slowly and walked each man to his hut with lagging steps. In a few minutes the great round balls of gum, with a little hole punched in each, through which a rotten line was passed, lay heaped upon the ground at Kûlop's feet. But the Sâkai had brought something as well as the *gĕtah,* for each man held a long and slender spear fashioned of bamboo. The weapon sounds harmless enough, but these wooden blades are strong and stubborn, and the edges and points are sharper than steel. Kûlop of the Hare-lip saw that the time had come for prompt action to supplement rough words.

" Cast down your spears to the earth, ye swine of the forest ! " he yelled.

Almost all the Sâkai did as Kûlop bade them, for the Malay is here the dominant race, and years of oppression and wrong have made the jungle-folk very docile in the presence of the more civilised brown man. The Sâkai chief, however, clutched his weapon firmly, and his frightened old eyes ran around the group of his kinsmen vainly inciting them to follow his example. The next moment his gaze was recalled to Kûlop of the Hare-lip by a sharp pain in his right shoulder, as the spear of the Malay transfixed it. His own weapon dropped from his powerless arm, and the Sâkai broke and fled. But a shrill cry from Kûlop, as he ran around them, herding them as a collie herds sheep, brought them soon to a standstill.

No thought of further resistance remained in their minds, and the *gĕtah* was quickly loaded on the rafts, and the plundered Sâkai, still wild with fear, began to pole them down the river, while Kûlop sat at ease on the last raft, which two of the shuddering jungle-folk punted carefully.

The wounded chief, left behind in his hut, sent two youths through the forest to bid their fellow-tribesmen prepare the poison for their blow-pipe darts, since he knew that no one would now attempt to kill Kûlop of the Hare-lip at close quarters. But the poison which the Sâkai distil from the resin of the *ĭpoh* tree requires some time to prepare, and if it is to be used with effect upon a human being, a specially strong solution is necessary. Above all, if it is to do its work properly, it must be newly made. Thus it was that Kûlop of the Hare-lip had time to load his rafts with *gĕtah* taken from two other Sâkai camps, and to pass very nearly out of

the Sâkai country before the people whom he had robbed
were in a position to take the offensive.

The Bĕtok River falls into the Upper Jĕlai, a stream
which is also given over entirely to the jungle-people, and
it is not until the latter river meets the Tĕlom and the Serau
at the point where the Lower Jĕlai is formed that the banks
begin to be studded with scattered Malay villages.

Kûlop of the Hare-lip knew nothing of the geography
of the land through which he was travelling, but he was
aware that running water presupposed the existence of
the habitations of men of his own race if followed down
sufficiently far. Therefore he pressed forward eagerly,
bullying and goading his frightened Sâkai into something
resembling energy. He had now more than a thousand
dollars' worth of *gĕtah* on his rafts, and he was getting anxious
as to its safety. To the danger in which he himself went he
was perfectly callous and indifferent.

It was at Kuâla Mĕrbau, a spot where a tiny stream
falls into the Upper Jĕlai upon its right bank, that a small
party of Sâkai lay in hiding, peering through the greenery
at the gliding waters down which Kûlop and his plunder
must presently come. Each man carried at his side a quiver
fashioned of a single length of bamboo covered with the dots,
crosses and zigzags and triangles which the Sâkai delight
to trace upon all their vessels. Each quiver was filled with
slender darts, about the thickness of a steel knitting-needle,
with an elliptical piece of light wood at one end to steady it
in its flight, and a very sharp tip coated with the black venom
of the *ipoh* sap. In their hands each one of them held a long
reed blow-pipe some twelve feet in length. These weapons
were rudely but curiously carved.

Presently the foremost of the Sâkai stood erect, his
elbows level with his ears, his feet heel to heel, his body
leaning slightly forward from the hips. His hands were
locked together at the mouthpiece of the blow-pipe, the
long reed being held firmly by his thumbs and forefingers,
which were coiled above it, while the weight rested upon
the lower interlaced fingers of both hands. His mouth
was puckered and drawn in, like that of a man who seeks
to spit out a shred of tobacco which the loose end of a
cigarette has left between his lips, and it nestled closely
to the wooden mouthpiece. His keen, wild eyes glanced
along the length of the blow-pipe shrewdly and unflinchingly,
little hard puckers forming at their corners. *Pit !* said the

blow-pipe. The little wad of dry pith which had been used
to exclude the air around the dart-head fell into the water
a dozen feet away, and the dart itself flew forward with
incredible speed, straight to the mark at which it was aimed.

A slight shock on his right side just above the hip apprised
Kûlop that something had struck him, and looking down he
saw the dart still shuddering in his side. But, as luck would
have it, Kûlop carried under his coat a gaudy bag stuffed
with the ingredients of the betel quid, and the dart had
struck this and embedded itself in it. The merest fraction of
a second was all that Kûlop needed to see this, and to take in
the whole situation, and with him action and perception kept
pace with one another. Before the dart had ceased to quiver,
before the Sâkai on the bank had had time to send another
in its wake, before the men who poled his raft had fully
grasped what was going forward, Kûlop had seized the nearest
of his Sâkai by his frowzy halo of elf-locks and had drawn
him screaming across his knee. The terrified creature
writhed and flung his body about wildly, and his friends
upon the bank feared to blow their darts lest they should
inadvertently wound their kinsman while striving to kill
the Malay.

"Have a care, ye swine of the forest!" cried Kûlop,
while he cuffed the screaming Sâkai unsparingly in order
to keep his limbs in constant motion. "Have a care, ye
sons of fallen women! If ye fire one more of your darts,
this man, your kinsman, dies by my *kris*!"

The Sâkai on the banks had no reason to doubt the
sincerity of Kûlop's words, and since they love their relatives
both near and distant, far more than is possible in more
civilised communities, they drew off, and Kûlop of the Hare-
lip went upon his way rejoicing. But he kept his Sâkai across
his knee none the less, and occasionally administered a
sounding cuff to him *pour encourager les autres*.

Thus he won his way out of the Sâkai country, and that
night he laid him down to sleep in a Malay village in the
full enjoyment of excellent health, the knowledge that he
was at last a rich man, and a delightful consciousness of
having successfully performed deeds well worth the doing.

For a month or twain he dwelt in the Jĕlai, at Bûkit
Betong, the village of To' Râja, the great up-country chief,
who then ruled that district. He sold his *gĕtah* to this man, and
since he was ready to let it go for something less than the
market price, the sorrows of the Sâkai were the cause of much

amusement to those from whom they sought redress, and whose duty it should have been to afford them protection.

But Kûlop of the Hare-lip had left his heart behind him in Pêrak, for the natives of that State can never long be happy when beyond the limits of their own country, and must always make their way back sooner or later to drink of the waters of their silver river. Perhaps, too, Kûlop had some one particular lady in his mind when he set out upon his quest for wealth, for if you watch, you will see that the best work and the most blackguardly deeds of a man are alike usually due to the woman who sits at the back of his heart and is the driving power which impels him to good or to evil.

One day Kûlop of the Hare-lip presented himself before To' Râja as the latter lay smoking his opium-pipe upon the soft mats in his house, and informed him that as he was about to leave Pahang he had brought a present " trifling and unworthy of his acceptance "—which he craved the chief to honour him by receiving.

" When dost thou go down-stream ? " asked To' Râja, for the Jĕlai is in the far interior of Pahang, and if a man would leave the country by any of the ordinary routes, he must pass down that river at anyrate as far as Kuâla Lĭpis.

" Thy servant goes *up*-stream," said Kûlop of the Hare-lip.

To' Râja started.

" What ? " said he, in a voice full of astonishment.

" Thy servant returns the way he came," said Kûlop calmly.

To' Râja burst out into a torrent of excited expostulation. It was death, certain death, he said for Kûlop once more to attempt to traverse the Sâkai country. The other ways were open, and no man would dream of staying him if he sought to return to his own country by land or sea. It was folly, it was madness, it was impossible. But to all these words Kûlop of the Hare-lip turned a deaf ear. He knew Malay chieftains and all their ways and works sufficiently well, and he had paid toll enough to To' Râja already to have no desire to diminish further the amount of his honest earnings. If he wended his way homeward through inhabited country, he knew that he would have to comply with the exactions of every chief through whose district he might pass, and this was a prospect that had few attractions for him. The Sâkai, on the other hand, he despised utterly, and as he was physically incapable of feeling fear at this stage of the proceedings, he laughed at To' Râja's estimate of the risk he would run. Nay, he saw in the chief's words a cunning attempt to induce him to penetrate more deeply into a land in which he might be plundered with the greater ease. Accordingly he declined to be persuaded by To' Râja, and a day or two later he began his return journey through the forests.

He knew that it would be useless to attempt to induce any one to accompany him, so he went, as he had come— alone. The dollars for which he had exchanged his plunder were hard and heavy upon his back, and he was further loaded with rice and dried fish, but his weapons were as bright as ever, and to him they still seemed to be all the companions that a man need desire. He travelled on foot, for he could not pole a raft single-handed against the current, and he had to trust to such paths as he could find, guiding himself for the most part by the direction of the river. He passed many Sâkai camps, which were all abandoned at his approach, and he halted in several of them to replenish his scanty stock of provisions, but he slept in the jungle.

It was on the evening of the second or third night that Kûlop became aware of an unpleasant sensation. The moon was at the full, and he could see for many yards around him in the forest, and though no one was visible, he became painfully conscious that somebody was watching him. Occasionally he thought that he caught the glint of eyes in the underwood, and every now and again a dry twig snapped crisply, now to the right, now to the left, now in front of him, now behind him. He started to his feet and sounded the *sôrak*—the war-yell—that pealed in widening echoes through the forest. A rustle in half a dozen directions at once showed him that the watchers had been numerous, and that they were now taking refuge in flight.

Kûlop of the Hare-lip sat down again beside his fire, and a new and strange sensation began to grip his heart queerly. It was accompanied by an uneasy feeling in the small of his back, as though he momentarily expected to receive a spear-thrust there, and a clammy dampness rose upon his forehead, while of a sudden the skin behind his ears seemed strangely cold. Perhaps even Kûlop of the Hare-lip needed no man to tell him that this was fear.

He replenished his fire and sat near it, trying to still the chattering of his teeth. If he could find himself face to face with an enemy fear would leave him, he knew ; but this

eerie, uncanny feeling of being watched and hounded by
foes whom he could not see struck him with palsy. As he sat
he glanced uneasily over his shoulder from time to time, and
at last he drew back against the trunk of a large tree, so that
none might strike him from behind. As he sat thus, leaning
slightly backwards, he chanced to glance up, and in a tree-top,
some fifty yards away, he saw the crouching form of a Sâkai
silhouetted blackly against the moonlit sky.

He leaped to his feet once more, and again the *sôrak*
rang out as he strove to tear his way through the underwood to the foot of the tree in which he had seen his enemy.
But the jungle was thick, he lost his bearings quickly, and,
weary with his exertions, torn with brambles and sweating
profusely, he was glad to make his way back to the fire again.

All through that terrible night Kûlop of the Hare-lip
strove to drive away sleep from his heavy eyes. The hours
seemed incredibly long, and he feared that the dawn would
never, never come. One minute he would tell himself that
he was wide awake, and a second later a rustle in the underwood startled him into a knowledge that he had slept.
Horror and fear had their will of him, and those who know
them are aware that there are no more skilled tormentors
than they. A hundred times he leaped to his feet and sent
the *sôrak* ringing through the jungle, and each time those who
watched him fled in panic. While he remained awake and on
guard the Sâkai feared him too much to attack him. His
previous escape from the dart which they had seen pierce
his side had originated in their minds the idea that he was
invulnerable, so they tried no longer to slay him from a
distance. This he quickly perceived, but fear clutched him
once more when he speculated as to what would happen when
he was at last forced to give way to the weight of weariness
that was now oppressing him so sorely.

Presently a change began to creep over the forest in
which he sat. A little stir in the trees around told him
that the bird-folk were awakening. Objects which had
hitherto been dark and shapeless masses in the shadows cast
into prominence by the white moonlight gradually assumed
more definite shape. Later the colours of the trunks and leaves
and creepers, still dark and dulled, but none the less colour,
began to be perceptible, and Kûlop of the Hare-lip rejoiced
exceedingly in that the dawn had come and the horrors of
the night were passing away.

All that day Kûlop, albeit weary almost to death, trudged

onward through the forest ; but the news had spread among the Sâkai that their enemy was once more among them, and the number of the jungle-folk who dogged his footsteps steadily increased. Kûlop could hear their shrill whoops, as they called to one another through the forest, giving warning of his approach, or signalling the path which he was taking. Once or twice he fancied that he caught a glimpse of a little brown form, of two glinting eyes, or of a straggling mop of frowzy hair, and then he would charge, shouting angrily. But the figure—if indeed it had any existence save in his over-wrought imagination—always vanished as suddenly and as noiselessly as a shadow long before he could come within striking distance. Kûlop of the Hare-lip found this far more terrible and frightening than the most desperate hand-to-hand fight could be, for the invisibility and the intangible nature of his enemy added the horrors of a fever-dream to the very real danger in which he now knew himself to stand.

The night that followed that day was one of acute agony to the weary man who dared not sleep, and about midnight he again marched forward through the forest, hoping thereby to elude his pursuers.

For an hour he believed himself to have been successful. Then the shrill yells broke out again, and at the sound Kûlop's heart sank within him. Still he stumbled on, too dead tired to charge at his phantom enemy, too hoarse at last even to raise his voice in the *sôrak*, but doggedly determined not to give in. But as he waxed faint the number and the boldness of his pursuers increased proportionately, till their yells sounded on every side, and Kûlop seemed like a lost soul, winding his way to the Bottomless Pit with an escort of rejoicing devils shouting a noisy chorus around him.

Another awful day followed, and when once more the night shut down, Kûlop of the Hare-lip sank exhausted upon the ground. His battle was over. He could bear up no longer against the weight of his weariness and the aching longing for sleep. Almost as his head touched the warm, dark litter of dead leaves with which the earth of the jungle is strewn, his heavy eyelids closed and his breath came soft and regular. This was his surrender, for at last he knew himself to be beaten. He was half-way up the mountains now, and was almost in reach of safety, but—

> " Ah, the little more—and how much it is,
> And the little less—and what worlds away ! "

Kûlop of the Hare-lip—Kûlop the resolute, the fearless
—Kûlop the strong, the enduring, was at the end of his
tether. He had been beaten—not by the Sâkai, but by
Nature, which no man may long defy—and in obedience
to her he surrendered his will and slept.

Presently the underwood was parted by human hands
in half a dozen different places, and the Sâkai crept stealthily
out of the jungle into the little patch of open in which their
enemy lay at rest. He moved uneasily in his sleep—not
because any noise on their part had disturbed him, for they
came as silently as a shadow cast over a broad forest by a
patch of scudding cloud—and at the sight the Sâkai halted
with lifted foot ready to plunge back into cover should their
enemy awake. But the exhausted man was sleeping heavily,
wrapped in the slumber from which he was never again to be
aroused. The silent jungle-people, armed with heavy clubs
and bamboo spears, stole to within a foot or two of the
unconscious Malay. Then nearly a score of them lifted their
weapons, poised them on high, and brought them down
simultaneously on the body of their foe. Kûlop's limbs
stretched themselves slowly and stiffly, his jaw fell and blood
flowed in twenty places. No cry escaped him, and the
trembling Sâkai looked down upon the dead face of their
enemy and knew that he had paid his debt to them in full.

They touched none of his gear, for they feared to be
haunted by his ghost, and Kûlop had nothing edible about
him, such as the jungle-folk find it hard to leave untouched.
Money had no meaning to the Sâkai, so the silver dollars,
which ran in a glistening stream from a rent made in their
bag by a spear-thrust, were left glistening in the moonlight
by the side of that still grey face, with the ghastly, pallid
lip split upwards to the nostrils. There the Sâkai took
their leave of Kûlop of the Hare-lip as he lay stretched
beside the riches which he had bought at so dear a price.

If you want some ready money and a good *kris* and
spear, both of which have done execution in their day,
they are all to be had for the gathering in a spot in the forest
not very far from the boundary between Pahang and Pêrak,
but you must find the place for yourself, since the Sâkai
to a man will certainly deny all knowledge of it. Therefore
it is probable that Kûlop of the Hare-lip will rise up on the
Judgment Day with his property intact.

LYNCH LAW IN THE WEST

By
J. MILLIGAN

THE winter we had when I was ten years old was reckoned to be the coldest ever remembered in Montana. Even the old-timers who came there first as pioneers in the days when they had to fight their way west against the Indians admitted it was colder than anything they'd known—so I reckon it must have been real cold !

My mother felt it, being a lone woman and working harder than any woman should work. There was never much more food in the house than would do for one, but she saw I didn't go hungry, so I guess she must have done, plenty times.

I knew she wasn't a widow-woman, and I knew there was some disgrace about my dad. He'd deserted her when I was just a baby, but I wasn't sure how it had happened. My uncle, though, who gave us the shack to live in and Mammy some chores to do round his farm so as she could feel she was earning something, used to say hard things about dad. When I asked about him, my uncle would say, " If your pappy hadn't left this country when he did, he'd had left at the end of the Sheriff's rope," so I knew my dad must have been a rustler, or horse-stealer, or something pretty bad.

Mammy would never talk about him. When I tried to find out more about him, she would say quiet-like, " Some men's square, and some's just naturally crooked. Guess your dad was one of the crooked ones. But you ain't got to think too bad of him, son. Maybe the devil tempted him more than most."

.   .   .   .

The shack Uncle Jed had given us was way up in the mountains by the Wheelbreak Pass. It was three miles down the trail to Uncle Jed's farm, and the three miles were a hard trial to my mammy after a day's work down at the farm.

It was six miles to Rolling Creek township, where I went to school, and I used to grumble about it, even though Uncle Jed's hired-man would give me a ride in the buggy for half

121

the distance. Mammy didn't grumble, though, and she didn't get mad when I complained. Kids are pretty selfish sometimes.

.   .   .   .

It was the night of the blizzard that my dad came home.

Up there on top of the range, the snow-drifts weren't so bad, and we hadn't to worry about being snowed-up. But it was cold : colder than I ever thought it could be. Even in our warm little shack, with a big log fire blazing, it was getting into my bones. I was crying with the cold. Afterwards, I was to know Alaska and the frozen Yukon, when the temperature was sixty below ; but I never suffered from the cold as I did that night.

Mammy slept in a big double bed by the window, and I slept in a tiny box-bed over by the corner next the door. Mammy was just getting my bed ready for me, heating a flat-iron before the fire and running it over the blankets to take the chill off them before I turned in. The blizzard was at its height. The wind was howling loud as thunder and bashing at the walls of the shack, so that the door kept crashing up against the thick bar across it until I thought it was going to split.

Suddenly my mother took her hand off the flat-iron and straightened herself, listening. I listened too ; and I thought I could hear another sound at the door, as if something else besides the wind was bashing at it. It was like somebody knocking.

I looked at Mammy, and I was scared.

" D'you hear that there sound, Mammy ? "

" 'S'only somebody at the door, son. I'm gonna open up right away. There ain't no call to be scared."

. . . But, before she opened the door, she went to the mantelpiece and took down my grandfather's old breech-loading rifle.

" Who's there ? " she cried out.

I heard a voice answering, but the blizzard muffled the words. I was real glad, though, to hear that the voice was human.

Mammy gave up trying to hear what the man outside was shouting. She laid down the rifle, and, using all her strength, lifted off the bar.

The wind came in like steam escaping after a boiler has exploded, and the snow billowed in in great clouds. And, along with the snow, something else was flung in by the storm. It was the big black figure of a man, and it flopped across the doorway like a felled tree.

The snow was all around my mother, swirling in queer patterns. I saw her wrestling hard to drag the man inside the shack ; then, when he was clear of the door, she flung all her weight against it so as to close it against the force of the wind, and called out to me to help put the bar up.

It was just about all we could do, but we managed it. Mammy bent over the man lying there on his face. The snow was sprinkled all over her hair, like the tinsel I had seen on Bert Gregg's grand Christmas-tree. She tried to turn him over on his back, but he was too heavy for her. His hair was black and very long, and it was spread out like a dark star on the floor.

I got the idea that my mother wanted to see the stranger's face. When she found she couldn't turn him over, she grabbed him by his long hair and pulled. His neck was bent back, and his face came into the light of the lamp Mammy was holding.

It was a broad dark face, and there was three weeks' growth of beard on it. The closed eyes were all wrinkled and fleshy, and the mouth looked thick and ugly.

" Shucks, Mom ! " I whispered. " Is he dead ? "

She was looking down at the stranger's face with a kind of faraway shine in her eyes. I was as much scared by that look as by the sight of the man's face.

" Mom ! " I shouted out, almost in tears. " Is he dead ? "

At that, she seemed to come to herself. She let go the man's hair, and his forehead hit the floor with a bang.

Mammy didn't seem to notice that bump, though. She turned to me with a kind of bright look that I thought was queer.

" Why, no, son ! He ain't dead. He's right as rain— only a little ways tired. Been walking round in the snow, I guess."

But I was still scared.

" I don't like that man ! Mammy, he looks a bad man ! Don't let him stay here. . . ."

Mammy was looking at me hard, and her face was drawn and tired-looking.

" You didn't ought to say things like that, Jimmy. This is your dad. . . ."

I felt as if my stomach was turning over inside me. Before I could know what was happening, I was crying, and Mammy was holding me against her tight.

Then I heard a sound—a sort of quiet choking sound. It was the man on the floor—my dad. . . .

Mammy let me go and bent over *him* again. I saw his eyes were wide open. They were pale blue eyes, wild-looking and hard as pebbles.

" Sarah . . . ! "

" Yes, Mick. So you've come back to your wife and child at last."

I thought that was a nice sort of thing to say ; and yet the way she said it made it sound like something bad.

" I'm sorry, Sarah. I know it's plumb late for me to talk this-a-way—but it's the truth. I reckon them last few years have been pretty long and hard for you—but I would have come back before—if I could. Honest, Sarah, I couldn't. You know—the Sheriff and the rest. God, though, I've wanted to come real bad sometimes ! "

His voice was rough and low, as if he needed a lot of strength to speak.

" Mebbe it was better for us that you didn't come," said my mother.

" Don't say that, Sarah girl ! You don't know the life I've had—never a day's peace—always on the run. . . . Gee, I was takin' a plenty big chance in comin' here, even with that blizzard blowin'. . . ."

" Why *have* you come ? "

" Why, jest to see you and the kid again, Sarah ! Reckon I'd go through a heap just for——"

" I want the truth. Why have you come ? "

My dad didn't answer for a minute ; then he said slowly :

" This was the only place I *could* come. They're after me again—Deputy Donkins and his posse. They near got me down by the Wheelbreak."

" I figured it was something more like that. Why are you back in this State ? I never thought I'd see you in Montana again."

" I couldn't help it, Sarah. They was after me in Idaho, too. The only thing I could do was to blow for the Bitter Roots, but they hunted me like bloodhounds, and I had to hit it over the border."

" So they was after you in Idaho, too. I guess it was for horse-stealing again. . . ."

" Rustlin' . . ." said my dad in a whisper.

My mother's voice was hard as a knife :

" Reckon it's just what Jed always said about you, Mick ;

you just naturally can't go straight. You're bad, Mick—every inch of you. I figure it was the best day in my life when you left me."

"Oh, Sarah, there ain't no call to be so hard. . . . Mebbe I ain't all I oughta be, but you didn't ought to speak that-a-way to me when I've come back after all them years. . . . I was all-in, Sarah, when I came to this shack. Reckon I couldn't have made another mile. I'm dog-tired—an' half-frozen. There's more need to be thinkin' about givin' me somethin' hot to drink and a place to rest than callin' me down."

My mother nodded slowly.

"Reckon it's as much as I could do for a dog on a night like this. Can you get as far as the fire?"

"Mebbe—if you help me. . . ."

He half got up, and she put a hand under his shoulders and helped him to get into the big chair in front of the fire.

"That's better . . ." he said after a minute. "But I'm still frozen inside."

Mammy was standing by the table.

"I'm just fixin' you something hot to drink."

"You ain't got whisky, have you, Sarah. I need it."

"Guess you do—for once. But I ain't got none. You'll have to make it coffee."

She put the coffee on to boil. My father seemed to be feeling better. He took off his big heavy coat, and then his mackinaw, and sat there in his shirt-sleeves.

I had been standing in the dark near the door, scared to make a noise, and listening hard to all they were saying. I was staring at my father, when he turned and saw me.

"My God!" he said.

He beckoned me.

"Come here, son. . . . You know who I am?"

I was too frightened to answer, but I went forward. His fierce eyes stared into my face.

"So this is Jimmy. Gosh, you're a big boy now, son—and you were just a baby when I saw you last. . . . Sarah, he's the spit and image of me. He's got my face and body—and he's got my way of lookin' at folks. . . ."

"I hate to see you touchin' him, Mick—though he is your boy," said my mother quietly. "Mebbe he does look like you—but I pray God he ain't got your ways."

My dad was still staring at me. He looked as if he was crying, and I was surprised at that.

" Pray God he ain't . . ." he repeated.

The coffee was ready now, and he drank fast, though it was scalding-hot. The door was still shaking, but the wind was not howling so loud. You could hear voices now when they weren't shouting, so I figured the storm wasn't so bad outside.

" So Deputy Donkins is after you again—it's the wages of sin, Mick. You'll get no peace till you turn to the paths of good—or till you're dead ! " said Mammy with tight lips. " Where did you say you left the posse ? "

" The Wheelbreak. Reckon they couldn't face the Pass in the blizzard."

" The blizzard's gone down now—listen. . . ."

We all listened ; and in that pause I seemed to hear a new sound from somewhere outside—the jingle of steel.

My father stiffened in his chair.

" Do you hear that ! That's a bridle-chain. . . . They've come after me ! "

" It's the first place they'd come—but I don't hear no bridle-chain."

" I do, Mammy ! " I cried out excitedly. " Reckon there's a horseman down by the fork ! "

" Christ ! They've got me caught ! " my father shouted, and his face had gone white. " Sarah, you gotta hide me ! . . . God, I'd figured they'd turned back at the Pass. . . ."

" Mind your language, Mick Milligan ! " my mother answered sternly. " And don't show yourself a coward before our boy. If they're still down by the fork, you've time to get away."

" Get away ! You mean leave the shack ! But I'd freeze to death on a night like this . . . ! "

" You gotta take your chance with God. Go outside, and climb on to the roof. If the Deputy comes, stay there till he's gone. Then you can come in again. If you stay near the chimney, you'll get some heat from it maybe."

My father sprang to his feet.

" Sarah—you wouldn't—give me away ? "

She looked at him scornfully, without speaking.

" I know you wouldn't," he said quickly.

Then, dressed as he was in his shirt and pants, he ran for the door and tugged it open. A flurry of snow—and he had disappeared. My mother closed the door and barred it ; then leaned against it, panting.

There was a long silence, except for the howl of the wind

and the little scrapings overhead that told of my dad climbing on the roof.

Then I heard a new sound. It was the chink of ponies' shoes on loose stones. The sound came closer. There was a mutter of men's voices ; then somebody beat on the door.

My mother's eyes looked at me in silent warning. I grabbed the clothes my dad had taken off and hid them under the blankets of my mother's bed.

" Who's there ? " she called out.

A deep male voice answered gruffly :

" Deputy-Sheriff Donkins here. I'd advise you to open up, ma'am—an' open up mighty quick ! "

The wind had dropped so much that I could hear every word quite plainly.

Without another word, my mother unhooked the bar, and the wind swung the door open.

Six men stamped in. Their faces were hard and watchful. In the hands of each one of them was a rifle.

" It's a wild night to visit with us, Sam Donkins," said my mother.

The face of the leading man was—to my eyes, at least— cruel and evil. He gave her a short nod.

" This ain't visiting, Mrs. Milligan. We're here on business. We came to find your husband."

As he spoke, his eyes were looking all round the shack. My mother laughed, but it sounded a queer laugh to me— hysterical-like.

" So you've come here a-lookin' for Mick Milligan. . . . That's a queer idea. I ain't seen him in ten years. If you find him, let me know. I'd like to know where he is myself ! "

" I'm sorry, ma'am, but we gotta search this shack," said the Deputy-Sheriff. " I hate to belie a lady, but I guess we just can't take your word for it that he ain't here—we trailed him as far as the Wheelbreak not an hour ago, and he was headin' this way."

He turned to his waiting men, and jerked his head.

" Get to it, boys ! "

" You'll have mighty little trouble searching," said my mother. " It ain't but a small place, and there ain't many places to hide—'cept under the beds. . . ."

As she said, the shack didn't take much searching. The men were soon finished.

" Well, Sam Donkins," said Mammy. " Are you satisfied Mick ain't hereaways ? "

" I'm satisfied he ain't in this shack at this particular moment," said the Deputy meaningly.

He strolled across to the fire, and warmed his hands at it.

" It's a mighty cold night, ma'am, and we've had a long ride. Ain't you got a little coffee to offer us ? "

My mother shook her head.

" There ain't as much as a pinch of coffee in the house. I'm mighty sorry."

The Deputy snatched up from the table the mug from which my father had drunk. He sniffed it.

" There was coffee in here."

" You heard what I said, Sam," my mother answered steadily. " There ain't no coffee in the house—*now*. That was the last we had."

Unconvinced, the Deputy replaced the mug on the table.

" Beg pardon, ma'am—but we're plumb thirsty. Ain't you got some apple-juice or something for us ? "

Again my mother shook her head.

" I ain't got nothing. We're but poor folks here—and you can't be hospitable when you're poor."

There was little more that the Deputy could say.

" That's so, ma'am." His eyes ranged the room once more ; and it seemed to me they rested a long time on the ruffled bedclothes under which I'd hidden my dad's clothes. " Guess we'd better be makin' the trail again. . . ."

With a nod to his men to follow, he walked towards the door ; then he stopped. He had seen something.

It was the rifle my mother had taken down from the mantelpiece. She had dropped it when my dad had come in, and the opening of the door had pushed it against the wall, where we'd forgotten it.

The Deputy picked it up.

" Reckon we ain't the only visitors you had to-night, Mrs. Milligan," he said in a hard voice.

Mammy looked scared, but her answer was steady :

" You reckon wrong. I took down that gun when I heard your knock—it's a lone place this, and I thought you might be bandits. I had to drop it to take the bar down and let you in."

The Deputy nodded again, but his eyes were suspicious. He turned the old rifle over in his hands.

I was shaking. The words, " Why don't you *go* ? " were ringing madly in my head. I was listening so hard that it hurt. It seemed to me I could hear, clear above the storm, little movements on the roof.

I reckon my mother was beginning to feel the strain, too.

"I'd be glad if you'd make up your mind about that rifle, Sam Donkins!" she said. "It's late, and my boy needs his sleep."

He did not even look at her. He just stood there twirling the old rifle, with his head bent to one side.

Suddenly I realised what he was doing—he was *listening*! My heart sank, for I knew that I was not imagining the sounds overhead. They were very small sounds, but they made it plain something was moving out there on the roof.

"Did you hear me speaking!" my mother demanded desperately.

Still the Deputy didn't answer. I was certain now that he knew that dad was up there—and I reckoned my father must have been nigh frozen already. How much longer could he stick it out . . .?

I got my answer quick enough. There was a sliding, scraping sound over our head—then a dull crash just outside the door.

The Deputy was strong, and it didn't take him the effort it had Mammy to get the bar off the door. Within a second, he had unhooked it and wrenched the door open.

The snow didn't blow in so much this time, and I could see my dad plainly. He was lying out there on his side, quite still.

The Deputy took a step outside and grabbed him. He dragged my dad inside the shack; and my dad didn't resist at all.

When he was back in the lamplight again, and the door closed, I saw the reason. He was frozen stiff. His body was crooked up in a set position, and his hands, claw-shaped as if to hold on to something, were rigid as wood. His beard was covered in a thick coating of ice, and there was a solid pool of ice on his upper-lip that extended up each nostril. He lay there, unable to move, unable to speak, with his tortured eyes staring at my mother.

The Deputy said grimly:

"Thought I heard you up there, Mickey. . . . Well, boys, we can't take an ice-man down to the gaolhouse. Guess we'd better thaw him before we take him along. . . ."

All crooked-up as he was, they laid him on the big chair.

His legs were doubled-up so that they didn't reach the ground, but they held on to his shoulders to stop him falling.

Before my eyes he began to thaw. The stiff legs gradually straightened at the knees, till the feet touched the floor ; and at the same time he began to shiver. He quivered and shook like a man on a switchback ; and the ice in his nostrils melted and ran over his mouth. The coating of ice on his beard moistened and thawed.

At last he spoke.

" Sorry you fellers had to take me—here. . . . Don't blame Sarah. . . . Guess she *had* to help me. . . . That God-damned roof—I hung on till I was numb, and I kinda hoped I'd freeze hard to the chimney—but I didn't. . . . I began to slide—and I couldn't stop myself. . . ."

The Deputy glanced at Mammy.

" Guess Mick could do with a hot drink, ma'am. . . ." he said doubtfully.

" I'll get coffee for all," said my mother, still trying to keep up her calm front. " I'm sorry I had to tell you there wasn't none in the house, Sam."

" I reckon you'll be forgiven for *that*," answered the Deputy.

She made coffee for all of them, and my dad didn't shiver quite so much after he'd drunk it. Then my mother went and got his clothes that I'd hidden in her bed. He put them on, and the men stood up to go.

My dad was still shivering a bit, but he smiled when he looked at me and Mammy.

" Thanks, Sarah. I owe you plenty—though it's a bit late to think about paying debts. I only wish they'd got me somewhere else but here. . . ."

He spoke carelessly—almost cheerfully. . . . And then the men took him away.

＊   ＊   ＊   ＊   ＊   ＊

I didn't sleep much that night. For hours I lay awake and thought of my father's agonised eyes staring dumbly at my mother as he lay there unable to move as much as a finger. I was mighty glad when I woke next morning, feeling tired and frowsty, that I hadn't to go to school that day.

But it seemed I wasn't to be spared the long trail down to Rolling Creek. Mother was up and about when I awakened, and I smelt pancakes.

" Jim," she said, " I'm fixin' up a big can of coffee and some flapjacks for your dad. He used to be powerful fond of flapjacks an' maple-syrup, and he always said nobody could make coffee like me. . . ." She broke off sharply. " Reckon your dad ain't having more than enough to eat in the cala-boose. So I reckon it's my duty to send him somethin' down he'll enjoy. Grease your boots, son, an' get ready to take this stuff down to him."

I was pretty sore about having to go all that distance after all, but I tried not to let Mammy see it. She looked blue enough already.

I slogged down as far as Uncle Jed's farm, but I didn't go in to see my uncle. Instead, I went round the back of the bunkhouse and got old Tom Akers, the hired-man, to hitch the pony in the buggy and give me a ride down to town. I had an instinct that Uncle Jed might not be too keen on letting me ride in the buggy, if I told him I was going to Rolling Creek to take food to my dad.

Tom pulled up outside the Silver Dollar saloon, and left me to go on to the gaol-house alone. The first thing I noticed when I got down was Sheriff Mills and Deputy Donkins going into the Silver Dollar with a crowd of other men. It was a fine clear day, but the blizzard had left a lot of drifts piled up against the houses.

I went on towards the gaol, and I noticed that there seemed mighty few folks about for that time in the forenoon. I did meet a couple of old ladies, though, and when they saw me they stopped to look at me hard and whisper to each other.

The gaol was at the other end of the street. As I drew near to it, I began to hear the sound of shouting, and I could see a crowd of men in front. I hurried on, for I felt pretty self-conscious with my coffee and flapjacks.

Then I saw that the crowd in front were all bunched round the gaol-house. They seemed mighty angry. Suddenly my heart started beating hard. I was close enough now to hear that some of the men were shouting my father's name. There was another word, too, that they kept repeating ; it was " lynch ! "

I could guess what they meant. My dad was a rustler and horse-stealer ; and, when one of that breed was caught, the cowmen who'd been his victims didn't always wait for the law to take its course. . . .

I hung about on the skirts of the crowd, scared that I should be seen. In my boyish mind was the fear that the mob might take it out of me as well as my dad.

Suddenly the crowd all yelled together, and some of them began firing off their Colts in the air. At the same moment a bunch of men spilled out of the calaboose, and I seemed to see among them another figure that they were dragging out. The mob went on shouting and screaming. It was like a pack of wolves after blood. I was so frightened that I dropped the can of coffee, and didn't notice I'd done so till a long time afterwards.

One man in the crowd turned away, frowning. I knew him. It was old Doc Summers, and he'd always been mighty nice to me. I grabbed his sleeve, and stammered out some question about what was going on.

" Lynch-law ! " he snapped. " It's a disgrace to the town. It's pure savagery. Whatever Mickey Milligan was——" He broke off and looked at me hard, as if he'd just seen who I was. " It's you, son. . . ."

" Is it my dad they're lynchin', Doc ! " I demanded.

He nodded seriously.

" 'Fraid it is, son. But I'll do what I can. I'll get the Sheriff——"

" I know where he is ! I saw him in the Silver Dollar with Mr. Donkins——"

" I'll go get him. Stay out of that there mob till I get back."

He was off, half-running, half-walking. I hung about uncertainly for a while ; and then a fearful loneliness came over me among that wild crowd, and I began to move after the doctor.

I looked back, and I saw that they'd mounted the black-haired unshaven stranger that was my father on a horse. They had tied him on facing the tail, so that his face was pointing my way. He sat up there, high over the heads of the crowd, and I thought he looked lonely too. He looked tired and very dirty ; but he didn't look scared.

Somebody grabbed my arm. It was old Tom, Uncle Jed's hired-man.

" Where's the Sheriff ? " I asked.

Tom didn't look happy.

" In the Silver Dollar. Doc Summers came in an' told him they had broke open the gaol and took your pappy out, but some other fellers there laughed an' said the Doc was jest tryin' to get the Sheriff away from his liquor. When I left, the Doc was calling him down something awful, but the Sheriff ain't moved yet. Reckon he don't *want* to believe

My father was swinging crazily in mid-air.

there's lynching goin' on. Or maybe he knew they was goin'
to lynch Mickey when he left the gaol-house. . . ."

His voice tailed away. He was looking up the street.
I followed his eyes and saw that the mob, with my dad in
the middle, was moving away. They were milling round him
like bees round a honeycomb, firing off their guns and
shouting at him. I couldn't hear what it was they were
shouting, but the sound of it chilled my blood. My dad was
nothing to me, but I was full of pity for him, propped up
there so quiet and tired-looking—and God ! how I hated
that mob !

I was deadly frightened, but mixed with my fear was a
kind of queasy curiosity. I followed the mob.

They took him about a quarter of a mile out of town and
stopped just on the edge of a big stretch of wood that was
there. I was shaking with a queer cold excitement.

I saw a rope go coiling up through the air like a snake.
The thrower had aimed to cast it over the projecting branch
of a big tree, but it only knocked off some of the snow that
was lying on the branch. Again the rope snaked upward.
This time it slipped cleanly over the bough. The crowd let
out a wild cheer.

A horseman rode up alongside my father and fastened
the noosed end of the rope round his neck ; then turned to
shout some order. The rope tightened, and my dad jerked
very upright in the saddle. The other horseman was propping
him up, and some other men were helping. They were making
him stand on his pony's back. My dad didn't resist. I guess
he knew that he'd have a quicker fall from a standing position
than from a sitting one : with the first there was the chance
of death by a broken neck, but the second meant strangula-
tion.

He was standing by now, and the rope slackened ever so
slightly. As it did so, the horseman alongside my dad held
up an arm, and somebody whacked my dad's mount. It
bounded forward ; and my father was swinging crazily in
mid-air.

The crowd hooted with delight. But it hadn't been
arranged well. They'd bungled the fall, and he was still
alive. . . .

I cowered on the edge of the jeering, roaring crowd,
but even from that distance I could see his face swelling and
darkening horribly. He was working his shoulders backwards
and forwards in agony, and the motion made him dance from

side to side like a marionette on the end of a wire. Some of the men laughed at that till they hurt their sides.

For what seemed hours—actually it must have been at least ten minutes—he jigged back and forth in that lunatic dance. He was a powerful man, and I reckon he'd bunched his neck-muscles to resist the strain of the tightening rope. His face was a horrible purple colour, and his eyeballs were bursting out of their sockets.

Quite suddenly his strength seemed to go out. His body relaxed and his mouth gaped very wide. His eyes stuck out more and more. Then his tongue came sliding down between the purple lips till it lay on his chin. I thought he was dead then ; but he suddenly jerked and began to kick. Several times he kicked, setting the rope swinging again ; then he ceased.

The rope swung gently now, and the body at the end of it rotated slowly. The eyes still stared wildly at the skyline, but they were dead eyes. My dad was dead.

Up to then some awful fascination had forced me to watch him ; but now the reaction set in. I began to vomit, and couldn't stop.

.   .   .   .

Taking the pancakes back home to my mother, I didn't stop in at Uncle Jed's to ask a ride for the rest of the way. I knew Uncle Jed was on the side of the Law—even if it was only lynch law, and I didn't want to listen to any mealy-mouthed cant about justice and retribution. Already I had banded myself on the side of those who are against the Law. My young mind was bursting with a ferocious hate against that bestial mob, and against the smug Sheriff who had deliberately left the mob to their victim.

Except in his death, my dad had no influence on me. Any acts I did afterwards which I ought to be sorry for had nothing to do with his bad example. But the manner of his death gave me, at ten years of age, a detestation and contempt for the Law that has been all too abiding. If he'd had a fair trial, I might have been a good citizen. But the way the Law pretended not to see, and the good law-abiding citizens denied him even the mercy of a bullet during his last agonies, put me finally and decisively on any other side but that of the angels.

WHERE PLATONIC LOVE MAY LEAD A MAN

By
MRS. BELLOC LOWNDES

O NE fine cold January morning the prosperous Antwerp barrister, William Bernays, kissed his little boy, said good-bye to his wife—he was not on kissing terms with his wife—and took train for Brussels.

Neither wife nor child ever saw him again.

William Bernays had said he meant to come back that same night, but no word was received from him to account for his absence. After two anxious days of waiting and of wondering what could have happened to prevent her husband's communicating with home, Madame Bernays informed the police of his disappearance.

Oddly enough, no one at first knew what business had taken the lawyer to Brussels ; but soon that trifling mystery was cleared up. An acquaintance whom he had met in the train, and who had travelled with him a short distance, remembered that Bernays had casually mentioned the fact that he was about to meet an important new client. " The man appears to be an American, in a big way of business," Bernays had observed. " I've not seen him yet, but we've been in correspondence, and he's already sent me a hundred and fifty dollars."

No trace of this unknown American client's letters, or of the cheque he had sent, could be found among the lawyer's papers, and the disappearance of William Bernays became a nine days' wonder in the town of Antwerp.

In such a case the very last thing that people are apt to suspect is what is popularly called foul play, and William Bernays' old friends and lifelong neighbours had more than one theory which might account for his temporary disappearance.

Not long before his mysterious journey to Brussels, the lawyer had become a Roman Catholic, and certain people thought it conceivable that he had gone off to a monastery.

Others recalled, under their breath—for his beautiful young wife was respected and even beloved—that William Bernays, like so many clever, brilliant men, had an ugly side to his nature—a very different one, that is, from his religious side. He had never been a man of high moral character. Madame Bernays was a saint, and from a sinner's point of view a saint is sometimes " gey ill to live with," as many an average man has discovered to his cost.

Was it not possible that Bernays had gone on a short illicit honeymoon ? If popular rumour spoke truly, this would not have been the first time. And Madame Bernays, noble woman that she was, had forgiven and forgotten. Many a man in Antwerp envied the lawyer his happy, successful, careless life, and his fair if austere wife.

But just a few members of his own family, and one or two trusted friends and confidants outside that narrow circle, knew that William Bernays was not the happy man he appeared to be.

True, he seemed to possess everything that makes for happiness in this world. He had a great reputation in his profession, he was blessed with plenty of money, he had a delightful home, and a little son whom both he and his wife worshipped.

But, unknown to the great majority of his fellow-citizens, Bernays was a profoundly unhappy and dissatisfied man—wretched in the one relationship that is all-important in adult life. William Bernays and Julia, his wife, each attractive, each clever, and each with a high if different ideal of duty, were utterly unsuited the one to the other.

Julia Bernays, the daughter of a noted Belgian statesman, was a refined, high-strung, and austere-natured woman. True, she was beautiful, but beautiful—so her husband had once described her to a member of his own family—as a statue is beautiful.

The marriage had been arranged in the French fashion, but the two young people, well suited by birth, fortune, and age, had seemed much attracted to each other—Bernays, indeed, fell passionately in love with his future wife.

From the day of the wedding, however, the bridegroom's jovial, familiar ways offended and displeased his bride ; and after about a year of disunion, and of the discomfort that such disunion brings, they actually discussed the possibility of a separation.

But already the little son whom they both loved with a

jealous love was born, and for the sake of their child, and because neither would consent to giving him up, in any real sense, to the other, they agreed to adjust their secret differences so far as to continue living in an outwardly friendly manner under the same roof.

Of this foolish and unnatural bargain ill was sure to come, and it soon did come in the shape at which the lawyer's acquaintances hinted among themselves when Bernays disappeared so suddenly and mysteriously from his home and usual haunts. The lawyer became frequently unfaithful to his wife, but in a furtive, shamed fashion which left it possible for those about them to hope and suppose that she knew nothing of these outrages on her wifely dignity. Outwardly William and Julia were on good and even cordial terms, and they kept the secret of their disunion hidden from every one save certain very near relatives and friends.

But a worse and an infinitely less-to-be-expected complication than Bernays' light conduct had followed the arrangement entered into by the husband and wife—that arrangement which made them strangers under one roof.

Indeed, what had come to pass even before the disappearance of William Bernays may well inspire a Browning yet unborn to write another " Ring and the Book."

II

IN the same town of Antwerp, united to the Bernays family by ties of a long acquaintance rather than intimacy, lived a widow lady named Peltzer. She was the proud mother of three handsome sons, each of whom was very popular with the town folk.

In due course all the young Peltzers set out to carve their fortune, and Armand, a brilliant engineer, eldest and cleverest of the band of brothers, went off to America, where he was soon well on the way to prosperity.

He met, however, with one rebuff from Fate. He married a charming girl, whom he had the misfortune to lose after a very few years. She left him, however, a little daughter.

The two younger Peltzers stayed at home and engaged together in business. But they did not prosper as Armand had prospered, and there came a day when bankruptcy— and, what was even more terrible to this honourable family, a fraudulent bankruptcy—stared the partners in the face.

The mother cabled the news to her eldest born, and Armand, without losing a day, left his work and his happy, successful life in America, and hurried home in order to save his two brothers.

The engineer had lost touch with what was going on in his native place, and when he asked in the town to what lawyer he should address himself in the difficult task before him, every one replied, " Go to William Bernays ! He is the only man who can get your brothers out of their dreadful scrape."

To William Bernays, Armand Peltzer accordingly went, and, thanks to the clever lawyer, the two young men came out of their trouble with honour, if not with fortune saved, and Armand ultimately found Léon, the cleverer of his brothers, a good post in America.

But he himself lingered on in Antwerp. He was in no hurry to go back to his adopted country. He had brought his little girl with him, and the presence of her son and her grand-daughter made his mother a happy woman.

He struck up a great friendship with Bernays, the lawyer who had saved his brothers from dishonour. Armand Peltzer was very grateful to William Bernays, and, as the engineer was a clever man, and an agreeable talker, the two soon became almost inseparable.

But what was surprising to those sufficiently interested in other people's business to take heed of such a thing was that Madame Bernays—the beautiful, reserved Julia—also became on terms of real friendship with Armand Peltzer. She welcomed him as she did no other of her husband's intimates to her house, and she took a close and tender interest in his little girl. As to him, we can perhaps guess what he felt as he gradually grew to find himself on terms of close friendship with

A lady, young, tall, beautiful, strange and sad.

Very soon the engineer became what a man so often becomes when he is on friendly terms with a husband and wife—the confidant, the adviser, and the sympathiser of both. Both, to him, broke their wise rule of silence, and he listened to the expansive, over-frank complaints and grievances of William, the aggrieved husband, and heard with eager, respectful sympathy the more reticent confidences of William's lovely and now neglected wife.

The position of such a friend—of a man, that is, who is intimate with a husband and a wife who have ceased to be intimate with each other—is very difficult and delicate. For such cases the French have an excellent proverb, which runs, " Between the tree and the bark do not try to thrust thy finger."

Armand Peltzer certainly did his best, early in the acquaintance, to bring William and Julia together again ; but his efforts, as any one but an eager young man would have known they would be, were quite unsuccessful. Indeed, his efforts only ended by widening the breach between the lawyer and his wife. Soon Armand himself became devotedly —he always declared, on oath and in the most solemn way, platonically—attached to Julia Bernays, to the wife of the man who had proved himself, since Peltzer's return home to Antwerp, his best and wisest friend.

Time went on, and still the young engineer lingered in the town where his mother lived. And only Madame Peltzer, with her keen mother instinct of what ailed her son, suspected who it was that was keeping him there.

It is on record that she warned him of his peril, but that he angrily repudiated her suspicions. True, he was constantly in the Bernays' house ; but if he paid long calls on Julia during William's business hours, he spent even longer hours in the lawyer's office, and the two men were always together in their spare time.

But there came a day when some cruel, mischief-making human being—it is said to have been the nurse of Madame Bernays' little boy—wrote an anonymous letter to William Bernays, asserting that his best friend, Armand Peltzer, was in love with Madame Bernays, and that all the gossips in Antwerp were talking about it.

Now Bernays, in spite, or perhaps because, of his wife's cold aloofness and his own secret flirtations, still loved his Julia quite sufficiently to be, or to become, violently jealous of her. The anonymous letter filled him with rage and suspicion, and instead of putting the coarse epistle into the fire, as he ought to have done, he kept it to show to his own family, and he wrote the following letter to Armand Peltzer :

ARMAND,—In spite of our friendship, I have to acquaint you with a painful but inevitable decision. I have received an anonymous letter concerning your friendship with Julia, and it is clear that I must safeguard the honour of my name. As your intimacy with my wife and myself causes low gossip, I must ask you to give up coming to our house.

My wife and I will henceforth live for our child. You also have the good fortune to be a father ; I wish you and your child all possible happiness. Let us never associate our children with our misfortunes.

I beg of you, Armand, not to answer this letter. I am too unhappy, too shaken, to bear any discussion concerning the painful subject. Believe me, it hurts me greatly to break with an old and what has become an only intimate friendship ; but I am sure that you will agree with me that, for both our sakes, it were better so.

I bid you farewell.

WILLIAM.

On the receipt of this letter Armand hurried round and insisted on seeing Bernays. He swore on what he held most sacred in the world—his child's life and his mother's honour —that he had never said a word to Julia that a brother might not have said, and further, that he regarded her with the highest veneration. His words bore such an accent of truth that William, ashamed of his base suspicions, humbly asked Armand's pardon. Nay, more ; he asked him to come and dine with him and with Julia the same night.

But the happy spell of innocent friendship between these three people had been broken. The lawyer went on receiving anonymous letters, and there came an evening when William thought that he detected a meaning and a secret smile between Armand and Julia.

He got up from the table, and, making—poor fool that he was—a violent scene in front of his wife, plainly told the other man that he could not bear his presence in his house any longer ; and the next day he wrote the engineer a letter in which he tried once more to express exactly what he felt about the whole painful matter :

ARMAND,—After all that has come and gone, I have to think, not only of what may be true, but of what may be said, and in view of the anonymous letters I continue to receive, I cannot doubt that your frequent presence in my house is making people talk. I beg you, therefore, in the name of my honour and of Julia's good name, to discontinue your visits. My wife and I live only for our son. You have also the good fortune to have a child. Let us never associate either of our children with any scandal. Pray send no reply to this letter. Neither speak

nor write to me about it. I am very sorry to have to sever
our friendship, but I am sure that you will feel with me
that we can pursue no other course.

Would that Armand Peltzer had obeyed the entreaty
contained in this letter ! It was, it must be admitted, a wise,
a dignified, and, on the whole, a high-minded letter for a
husband to write to the friend who, now that the scales had
fallen from that husband's eyes, was soon by him to cherish
a violent if a still respectful passion for his wife.

But Peltzer did not receive the letter at all in the spirit
in which it had been written. He chose to read in it an
intolerable insult. His friendship for the lovely, neglected
young married woman had become to him the noblest, as
well as the most absorbing, passion of his lonely life. Nay,
more ; he told his mother—his unhappy, anxious mother,
who alone had suspected the truth almost before he knew it
himself—that it would be ignoble on his part to give up his
acquaintance with Julia Bernays.

Armand sent no answer to his old friend's letter, but he
evidently communicated its purport to his old friend's wife ;
and she, angered, as will be understood by every woman
who reads this strange and terrible story of love and hate, by
what she took to be a most unworthy and shameful suspicion,
went straight to her husband with the news that she now
intended to obtain a divorce.

Bernays was bewildered and horrified by his wife's threat.
He eagerly declared that he did not suspect and never had
suspected Julia, and further that he even acquitted her of
imprudence.

He confessed to a morbid fear of gossip and scandal.
Were he and Julia, he asked reproachfully, to part because
of a foolish quarrel brought about by scurrilous anonymous
letters ? Was their home, all the dignity of their joint life,
to come to an end just as their little son was growing old
enough to understand what it means when a father and
mother are divorced and the home is broken up ?

Nay, more, thoroughly sobered by his wife's cold anger
and virtuous indignation, William Bernays sought out his own
and Julia's lifelong friend, the President of the Belgian High
Court, Monsieur Longé.

To this wise old man he told the whole story, and how
little the whole story seemed when it was put in plain
language !

Monsieur Longé reasoned with Julia. He showed her that her sudden wish for a divorce was cruel to her child, and finally, with her consent, he drew up a sort of informal deed which both husband and wife were to sign and leave with him.

The first clause in the deed expressed Bernays' great regret at having unjustly accused his wife of indiscreet behaviour, and recognised the utter falsity of the accusation.

The second clause arranged that the husband and wife should each inhabit a separate suite of apartments in the same house, and it even stipulated that their meals should be served apart unless, for the benefit of the child, either thought it advisable that they should meet occasionally at luncheon. Together, also, they were to settle everything that concerned the little boy's health and education.

Madame Bernays, on her side, undertook to behave exactly as a wife should behave when her husband's friends came to the house. But she stipulated that she was *to be perfectly free as to the choice of her friends*.

Finally, husband and wife agreed never to engage in painful discussions the one with the other, and to allow Monsieur Longé to arbitrate between them in case of any difference of opinion.

Julia Bernays' first act after the deed had been signed was to invite Armand Peltzer to dinner.

She was " *to be perfectly free as to the choice of her friends*," and it seemed to this wrong-headed woman that her womanly honour demanded of her that she should break the spirit, while obeying the letter, of the new agreement into which she and her husband had entered together.

As soon as Bernays heard what she had done he made matters worse by preparing to break the letter of the law to which he had agreed.

" No," he said firmly ; " I will not tolerate the presence of Armand Peltzer in our house. His coming is bound to lead to fresh difficulties and troubles."

Thus, before the ink on their signatures was well dry, husband and wife were disregarding, the one the spirit and the other the letter, of the deed.

In vain their trusted friend, Monsieur Longé, implored Julia to give way, and told her that she was doing very, very wrong. She insisted, on the contrary, that she was doing right, and that only Armand Peltzer's presence in their house would make her feel that her husband no longer suspected her.

She also considered it her duty to inform Armand of what had followed on her invitation to him. This naturally set him afire too. He sat down and wrote an angry, and yet it must be admitted a dignified, letter, in his turn, to William Bernays :

> WILLIAM,—After the interview in which you begged me to forgive your unjust and dishonouring suspicions of your wife and of myself, I thought all was right again between us. But there came, as you know, further trouble. I learn that in the deed you and your wife have signed it is expressly stipulated that Julia may choose her own friends. Now she chooses me to be her friend, and frankly asks you to receive me as such. You refuse to do so, and that is a gross insult to me.
>
> Your wife, who has a noble heart, is devoted to my little daughter. In her interest, and in the interest of my child, also in the interest of yours, I consent to hold out my hand and again to forgive you. Thus will be prevented any foolish talk about the noble and pure-minded woman who bears your name. You have indeed acted ill to your only friend—that is, to me, and I can never, never hope to forget your conduct in this matter.

Bernays returned this letter unopened, and the same evening Armand Peltzer sent the lawyer a formal challenge to a duel.

Now, Bernays, either because he was physically a coward, or because he dreaded the wave of talk that a duel always provokes in foreign society, was horrified by the receipt of Armand's challenge, and he actually sent his one-time friend a written apology for what he termed his " unjust suspicions."

Bernays, however, remained firm as to the one thing that really mattered to them all, and on which his wife and Armand Peltzer were determined to make him yield. Though he seemed willing to meet his wife half-way as to almost everything concerning their joint life, he would not give in about this one matter. He refused to receive, or to allow her to receive, visits from Armand Peltzer.

In a letter to the venerable President of the Belgian High Court, a personal friend, it will be remembered, of both his own parents and those of Julia, Bernays endeavoured to explain exactly how he felt about the matter :

I am willing to accept all my wife's conditions and to observe them faithfully, with one exception ; I must refuse to receive Peltzer as a friend. Julia must not push me too far. She must not ask me to do what is above my strength. Unless the fact is pointed out to them, no one among our friends will notice whether we receive Peltzer or not. As long as Julia is in my house, living with me as my wife, she will neither be suspected nor talked of unpleasantly. It is absurd to say that for her sake I should put up with the society of Monsieur Peltzer ; it would only lead to fresh trouble.

Peltzer could not make up his mind to this complete separation from the woman he had grown to love with a love which, as he always solemnly declared, though absolutely pure, was none the less ardent and absorbing. At the end of a month of separation he wrote the following letter to Bernays :

WILLIAM,—I understand that you have signed an agreement by which you allow your wife complete freedom in the matter of receiving her friends. Further, you will remember having told me how very sorry you were for your unjust and ignoble suspicions. How amazed am I now to learn that you have made up your mind to a brutal and violent rupture between us ! I might have challenged you to a duel, and I felt greatly tempted to do so ; but that would have made talk, and would have greatly injured the reputation of your wife, whom I respect and esteem. I did, however, ask my brother to arrange an interview between us. We could then have had a frank and loyal explanation. You refused ; thus confirming your first insult.

For the sake of Madame Bernays, whose noble character I venerate, and because of the gratitude I shall always feel for her kindness to my little girl, I still consent to meet you and to be seen in public with you. In that way we will both avoid being parties to a low and infamous machination which has had for object that of attacking the name of a woman who is, above all women, high-minded and pure.

ARMAND PELTZER.

This letter Bernays sent back unopened to the writer, and to a friend the barrister wrote, " I cannot tell you the hatred and contempt I feel for that man ! " And to the same friend he sent a good many documents—various letters he had had from his wife, and so on.

Very soon the position between the husband and wife became so strained that Bernays, at last utterly disheartened, begged his wife, in his turn, to consent to a divorce for incompatability of temper. But, to the great surprise of the few who were in their secret, Madame Bernays now absolutely refused to consider the question of a divorce.

When we think over and try to pierce the psychological mystery which is perhaps the most extraordinary feature of this extraordinary story, this final refusal of Julia to free herself from her husband is seen to have played a great and sinister rôle in the dread drama that followed.

And yet, who can doubt that had Julia Bernays desired to marry Armand, who by this time was madly in love with her, and for whom she seems to have cherished a very warm feeling of friendship, nothing would have been easier than for her to accomplish her purpose.

But in that case Julia would have had to give up her little son, or, at the best, to have shared him with her husband. According to the French and Belgian law, after a divorce has been granted, the father and mother of any child issued of the dissolved marriage have a right to their child's companionship for alternate months of each year.

Julia Bernays wrote to her old and trusted friend, President Longé :

> I entirely refuse to divorce William, because to do so would partially separate me from my child. I know my duty as my boy's mother, and it is a duty made the more incumbent on me owing to my profound contempt for the man who has behaved to me as Monsieur Bernays has done. He refused to defend my honour when it was odiously and basely challenged, and if he dares to institute a suit for divorce I shall know how to defend myself.

And so once more these unhappy people attempted to live together for the sake of their child and his future ; and if Armand Peltzer had played a manly part and had gone away, as many a man situated as he was situated had done, all would have been, if not well, at least unshadowed by a terrible crime.

III

BUT human nature is a strange and complicated thing. Armand Peltzer had persuaded himself that his love for Julia Bernays was a noble passion of pity for an innocent woman hardly used by fate. Deep in his heart he knew that he loved her ; he desired ardently to marry her, and he wished that she should be free to consider him kindly.

When he found that her love for her child made divorce impossible to her, it became clear to him that there was but one way—albeit an awful and a dangerous way—in which to cut through the tangle in which he found himself.

William Bernays must be made to disappear, and the secret of his disappearance must be solved by the discovery of his death. Only as a widow could Julia become a happy wife.

And Bernays, as we know, did disappear. He took train to Brussels on that bright, sunny January day, and thenceforth he seemed obliterated as completely as if he had never existed.

An exhaustive hunt for the vanished man took place all over the continent of Europe. But the mystery remained impenetrable, and there followed nine long days of anxious waiting on the part of Julia, her little boy, and Bernays' own family, which included an aged father and mother.

On the last of the nine days the Chief of the Brussels Police received the following strange letter. It was dated Basle, and ran as follows :

SIR,—I am horrified to learn in the papers that the letter that I wrote you—indeed, the letters I wrote you, for I have written two—did not reach you ! Monsieur William Bernays, alas ! has not disappeared. He is dead. He was killed by accident in my Brussels office, 159, Rue de la Loi. The accident was entirely my fault—or, rather, the fault of my carelessness. He came to see me by appointment to talk over an important business matter. There was a pistol lying on my desk, and I foolishly took it up and began playing with it. Monsieur Bernays had already turned to leave the room when the trigger went off, and, to my intense horror, Monsieur Bernays fell at my feet. I thought—I hoped he was only wounded, but soon, alas ! I saw that he was dead—and dead by my hand !

My first impulse was to send for the police. Then I remembered how very awkward and unpleasant would be my own position. I am an American, without a single friend or acquaintance in Brussels.

I therefore made up my mind that I had better leave Belgium and communicate with the police from a distance. I did so. But my letters seem to have miscarried. I am now very sorry that I behaved so foolishly. Still, I shall be able to prove that all I say is true, and I beg you to tell Monsieur Bernays' unfortunate family how deeply I sympathise with them, and how terribly sorry I am at having been the involuntary cause of his death.

I am, Sir, your obedient servant,

HENRY VAUGHAN.

Henry Vaughan! Who was Henry Vaughan? No trace of him could be found in the hotel registers of the town, and at first (so unlikely and unreal did the contents of this letter seem to be) the police took it to be one of those letters, often quite intelligently worded, which always follow on the commission of any widely advertised crime or disappearance, and which are the work of foolish or morbid practical jokers.

Still, as Rue de la Loi is a well-known street, it was thought worth while to send a couple of detectives to the address.

They found No. 159 to be a large, respectable house let out in business offices, and, after a certain amount of search and of inquiry from the porter, they further discovered that an American named Henry Vaughan had indeed hired an office in the building. This, however, only confirmed their belief that the letter had been written by some practical joker who wished to annoy Henry Vaughan.

Giving no hint of their dread mission, the two men made their way to the room which they were told was occupied by the American.

They knocked. There was no answer. Quickly and quietly they forced the lock, and there, huddled up in an arm-chair in front of a large desk on which lay a pistol, sat William Bernays—dead. He had been killed by a shot from behind, for there was a deep wound in the back of his neck.

Everything in the office was in perfect order. Bernays' heavy overcoat and his hat still hung on a stand near the door. A good deal of blood had gushed out on to the thick carpet, and there was the imprint of a man's boot-sole in the dried and coagulated blood. But that, though a painful detail, was natural enough. It was odd, however, that Henry Vaughan, after the accident, should have picked the dead man up and sat him down in the chair. Still, perhaps he had done so hoping that Bernays was still alive.

In the unfortunate lawyer's pocket was found a certain amount of money, and the following letter, which confirmed the mysterious American's story :

> SIR,—By the favour of an English friend I have obtained your name and address. They tell me you are the best lawyer in Antwerp, as well as an authority on commercial and maritime matters. This is why I ask your assistance concerning the state of Belgian law as to the following points.

Then came a number of highly technical questions as to the Belgian commercial and navigation laws and usages. The long letter concluded with the words :

> I shall be much obliged if you will kindly answer the above by return, for I am engaged, as you will understand, on a very important piece of business. As an earnest of my wish to avail myself of your legal assistance, I enclose a hundred and fifty dollars. I am told you are conversant with English as well as French. Pray write to me in either language.
> I am, Sir, your obedient servant,
> HENRY VAUGHAN.

Yes, the story told in Henry Vaughan's letter was borne out by the facts—indeed, it was probably true in every particular. After all, truth, especially in criminal matters, is often far stranger than fiction.

But had the lawyer really died as Henry Vaughan declared he had done ? The position of the wound gave the lie to the story—unless, of course, which seemed very unlikely, Bernays had suddenly turned away and so received the shot in the back of his neck instead of in his breast.

At any rate, there was but one thing now to do, and that was to get hold of Henry Vaughan.

The police soon discovered that the mysterious American was known to quite a number of important people in Belgium. Traces were found of him, not only at Basle, where his letter had been posted, and where he had stayed at a good hotel for some time, but also in various Belgian and German towns. He appeared to be, as he had said in his letter, an American man of business travelling, however, on behalf of an important business concern in Australia.

But what had happened to him after he had left Basle, which he had apparently done within an hour of posting his letter, remained an impenetrable mystery. In fact, it seemed fairly obvious that " Henry Vaughan " had taken the wise if not very noble course of leaving for America immediately after he had written the letter—that curious, prudently worded letter—telling of the dreadful thing that had happened to him.

IV

DAYS and weeks slipped by. The body of the unfortunate William Bernays had been brought home to Antwerp and buried, amid marks of widespread sorrow and esteem, while among the chief mourners walked Armand Peltzer.

Madame Bernays and her little son went into deep mourning, and began to live the quietest and most retired of lives.

And then suddenly anonymous letters, bearing the postmark of Antwerp, began to rain in on the Brussels police ! These letters indicated, in language that became plainer and plainer, that a certain Armand Peltzer, an engineer who was now courting Madame Bernays with a view to persuading her to make a second marriage, had had a deep interest in the death of William Bernays. Nay, more ; they suggested that the letter signed " Henry Vaughan " should be compared with the handwriting of Armand Peltzer !

Again the Chief of the Brussels police thought he was being hoaxed, the more so that a very few inquiries in Antwerp made it clear that the Peltzers were people of consequence and respectability. It was also ascertained that at the present time two sons were living with their widowed mother—Armand, the distinguished engineer, who had come so nobly to his brother's help some years before, and Léon, one of the brothers who had been in trouble. Léon, who was making a good livelihood in America, had come home on a holiday.

Still, in view of the fact that the Brussels police had never been wholly satisfied as to how Bernays had met his death, specimens of the handwriting, not only of Armand Peltzer, but also, incidentally, of his brother Léon, were secretly procured.

A great, an overwhelming surprise, was in store for the official in charge of the affair.

While it did not require an expert to see that there was nothing in common between the handwriting of the mysterious American and Armand Peltzer, the handwriting of Léon Peltzer and that of "Henry Vaughan" were absolutely identical !

A few hours after this fact had been ascertained, the two brothers were arrested, to the extreme amazement, even the wrath, of many of their fellow-townsmen with whom they had been popular from childhood onward.

And then there followed one of those close, ruthless, brilliant investigations that have become the glory of the modern detective forces of France, America, and England.

Once a clue is found, their task is often pitifully easy. But this time the law had as antagonist a really able man who had thought out every detail of his plot with marvellous ingenuity. Had Léon possessed the intellectual capacity that distinguished his eldest brother, Armand would almost certainly now be living an honoured citizen of Antwerp, the devoted and happy husband of the beautiful Julia, widow of his one-time attached friend, William Bernays.

Amazing, almost incredible, in its cold, reasoned cleverness, was the story that was gradually unrolled—and the more amazing in that neither brother gave himself or the other away. Not only did they each protest their innocence, but they did more ; they behaved, while in prison awaiting trial, in a way to convince some of those who saw them that they were innocent and that their consciences were at ease.

And yet, as the links in the chain became slowly but surely joined up, Armand and Léon must have known, only too well, that their sinister plot had only miscarried through Léon's folly. Had he not written the letter signed "Henry Vaughan" with his own hand—had he, for instance, had it typewritten, the Brussels police would never have obtained the clue which finally led to the brothers standing their trial for the murder of William Bernays.

V

ACCORDING to the prosecution the following were the facts of the case :

Léon Peltzer, after the serious business troubles from which his eldest brother had so cleverly extricated him, had been for a while a rolling stone.

He had stayed for varying periods in Manchester, in London, and in Buenos Aires. At last he had settled down in New York in the employment of a big and respectable firm ; and it was there, on an October day some three months before Bernays' disappearance, that the young Belgian suddenly informed his employers that he must leave them at a moment's notice. The reason he gave was that a Canadian friend, who had once been very good to him, had telegraphed for his help in a serious difficulty.

But Léon Peltzer did not go to Europe via Canada. The 1st of November found him on board the *Arizona*, bound for Liverpool, under the false name of Prélat. He probably found a letter waiting for him from his brother, for he went straight on to Paris, and there met Armand, and although both men stayed at the same hotel they used different names.

They spent four days together in Paris, and then Armand, who was throughout the directing intelligence, and who evidently found in Léon a very willing instrument, went home to Antwerp.

Léon Peltzer at once moved to another Paris hotel, again changing his name. It was from there that he went to a hairdresser, and, explaining that he was going to a fancy dress ball, bought a wig and a false beard. He waited a day or two, and then, on the day he said the ball was to take place, he went back to the same hairdresser from whom he had bought the wig and beard, and had himself thoroughly well " made up." He even went to the trouble of having his face stained a dark olive colour.

When he finally left the shop, Léon Peltzer was so entirely unlike his usual self that not his own mother, or so he was assured, would have known him. From a fair Belgian he had become in appearance a South American Spaniard.

His next step was to write a letter to Armand, dated " November 18—San Francisco." This letter Armand showed to several family friends in Antwerp. In it the writer described his busy, prosperous life, and announced that he would soon come home for a short holiday.

But Léon stayed on in Paris some time longer, and there, under the name of Viberg, he bought seven revolvers and three boxes of ammunition. After doing this he destroyed everything—clothes, papers, and so on—that he had brought from America, and, under yet another new name—that of Valgrave—he purchased an entirely new outfit, including a quantity of good underclothes, but all these were marked, by his order, in the name he finally adopted, that of Henry Vaughan.

Thus equipped with a new name and a new personality, that of a traveller for Messrs. Murray and Co., of Sydney, come to Europe to organise a new service of steamers between Bremen, Hamburg, Amsterdam, and Australia, Léon Peltzer started on a series of cleverly planned journeys.

"Henry Vaughan," the dark, bearded, middle-aged-looking South American, left Paris on December 1, and for three weeks he travelled all over Holland and Germany, staying, among other places, at Hamburg, at Bremen, and at Amsterdam, seeing a good many business people—especially lawyers—and making all kinds of arrangements that had the appearance of being absolutely genuine.

He stayed in good hotels, and seemed to have plenty of money with which to entertain new business acquaintances.

Never, in the long history of murder as a fine art, was murder more intelligently, and in a sense more intellectually, planned than was that of William Bernays. Neither time nor money—the two accomplices that are generally lacking to the murderer—was absent from the sinister tryst. Indeed, had Léon Peltzer possessed a tithe of his brother Armand's intellect, the two would certainly have succeeded in the scheme so cleverly imagined and so carefully and patiently carried out.

The fact that there were so many lawyers ready to come forward and say that they knew Henry Vaughan quite well, and that he was a respectable business man, had been naturally instrumental in causing the Brussels police to drop all inquiries until there came the anonymous letter clues from Antwerp.

But to return to the doings of "Henry Vaughan." After having thus created for himself a new and honourable personality the pseudo-American went to Belgium. He travelled about for a while, then settled down in Brussels. There he hired an office in the Rue de la Loi, and he purchased, not only a certain amount of office furniture, but also a thick carpet, and even a pair of thick curtains to hang over the door. He also remembered to get a hat-and-coat stand. This was in order that Bernays, on coming into the room, should hang up his heavy overcoat, which, if he had kept it on, might have deviated the course of the bullet.

As to what actually occurred on the morning of the murder, it remains, and will always remain, a mystery.

Was William Bernays shot by Léon Peltzer or by Armand? Many Belgians believe that the engineer arranged to give himself the satisfaction of killing the man whom he had come to regard as his deadly enemy, for it was the imprint of the sole of Armand's boot which was found in the coalgulated blood on the carpet.

According to the medical evidence, Bernays was not killed in the arm-chair where he was found. He was shot standing, and his body probably remained on the floor for twenty-four hours. Then either Léon or Armand, or possibly both brothers, came back, and so arranged the body as to make his death appear an accident.

But it may be objected that though this story of all that may have happened is very cleverly imagined, how was it *proved* that Armand Peltzer was directly concerned in the murder? The boot-sole imprint would be a very slight piece of evidence on which to condemn a man to death.

It is true that, owing to Armand's acute and foreseeing intelligence, and also thanks to his brother's steadfast loyalty, the police found it very difficult to involve the elder Peltzer in the net of proof as surely as he himself had drawn his enemy into his snare. It may be doubted if, but for the existence of telegraphy, they could have succeeded.

Armand was doomed when at last the police discovered the telegrams which the brothers exchanged when about to meet in Paris. In Paris the detective's task was easy, for the French hotelkeeper at once recognised Armand as the man who had stayed with him at the same time as Léon. During the whole of Léon's peregrinations through Holland, Germany, and finally Belgium, the brothers were in constant communication, almost daily telegrams passing between them, Armand using an assumed name, that of a woman.

Yet another fact which told terribly against the elder brother became known to the police. On December 23 he had begun practising pistol-shooting in his mother's house. Their neighbours complained of the noise, and Armand soon desisted from his strange diversion ; but, hidden in a secret place, there were afterwards found a large number of cartridges which were proved to be those which Léon had bought in Paris.

It is a curious fact that none of the seven revolvers bought in France seems to have satisfied Armand as being suitable for his purpose, for Léon made a hurried journey from Brussels to London, and it was with a revolver bought from an English gun-maker that William Bernays was shot.

On the very morning of the murder the younger brother addressed to the elder the following telegram :

" Thanks for your charming proposal. I hope to see you Saturday.—Marie."

This, being interpreted, meant, " He has accepted my proposal : I hope to see him to-day."

Armand declared that it had been sent him by a woman whom he had met by chance, and with whom he had made an assignation. Unfortunately for him, the original draft of the telegram was found in the Brussels post office, and it was in Léon's handwriting !

VI

WHEN at last the two brothers were put on their trial, the case excited most extraordinary interest, not only in Belgium, but all over the Continent.

The trial lasted a whole month, and, as is the custom in France and Belgium, numberless witnesses were called who in America or in England would have been considered to have little or no connection with the case.

Practically all of the relatives of each of the parties—of the murdered man, of his wife, and of the two men in the dock—were heard at length, and even asked for their opinion on the affair.

Each of the brothers also gave in the witness-box his own explanation of what had taken place, and it is a curious and rather touching fact that the object of each seemed to be to guard and to exculpate the other.

" Is it likely," cried Armand, " that Léon, who had absolutely no interest in Bernays' death, should have murdered a man simply because I disliked him ? " And then, in eloquent language, he went on to assert the purity of his affection for Madame Bernays, much in the same noble words that Browning put in Caponsacchi's mouth when addressing the judges :

You know this is not love, sirs—it is faith.

Léon also tried to shield his brother. " I shot William Bernays because he penetrated the disguise I had assumed in order to carry out a fraudulent bit of business," he declared coolly. " It is probable, it is even conceivable, that my brother Armand should have desired to murder Bernays, considering that Madame Bernays had the power of divorcing her husband ? "

The most exciting moment of the trial came with the appearance of Julia Bernays in the witness-box.

Dressed in widow's weeds, her splendid golden hair tucked away out of sight, her large blue eyes red-rimmed with long weeping, she looked more ethereal, more spiritually beautiful than ever.

" I am here," she said in a firm, low voice, " not to accuse, but to forgive——" There was a pause, and then she went on, " It is my husband I try to forgive for his infamous conduct."

She denied, in the most moving and solemn way, that her feeling for Armand Peltzer had ever been anything but a pure and high-minded friendship—" and it is a friendship," she concluded, " which has never faltered, and which is as constant, true, and pure to-day as it ever was." And then she exchanged a long, sad, ardent glance with the fine-looking young man who stood, with folded arms, in the dock.

The two brothers were defended by the leading barristers of the day ; but nothing could avail them in the face of the irrefutable evidence which had been pieced together as the result of Léon's one act of carelessness.

The verdict was never in doubt.

The judge asked the prisoners if they had anything to say.

" I have to say," replied Léon Peltzer eagerly, " that I accept the condemnation. But my brother Armand is absolutely innocent, and the jury have committed a judicial crime in condemning him."

Armand, turning to the twelve men who had just pronounced his fate, cried in a loud voice :

" On the jury will lie for ever the curse of my child ! "

THE END OF THE BARON

By
R. McKINLEY

The " Baron " was the name under which went the leader of one of the most highly organised gangs in the United States, and who controlled and directed rum-running operations over 2,000 miles of the Pacific coast. He had corrupted many high officials, but the Federal authorities are on his track and he has just learned of the failure of some of his plans and of the warrant which is out for his arrest. " H.D." was the Baron's right-hand man, and the writer was employed as the Baron's wireless operator.

THE Baron went tearing off to his luxurious home, which had been left in the care of a couple of men-servants, bent on strengthening his organisation. Scarcely had he reached his home than the telephone bell rang. It was a call from police headquarters. The Baron was ordered to report immediately. This was something quite new to him. For the police to issue orders to the chief rum-runner on the Pacific coast was something approaching insolence to his point of view.

" Hell, and who do you think you are, to give me orders ? " he asked, slamming the receiver down, and promptly picking it up again put a call through to the political boss.

" Say," he declared, " it's just coming to something when your police fellows phone me and order me to report to them instantly. Just keep them in order or there'll be trouble. Understand ? "

The reply which the Baron received, however, caused him to change his tone considerably. A very serious charge had been brought against him, not with the police, but with the Federal Authorities, who were about to act. America was no longer a safe place for him to remain in, and the sooner he made his get-away the better for himself.

The political boss could do nothing for him, save give him warning of what was taking place.

Speed of movement was vital if arrest were to be evaded. There were only two ways out of the city for him to make to

Mexico, which was the only place he could hope to find safety—the long coast road, and the railway. But already both these were being watched by Federal agents, who had learned of the Baron's return to the city. They had been searching for him, and were already on their way to his home in fast motor-cars to execute the warrant which they held under the dreaded Mann Act.

I must explain here that in the United States there are, broadly speaking, two classes of law, Federal and State. A Federal law covers every State in the country, and Federal agents are appointed to see that these laws are carried out. State laws are very different. They only apply to the particular State in which they are enacted. Thus, were we similarly situated in this country, we should be in the strange position of having a totally different set of laws in every county in England. Take the cases of two men, one living in Kent, and the other on the opposite side of the street, which might happen to be in Surrey. Each man commits a certain act. That act might not be regarded as an offence under the laws of Surrey, with the result that nothing would happen to the Surrey dweller, though his unfortunate Kent neighbour might suffer a long term of imprisonment. In America, the local, or State laws, are enforced—that is, more or less, according to the way in which grafting is done—by the local police, who can be called upon to assist Federal agents to enforce Federal laws, or ordered by the political boss to enforce Federal laws if those particular Federal laws suit his particular political party. We talk about the muddle of the British legal system, but in this country we are at least honest and just in enforcing laws. A very different state of affairs prevails in the U.S.A. Political opinion and graft count for far more than law and order.

The Mann Act, under which a warrant for the arrest of the Baron had been issued, is one of the most infamous of the many Federal laws in America. Actually, the Act is aimed at putting a check to the operations of White Slavers, but so wide are the powers under it, that there is scarcely a man in the States who could not be arrested and charged under it with some form of crime or another. For instance, for a man to take a girl from one State into another, even though the trip is made with the consent of the girl's parents, renders him liable to a White Slaving charge. If the two decide to stay for a holiday in the State which they have visited, and return later, the man is liable on conviction to fifteen years' penal servitude, and this, even though he has married the girl.

It was under this dreaded Act that a warrant had been issued against the Baron. The offence concerned Rosaline ; according to the information which the political boss gave the Baron, information had been laid against him by some unknown person with the Federal Authorities, that on different dates he had taken Rosaline from the State, into Ensenada in Mexico, and had stayed with her there at an hotel, passing the girl off as his wife, and further that he had taken her to the Canadian border with her child, and he had left her there.

It was a charge which the Baron could not possibly contest. The pair were regarded as man and wife, though, actually, the Baron had a wife living in Mexico, and they had spent scores of week-ends in Ensenada and other places outside the State. And even now, the girl and her child were staying on the Canadian frontier. With the prospect of from fifteen to twenty years' penal servitude looming before him, the Baron was by no means happy. Escape from the city was the only thing which mattered now ; escape into Mexico, a matter of some eighty miles, meant liberty. How to effect that escape was another problem, with both the road and the railway station being watched.

With the exception of the two men-servants who had charge of the house, the Baron was alone. Both men were old associates of his, who worked with him in his mule-driving days, and were now in the guise of servants assisting him in the bootlegging business. They could be trusted absolutely, for the trio had been in many a tight corner before, and there were but few of the Baron's secrets which were not shared by the other two men. Both were, like the Baron, of Spanish origin. One man filled the rôle of butler-valet, while the other combined the duties of odd man about the house and gardener. There were other duties which the men undertook, but they were of a far more adventurous type, and usually necessitated carrying a gun in their hip pockets. To them the Baron told his dilemma, and a way out was discovered.

The butler-valet should take his place when the Federal agents arrived to search the house. Already the agents' cars were outside the door, and the Baron smiled grimly as he looked at the men who had come to arrest him. He was safely hidden behind the thick window curtains. For some time no heed was paid to the loud hammerings on the door.

Then, when they were repeated with threats, the Baron shuffled to open it.

Six men, all strangers to him, stood at the door.

"What do you want?" he asked, speaking in broken English.

"We're Federal agents," explained the senior of the gang, displaying his badge. "Where's the Baron?"

"He 'aint here, boss," lied the Baron. "Gone to Canada, I heard."

"That so," drawled the agent, "then in that case we'll jes' take a look round."

"Tain't no use, boss," declared the Baron. "He's no here."

The Baron was roughly pushed out of the way by the six agents, who forced their way into the place. "Got any booze here?"

"No, boss," said the Baron weakly. "The Baron sees there ain't no booze left about for us folk."

The Baron followed the six men as they began their search of the house, protesting that the Baron had not been home for some days.

"What do you want 'im for?" he asked.

"Mann Act," bluntly replied one of the agents.

"Say," drawled the Baron, "and whose given him away?"

"A woman, of course, the bride's mother, in fact," and the man gave a hearty laugh.

But he had told the Baron all he needed to know. The secret of the many failures was laid bare. "H.D." had not talked. There was only one person in the world who might have discovered his plans, and that one person the old harridan whom he had ordered out of his house, and who had sworn vengeance on him. She was his enemy and had blown his game to the Federal authorities.

Half a million dollars had been the price which she had demanded of him. He had refused to give this sum of money, as hush money, and now she had turned on him. Rosaline must be in on this too. From her the Baron had no secrets, to her he had talked freely and openly. She must have passed on the information to her mother. He would deal with the pair of them when he was free from his present difficulties.

But the Baron was careful not to betray himself to the agents. He was merely the Baron's servant, and as such he played his part with the skill of an experienced actor.

F.T.S.   L

While two of the agents remained posted in the hall to prevent any one from entering or leaving the house, the Baron was forced to accompany the other four in their search. Every room was carefully examined, furniture moved, and walls tapped to discover whether any secret doors existed. A wardrobe in the Baron's bedroom was found to be locked. Ruthlessly this was burst open, the woodwork being splintered and smashed. Half hidden in the folds of clothing hanging there was the butler-valet.

Roughly he was dragged from his hiding-place.

The Baron gasped a startled cry. " Boss," he exclaimed. " I didn't know you was back in the house."

" Have I got to tell you when I come to my house ? " retorted the supposed Baron, who was being held by two of the agents. They had no time to parley words.

" Thought you'd made a good hide, didn't yer ? " he was asked.

" You're coming with us, Baron."

" What for ? "

" Charges under the Mann Act. You'd better come clean. Goin' to blow it ? "

" When I gets to headquarters," was the reply.

A pair of handcuffs was slipped over his wrists, and protesting that he would make no trouble, the man was dragged from the house, and dumped into the waiting car.

Pleased with their capture, the agents drove away, leaving the real Baron standing gaping at the door of his home. Now there was not a second to lose. Rushing through the house, the Baron jumped into one of his own cars and raced madly down town to " H.D.'s " office.

" Get my automobile away quick," he ordered his second-in-command, as he dived into the office.

A moment later he was busy on the phone, ringing one of his many garages on the great coast road.

That afternoon a heavy farm lorry stopped outside the office where " H.D." conducted his " real estate business," and a dirt-covered farmhand wearing dungarees climbed into the seat beside the driver. The lorry rumbled off along the coast road, heading south for the frontier.

The lorry halted at a petrol station on the road to refill its tank, and the grimy farmhand slipped from the cab and disappeared, while the lorry resumed its journey.

Some time later a well-appointed automobile, driven by an immaculate chauffeur and conveying " H.D.," Real

Estate Agent, to Ensenada, drove rapidly from the garage. The smartly dressed chauffeur knew his business, and drove without regard to speed limits till the frontier was reached.

Once over the border, the car stopped outside a notorious hotel. The chauffeur got out, threw open the door of the car, " Come on, ' H.D.,' we'll drink to the health of Uncle Sam and his policemen," he exclaimed. For the moment the Baron was safe.

The news of the arrest of the Baron under the Mann Act spread like wildfire through the town, and was published in big type in the early afternoon papers.

Then followed later editions with reported confessions, and finally, much to the chagrin of the Federal agents, the full story of how they had been tricked.

They could do nothing with the man they had arrested in the place of the real Baron, for once at police headquarters, he had declared that he was not the Baron, but one of his servants.

His attitude was that he had never even pretended to be the Baron, and his explanation for being found hidden in the locked wardrobe quite a simple one.

" I heard the Baron come in, and knew I had no right. in his room, where I was searching for whisky," he said, " I heard him coming upstairs, so I hid in the cupboard."

Asked to explain why the man who had opened the door to the agents exclaimed " boss " when the cupboard door was opened, the servant said his name was " Bonze," and the agents must have misunderstood the word and taken it for " boss."

It was all very simple, though perhaps unconvincing. To the discomfort of the Federal men, it had to be admitted that they had not asked either the prisoner or the other men in the house whether the man they had arrested was the Baron or not, and took no steps to establish his identity till they had reached police headquarters.

In the end the man had to be set free, and he returned to the Baron's house to await orders, while the Federals recommenced their search for the Baron, now safely over the frontier.

" H.D." returned to Los Angeles that night, driving himself in the car which he and the Baron had used earlier in the day, and I received a phone call, ordering me to report to him immediately. When I reached the " real estate agent's " place, I was told that the Baron was going to establish his headquarters, for the time being, at all events, in Ensenada, while I was to pack up and go to San Diego ; there stand by at certain hours to pick up messages from the Baron, and send them forward according to instructions. He was making the necessary arrangements for transmitting messages from Ensenada.

" H.D.," too, had received very definite instructions regarding Rosaline's mother, who had given him away to the Federal agents, but the nature of those instructions he kept to himself.

Less than a month after his departure from the United States, I read in a Los Angeles newspaper that the old woman had been found dead. She had apparently poisoned herself, in a boarding-house where she had been staying, and the Coroner decided that she had committed suicide. The Baron and his gangsters knew how to deal effectively with people who dared to cross swords with them.

It did not take me long to establish myself comfortably in San Diego, and in three days I had my wireless station working.

The authorities were totally unaware of its existence, and I was thoroughly enjoying life. Each night I had about three hours' work to do, taking down code messages, and transmitting them, either by wireless to ships at sea, or by phone to Los Angeles. I began to flatter myself that at last I had found the job of a lifetime.

But soon I received startling news over the phone. The Federal agents had discovered the whereabouts of the Baron, and were making every effort to get him back into America, where his arrest could be effected. Further warrants had been issued against him, charging him with bootlegging and conspiracy, both, of course, being Federal charges.

The Baron's secret wireless station in Ensenada was on board a Mexican ship lying in the harbour there, a fact which the police soon discovered. Under Mexican law it is an offence for a ship in harbour to make use of her wireless, and this was seized upon by the Federals as an excuse to approach the Mexican authorities. Naturally, they did not expect to get the Baron out of the country in this way, but were seeking to make it as difficult as possible for him to carry on his bootlegging business.

But the Mexican authorities are slow to act, and slower still when officials are paid a good price to be slow.

Nothing happened, and night after night messages came

through in the usual manner. The next move was a demand for his extradition for trial in the United States. Weeks of arguing followed, during which time the Baron did some heavy bribing, which resulted in the extradition being refused ; the authorities, however, were determined to have the Baron by any means.

The Baron had been staying in a little place called Tiatuana, about eighty-seven miles from the frontier. The hotel where he was located was commonly known as " Aunt Jane's " and was well known to thousands of Americans. Late one night I was seated at my wireless when a message came through. It read, " Boss missing since an hour ago. Have you news ? " Instantly I replied, " No. Find him."

Minutes, which seemed like hours, elapsed, till the receiver buzzed again.

" Stand by," came the message, and then followed, " Been doped and carried away by Federals. In big car heading coast road north. Report Los Angeles at once."

I rushed to the phone and put through a call to " H.D." I found the Baron's lieutenant at his home, and quickly told him the news.

" Say, that's clever," he said. " O.K. I'll get busy right away. Try and get the number of the car he's in."

I went back to my radio, and gave the call signal for Ensenada, and, having got a reply, asked if they could give the number of the car. Five minutes later I was given not only the number but a good description of the motor and its occupants. Apart from the driver of the car, there were four policemen in it, hefty fellows wearing wide-brimmed hats. At once I passed the news on to " H.D.," who replied that everything was set. He appeared to be in no way excited or anxious, but just his ordinary, careless, slow-moving self.

I could not resist the temptation of taking my old car out, for I knew now it was scarcely likely I should be needed for further messages that night.

I put a gun in my coat pocket, and started the car up, heading for the coast road, in a northerly direction, in the hope of picking up the rescue party, which I felt convinced " H.D." would send out in cars from Los Angeles. Good luck was with me. After an hour and a half's run I saw the headlights of two cars approaching, and drew to the side of the road. The driver of the first car saw my lights, and, considering from the fact that I had stopped and drawn clear of the road I had acted suspiciously, decided to stop and investigate.

The car was pulled up, and two men alighted. I recognised the first man, it was the butler-valet, the man who had been arrested at Los Angeles in mistake for the Baron.

I jumped out of my ancient car and shouted a welcome to him.

" Hell, Mac," he returned. " We thought your car was one of the Federal's. You were for it." He pulled an ugly-looking gun.

" Seen anything of them ? " I was asked.

The coast road, a huge, wide highway, ran straight as a die for miles north and south. That night it was deserted, and the lights of any approaching cars could be seen for fully five miles either way.

The spot where we had pulled up was ideally situated for the hold-up of the bulls' car when it came.

Already the gangsters had decided upon their plan of campaign. There were eight of them in the two cars, and each man was armed. In the back of one of the two cars were a couple of sub-Thompson machine-guns, firing tracer bullets, which would be used if the need arose.

That the Federals with their prisoner would come tearing along the road within the next hour or so, none of us had any doubt. It was their only road into the States, and they would not be likely to delay their return until daylight ; darkness suited them far better, and speed in getting their prisoner safely under lock and key in one of the American police headquarters was of vital importance, in view of the fact that his gang would soon learn of the kidnapping, and be certain to make some attempt at rescue.

My arrival on the scene, however, had caused a slight change in the plan of operations.

It had been intended, so I was told, to stage a smash and thus block the road, to pull the bulls' car up. But now I had arrived with my old Lizzie, she was to be sacrificed ; the old tub was not worth a couple of pounds. The cars which the bootleggers were using were both high-powered, modern automobiles with plenty of good service in them.

With the lamps of the cars extinguished, we stood in a group beneath the trees, arranging the details of the scheme, at the same time keeping a watchful eye to the south for the headlights of the car approaching from the border. The one chance which we had to take was that we might make a mistake and hold up a wrong car, but that chance had to be taken. Had the wrong car been stopped, it would have been a nasty experience for the occupants, who would have had to be held up till we had done the job we were bent on.

And even when we had completed it there would of necessity have been a further delay, since it would not have been safe to allow spectators to go immediately, but this did not happen.

While we were talking we saw the headlamps of a car approaching far away to the south. It was being driven at terrific speed. Instantly the old car was pushed into the middle of the road, and toppled on to its side, the petrol running out of the tank beneath the bonnet, and forming a pool in the roadway. A match was thrown into the pool, and a second later old Lizzie was going up in flames. The other two cars were hastily swung round as though they had been coming from the Mexican frontier and were making for the States. Three men knelt by the roadside, and swathed my head and face with bandages as I lay, the supposedly seriously injured victim of the smash on the grass bank.

The strange car was nearing the spot, when one of the " bandagers " darted from my side and commenced to wave his arms furiously, signalling to the oncoming car to stop.

There was a sudden heavy grinding of brakes, and the car stopped not twenty yards from where the Ford still blazed. Two Federal agents jumped out.

" Accident ? " asked one.

" Yes, a nasty one. Stick 'em up ! "

The agents found three guns pressed up against their chests, and promptly raised their arms. At the same moment the five gangsters rushed from their hiding-places, surrounding the car, threatening the other agents in it, and one by one the men got out, their hands up in the air. Each man was searched and his gun taken, two of them had handcuffs as well. In the back of the car was the Baron, handcuffed and unconscious.

Quickly he was lifted out, and transferred to one of the two cars which had brought the gangsters from Los Angeles, and the handcuffs were taken off. Three pairs of handcuffs, and four Federals. The rest was easy. The men were made to stand back to back, and the bracelets slipped on to their wrists and snapped tight.

" Sorry to put you to such a lot of trouble," laughed the " butler," " but we just couldn't let you take the Baron like that."

" We're Federal agents," warned one of the gang.

" What of it ? " " we laughed.

The four men were marched off and were made fast to a tree with a rope passed through their handcuffs, and well out of sight in the darkness. Then their car was deliberately set on fire and left to burn.

The nine of us, with the unconscious Baron, crowded into the two cars, and dashed back to the Mexican frontier.

Ten miles from the frontier we met the first car that we had seen on the road, an old car with an ancient man driving, and whom I for one sincerely hoped would be the first to find the unhappy bulls we had left tied up miles back.

We reached Tiatuana safely as dawn was breaking, and carried the Baron up to bed at " Aunt Jane's " before sitting down to discuss the event of the night, and enjoy a hearty breakfast.

From the proprietor of " Aunt Jane's " we learned later in the day of what had happened to the Baron.

He had been seated enjoying his drink on the terrace in the cool of the evening, discussing events with a stranger who had been staying in the house for a couple of days. The stranger, unknown to any one at " Aunt Jane's," was actually one of the four men we had left tied up on the road. He had managed to dope the Baron's drink, and as he became unconscious, he was carried off by the other men who had been waiting for the signal in a car close by. The Baron had been away half an hour before he was missed, and the alarm raised. Scouts who had been sent out soon learned that he had been seen in the car with the Federals, and had got the number of the car.

" It was a mighty good thing you were at your radio, Mac," the Baron said later in the day when he had come round, and was laughing over the story of his rescue. " If you'd been away having a few drinks I'd have been caught long before this. Drink is a terrible thing, Mac. Keep off it. Have nothing to do with it. Now, have a drink ? "

Although the Baron tried to make light of his position, and declared that every one had a bad patch of luck at times, it was plain to us all that he was more than ordinarily worried by the turn of events. Far too much was known of his business methods by Federal agents for him to hope that his luck would turn. Again, every day he remained in Mexico, unable to direct operations at headquarters, strengthened the position of his rivals, and the Federal agents knew this as well as he did. Worse still, though we had succeeded in rescuing him on the Pacific road, the Federals were still crying out for blood. At all costs they were bent on getting hold not only of the Baron himself, but of the members of his gang who had staged the successful hold-up. They had got hold of the burned number-plate of my ancient car, and had traced me through it. I was now wanted for a serious crime which would, were I caught, result in my being sentenced to about twenty years' penal servitude. Acting on the instructions of the Baron, I reported to the Mexican police the fact that my old Ford had been stolen, and this was placed upon the official records, together with a very circumstantial account of the supposed theft.

The Baron was not anxious for me to remain a fugitive from the United States. But things went from bad to worse. Cargo after cargo of rum was seized by the Federals as it was being landed, or in the speed-boats off the coast. Scores of times speed-boat men were obliged to dump the precious spirits when they were within an ace of landing the stuff. Then came the heaviest blow of all. The Federals applied for another extradition order again the Baron, this time in connection with the hold-up on the Pacific road. We learned of this move from a Mexican police official. But happily Mexican officials are no more averse to taking bribes than the Americans, and the Baron was able to buy his liberty for the time being, and learn the details of the Federals' moves. Their spies were swarming in the country, and were constantly on the track of the Baron and the rest of his gang in Tiatuana.

Late one night we held a council of war in " Aunt Jane's." The Mexican official who had been passing the news of the latest moves of the Americans was becoming more and more greedy in his demands. Now he was asking for an immediate payment of the equivalent to £500 to ensure the safety of the Baron, threatening that unless the cash were paid he would not have any alternative but to arrest him.

There were five people other than the Baron and myself present at the council of war, when the whole of the details of the present position were discussed. Each was agreed that, given time, the necessary cash could be raised, a week or perhaps a fortnight at the most would be needed, but during that period the safety of the Baron was threatened at every moment. We phoned to the Mexican official, and tried to explain the position to him, but he declared that unless the money was forthcoming by the morning he would have to do his duty. Of course, he said that he did not need the cash himself, but was being pressed by the men who were acting for the Federals. They had threatened to report him and get him imprisoned unless he handed over the cash.

At all costs the Baron had to be saved from extradition, which would automatically follow his arrest by the Mexicans, who never dare oppose the power of the Americans when it comes to a law case. If we could get him away for about a fortnight, hidden from both the Mexicans and the Federals, everything would be O.K. At Ensenada, some eighty miles distant, there was a little steamer belonging to the Baron. She was registered under the Mexican flag, and had regularly been used by the Baron and his gang as an intermediate boat running out to the mother ships at sea with orders from shore. *White Label* was the name of the craft. Of 90 tons register, she was little larger than an ordinary Thames tug, but one of the stoutest little sea-boats afloat. Time and time again has she steamed out to mother ships lying 120 miles from the coast, and returned safely to harbour. Lying off Los Angeles, though naturally well outside the territorial limit, was a large steamer loaded with whisky, the last purchase the Baron had been able to make. By the sale of the cargo of this ship the Baron had hoped to recoup some of the heavy losses which he had sustained. Once we could get him aboard the ship he would be safe from arrest, so at the council of war that night we decided to make an attempt to get him aboard her.

The *White Label* was fitted with wireless, which, despite Mexican regulations to the contrary, she continually used while in port. She was at that moment lying snugly in Ensenada Harbour, and with the set which was fitted in " Aunt Jane's " and used regularly by the Baron, I got into touch with her, ordering her to get steam up and be ready to go to sea.

From the skipper of the *White Label* I received an O.K. message through, and arrangements were made to smuggle the Baron out of the hotel. As usual at week-ends, the place was crowded with Americans. Men and women, boys and girls, many of them still of school age, were dancing and drinking. They had come to " Aunt Jane's " for the usual week-end riot of jazz and whisky.

If we were to get the Baron away, now was the opportunity, while the dancing and whisky-drinking was at its height. The proprietor of " Aunt Jane's " had hitherto been in the confidences of the Baron, but he was no longer to be trusted. In the past he had assisted us in every way, but during the last few days he had seemed rather too anxious to discover what our arrangements were.

In order that he might be thrown off the scent, the Baron ordered further supplies of whisky to be brought to his room, and invited the proprietor to join the party.

Fortunately for us, owing to the week-end riot in the hotel, our host was unable to remain long with us, but he did stay long enough to consume about half a bottle of whisky, and learn from the Baron that a further sum of £500 was to be paid immediately to the agents to ensure his safety in Mexico. Meanwhile, I left the apartment and made my way to the garage where the big car which the Baron used was stored. I filled the tank with petrol, and brought the car round to the back of the hotel, hiding it in a lane nearby, and returned to the Baron's apartment to meet the proprietor of the hotel who was just leaving.

" I'm mighty glad the Baron can find the cash to keep the Federals off," he said, as I greeted him.

" Things are a bit difficult," I laughed.

When I entered the apartment I found the Baron seated, gloomily staring at a half-empty whisky bottle.

" How are things, Mac ? " he inquired.

" Everything is O.K.," I answered. " I've got the car outside."

Ten minutes later, the Baron and his men were cautiously creeping through the grounds of the hotel to the lane where the car was waiting. He had locked the door of his apartment on the inside and had left the lights burning, to allay suspicion should any one trouble to look up at the windows from the garden.

Ensenada lay eighty miles away, and I drove the car at breakneck speed through the darkness.

We reached the harbour at daylight, the *White Label* lay alongside with steam up, ready to put to sea. No time was lost in getting the Baron and two others aboard. I was left to put the car in a local garage, and ordered to get busy with my wireless, passing on the vital information to others of the gang who were still in Los Angeles.

But, cautious though we had been in our arrangements for the Baron's flight, our plans had become known. An hour after our departure from " Aunt Jane's " some one tried to get the Baron on the phone in his apartment, and when no reply could be obtained, a man was sent to his apartment, to find the door locked. An entrance was forced, and the apartment found empty. By wireless and phone word was passed that the Baron had escaped from Tiatuana, and both Yankee bulls and Mexican agents joined hands in the search for him.

While we imagined that he would be safe aboard the *White Label*, an American cutter was speeding after her. The *White Label* was a Mexican ship, and actually in Mexican waters, but such details never seemed to worry the Americans.

The cutter came up with the little steamer, which could not do much more than five knots against the cutter's fifteen. No signal was made, till too late. The cutter crashed into the *White Label*, tearing a big hole in her side and damaging the propeller. This " accident " occurred on the first night out at sea, and no attempt was made by those aboard the cutter to give any assistance. Immediately after the " accident," so the Baron and skipper of the *White Label* both swore in affidavits made in Mexico, the cutter turned and steamed off, leaving the little ship helpless.

During the night wireless calls were sent out for assistance, and efforts made to repair the damaged propeller.

The wireless call was answered by a Japanese fishing craft which, incidentally, had taken part in rum-running operations. It was impossible to repair the propeller while the ship was at sea, and sail was rigged up, and attempts were made to beach the vessel sailing under canvas, with the Jap boat standing by. The Baron was transferred to the Japanese fishing vessel, in case the cutter came up again and tried to get him, and slow progress was made before the wind, which fortunately was blowing towards the Mexican coast.

Early next day a heavy sea got up, in which the *White Label* floundered and wallowed. It was impossible for the two little ships to keep company, and since the Jap had four drums of whisky aboard her, which had been taken from the Baron's ship, it was thought wise for her to make for a fishing village on the coast, where there was a prospect of the Baron being safely hidden for a time, till the fishing boat could make the mother ship again.

Soon after the ships parted company the propeller shaft of the *White Label* pulled out, and was lost. Fortunately, the engineer had foreseen that this might happen if the seas increased, and had taken precautions to prevent a sudden inrush of water. Although the ship was leaking badly, they managed to keep the water down, till the arrival of an American cutter, which came alongside and got a line aboard. The cutter commenced to tow the *White Label*, making for Ensenada Harbour, a distance of about thirty miles. The two vessels had just reached the entrance to the port when there was a sudden inrush of water, and the tow rope had to be cut with an axe to save the cutter from being dragged down as the little rum-runner sank. Her crew swam to the cutter, all being picked up safely. Whether the cutter which towed the crippled ship in was the same one that had caused the damage was never discovered. Some days later information was laid against the *White Label*, and after she was raised, she was confiscated by the Mexican authorities, and her skipper and mate were both sent to prison, a state of affairs that would never have happened had the Baron been able to pay the money demanded. Meanwhile, luck was still against the Baron. He had succeeded in landing in the fishing village and had got the four drums of whisky ashore and safely hidden. For four days he remained there, waiting an opportunity to get away, and at the same time to get the whisky to the man who had ordered it.

On the fifth day he was aroused from his sleep by a Jap.

"Come quickly, Baron," he shouted, "the Mexican police are looking for you, and they have found the rum."

The Baron jumped out of bed and followed the Jap to the beach, where he was hidden beneath a pile of nets and fishing gear, while the Mexican police searched for him. Unfortunately, in his hurried flight, the Baron had to leave behind him all his clothing, together with his wallet, containing several hundreds of Mexican and American dollars.

That afternoon, dressed in the rough clothing of a Japanese fisherman, the Baron sailed in a Japanese fishing boat, to try and reach the mother ship, promising the Japs a reward once they put him aboard.

It was not until the Baron finally reached the mother ship, some 120 miles off Los Angeles, that he learned by wireless the full extent of the disaster. No less than four thousand cases of whisky which were being run from the ship had been seized by the Americans, and warrants for his arrest were issued both in America and Mexico. So far as he was concerned he had reached the end of the road.

For the next month I remained in Ensenada, hoping for the best. I had little or nothing to do, save drink and waste my time in the saloons. Funds were beginning to run low, and I got into touch with the Baron's second-in-command at Los Angeles, over the long-distance phone. From him I learned that the Baron had, after a long chase, been arrested, and was at that very moment in the lock-up. I was out of a job.

A RACE FOR A BRIDE

By
H. K. HALES

I ONCE rode a race for a bride. Not my bride—she belonged to a friend of mine. It happened like this.

It was Christmas, 1902. I was dressing for a party late one evening when the telephone rang. Over the wire came an agitated voice.

" I'm in a fix, H.K.—a desperate fix. Can you help me ? "

" What is it ? " I asked. " Who are you ? What's the matter ? "

" I'm in a terrible fix," said the voice again. " I've got to get married ! "

" Have you, now ? " I said. " The dickens you have ! That'll teach you a lesson. But what can I do about it ? "

" It's to-morrow," said the voice, "—two o'clock sharp to-morrow. And you're the only man who can help me ! "

Now by this time I had recognised the agonised accents as those of a friend of mine, a good fellow not given either to strong drink or to hasty marriages.

" You old idiot," I said. " Calm down and tell me what's wrong. Start from the beginning."

" I'm due to be married to-morrow," he said. " Ashby-de-la-Zouch—and there's only a Sunday train service, so I can't possibly get there in time."

" Oh, so that's the trouble. What do you want me to do ? "

" Drive me there in your car," came the cool though anxious voice.

" All right. Meet me at six outside the ' George,' in Hanley," I said—and rang off.

I shan't forget that Christmas day in a hurry. To start with, I overslept and did not get dressed until well after the time I had named. Hurriedly putting on my cap and motor coat, I sallied forth complete with goggles on my errand of mercy. It was a tough proposition, and I knew it.

I picked up the fretting bridegroom in Lichfield Street, Hanley. He was in a profuse perspiration and as I approached

I noticed that he had his watch in his hand and was weighing up his chances of getting to the church in time—and that, judging from the expression on his face, he thought the odds were against him.

He pitched his bag containing his wedding clothes into the car. "I'll change at the girl's house," he gasped and hopped in beside me. Then began the battle with the miles and the ticking song of time.

The bridegroom writhed in his seat. He clung to the swaying car with one hand while in the other he held that confounded watch of his. I got to hate the fleeting glimpses of that dial. It seemed to point with fingers of doom at me and my old car. My companion was so anxious about the time that he looked at nothing else and did not notice the risks I ran. He just clung there almost sobbing, and the perspiration dripped down his face as he watched the minutes and the hours pass all too quickly as we sped along.

Up hills we panted and down hills we scorched. We swung round bends with two wheels off the ground. Birds, beasts and humans fled before us. Drivers of carts and carriages heard our approach from afar and drew into the hedgerows till we had flashed by. Never had my old De Dion done so bravely, never had her single cylinder barked so well. At one village a policeman rushed into the roadway to stare at us, but we were gone beyond his reach before he could invoke the law. Not long afterwards we struck a bad patch of half-melted snow and spun round so fast that we finished up headed homewards. A mile further on we came to a halt in a sea of mud at the foot of a hill and it took every ounce of our strength to get going. But our worst scare was when we nearly skidded into a deep and watery ditch.

The bridegroom was white as a sheet.

"Cheer up," I remarked at last. "I remember this bridge. We are almost in Burton-on-Trent."

This was fatal. Just as we reached the bridge the car stopped. Without a murmur it slowly came to rest and there we sat in silence in the hush of that Christmas noon. But only for a moment. The bridegroom jumped out and fairly danced with anxiety and worry. "Now you've done it," he shouted ungratefully. "Here we are, stranded, with nine miles to go and no chance of getting there—and only an hour left."

"You'll get there if I have to carry you," I shouted, and rushed ahead to look for some sort of conveyance. I charged into a neighbouring inn-yard and there, thank heavens, was a pony and trap. A small lad held the reins.

" Get out," I shouted. " I want this quick."

The lad looked scared but stuck to his reins.

" You can't have it. Master wants it—he's going for a run."

" No, he isn't," I retorted. " Get out. I must have it."

" What's up now ? " shouted the proprietor who stood in the hotel doorway.

" I want your trap to drive to Ashby-de-la-Zouch."

" The devil you do ! Well, you can't have it," was the ungracious answer. " I am just going out myself."

" That's all right," I said. " I will bring it back soon. You can have my motor. It's stopped on the bridge. Here's a fellow who has to be married in an hour and I've got to get him to the church."

The sight of the bridegroom settled the matter. Poor chap, what with the anxiety and the swaying about in the car, he looked half dead. We got the trap without further bother. The pony was a little one—little more than the size of a Shetland—but he was plucky. He covered the nine miles into Ashby in record time. He had no intention of breaking records, but when he found that I was prepared to break a whip he needed no further encouragement to enter into the job thoroughly. Whether it was my shouts or the bridegroom's groans that did the trick I don't know, but anyway we had covered the nine miles by five minutes past two, and were at the door of the bride's father. Inside the wedding party were waiting with anxious faces, all dressed up for the show.

There was no time to enter into explanations. " Dress him quick and get him ready," I shouted, " while I drive on and tell the parson there has been a delay." I rushed out of the house and gave the pony the whip. I still had four miles to cover to the church. The pony seemed about to drop, but if the ring was not on the bride's finger by three o'clock there would be no wedding that day.

I stood up in the cart and urged the animal on. A crowd had gathered at the doors of the church awaiting the bride and groom. Astonishment was written on every face when they saw, not the expected happy couple, but a man dressed in motoring coat, goggles and cap standing up in a swaying trap. In one hand I held the reins and in the other four feet of whip handle. Somewhere on that hectic journey the lash had become entangled in the wheel and torn off and I had not noticed that I had been thrashing the empty air.

I leapt out of the trap and pushed my way through the crowd into the church, ran up the aisle and button-holed the waiting clergyman to explain the delay. Then I flopped into a pew and rested. Half-past two and still no sign of the couple. All too soon the clock struck the quarter to the hour but at the same time I heard something which fell on my ears more pleasantly than any wedding march—the rattle of the wheels of a carriage on the rough surface of the road outside. They had arrived. My labours had not been in vain—or had they? Even now the business had to be completed before three o'clock. I rushed up to the patient clergyman and begged him to put back the minute hand of the clock. But he, upright soul, would not have it. So I sat and sweated in the pew while the wedding service commenced. Every second I expected that wretched clock to strike and so negative all my struggles. . . . The groom slipped the ring over the girl's finger. Hardly had I said a fervent " Thank God ! " than the clock in the old tower struck the hour. We had won—by the shortest of heads.

Never have I earned a kiss so well as that which the bride bestowed upon me after the ceremony was over. As for the bridegroom, he shook my hand so hard that it hurt. Though not superstitious he believed in signs, and he had made up his mind that were he to miss his wedding it would foretell disaster.

" Send for me if ever you feel like bolting," I said. " I'll drive even faster."

I think that threat did much to keep him faithful. He certainly never forgot our race for a bride.

ILLEGAL CARGO

By
JO HALLAM

The author and his friend, Doolie, are out of work in 1902.

WE'D been back in Liverpool about a month when Doolie arrived back at our boarding-house one night full of excitement.

"What's up?" I asked.

"Ho, ho!" he roared. "You may well ask 'what's up.' Why, the luckiest break that you or I have had in our lives!"

"Well, what is it?" I asked impatiently.

"Jo," he said impressively, "how would you like to earn 150 dollars a month, and at the same time have an adventurous, healthy life. How would you like it, eh, Jo?"

I replied that there was nothing I would like better.

"Well, we can get it, both of us," he continued excitedly.

And then he told me he'd met a man down in a pub near the docks who was an agent of a big gun-running concern. He had seen the man down there quite often before, as a matter of fact, but had never spoken to him before. Doolie had noticed, however, that the man had taken an interest in everything he'd said and had evidently been studying him carefully before he decided to broach the subject to him. Doolie had jumped at the idea, and had told the man that he had a friend with vast seafaring knowledge and great discretion (this was meant to be a description of me!), who was also looking for a job, so the agent said we'd better both go along to a Mr. C., a Spaniard, who was at the head of the organisation in England.

I was not so enthusiastic as Doolie about it.

"It's crooked, isn't it?" I asked.

He stared at me for a moment, and then roared with laughter.

"What does that matter to you or me?" he said. "We draw our pay, and do what we are told, and that's all there is to it. Besides, what business isn't crooked? Every really successful business is crooked, or has been, at one time."

I knew there was truth in what he said, and I knew also that there was so much arm-running going on that it was more or less an open secret—as it is to-day !

Mr. C. apparently approved of us, for he signed us on. We were to travel to San Francisco on a ship which left in a week's time. There would be six of us going out on the same job.

"And you will—of course—be discreet ? " he smiled as we went out.

"Of course," we echoed.

"There is no need to assure me of that," he purred in his soft, rather sinister, voice, "*I have made arrangements in case you are not.* I hope you will be comfortable on the voyage out to San Francisco. There will be two valets in attendance. Good-bye."

"What on earth was he talking about ? " I asked Doolie when we got outside the door. "What do we want with valets ? "

"They're probably part of his *arrangements*," Doolie suggested.

He was right. They were !

The two servants were Chinese. Their names were Tung Chow and Chang Chow. They weren't a nuisance to us on board but they were inscrutable ; you couldn't tell what they were thinking ; you never knew when and where they were going to appear. All the same, they were excellent servants, and it was a new experience for me to be waited on. Doolie was highly delighted with them and was always ordering them to do little unnecessary things. In fact, Doolie was highly delighted with everything, and lorded it about the ship in such an arrogant way that he became quite unpopular with the rest of the passengers.

There were four others, all Englishmen, who were going out on the same job as ourselves. Three of them were quite decent fellows. One was a nasty little weed of a fellow, whom all the others seemed to dislike as much as I did. Why Mr. C. chose him to go, I can't think, except that he had the qualifications which no one else had, that he had done gun-running before. He seemed to know more about the present business, too, than any one else. He told us we were going to carry American arms into China. When Doolie asked him why Englishmen were wanted in the crew, he said that it was always the custom on any gun-running boat on which he had served to collect foreigners to form the main part of the crew—men who have no interests in either of the two countries.

The crew on a gun-runner, he said, were always very carefully picked, and usually only discreet and reliable men were picked. In spite of the general dislike of this weedy little man, he certainly gave us a lot of information. He kept impressing on us the urgent need for secrecy.

"They're a powerful group who are on this job," he said, "that's why they can pay us big money. And that's why they wouldn't stop at killing a man who was blabbing."

He said that the Chinese servants knew everything that was going on and wouldn't hesitate to get rid of any one who began to talk rashly. He had known the trick of the "valets" before.

"So," he would say, his dirty teeth showing a dull yellow smudge as he grinned, "so, if one of us is found with a knife in his back, the others will know the reason why."

We couldn't understand at the time how this little man, whose name was Simon Raikes but who was always known as Weedy, knew such a lot. Even Doolie was suitably impressed by his constant warnings about secrecy, and every time I saw the Chinese servants a sort of cold shiver used to run up and down my back.

Thinking it over, I can't understand why we didn't suspect Weedy at the time of being a spy of Mr. C.'s set amongst us to see that we kept our mouths shut, and at the same time to impart a little information about the business we had let ourselves in for. Although we never knew for certain afterwards, I have very little doubt now that that was what he was.

If that was true, and I am pretty sure it was, it meant that there were three men set to watch over the five of us ; and though this may sound ridiculous I can assure you that it isn't. The utmost care to prevent any kind of leakage is essential in such a dangerous and internationally important game as gun-running. I realised afterwards that this particular organisation was enormous, with agents all over the world, and their methods of preventing leakages were thorough in the extreme.

When we arrived at San Francisco a close watch was kept on us in just the same way. We were met by a Chinaman whose name was Lung Hi. He, I believe, was the chief agent of the organisation. We were accommodated by him at an

Oriental boarding-house kept by one Hu Nan, and wherever we went we were followed.

Doolie thought this was a great joke and would take enormous walks all over the town in order to tire out our pursuers, but it made me anxious, for it brought home to me the seriousness of the job we had undertaken.

"Now, none of that nonsense, Jo," Doolie said when I expressed my fears. "We've got a darn good job, and we're lucky to have it. These Chinks don't mean us any harm. Forget you're going arm-running. Try and think it's a cruise for the sake of your health."

And he let forth his customary bellow of laughter and refused to listen to anything more I had to say.

For obvious reasons I cannot tell you the name of the gun-running ship or her captain. He may be alive now for all I know, and perhaps even engaged in the same trade. There is, I am sure, as much opportunity for him to earn a good living by arm-running now as there was thirty years ago ! I will call the captain, who was a South American, Mr. X., and the ship herself I will call the " T."

The " T " was an ordinary cargo-boat which during the last two years had not been seen on the high seas. In those two years she had been laid up no one knew where, and had had many extraordinary alterations made to her.

Her cargo on this particular voyage was hams ; she was, in fact, a junk-ship. One of our first duties was to load these hams into the holds. This job was very strictly supervised. To a casual glance all the hams looked exactly the same, but if you examined them closely you would find that the short piece of string which was attached to the knuckle of each ham differed in many cases in one important respect. Some of the hams were tied with one knot ; the rest were tied with two knots !

The top two layers in each compartment must contain only hams with one knot on them. The rest must be evenly distributed. Another curious fact that would not strike the ordinary eye was that many of the hams were rather fatty—decidedly more fatty than the top two layers !

The explanation of these peculiar facts I guessed, but didn't know it fully until Weedy told me when we were safely on our way to China. The explanation was this : the hams that were tied with a single knot were just ordinary hams ; the hams tied with two knots contained a revolver and ten rounds of ammunition ! It was a delicate and highly skilled job secreting these arms inside the hams, and it was done like this. The hams were split open and hollowed out, and the revolver and ammunition placed inside. Then hot fat was poured in and the ham pressed together again so that it was impossible to tell that it had been tampered with. Not a single ham was split in exactly the same place, so that the streak of fat did not give the show away by always appearing in the same position. It was a very ingenious method of secreting arms, and one we practised without detection for many years.

In addition to the ham-method, arms were also secreted in artificial ballast-tanks, and in there also was the greater part of the ammunition. Altogether we carried about half a million rounds of small-arm ammunition, about five thousand revolvers and a small number of rifles.

Both Doolie and I were glad when we heard the " T " was about to start on her voyage for we both disliked the boarding-house in which Lung Hi insisted we must stay. It seemed to us that the place was full of a lot of scoundrels, mostly Chinks, who did nothing except take opium and lie about in ugly slumbrous positions. We were offered opium on several occasions but wisely neither of us accepted the offer.

But if Doolie and I thought we were to get away from these low and evil-looking characters when we got aboard the " T " we were very much mistaken. To our horror we discovered that most of the crew were to be made up of Chinese and most of them looked remarkably like the ones we had known in our boarding-house, though neither of us was very good at distinguishing one Chink from another ! We did not actually meet the captain until we were well under way ; this, I suppose, was only another instance of the elaborate, and for the most part purposeless, precautions that were taken for secrecy.

I first saw the captain, Mr. X., when the customs-men came aboard. I happened to overhear part of their conversation with him.

" I haven't seen the ' T ' in these parts lately," one of them said.

" No," answered Mr. X., " she's been laid up a long time. We've had a lot done to her. She's almost a new boat now."

" Yes, she looks spruce enough," the customs-man said.

He was just moving off when there was a loud yell and a sound of scuffling from the Chinese quarter of the ship. (Much to the relief of Doolie and myself we had found that

the Chinese element on board was to be separated from the
ordinary crew.)

"Go and stop those —— scoundrels from squabbling!"
Mr. X. shouted harshly to his first officer.

After a minute the noise stopped.

"Mighty queer lot you've got on board," said the
customs-man.

"They'll be all right when they settle down," Mr. X.
answered casually, but I could see a dangerous light in his
eye that bodied ill for somebody.

I felt relieved when we left San Francisco behind, for I
had had a sort of feeling that we should be stopped before
we got away at all.

Our destination was Canton, but apparently in order to
avoid the risk of being stopped by a gunboat, we did not
follow a straight course but kept southwards through the
Philippines.

Although I was on the "T" arm-running for five years
none of the many voyages on which I went stands out in my
memory like the first one. This is partly, I suppose, because
the whole business was new to me and therefore everything
impressed itself on my memory more vividly than later when
I had got used to the life. But it is also because that first
voyage was the only one in the whole five years of my service
on which we were fired at and nearly detected by a gunboat, and because it was marked by more brutality and
disgusting behaviour than on any later voyage.

It is almost impossible to give you an adequate impression
of the horrible atmosphere that was to be found on the "T."
Doolie, who had been used to that sort of thing before, didn't
mind it as much as I did. But I, who had been used to Andy
McNabb's genial ruling of the *Angus McVite*, and to my father's
hard but very moral and fair ruling of the *Kanyan Candy*, was
astounded by the general brutality and lack of fair judgment
in Mr. X. and his officers.

I had already seen a dangerous look in the eyes of Mr.
X., but it had never occurred to me that he intended to mete
out savage punishment on the Chinks who had been fighting.
But on the first night, when all except those on duty were in
their bunks, I was woken up suddenly by the sound of
hysterical laughter from somewhere up on deck. I slipped
out of my bunk and stealthily made my way to the deck.
I saw there the most disgusting and revolting sight.

Mr. X. was lounging against the rail smoking a cigarette

and there was a cruel smile on his lips that was not good to see. He was looking intently at his first officer and the naked Chinamen beside him. There were two Chinamen there, bound to the rail stark naked. The first officer, whose name and nationality I do not care to disclose, was flogging them brutally with a knotted rope.

The night was silent except for the heavy thudding of the rope as it hit the men's bare backs, the heavy breathing of the officer, whom I will call Mr. Y., and his occasional bursts of hideous hysterical laughter. He would dart from one man to the other, giving the first man some strokes and then flinging himself upon the other with renewed frenzy.

I could not understand why the men did not scream out. I thought that they might have fainted, but their bodies were taut and only sagged as the rope bit hideously into their flesh.

I felt sick with hatred at the brutality of these men, but I could do nothing. I dared not move or make any noise. I could not understand why no one else had heard the noise and come up to investigate as I had done. But there was not a sign of any one. The ship slowly pursued her course. The moonlight flickered on the deck and for an instant lit up the men by the rail. It revealed for an instant the terrible weals on the backs of the two Chinamen, and I shuddered at the thought of the agony they must be suffering.

Just as I was about to turn away, Mr. X. held up his hand. "That's enough," he said. "You're getting excited. You'll be doing something rash if I let you go on any longer."

Mr. Y. flung the rope down on the deck and, staggering across to the Chinamen, kicked them savagely. With one stride the captain was beside him and flung him roughly away.

"That's enough, I said," he snarled, his eyes narrowing. "When I tell you to stop you've —— well got to stop, d'you hear?"

Then Mr. X. undid the ropes that bound the men to the rail and pulled gags out of their mouths. So that was why the men had made no sound! The instant the gags were taken out, one of the Chinamen started squealing like a pig. The other moaned softly as he straightened his wounded back.

"Stop that row," the captain muttered threateningly. "You've had your punishment, and let that be a lesson to you not to fight and squabble among yourselves. Put some clothes on and get back to your bunks."

I didn't wait to hear any more but hurried back to my own bunk feeling angry but helpless in the face of such cruelty. As I padded noiselessly back I could hear the first officer chuckling to himself as he leant against the rail.

.   .   .   .

That was the first example I had seen of the brutality of the officers. But it was by no means the last ! I am not going to tell you very much of the life on board the " T " because I find it unpleasant to recall, and I am sure it must be unpleasant to read. It is sufficient to say that conditions improved greatly as the years passed, and though Mr. X. was still captain when I left the ship, most of the old officers had given place to new ones ; and, though floggings still continued, they were administered by Mr. X. and no one else. That does not mean that they became any less savage, however, for the captain had a lusty arm and an evil temper.

The first officer came to a tragic end, but I am afraid I couldn't feel in the least sorry for him.

He became insane and, after running riot amongst the crew with a knife, leapt overboard, and mercifully was never picked up. This happened less than a year after I joined the ship and I feel now that he was not altogether sane when he flogged the Chinamen on that terrible night I have described. I cannot believe that a sane man would have laughed while performing so dreadful a task. I do not blame him so much as I blame Mr. X. for allowing him to do it.

I fully expected the Chinamen to mutiny when they saw what had been done to their companions, but to my amazement everything was quiet the next day, and there was no sign of unrest among any sections of the crew. I suppose they were used to it. There was a certain amount of furtive whispering, it is true, but no more than usual ; for there was always furtive whispering going on on board the " T ; " there was never much work to do, and men stood about in groups talking softly. It was an uncanny atmosphere—until you got used to it.

I told Doolie the next day what had happened during the night. It was strange, I remarked, that no one else had heard anything.

" No one heard anything ? " he echoed. " Why, I should say the whole ship heard. I certainly did."

" But didn't you want to know what was going on ? "

" I guessed," he replied laconically. " You must have had a lot of soft jobs in your time, Jo, if you can't stand

anything like this. I've had to stand many a flogging like
that myself and I'm none the worse for it."

"But this is terrible," I argued, " the man was shrieking
with laughter the whole time."

"Forget about it, Jo," Doolie said. "We're both of us
getting splendid pay, and as long as we keep out of the way
of trouble, we've got soft jobs. You wonder why the Chinks
don't kick up a fuss about these floggings. Well, I'll tell you
why. It's because they're getting an enormous wage for doing
next to nothing, and they know if they lose this job they'll
probably never get another one, for most of them are worthless good-for-nothings. Half of them deserve to be flogged
simply for being such miserable specimens of God's creatures !
They drug themselves stupid most of the time, and when
they're not drugged, they're fighting."

Although I certainly didn't feel as happy as Doolie over
the affair, I had to admit there was some truth in what he
said. The Chinks on board the " T " were a pretty foul lot.
Mind you, I haven't any kind of racial prejudice against the
Chinese. I have known men of a great many different races,
and the worst types I've met haven't been coloured yellow,
or black either. I have known men who have been white
men outside, but inside as black as sin, and vice versa. No,
it wasn't racial prejudice that made me despise the Chinks
on our ship ; it was just that they were rabble, and worthless
rabble at that.

The big excitement of that first voyage was our encounter
with an American gunboat. We were only ten days out when
she first hailed us. I remember I was doing a bit of painting
up on deck when her smoke was first discerned on the
horizon.

Our captain couldn't understand what vessel she was, for
he was steering clear of all regular craft. She came nearer
and nearer until it was impossible to ignore the fact that she
was signalling for us to stop. But, rather foolishly I think,
Mr. X. only increased our speed in the hope of getting away
from her. He wanted to avoid the risk of a search if it was at
all possible. But it wasn't possible. The boat behind us was
determined to stop us. She was evidently a very fast boat for
she was gaining on us rapidly.

"What is she, skipper ? " Doolie asked boldly.

"She's a gunboat all right. American," he rapped out.
"We'll have to stop."

At that moment a shot rang out.

" She's firing at us, b— her ! " he raged. Then he roared
out orders and we slowed down and finally stopped.

The gunboat sent out a boat with half a dozen men in
it. They came on board—and it was nearly three hours before
they left again ! I think they were absolutely convinced that
we were carrying illegal cargo, and it says something for the
ingenious methods we employed that they were sent back to
their gunboat with nothing to report.

Doolie and I were full of excitement at this sudden turn
of events, but a lot of the crew were in a pitiful state of terror.
The captain, however, had lectured us so often on how to
behave in case of an emergency like this that they managed
fairly effectively to conceal any signs of alarm.

I will say this for Mr. X., that during this emergency he
behaved wonderfully. He kept splendidly cool although he
was under a constant barrage of questions from the officials.

Our papers were examined. All the crew were lined up
and the officers interrogated. They got no satisfaction from
this, however, so they started a long, careful search of the ship.

" I want some of your men to come round with us as well
as yourself," one of the officials said to Mr. X. " They may
be needed for moving cargo."

Doolie and I both happened to be near when he said
that, so we and a couple of other men were given the job
of accompanying the officials round the ship.

" Well, we'll be in at the kill if they find out anything,"
Doolie whispered to me, and then burst out into one of his
uncontrollable chuckles.

The officials stared at him, and, as for Mr. X., his eyes
narrowed and he looked like the Devil himself the way he
glared at Doolie. I felt decidedly uncomfortable. That means
a flogging for Doolie afterwards, I thought. But I was wrong.
Mr. X. was so pleased at getting rid of the officials that I
suppose he forgot all about the incident ; anyway, he never
said anything about it.

When the officials started examining the hams I felt myself
quivering with excitement, but Doolie and the captain seemed
quite cool and self-possessed.

" I want to see that there is nothing concealed beneath
those hams," one of the officials said. " Get your men to
remove some of them."

The four of us set to, and, handling the hams as gently as
we could for fear that they should split open and reveal their
secret, we soon convinced the officials that there was nothing

but good, solid, innocent-looking hams from top to bottom.

They continued their search, however, and there was still a danger that they would discover the false ballast tanks ; but nothing was discovered, and as the time passed, the officials became more and more apologetic. Doolie and I went off, and as we went I heard Mr. X. asking them if they'd like to come into his cabin and have a drink while they were waiting. They all disappeared into his cabin and did not appear again for about half an hour. Doolie and I hung around to see what was going to happen next. To our amusement we heard Mr. X. asking them if there was any part of the ship they'd like to go over again.

" No, we've finished our search," the chief official said. " We're not going to waste any more of your time, or of ours either. I trust you. I know you're only carrying honest cargo. I'm sorry we've had to delay you so long."

" Oh, that's all right," Mr. X. said graciously, " it's been a pleasure to have your company."

He shook hands with them all, and they returned, with nothing to report, to the gunboat.

Mr. X. was in a splendid humour for some days after that, for everything had gone to plan and not a single hitch had occurred. The organisation on the boat had been proved perfect.

THE MYSTERY OF THE "EAR"

By
CAPTAIN RAGNAR NYBERG

WE came in through a little narrow door, Jimmy, "Scotty," and I, and peeped around full of curiosity. We found ourselves in a little dimly-lit room, with a row of similar rooms opening out of it. In each room there were two or three tables, or counters, with a motionless, expressionless Chinaman behind each. The light was so bad that they merely appeared as shadows against the shelves behind them.

The tables were littered with odds and ends, curios and knick-knacks of every kind, worthless rubbish and precious works of art all jumbled together. The whole place smelt of sandalwood and a multitude of other Oriental scents and smells unfamiliar to our Western nostrils, but not actually unpleasant. Besides the smell of sandalwood, which I had learnt to recognise since it seems to be inseparable from all Chinese houses, there was another smell which I particularly noticed. It was both sweet and sickly, heavy and almost soporific. I tried in vain to analyse it.

In the depths of the innermost room, crouched on a high chair behind an old-fashioned writing-desk, sat a wrinkled old Chinaman, thin as a rake.

This was Tai Sang himself, the owner of the shop. My shipmate Jimmy, who was English but born and bred in Shanghai, had told us a great deal on the way there about Tai Sang, the little man from Canton who had come to Shanghai with empty hands, and had worked his way up until he now was the owner of one of the most famous and flourishing shops in the native town. He had made Tai Sang out to be a business genius, but had also pointed out that he was famous for his incorruptible honesty. Perhaps it sounds paradoxical in European ears, but it is a fact that Chinese business men as a rule are honest.

While Jimmy went into the inner room to talk to old Tai Sang, Scotty and I wandered from table to table looking at the wares. The wooden-looking assistants did not take the slightest notice of us, but this did not surprise us so much. It is the same in all Chinese shops : you must find things for yourself ; the assistant does not trouble to ask what you want, or show you anything not already on the counter.

When Jim approached Tai Sang's "holy of holies," a curtain was quickly drawn across the doorway and immediately afterwards Tai Sang came out, offered him a chair—on this side of the curtain—and sat down beside him. Jim had assured us that he was a good friend of Tai Sang's, and this was obviously no exaggeration. They talked together for some time, while the two of us made up our minds what to buy. When at last we had finished and turned to the assistant, who still did not move a muscle, another Chinaman appeared beside him—heaven knows from where—informed us in polite whispers as to the price, and took our money. There seemed to be no shortage of staff in Tai Sang's shop.

Our visit was in fact both interesting and profitable—for Tai Sang's prices were decidedly more reasonable than in a good many shops in the foreign quarter ; and on our way back I thanked Jimmy for taking us with him, and at the same time I asked him what he had talked about to the old man.

"A little of everything," Jimmy answered. "Old Tai Sang doesn't look like much, but he has had a full life and knocked around a lot. He talks as good English as you or I. Like all Chinamen, he is talkative when he feels like it, and as impenetrable as a brick wall when a subject comes up that he doesn't want to talk about. As a matter of fact, I tried to get him to talk about 'The Ear's' latest exploits, and asked him if he wasn't afraid of a hold-up, since his shop is right in the district where the Ear gang seems to work as a rule—but you should have seen the old boy shut up like an oyster, and keep silent until I realised I had dropped a brick and changed the subject ! It really does surprise me that The Ear hasn't tried to squeeze Tai Sang. There must be pots of money in his shop for the gang to take.

"Who is this 'Ear' really ? " I asked. "Every one is talking of his daring coups—for example, that last raid of his on the foreign settlement, and all the rest of it. Is he some kind of Chinese Arsène Lupin ? "

"Well, not exactly that," said Jimmy thoughtfully. "No one knows exactly who The Ear is—just that he is the leader of the most dangerous gang that has ever existed in Shanghai. So far nobody has managed to trace either him or any of his followers—between the raids they seem to vanish into thin air. But in any case he is no ' gentleman thief.' The Ear and his men are nothing but a crowd of cold-blooded murderers. Their method is so straightforward that it sounds clumsy—but it is highly effective, I can tell you ! One or two of the members of the gang come rushing into a shop, shoot down every one there, take possession of the till, and disappear as quickly as they came. They seem to be extraordinarily well informed, both here in the Chinese town and up in the foreign quarter ; they know to a ' T ' when their victims have plenty of money in the safe—and when the police are busy elsewhere. I know that their activities have worried the police authorities seriously lately, and that there have been a number of attempts to trace and break up the gang, but so far they have had no success. The entire Chinatown is terrified of these brutes."

Some time later I met the young Latvian policeman from whom I had heard the solution of the mystery of Ching-ki and the counterfeit silver coins. He belonged to the police force in the foreign quarter, but was stationed in the native town to keep watch over the safety of the Europeans there. Although it was not really in their province, the European police were often obliged to take a hand in criminal affairs which only concerned the Chinese, such as, for example, the Ching-ki business.

This Latvian friend of mine had very often some exciting episode from his work to tell me, and this time he made me more than usually interested and curious when he happened to mention Tai Sang's name in connection with an attempt at blackmail and robbery : This is what he told me :

Some time back Tai Sang had had a threatening letter from The Ear—or from some one calling himself by that name —in which he was advised to pay a large sum to the gang within a certain time, or they would call on him in his shop. And it was not hard to guess the results for Tai Sang and his staff of such a visit.

A couple of days later Tai Sang had, sure enough, gone to the bank and drawn out a fairly large sum. Tai Sang told the bank clerk about the threatening letter, and said—rather boastfully, they had thought—that he would see to it that all the notes were marked, and inform the police of the blackmail.

Tai Sang did not even reach home with his money. On the return journey his rickshaw was in collision with another, the old man was thrown out, and in the confusion that followed some one snatched his money-bag from him and disappeared with it. Tai Sang drove straight to the Chinese police station and notified them of the robbery, or loss, whichever it should be called. He was positive that it was The Ear's gang that had been in action ; and at the same time he told the police a number of unpleasant truths about their inability to put an end to the reign of terror caused by this daring criminal.

Apparently the police force did not like this, and a thorough, but unfortunately quite fruitless, search was organised.

It began to be rumoured in the native town that The Ear had condemned Tai Sang to death for his temerity in notifying the police, and the bandit's next move was awaited with tense excitement. There were those who thought that Tai Sang ought to close his shop and leave the town, for The Ear had an unpleasant habit of carrying out his threats. But Tai Sang refused to be worried—visibly, at any rate. His shop was kept open as usual ; the eternally sleepy and wooden assistants still stood in their places behind the tables, and in the " holy of holies " old Tai Sang sat, day after day, in the same place behind his desk and kept watch over his domain. Every one who passed by in the street could see him through the ever-open doorway. It looked as though Tai Sang intended to challenge The Ear—and Death.

A fortnight passed—three weeks—and nothing happened. Tai Sang's shop was still open to bandits and honest customers alike, but The Ear and his gang seemed just lately to have retired from business. The first day or two after the theft of Tai Sang's money there were still a few cases of assault and robbery to report, but after that everything was quiet. In the police force they really began to wonder whether The Ear had actually drawn in his feelers after Tai Sang's report. Not that it would be like the daring gang to take fright. They expected real fireworks, and were afraid that Tai Sang would not escape unharmed when the time came.

But, as I said, three weeks passed without the expected catastrophe. And when at last something did happen, it was the very last thing they had expected.

One day a little lean and wrinkled old Chinaman put in an appearance at the headquarters of the foreign police, and asked permission to see the Commissioner himself. And this was granted after a good deal of humming and hawing.

F.T.S.   N

The old man introduced himself as the merchant Tai Sang from Li-Yuen Street. This made no impression worth mentioning on the Commissioner, who as a matter of fact had not heard a word about Tai Sang's quarrel with the Ear —since the theft had been reported to the Chinese police, who, although they worked with the force in the European quarter, were not in the habit of reporting matters in which no white man was involved.

The Commissioner asked rather impatiently what Tai Sang wanted.

" Most honoured Commissioner, your humble servant has caught The Ear and all his gang," Tai Sang told him respectfully.

" What ! " shouted the Commissioner. " What on earth do you mean ? Where have you got them ? "

" In the cellar under my shop, your Excellency," Tai Sang replied.

The Commissioner of Police scratched his head with his paper-knife. This really did sound altogether incredible. Could an old Chinaman have succeeded alone, where two entire police forces had failed ? The Commissioner had on several previous occasions come up against the curious Chinese idea of a joke and their tendency to make up fantastic lies. It was not without reason that he looked at Tai Sang as if he were some kind of Chinese Münchhausen.

But Tai Sang was not to be shaken. He repeated, time after time, patiently and politely, that he had caught The Ear and all his gang : that was the sober truth.

At last the Commissioner did not know what to think. To be on the safe side, he advised Tai Sang to consult the Chinese police, who were the suitable authorities to take charge of the affair.

But Tai Sang shook his head energetically. No, he would not go to the Chinese police in this case ; he mumbled something about there being so much illness in the force at the moment. This sounded absolute nonsense, of course, and the Commissioner once more almost made up his mind to turn him out.

Just at that moment one of the police officers happened to come in. He belonged to the European police stationed in the native town, and the Commissioner ordered Tai Sang to repeated his story to him.

Now it was the officer's turn to scratch his head. But on one point he could confirm Tai Sang's story : there had actually been an unusual number of cases of illness among the Chinese policemen just lately. They had disappeared from their posts one after the other, and the foreign police had been obliged to go alone on their rounds. The police officer guessed at some epidemic.

After thinking it over for some time, the Commissioner promised to send two policemen with Tai Sang. He informed him that if he had not spoken the truth they were to bring him back with them, and he should pay dearly for his mistaken joke.

One of the European policemen told off to accompany Tai Sang happened to be my good friend the Latvian. The other was English, a former sailor called Jack Irvin. I heard the rest of the story from my friend, and I shall try to tell it in his words.

" On our way to Li-Yeun Street we tried to worm more details out of Tai Sang about the strange capture he said he had made ; but he only wagged his head, and mumbled that we would find out all about that when we reached the shop.

" Of course we knew Tai Sang to be a reliable and honest man who ought not to make up any fairy-tales ; but, on the other hand, it seemed improbable that he should be able, without assistance, to outwit and capture the dreaded gang.

" The door of Tai Sang's shop was open as usual. We went in and peered around full of curiosity, but could not discover anything odd. However, I dare say that we were a bit on edge, for when Tai Sang suddenly shut the door and locked it, I jumped, and I saw that Jack did too.

" Then we made an extraordinary discovery. There stood Tai Sang, little and bent, beside us, but—seated at the desk in the inner room was also a Tai Sang, staring with expressionless eyes at the room and the motionless assistants. What was the meaning of all this ? Had Tai Sang a twin, or a double ?

" I turned angrily to Tai Sang to demand an explanation, but at that moment he touched my elbow and pointed to the floor in front of the desk where his double sat.

" In his usual quiet manner the old man then told us to draw our revolvers and be prepared to shoot. We obeyed mechanically. Tai Sang tripped over to a curtain and disappeared behind it. Next moment the floor creaked, and the place Tai Sang had pointed to was suddenly changed into a square, yawning hole. A trap-door !

" At the same time we heard Tai Sang's voice, which now seemed to come from the immovable figure at the desk.

" ' Kindly wait a moment, my honoured sirs,' the voice said, and next minute he once more appeared from the curtain beside us.

" We no longer knew what to think. We had the impression of being transported to some sort of Theatre of Mystery. Everything seemed so unreal ; the dim room, the motionless, puppetlike assistants, and, not least, Tai Sang's double at the desk—with the open trap-door in front. Had Tai Sang gone mad after all, and planned to catch us in some diabolical trap ? I was just beginning to wonder whether to level my revolver at the old man, when he drew a torch from his pocket, shuffled over to the trap-door, and flashed the light into it. He signalled to us to come closer and told us to peep down— but carefully, for he could not guarantee that those who were down there would not make use of their weapons !

" ' Do you mean to say that they are . . .' I exclaimed in amazement.

" Tai Sang nodded contentedly.

" ' Just so, my masters,' he said. ' Down there you have the gang of The Ear ; twelve of them ; and as far as I know that is the lot ! '

" Now at last I began to think that there must be some truth in Tai Sang's astonishing story. But still I was not quite convinced. Perhaps if the truth were known it was still a scheme to get us down into the cellar.

" I pulled out my own torch, knelt down and examined the floor in front of me carefully with it, to be sure that there were no more trap-doors, before I crept forward to the edge of the black hole. When I got nearer the trap-door I could hear that at any rate something living was down there in the cellar, for strange moaning sounds came up from its depths.

" I held my torch over the edge and let the beam of light shine into the darkness. I had given Jack a sign to stay a few paces behind me, and I hoped that he was keeping an eye on Tai Sang in case the old man should try to push me into the hole.

" At first I could not make head or tail of the sight that met my eyes when I poked my head forward carefully and peeped down. The light was reflected on some black and glittering substance, which looked like a floor of polished black marble. But out of this floor jutted several extraordinary figures. The first of them was not far from the opening, and when I let my light shine on it I saw that it was the upper half of a human being, or at least a figure of vaguely human shape. It was completely covered in some brownish, semi-transparent glaze or varish.

"And this strange apparition was alive! Its head and arms moved slowly and helplessly! And from the creature's mouth came a half-choked moaning.

"I shone my light over the farther parts of the cellar and discovered several other similar figures, some singly, others two and two together, leaning against each other as if seeking a resting-place. There were twelve in all, just as Tai Sang had said. I was struck by the strang, strong smell from the cellar; it had an unpleasant, suffocating sweetness. I had noticed it already when we first came into the shop.

"I signed to Jack to come and look, and then turned to Tai Sang for an explanation of the whole thing. Tai Sang wagged his head, rubbed his bony hands together so that they rustled like dry grass, and started to tell his story. I will tell it you from the beginning.

"When Tai Sang received that threatening letter from The Ear, he made up his mind to carry out a plan he had formed long ago. He was going to catch The Ear and his gang!

"The first step was to exasperate The Ear. This he achieved by stage-managing the theft of his ransom! Yes, the man who ran into Tai Sang's rickshaw on his way home from the bank, and who snatched away his money-bag, was none other than one of Tai Sang's own assistants. Of course Tai Sang reckoned that The Ear would soon see through the bluff and open the attack in full fury.

"And Tai Sang was ready to receive them! With genuine Chinese ingenuity and Oriental patience he had perfected the complicated trap in which he intended to capture The Ear and his gang. He had let his assistants make life-size wax dolls, and these were placed behind the counters instead of the real assistants. They were so cleverly made that in the dim light they were indistinguishable from living people.

"Finally he provided himself with a double, too; a puppet placed in his usual place behind the desk, and supplied with a speaking-tube leading behind the curtain where we had seen Tai Sang disappear.

"The trap-door was there already; it was nothing more nor less than the ordinary way down to Tai Sang's cellar, but now he provided it with a spring so that it would fall down when any one trod on it.

"Down in the cellar was the most cunning detail of his bandit-trap. He had thought of it accidentally. For a long time he had had a supply of treacle standing there in large barrels. It was not the palatable and refined treacle that we are used to in Europe, but a raw product, dark brown in colour, only just liquid, and stickier than any glue in the world.

"Once upon a time Tai Sang had been forced to accept this treacle in payment of a debt, and he had not since been able to get rid of the stuff. After a while the barrels began to leak, and the whole floor in that part of the cellar had gradually become coated with a sticky layer of treacle, to the great annoyance of all those who had to go down there. Their feet caught in it, and it was with the greatest difficulty that they managed to get free again.

"It was this that finally gave Tai Sang a brilliant idea. He had a wooden enclosure made round that part of the cellar, and then he broke up all his barrels of treacle ! It flowed out and spread itself in a layer almost a yard deep inside the barrier. The bandit trap was ready ; The Ear and his gang were welcome !

"Day by day Tai Sang sat waiting like a spider in its web. The shop door stood temptingly open ; behind the counters you could glimpse the assistants—or rather, their waxwork copies—and at Tai Sang's desk sat the puppet with its speaking-tube and kept watch over the room. Tai Sang himself sat behind the curtain, staring patiently into a cunning home-made periscope—or, to be accurate, a series of mirrors—which made it possible for him to see who came into the shop. If it was an honest customer one of the assistants had to creep out from his hiding-place and attend to his wants, and if the visitor was one of his friends it might happen that the puppet said a few words with Tai Sang's voice.

"Then one day two Chinamen rushed into the shop, drew their revolvers and opened fire. The attack was unexpected and quick as lightning, and came at a time when the street happened to be quite empty.

"The wax puppets behind the counters fell down most naturalistically, thanks to an intricate mechanism worked by the real assistants from their hiding-places behind the shelves. The robbers then made for the desk where ' Tai Sang ' sat, and fired a couple of shots at him—with no visible result !

And as if this were not enough, Tai Sang burst into derisive laughter and told them to get out !

"Of course they did not listen to him, but instead rushed at the desk to finish him off—and tumbled headlong into the mess of treacle ! And there they had to stay.

"For Tai Sang was determined to do his job thoroughly and he counted on more than one visit from the gang. And he was right. Two days later the scene was re-enacted with practically no variations, and with the same result. Now he had four captives in his treacle.

"But still he was not satisfied. He wanted the whole gang, and he was convinced that there were many more of them. It may seem odd that he should be so sure that one after another would be lured into the same trap without the suspicions of the remainder being aroused ; but Tai Sang was of an analytical mind. He had worked out that the effect on the others would be to think that the vanished members had found it more profitable to make a private bargain with the old man, to extract as much money from him as possible, and then to disappear without sharing their spoils with their comrades.

"In the course of a fortnight Tai Sang caught twelve robbers in six raids—and then there were no more. He waited a week, and then concluded that he had caught the entire gang. Besides, he had during this time extracted confessions from his captives in the cellar by promising them water if they would tell him how many of them there were, who they were, and where they had hidden their spoils. No doubt one grows very thirsty if one spends a fortnight firmly stuck in treacle, and little by little Tai Sang succeeded in finding out all that he wished to know.

"When he was quite sure that he had caught the whole gang and that he knew everything worth knowing about their misdeeds, he went to the foreign police and reported the matter.

"Jack and I realised that we two could not alone deal with the bandits, and sent to the Chinese police station for help. It took us practically a whole day to fish the ' candied ' robbers out of the treacle. And I will say it was a surprise, both for us and for our Chinese colleagues, when we had a closer look at the ugly fishes.

"For they were one and all members of the Chinese police force—Jack and I had patrolled the town with several of them for months ! It was obvious that Tai Sang enjoyed our amazement, for he rubbed his bony hands contentedly. He had found all this out long ago, but had saved it as a crowning flourish for the end ! ''

This was the story my Latvian friend told me.

The Ear was found to be an officer in the Chinese police force, and the eleven others were attached to the same station. This explained why the gang had been able to carry on for so long without being traced, for, of course, no one could suspect that the same policemen who took part in the hunt for The Ear and his gang became, when off duty, those same dreaded bandits.

The resulting trial caused a stir throughout China, and the inhabitants of Shanghai gave a sigh of relief when the ten surviving bandits—for two had died while imprisoned in Tai Sang's cellar—were condemned to death. The execution took place while I was at sea, but I read in the papers that '' all Shanghai '' had witnessed the event.

Later on I talked over the case with my Latvian friend, and asked him whether he could explain why these men should have taken up such a horrible profession. He replied that there was quite a plausible explanation.

It appears that the Chinese police in Shanghai were very poorly paid at this period, and it frequently happened into the bargain that the Chinese authorities were unable to pay their wages. The European force, on the other hand, were well paid and always received their wages punctually. When the constables from these two forces came in contact with each other in the execution of their duties, it is easy to understand that the underpaid Chinese were filled with envy, and began to speculate on some other means of claiming their dues from society. It was under conditions such as this that The Ear gang—the most dangerous group of robbers that has ever plundered in Shanghai—came into existence. And had it not been for old Tai Sang things might have turned out very differently.

For my part I am practically certain that Tai Sang had been tricked by them, at least to some extent. He insisted that he had had nothing to do with The Ear until he received that threatening letter ; but I believe that the gang had extorted money from him before this, and that he had brooded over his plans of vengeance for a long time before he put them into action. The Chinese are like that : incredibly patient and extremely peaceful by nature—but they never forget an injustice and grudge no pains nor expense to obtain vengeance.

Some time after this affair old Tai Sang sold his business and moved to his native town, Canton, to settle down and enjoy his old age, as befits a Chinaman who has completed his life's work, made a name for himself, paid his debts—and settled his account with his enemies.

The puppets that he used so as to lure The Ear and his gang into the trap may to this day be seen in the criminal museum in Shanghai.

THE LUCK OF AN EARTHQUAKE

By
FRED WALKER

WE came through the Golden Gate at sunset, which is the right time to see it, for the calm sea is golden and wonderfully beautiful. Even the dingy ships in this landlocked harbour are magically transformed into fairy craft, the golden touch of the sinking sun hiding the cracked paint on their sides and softening their ugly lines. Glistening black shapes dodge in and out of the water—the seals playing on the rocks. Not having the mind of the good tourist, I am usually too busy with more mundane things to bother about sightseeing, but on this occasion the calm beauty of the scene took my breath away.

I found that San Francisco itself did not live up to the promise of its magnificent portals. Compared with the cities I had already seen, it was much less interesting than some and no more beautiful than most. I noticed that the buildings, in the main, were smaller than usual ; there were no skyscrapers, which I thought suggested lack of enterprise. As after-events proved, though, this fact turned out to be a blessing in disguise.

We booked a room at a good-class hotel at the corner of Kearney Street and California Street, and as soon as we had eaten we went upstairs to our room. There I was surprised to see Carlos begin to take off his jacket.

" Hallo ! " I said. " What are you supposed to be doing ? "

" I am going to bed," he answered. " I am very tired."

" Don't be silly ! I want you to come with me and have a look at the town."

" Ugh ! " He made an impatient gesture. " Who wants to see the town ? I have seen it before. There is nothing to see. Streets and shops and people, and more streets and more shops and——"

" Shut up ! " I interrupted. " What about the Chinatown I've heard so much about ? "

" You saw the Chinatown at Isleton ? It is like that.

When you have seen one Chinatown you have seen all of them."

But I refused to be deterred from my original intention, and, crossing over to him, began to drag his clothes on him again. He struggled, and we had a friendly brawl before, with a characteristic shrug of his shoulders, he capitulated.

" I am too tired to fight," he said, with a smile. " Otherwise I would throw you out of the window. As it is, for the sake of peace and quietness, I will come and see this Chinatown you are so anxious to visit."

" That is what I like to hear," I said approvingly. " I bet we'll have such a good time that you'll thank me for making you come."

It was a remark made at random, but it turned out to be a prophecy. Carlos did thank me, and very heartily too, for in forcing him to go sightseeing, instead of leaving him to go to bed, I saved his life.

The Chinatown of San Francisco lies round about Grant Avenue, which runs parallel to Kearney Street, and was thus just a short distance away. In those days the Chinese were a picturesque people, and, what with sing-song babel of sound, the strange notices over shops, the pigtails, the loose, colourful garb, and the fact that you saw about one white man per mile, I found it difficult to believe that we had not been magically transported into the heart of Hong Kong.

But in those days, too, life in Chinatown was much more like the pictures painted by fiction-writers than it is to-day, and dreadful things happened in the opium dens in Grant Avenue. In the streets leading to the district large police notices were fixed to the lamp-posts-cum-telegraph-poles, stating that tourists who went into the Chinese quarter without an official guide did so entirely at their own risk.

Carlos and I were so used to doing things " at our own risk " that we paid little attention to the warnings, and turned down a narrow, evil-smelling alley that led into the darkness. When we had gone some distance we saw a patch of light coming from a small door in the side of a house over which we could faintly discern a sign-board. The Chinese inscription meant nothing to us, but when we saw the word " Restaurant " beneath it we knew that we had found what we were looking for.

We opened the door and descended some steps, to find ourselves in a long, stuffy basement room. The pungent smoke from dozens of long Chinese pipes caught our throats and

made our eyes smart, but as we became used to the heady
atmosphere we realised that we were in a gambling saloon.
Although packed with men, the room was quiet with an
ominous quietness. Occasionally the silence was broken by
the sing-song chant of a Chinese counting the score or making
a bid, but, for the rest, the players remained still and silent.

Carlos and I joined the crowds grouped round the tables,
where, in the light of the big kerosene lamp, a game was
being played with counters and strips of cardboard of various
shapes.

"What are they playing?" I whispered to Carlos.

"Fan-tan," he answered.

I had heard of this favourite Chinese game, of course, but
I had never before seen it played, and I watched closely, in
the hope of picking up its intricacies. The movements of the
queerly shaped "cards" were fascinating enough, but I am
afraid I learned very little about the game, and have no idea
yet as to how it is played.

After watching for an hour or so Carlos and I went in
search of something to eat and drink, and found, on returning
to the tables, that two Americans had come into the saloon.
They joined two Chinese in a game of poker, and when one
dropped out for a spell I took his place. I soon found that
it is asking for trouble to play with members of the most
poker-faced race on earth, and when the other player
returned I relinquished my hand, and settled down again to
watch. As the cards were running evenly play became very
dull, and after a time I joined Carlos, who was standing by
one of the fan-tan tables.

Suddenly the quietness of the room was shattered by a
hoarse shout of rage and a squeal. Jerking round, I caught
a glimpse of one of the Americans pulling a revolver from
his hip pocket. There was a loud report, and the lamp over
the poker table split and went out. Another shot, and——
But by that time I had grabbed Carlos, and we were running.

Knives began to flash, and the whole saloon became a
seething mass of struggling, shouting men. Squirming and
fighting our way through the crush, we made for a door, and
were just able to open it before the last lamp was shot out.

We were now in pitch darkness, and gingerly put out our
hands to try to establish our position. As far as we could
make out, we were in a passage. Having no inclination to
loiter, we blindly groped our way forward, bumping against
walls, falling over objects, until it seemed that we had been

going for miles. Suddenly, and without warning, we came into violent contact with a horde of Chinese, also fleeing from the *mêlée*. In their panic they knocked us down as they swept swiftly onward. Bruised and thoroughly shaken, we lost our heads completely, and started to run as hard as we could in the darkness, without thought of direction or the obstacles that might lie in our path.

Crash!

We had banged violently into something that split under the impact, and showers of dust rained down on us. Once more we picked ourselves up from the floor, and the sight that confronted us was so unexpected that, in spite of our dilemma and discomfort, we stood still and roared with laughter.

We had crashed through a *papier-mâché* wall into the next house, and had fallen into a dimly lit bedroom, to interrupt a domestic scene of a most intimate nature. It was the sight of the man's startled face suddenly appearing over the edge of the bedclothes, and a feminine shriek, that sounded from under the sheets, that dissolved us in laughter—but that laughter was short-lived.

Angered at our impolite intrusion into his private affairs, the Chinese began to shout at us. We could not, of course, understand a word that he was saying, but the action that followed his remarks made the meaning only too clear. With a lithe bound he was out of bed, and snatching up a murderous looking knife from a chair, he came at us with a rush. With a quick movement that saved the situation, Carlos stuck out his foot and sent the Chinese sprawling. By the time that enraged gentlemen had disentangled himself from the folds of his voluminous nightgown we were out of the door and flying through a further succession of narrow, evil-smelling passages.

At last, by mere chance, Carlos found a door that opened on to a dingy alley, and, as we could hear no sound of pursuit, we rested a few moments to regain our breath. Suddenly I became conscious of a peculiar stillness in the air, and was assailed, quite inexplicably, by a violent headache.

" Do you notice how still the air is ? " I asked Carlos. He nodded his head in a perplexed sort of way.

" It is cold too," he commented. " I do not like the—the smell."

He did not refer to the smell of decaying refuse that

permeated the alley, but to a strange sense of tautness that seemed to be in the atmosphere itself.

He gave a shiver.

"We have had enough excitement for one thing," he remarked. "Come on! Let us go back to the hotel."

We had taken no more than a couple of steps when out of the stillness came destruction.

Without warning, the earth began to shake beneath our feet. I staggered like a drunken man, and pitched violently into a wall. From all around us came the sound of heavy objects crashing and breaking, of cries and panic, of people beginning to run, while the earth writhed beneath our feet.

It is impossible for me to describe the exact sensation of that appalling first shock in the catastrophic San Francisco earthquake. I felt as though I was a pebble being tossed about in a violently shaken sieve. The earth did not roll or heave; it vibrated as though it had been suddenly seized with an acute attack of the ague.

Instinctively Carlos and I made for a more open space, where we should be clear of the flying *débris*, and it was just as we reached Grant Avenue again that the second shock occurred. We tried to run while it was happening, as did thousands of other people, but it was impossible to keep one's balance, and we were thrown about like ninepins. Buildings tumbled, clouds of dust drifted everywhere, and as we turned into Market Street—the city's main thoroughfare—we were horrified to see, at the far end of it, a red glow in the sky. Fire!

The streets were full of half-clothed people, some clasping children, others bits of their personal belongings, and many of them were shouting and screaming in their panic as they blindly made their way to the lower end of Market Street, which leads to the ferry buildings and the sea.

The third shock occurred as we were running with the crowd down the hill, and it was the worst of all. With my own eyes I saw the street split open, and a horse and cart disappear in the yawning crevice, to be followed by dozens of panic-stricken people, who were pushed forward to their death by crowds that followed at their heels. Their screams ring in my ears to this day.

Try as I will to recall my impression as I ran down Market Street towards the sea, I cannot remember possessing any feelings at all other than those of sheer panic which numbed my brain. Blindly, and without thought of direction, I ran

I saw the street split open.

with the crowd, heedless of the people whom I was treading underfoot. Every man was for himself in those moments of terror, and thoughts of self-preservation predominated in every mind.

At the ferry buildings frenzied people crowded into boats, and most of the overburdened craft that attempted to ride the heavy seas capsized. Many, many lives were lost in the harbour on that never-to-be-forgotten morning.

Three shocks, and the earthquake was over. Ten minutes from the time when Carlos and I felt the first tremor the earthquake was a thing of the past. And yet in that short time a trail of destruction had been laid that ultimately resulted in the loss of a thousand lives, and damage to property to the extent of some five hundred million dollars.

As is so often the case, it was fire, and not the earthquake itself, that did most of the damage. Many of the buildings were constructed largely of wood, which burned like tinder once the fire had got a hold. A stiff wind had sprung up, dispelling the sullen atmosphere that had preceded the first shock, and as I ran down Market Street I could see the flames spreading down Nobb Hill at an alarming rate.

After the third shock the panic began to subside, for it was instinctively felt that the 'quake was over. The crowds began to thin out, and Carlos and I were able to push our way through towards Nobb Hill, at the end of Market Street. Already the fire-fighting forces of San Francisco were hard at work. Handicapped by the determined wind that was blowing the flames inland, the black-helmeted firemen, calm and efficient, as if an earthquake was all part of their day's work, were busily engaged in blowing up buildings, to prevent the fire from spreading. Had those courageous men been seized with the general panic the whole city would undoubtedly have been wiped out.

The entire population of San Francisco seemed to be in the streets that morning, and terribly sad were many of the scenes I saw. Not for some days did I get used to the sight of a hand sticking out from beneath a pile of fallen masonry . . . or the crushed body of a child. . . .

When Carlos and I managed at last to reach our hotel we surveyed the spot without speaking. The building had collapsed, and was now a total ruin. Everybody in it had been killed. We had no thought for our lost baggage or the week's room rent that we had paid, but surveyed the scene with feelings of thanksgiving that we had escaped the fate that had so suddenly overtaken the hotel inmates.

It was three o'clock on a morning in April, 1906—the blackest morning in my life.

II

Dawn broke, and with it came visual realisation of the appalling havoc that had been caused by the earthquake. The fire still raged, feeding hungrily on once imposing buildings, while the firemen concentrated on preventing it from reaching farther into the city. Dead and injured were being taken from beneath ruined buildings ; demented people were walking the streets ; great gaps in the road told of the burial-place of many unfortunates ; one wall and a huge pile of shattered bricks were all that remained of many of the city's largest business buildings. Although the wealthy residential part of San Francisco had escaped with just a few smashed coping-stones and broken windows, the whole of the middle-class and Chinese district had suffered extensively, and on all sides frantic people, many of them still in their night attire, could be seen scrabbling about the ruins, dragging out precious pieces of furniture or—more often than not—the remains of a relative.

I saw a youngish man walking up Market Street in a long nightshirt and a battered top-hat, solemnly trundling a wheel-barrow to some unknown destination. There was a blank expression on his face, and every few steps he kept repeating, " Jesus Christ ! Jesus Christ ! " He was just one of many whose brains had been turned by the catastrophe.

Sad, terribly sad memories crowd through my mind as I look back on that dreadful experience, but tribute must be paid to the authorities of San Francisco for the way that order was brought out of chaos and the homeless housed and fed ; to the nurses and the doctors ; to the police ; to the indefatigable officials and organisers who brought a measure of comfort to a stricken city.

Scarcely had the third shock died away before the ambulances were out, carrying the injured to hospital and tending to the dying. Nurses appeared from nowhere ; doctors in their night-clothes administered anæsthetics to the victims imprisoned by the falling masonry, and performed operations on the pavement to enable them to be released ;

laymen assisted with a willingness and energy that made up for their lack of skill. Nobody with a scrap of medical knowledge failed to give his fellow-men the benefit of it that morning. And at the hospitals and infirmaries every doctor worked like four men, every nurse ran herself off her feet.

Of the firemen I have already spoken. Theirs was, perhaps, the most important task of all, for, had they been unable to check the progress of the flames, certain it is that the death-roll would have been considerably higher. They worked as I have never seen men work before, and, although the ruins smouldered for many days, the worst of the fire was over within a few hours.

Then there was the relief organisation, in which the police and the municipal authorities were jointly concerned. Dawn was just beginning to gild the sky when workmen suddenly appeared, to begin digging feverishly in Golden Gate Park—one of the largest parks of its kind in the world.

Carlos and I, miserable, tired, and hungry, watched them at their labours, and I went up and spoke to a man who seemed to be a foreman.

" Any work going ? " I asked.

" Apply at the Town Hall," he answered. " There'll be plenty of work for every able-bodied man in 'Frisco for months to come."

" What's happening here ? " I questioned, indicating the scenes of activity around me.

" We're building a camp for the homeless," he explained.

The camp was ready for occupation that afternoon, and consisted of a number of large tents, rather on the lines of a military camp. I believe I am right in saying that the Red Cross organisation was mainly responsible for running the camp, and for attending to the hunger and distress of the thousands of unfortunates who flocked to it.

Anxious to help when there was obviously so much for which help was needed, Carlos and I made off for the Town Hall, and as we went we saw several motor-cars coming from the direction of Nobb Hill—the aristocratic quarter of the city. In those days motor-cars were a rarity, and these particular cars attracted a good deal of attention—not only from us, but from the vigilant Red Cross people. The occupants were brusquely ordered out of their seats, and the cars commandeered for use as ambulances. I could not help being amused at the discomfiture of the owners, who, for the most part, had come to look at the damage. Sightseers at such a time could hardly be encouraged.

At the Town Hall we found that we were not alone in thinking that there might be work going. Hundreds of other young men were waiting to apply, and it was some hours before we were able to reach a harassed official who enrolled us as special police. We were each given an armlet and a revolver, and, in charge of a regular policeman, were told off to guard a bank which had been so badly damaged that its vaults and strong rooms were gaping open, for the attention of any thief who might happen to pass by.

Our orders were brief but comprehensive.

" Unless we take a firm stand from the beginning," the Chief explained, " this town will be overrun by unprincipled looters. You've got to stop 'em. And when I say ' stop 'em,' I mean—shoot to kill, if necessary."

I thought the instructions a little drastic, but I had not been on duty very long before I realised that I had completely over-estimated the godliness of some people. Possibly the sight of so many men and women working unceasingly to safe life and mitigate suffering had unconsciously led me to think that everybody would rally round to do the same. I forgot for the moment that this world also contains men and women who will thieve, kill, and mutilate for a paltry gain, but I realised my error when I took an active part in a particularly gruesome incident.

There were four of us on duty outside the bank, one at each corner, and my position was at an end near to a building that had been completely ruined. Idly surveying this during the morning, I noticed a man busily engaged in digging among the wreckage, and, more out of curiosity than because I suspected that anything was wrong, I walked over to see what he was doing.

So intent was he on his task that he did not hear me approach. Looking over his shoulder, I could see, half-buried among the ruins, the body of a young woman. The man was bending over it, and, holding one of her cold hands in his, was clumsily hacking with a jack-knife at a finger that was encircled by a beautiful diamond ring.

I felt physically sick, but the nausea was quickly succeeded by the acute coldness of something more than rage. I drew my revolver and shouted. The man turned to face me. Without any compunction I shot him through the head, and was glad to see him fall.

Unfortunately, this was by no means an isolated incident, although it was the only case of looting in the punishment for which I was actually concerned. The rifling of dead bodies was prevalent, and there were many pitched battles between the city's defensive forces and gangs of hooligans who tried to break into damaged shops and other buildings.

It was quickly realised by the authorities that, with so many of the city's shops out of commission, the tradesmen who were still able to do business would be in a position to charge exorbitant prices for their goods, and forceful steps were immediately taken to prevent any such profiteering. All shops were closed ; all private trading was forbidden ; and along the notorious Barbary Coast—which had suffered no damage—the saloons were shut down. No work was allowed to be carried on except that which concerned itself with public relief or the rebuilding of the city, and the saloons were closed chiefly because the authorities did not want the attentions of its workmen diverted into idle channels. The immediate needs of the people were food and shelter, and an efficient organisation was set up to make sure that everybody got his share and no more, irrespective of social status or financial position. Meals were procured by tickets only, and we of the special police were also fed and housed at the camp.

The San Francisco municipality did not believe in cheese-paring methods where the virtual rebirth of their city was concerned. They paid good wages, and in return received that earnest service that they most urgently needed. We received five dollars a day and all found, but the labour forces engaged in clearing away the *débris* received double that sum.

In other directions too, the authorities were busy. Immediate appeals had gone out all over the country, and from Washington and the East money came pouring in to help the stricken city. Until quite recently I had in my possession a number of specially designed postage-stamps that I kept as a curiosity. They bore a red cross and the words " Help San Francisco."

An official guard was put right round the city, and nobody was allowed to enter or leave it without a permit. San Francisco wanted its population to stay and work, and the authorities were determined to keep out that floating population of undesirables which always follows closely in the train of disaster of this kind, and is the bugbear of law and order.

After a fortnight as special policemen Carlos and I applied for a transfer to the labour forces. The higher wages appealed to us, of course, but we were sick to death of the monotony of guarding a building that needed just our inactive presence.

The request was readily granted, and we were set to work clearing away wreckage. Although we did not mind the hard work once we had got used to it, we could never suppress a shudder when our spades came into contact with anything that was soft and yielding, and this happened many times.

Altogether we stayed in 'Frisco for three months after the earthquake, and by that time the normal life of the city had reasserted itself. All the emergency restrictions had been removed, and buying and selling was freely resumed ; people were coming and going out of town as they pleased, but the camp for the homeless still stood in Golden Gate Park, and there were still hundreds of destitute people whose needs had to be provided from public funds.

Satisfied that we could now leave the city with a clear conscience, Carlos and I decided to move on.

HOW THE GERMAN SPY ORGANISATION WAS SMASHED

By

EX-SUPERINTENDENT P. SAVAGE

WHEN the Great War broke out and convulsed the world, the vast spy organisation which for a number of years the Germans had established in this country lay in ruins.

With one or two minor exceptions the officers of the British Intelligence Department were in possession of the names and addresses of all foreign agents, who had been assiduously and by all manner of crafty devices endeavouring to learn our most cherished naval and military secrets. So intimately were we acquainted with their activities and whereabouts that, simultaneously with the declaration of war, twenty spies were arrested in different parts of the country, and more than two hundred who were suspected of spying were interned. In addition, Germans and Austrians of military age who had failed to return to their home country were regarded as potential spies. They were all rounded up, and within a very short time no fewer than nine thousand were detained in concentration camps as prisoners of war. So effectively had this widespread espionage system been demolished that not a single item of military news got through to the enemy, and even at the end of August the Germans were still ignorant of the despatch of the British Expeditionary Force to France.

Not only was the old German spy organisation smashed, but precautions were taken to prevent any new organisations from arising out of the ashes. Spying was made a military offence punishable by death ; aliens were cleared out of certain areas ; a postal and cable censorship was established ; the use of wireless and any other form of signalling was prohibited.

A few spies in the guise of neutrals did manage to creep into the country, but they were very quickly detected. Karl Lody, admittedly one of the cleverest of spies, was watched almost from the time he landed, and he was purposely allowed to send by post and even by cable certain information which he had gleaned and which was considered more harmful to Germany than to Britain. To give one example, in a famous letter he sent to one of the Kaiser's agents in Stockholm he reported quite seriously that he had seen the phantom army of Russian troops passing through England on the way to France. He was so precise in his information that he gave the actual number of men and the number of trains which had conveyed them from northern to southern parts.

I am not, however, dealing with the stories of the many spies who fell into the very wide nets laid for them. I want to show how a very clumsy German spy named Heinrich Grosse, whom I arrested at Portsmouth in 1911, was instrumental in placing in the hands of the British authorities the weapons for the destruction of the whole elaborate espionage system of the German Intelligence Department.

In 1909 I was sent from New Scotland Yard to Portsmouth dockyard as detective-inspector in charge of an area which embraced Portsmouth, Southampton, Isle of Wight, and Weymouth (Portland), and part of my job was to keep a vigilant watch on the activities of certain Germans resident in those districts. Just about that time much anxiety was being displayed in this country owing to the growing strength of the German fleet, and members of parliament reflected the concern of the public by frequent questions to responsible ministers.

In the following year (1910) amazement was expressed at the arrest by the German authorities of two English officers who were accused of espionage on the Isle of Borkum. They were Captain Trench, R.M.L.I., and Lieutenant Brandon, R.N. They were tried at Leipzig and sentenced to four years' detention in a fortress. Later a further sensation was caused by the arrest at Bremen of Mr. Bertrand Stewart, a London solicitor and a young Yeomanry officer of brilliant promise. He was convicted at Leipzig for attempting to obtain information injurious to the interest of Germany, and he was sentenced to detention in a fortress for three years and six months.

The cry was raised : What about the German spies in this country ? Why aren't they arrested ? As a matter of fact there was some ambiguity about the Official Secrets Act of that time, and the Government amended it in order to strengthen the law against espionage by extending the definition of places prohibited to the public, making it an offence to obtain and convey to a possible enemy information, which might be useful in war, allowing arrest on a magistrate's warrant, and requiring suspected persons to justify their actions when incriminated. This helped considerably the work of the contra-espionage department which had been formed by the establishment of a Special Intelligence Department comprising Admiralty and War Office officials, the Metropolitan Police, and various constabularies.

Towards the end of 1911 I received information about a mysterious German who called himself Captain Grant, and who resided in a private hotel in Green Road, Southsea. He was a stockily-built man, typical of the merchant service to which he said he belonged, with a round, jovial face, and a geniality that disarmed suspicion. He spoke perfect English with only a slight trace of German accent. He told his land-lady that his father was a judge, that he had received a univer-sity education, and that he had travelled about the world pretty extensively. He explained that he had come to England to write a book about coal, and after completing the work he hoped to settle down in Southsea as a teacher of German. He was well supplied with money, and he had two hobbies— fishing in the daytime and solving picture puzzles in the weekly papers at night. He used to go out with his rod and line and for hours would take up a position on the South Parade pier of Stokes Bay fishing for whiting and flatfish. Like a true fisherman he possessed infinite patience, and as a rule he had remarkably good catches which he took home to his landlady. I watched him very closely—I am an enthusi-astic angler myself—and soon came to the conclusion that he was angling for something more important than flatfish. He also chose a position from which he could easily note the movements of naval ships and lighters and stores.

My staff consisted of keen officers of tireless energy, and they kept him under constant observation. So well did they perform their task that he never once suspected their purpose, nor did he know that we had ascertained that his real name was Heinrich Grosse.

About the middle of November a naval pensioner named William Salter, who was employed as a telephone operator on H.M.S. *Vernon*, inserted an advertisement in a local paper stating that he was willing to undertake private inquiries. Grosse wrote to him in the name of Grant, and they met by appointment. Grosse asked Salter to find out the amount of coal in different ports, both for Government purposes and shipping, and also the number of men who would be in the naval barracks at Christmas. Salter listened to the questions with concealed amazement. "Some people," said Grosse, with a view doubtless of salving Salter's conscience, "would call this spying, but it is not spying from a war point of view. It is nothing to do with the army and navy. It is spying for commercial purposes only." He added by way of further elucidating his point that if there was a miners' strike in England, German merchants would be able to send supplies of coal over here at enhanced prices.

Salter pretended to enter into the spirit of this strange adventure, and said he would try and get the figures. He promptly reported the conversation to the Admiral Superintendent of the dockyard and from that time Salter acted under instructions. We continued our observations, and Salter was officially provided with certain figures which he gave to Grosse, who appeared to be very pleased with them. Later, he made a similar inquiry at a stationer's shop, and then he turned his attention to Southsea Castle, where he tried to find out from a gunner the calibre and positions of howitzer guns.

On December 1st we followed Grosse to Southampton, where he entered a shipping office and asked about a return passage to Berlin. We decided to act before he had an opportunity of escaping to his own country, and having obtained a warrant I arrested him as he was about to enter his rooms at Southsea. We then made discoveries of the greatest importance. In the pocket of his trousers was a letter in cypher. Two other letters were in a writing-table, a sketch of Portsmouth harbour was under a blotting-pad, and a fully-loaded six-chambered revolver was in a chest-of-drawers with a box of cartridges.

When the letters were deciphered they proved conclusively that Grosse was a spy employed by the famous Steinhauer, the Kaiser's master spy, to whom he had been sending information through the medium of an agent named Petersen, of Rotterdam.

Attached to the staff of the Special Intelligence Department were certain able officers who had made the decoding of cyphers a lifelong study. Their skill was such that I think I am right in saying that no enemy cypher, however cunningly contrived, baffled them. In the case of Grosse's letters the cypher was described in court as a very simple one. The key was the sentence : " Pack my bag with five dozen liquor mugs." By an easy arrangement of numbers the letters in the sentence could be made to correspond with the letters of the German alphabet. When decoded the correspondence showed quite clearly the nature of the correspondence between Grosse and his employer, Steinhauer.

One of the letters, signed by Petersen, said : " Portsmouth and the immediate neighbourhood is the spot that I am keenest about. Kindly let me have your address as soon as possible and let me know whether to send registered letters there. You will then receive the remaining £5. I do not want to send the whole amount to the hotel. Mr. Stein (Steinhauer) has informed me of your idea of sending me a short diary. I shall be glad to get it."

Another letter revealed the whole scope of Grosse's activities. This also was written by Petersen and was as follows :

" I hope you received the registered envelope which I sent you the other day with its enclosures. One of my friends told me that your recent information was accurate and without any personal embellishment. I hope you will take trouble to make our joint business a good one in future.

" You will see from the newspapers that there is special interest at present about things relating to England and Germany. This happens most opportunely for you, and you can see that the field of operations will be a valuable one. I do not want to hurry you too much, but I am now giving you some questions, the answers to which I consider will be very useful to me.

" 1. Is it really true, as stated in the newspapers, that the new submarines are being fitted out with guns ? How and where are they mounted ?

" 2. Where are the guns stored for arming merchant ships in time of war ?

" What sort of guns have the mine-laying cruisers *Naiad*, *Thetis* and *Latona* ?

" 4. Have these got wireless telegraphy ?

" 5. How much coal is there on shore ? Is there no more coal in the dockyard than what is stated ?

" 6. More details are required about the system of rangefinding. The information about a floating conning-tower is surely imaginary.

" There is therefore work and stuff enough. I wish you every success in my branch of work. P."

Grosse was the first man to be accused under the provisions of the amended Official Secrets Act, and his trial took place

at Winchester before Mr. Justice Darling in February, 1912.
So much importance was attached to the proceedings that
Sir Rufus Isaacs (Lord Reading), who was then Attorney-
General, conducted the case for the Crown. In the course of
his opening speech he hinted at the secret trial in Germany
of Mr. Bertrand Stewart and contrasted it with the present
public trial. " In this country," said the Attorney-General,
" when a man is prosecuted he is brought to trial in open
court before one of his Majesty's judges and a jury."

Grosse gave evidence in his own defence, and denied that
he was making inquiries to help a possible enemy of this
country, but he made a feeble show in cross-examination.
It was proved that while he was in prison he received a letter
from Petersen, to whom he had appealed to defray the costs
of his defence. This letter, the reading of which caused roars
of laughter, was as follows :

" According to your wishes I will send to your solicitors
£80 for your defence. I must confess that this amount for
your defence seems to me to be very high. I fear the benefit
is out of all proportion to the expenditure. In no circumstances can I do more for you."

The jury returned a verdict of guilty, and the Attorney-
General then revealed the fact that Grosse was in 1898 tried
at Singapore for uttering forged notes and was sentenced to
ten years' imprisonment.

Mr. Justice Darling, in passing sentence of three years'
penal servitude, said the offence of spying struck at the security
of the country. " Beyond that," he continued, " these offences
have deplorable consequences. The practice of spies intent
on discovering secrets which another thinks it essential to
keep can but create and inflame hostile feelings. Those who
engage in this traffic may possibly justify themselves on
patriotic grounds, but the harm they do is irreparable and
may lead to war."

It was as a direct consequence of Heinrich Grosse's arrest
that the Special Intelligence Department came into possession
of information which was the means of enabling them to
shatter the foundations on which the German espionage
system was based. One of Grosse's colleagues was Karl
Gustav Ernst, who had a hairdresser's establishment in Cale-
donian Road, King's Cross. Inquiries proved that Ernst
was, like Grosse, in the pay of Steinhauer, and that he was
the medium through whom Steinhauer communicated with
all his agents in England. Letters addressed to the agents

and stamped with English postage stamps were sent under separate cover to Ernst, whose job it was to post them in various parts of London. This discovery was made immediately after Grosse's arrest in 1911, and from that time the authorities not only knew the names and addresses of all Germany's spies but the nature of the information which they were anxious to obtain. An occasional arrest was made, but only when it was considered absolutely necessary. We judiciously allowed the majority of spies to carry on the good work of transmitting information which was not only inaccurate but harmless to this country. In other words, we just played with them.

As I have explained, on the day war broke out twenty spies were put under lock and key. The first man arrested was Ernst, who was seized by the late Chief Inspector Ward and Sergeant Cooper at his shop. He was interned, but he claimed to be a British subject on the ground that although his parents were German he was British because he was born at Hoxton. It was therefore decided to deal with him under the Officials Secrets Act, and in November, 1914, he was tried at the Old Bailey on an indictment charging him with inciting another man to communicate to Steinhauer information relating to the movements, armaments, and disposition of British vessels which was calculated to be useful to the enemy.

Sir Archibald Bodkin, who appeared for the Crown, referred to Steinhauer as a person high up in the secret service of the German Government. Since 1911 the officials at the Post Office had had strict orders to pay particular attention to Ernst's correspondence. Letters addressed to him not only in his own name but in the name of Walters and Waller were opened by the Post Office officials, and after their contents had been copied were sealed up again and reposted to Ernst. Similar letters posted in this country by Ernst and addressed to a person in Potsdam in the name of Reimers were opened and copied and then forwarded to their destination. Counsel described Ernst as Steinhauer's forwarding agent, a position for which he received a payment of 20s. a month which was afterwards increased to 30s. a month. All the envelopes of the letters sent under cover to Ernst were addressed and stamped with English stamps, and Ernst's duty was to post them in different parts of London. He was also detailed to make inquiries about persons supposed to be connected with the British Intelligence Department, and to report the result of his inquiries to Steinhauer.

Ernst himself provided an interesting sidelight on a visit which Steinhauer paid to London. "I have only seen Steinhauer once," Ernst remarked to a detective after his arrest. "That was just before Christmas, 1911. He came to my shop one Sunday morning. I had several customers there. He said : 'You are Ernst. Do you know me ?' I said : 'No.' He said : 'You have heard of me. I am Steinhauer. I want to have a quiet chat with you. I will come back after the shop is closed.' He returned later and we sat down and had a long chat."

In the witness-box Ernst denied having attempted to procure any information concerning his Majesty's ships. His cross-examination revealed some astonishing facts which our Intelligence Department already knew. Ernst admitted that he began to act for a Mr. Stein in 1910, but at that time he did not know that his principal's full name was Steinhauer. He could not tell the exact number of letters which he had addressed to Steinhauer in Berlin, but he thought it was about two hundred. The letters he received from Steinhauer for posting in this country also numbered about two hundred.

In a letter written by Ernst to Steinhauer and dated December, 1911, there was a reference to the Heinrich Grosse case. "The newspaper placards were very interesting this evening," wrote Ernst. "Another German spy in court. German officer arrested at Portsmouth.' I enclose you the cutting."

"Did you regard Steinhauer as a representative of the German Government ?" asked Counsel for the Crown.

"I did," replied Ernst.

"What sort of representative ?"

"I thought he was making inquiries in this country concerning fortifications or whatever it might be."

"And ships ?"

"I did not think it was ships then. I did not know at this time that Steinhauer was a German secret service agent."

"You are a mean, mercenary spy," said Mr. Justice Coleridge, in sentencing Ernst to seven years' penal servitude. "You were ready to betray your country to the enemy for money, and equally ready, I dare say, to betray Germany to us for an increased reward."

SECRETS OF THE CARDS

By
DARE DU BOIS PHILLIPS

SHORTLY after the war, I was coming from New York to England on board the *Mauretania*. The first night we went aboard, I met a most charming Southerner in the smoking-room, and we became firm friends. He hailed from Virginia and was in the early thirties. I shall call him Campbell. Early on, he told me that that was his first trip to Europe and he was looking forward to it with much excitement.

" I have had a hard life," he told me, " but I have been lucky, and even though I'm quite young, I am now in the happy position of being able to pack up work and go and enjoy life."

As he had a lot of money, I thought it as well to give him some parental advice about the kind of person who would be only too eager to help him enjoy himself, and while he undoubtedly appreciated the motives that impelled me to utter such a warning, he came back the usual phrase : " I am old enough to look after myself, and I think I'm more than a match for any sharper who tries to be funny."

I shrugged my shoulders, and we left it at that.

During the crossing we passed the evenings away by making up a nice little poker-school. It nearly always happens on board ship that a few of the passengers get together and play cards regularly in the evenings, and also in the afternoons when the weather is bad. The stakes were not very high and our losses so small that it was obvious that, if there was a sharper in the school, he had not yet started any of his tricks.

Naturally, I kept my eyes skinned for any signs of funny business, and the only peculiar aspect of our games was the rude behaviour of two of the school to each other. They were —so it appeared—total strangers, but they always seemed to be getting into trivial disputes with one another and losing their tempers in the process. Before the voyage ended they had become bitter enemies ; always bickering and quarrelling, and insulting each other.

To my practised eye, this behaviour was definitely
suspicious. I had seen the gag worked before, and I knew
that something was on foot. Usually, when two sharpers
are in league together to fleece a victim, they take great
pains to encourage that victim to think that they are strangers
to each other—and antagonistic strangers at that. I have to
give them credit—they were first-class actors, and their
methods were so natural that, had I not been on my guard
for things like that, I would assuredly have thought what all
the rest of the school thought—that they were men who had
taken a violent dislike to one another, and that no friendship
was possible between two such enemies.

About a day before we reached Cherbourg, I asked
Campbell where he was going, and he told me that he
proposed to see the bright lights of Paris for a few days, after
which he intended to go on to Vichy. By a coincidence—a
real one, I assure you—I was to go on to Vichy ten days
afterwards, and I told him so.

I went on to tell him that I would be staying at the Hotel
du Parcq, and he promised to look me up.

We parted at Cherbourg, as I had some business to attend
to, and about ten days later I duly arrived at Vichy. There
I found my friend staying at the Hotel Rhul, and on my
telephoning him there, we met for dinner that evening and
renewed our friendship most congenially.

On the next day, Campbell and I went to the Golf Club
where we played, and during lunch there, I was interested
but not particularly surprised to find, dining at a nearby
table, one of the members of our little poker-school on the
Mauretania. He was one of the two men who had made
themselves conspicuous by their continual quarrelling, and
I determined to keep my eyes open more than ever now.
Of course, it *might* be sheer coincidence that he happened to
be staying in the same place as the rich Virginian, but I
doubted it.

Campbell was delighted to see him, and nothing would
satisfy the newcomer but that we should dine with him that
evening at his place at Nevers—a quiet little resort about
one hundred and forty kilometres from Vichy.

We had a wonderful dinner together, and in the course of
conversation I told him that Vichy seemed so dead then
that I proposed leaving it and going up to a little place called
Cautrets in the Haute Pyrenees. This is only a small town,
but it is very lovely. There is always plenty of amusement

going on and the amenities of the town include a good theatre
and a very nice little casino.

My two companions evidenced much interest in this little
spot, and I got out a map there and then and showed them
exactly where it was.

" How about all of us going along there ? " suggested
Campbell. " I'm not particular where I stay, and I quite
agree with you, Captain, that Vichy is a very dull spot just
now." He turned to the other man. " What about you ? "
he asked.

The newcomer, whom I shall call Mr. A, thought it an
excellent suggestion, and, when I offered to drive them up
in my car, he suggested that we all go with him as he had
a very large Hispano-Suiza—a luxurious new model which
he must have bought on arrival in Paris.

After a little good-natured wrangling, he and I compromised by having all the luggage put in my car, and
actually travelling in his.

Our route went through Toulouse, and I must give Mr.
A credit that the arrangements which he took upon himself
to carry out were admirable. Rooms were reserved for us
when we arrived at Toulouse, and when we came to leave
on the next day, Mr. A had already settled the bill and would
not hear of our paying our own shares. The Virginian thought
that he was undoubtedly a king among men, but I had my
own opinion.

On arrival at Cautrets, we booked rooms at the Hotel
Angleterre, and, after a very good dinner, went over to the
casino where Mr. A had a colossal run of bad luck and lost
about 100,000 francs. Afterwards, we all went into the
adjoining ballroom, and, from the interest that Campbell
took in the many charming ladies that were adorning the
room, it was obvious that he had a leaning towards the fair
sex.

I now see how carefully Mr. A had laid his plans, for as
soon as he realised Campbell's little weakness, he suggested
going to Biarritz the following day and putting up for the
week-end at the Carlton Hotel. I was a little surprised at
his choice, because the hotel at which one usually stays in
Biarritz is the Hotel du Palais, but he explained his selection
by telling Campbell that he knew two wonderfully attractive
American girls who were staying at the Carlton and to whom
he would gladly introduce us.

This was a proposition which did not fail to appeal to the

susceptible Southerner, and it was rather amusing to see the way that he pushed ahead the preparations for our departure.

When we arrived at Biarritz, we went over to the Hotel du Palais for dinner, and sitting at a table a little distance away from us were two of the most beautiful girls I have ever seen. Dark, tall, exquisitively dressed, and with faces that did not rely for their beauty on the regularity of features so much as on the character and the intelligence that they so attractively showed in their demeanour and bearing, these girls needed no pointing out to the Virginian. As soon as he came into the dining-room, his eyes fastened on the two lovely creatures, and, throughout the meal, we had the utmost difficulty in extracting any sort of sense out of him.

When Mr. A realised Campbell's admiration, he smiled with a worldly contentment, and remarked :

" Didn't I tell you that they were worth coming a long way to see ? "

Campbell came out of his reverie with a jerk.

" Eh ? " he queried vaguely.

Chuckling, Mr. A repeated the question, and then elucidated it by telling us that these two girls were the American beauties of whom he had told us about earlier.

" Can you introduce me ? " asked the Virginian eagerly.

" Certainly I can," replied Mr. A, and his face took on a grave expression as he went on talking. " Before I do this, though, I really must warn you of one thing. Both these girls have always been accustomed to having everything they want in life. They both have independent incomes, they are extremely extravagant and they are inveterate gamblers. So —be careful ! If you want to live up to the life they lead, it may cost you a pretty packet."

I doubt whether Campbell even heard this well-meant advice ; he nodded in a perfunctory sort of way, and only came to life when Mr. A, with a resigned shrug of his shoulders, effected the introduction.

The girls were as charming as they looked, and that evening we all went over to the casino, where there happened to be some excessively high play. A very well-known Spanish nobleman was the centre of attraction, for he had had some phenomenal luck, and had run a baccarat bank into about two and a half millions francs. When a man is winning like this, it is the natural instinct to try to punt against the bank and change his luck. Of course, it is usually disastrous, and in our case proved to be particularly so, for we lost a good deal of money between us, and the Virginian, as a matter of fact, had to go several times to the *caisse* and change some big notes.

Looking round the table, I was a little surprised to see yet another member of our poker-school on board the *Mauretania*, and it was then that I really decided that this whole business was something more than a series of mere coincidences. It was the same man who had been so hostile to Mr. A all the way across, and when we all greeted him again, he still retained some of that antagonism. But as the evening wore on, they patched up their differences and we all got along quite well together.

This newcomer (I shall call him Mr. B) said he was most delighted to run into us again as he had been having a very miserable and lonely time in Biarritz. He knew nobody in the town, and had found very little to do except to gamble his money away. He explained that he had left Berlin much sooner than he had anticipated, and now had two months to loaf about in before he returned to the United States.

We added Mr. B to our party, and arranged various dates together to occupy him and us for some time to come.

That night, as I was on the point of going to bed, Campbell asked me if he might come up to my room and have a chat. I assented willingly, and he confessed to me that he had fallen desperately in love with the younger of the two sisters. Her name was Eileen, and I was regaled with a description of her beauty and her intelligence that set me yawning even more energetically than I had been doing when I first decided to go to bed.

As soon as I could get a word in, I said :

" Look here, old boy, I understand how you feel, and I don't blame you for falling in love with such a charming girl. But take your mind off romance for half a minute, and tell me whether you don't think it's rather extraordinary that we should meet here the other member of our poker-school ? "

Campbell looked at me in surprise.

" Why should it be extraordinary ? " he asked. " The fellow's got as much right to be here as we have."

" I don't agree with you," I told him bluntly. " That little man is only here because *you* are here ! This is your first trip abroad, and I must warn you that it is dangerous to take strangers on their face value. Don't think that I am making a direct accusation because I have no definite proof, but if you took it into your head to think that Mr. A and his new friend and even the two American sisters were all members of a gang of international confidence tricksters—well, you would be on the safe side ! "

The Southerner wheeled round on me, his face contorted with anger.

" Are you trying to tell me that Eileen is a swindler or has anything to do with swindlers ? " he raved.

" My dear boy," I soothed him, " I am not saying that she is or she is not ; I am just saying that it would be a good idea to think of her as such."

" I don't see how on earth you can make such an unwarrantable and ungentlemanly insinuation," he remarked frigidly.

" I don't mean to annoy you," I assured him, " but it is certainly extremely suspicious that the two men from the *Mauretania* should pick up with one another again here. And, because I am suspicious of them, I cannot help being suspicious of any young ladies—however charming they might be—whom they introduce to us."

Campbell stuck his jaw out and looked as if he were about to hit me. He controlled himself, however, and marched out of the room, pausing only at the door to say :

" If you and I are going to remain friends, don't you ever dare say that Eileen is mixed up in anything so disgraceful. It's a damnable insult."

The door that he banged after him shut out not only the Virginian, but all his hopes of ever getting another warning from me. I am as much a gentleman, I think, as the next man, and I would not bring a lady's name into a conversation like that unless I had fairly good grounds for my suspicions. However, I had done my best and now let Mr. A and his beautiful friends take care of my friend.

On the next day the atmosphere, as far as it affected Campbell and myself, was a little strained, but we all went over to the casino at San Sebastian and, as he hired a car and took Eileen with him, we following later, his ruffled temper had been soothed by the pleasantness of his companion before I saw him again.

We were already playing a fairly high game of *trente et quarante* when Campbell and his lady arrived, and they sat down to join in. I was sitting close by and I noticed that when Eileen opened her bag, consternation was written on her face.

" Good gracious ! " she ejaculated, " do you know what

I've done ? I've brought my wrong handbag out and left all my money behind ! "

The Virginian was only too happy to help her out of her difficulties and he gave her immediately twenty-five thousand francs with an eagerness that only showed how much in love the poor sap was !

" Thanks ever so much," she acknowledged. " Here's my cheque for that amount."

He waved it aside with a chivalrous gesture, but she insisted, saying :

" If you don't take this, I am afraid that I shall have to become a spectator and my whole evening will be ruined. I never take money from anybody to gamble with."

After a certain amount of quibbling, the Virginian gave in and the cheque changed hands. They entered into the game immediately, and although the play was fairly high, the evening could not be called sensational by any stretch of imagination. Before we repaired to the Hotel Christina for dinner, as guests of Mr. B, Eileen had won about 15,000 francs, and the rest of us had lost odd little amounts.

While we were having our meal, the Virginian, all unknowingly, put the rope round his own neck. He remarked :

" Honestly, this game down here is hardly worth playing. It doesn't interest me a bit. Now, what really *would* strike me as an attractive proposition would be for the five of us, and possibly two or three other people that we can rope in, to take a private sitting-room here and have a game of *chemin de fer* on our own. Then we should not have to have ten per cent. taken off our winnings all the time."

I could not help smiling at this naïve admission, but my face sobered as I realised the seriousness of what he was doing. If, as I so confidently expected, these people were crooks, he was playing into their hands, and signing his own death-warrant. What come-back would he have if they swindled him ? *He* had suggested playing, and on his head would be the consequences.

Mr. A proved his knowledge of human nature by vetoing Campbell's plan.

" My dear fellow," he said, " I don't think much of your suggestion. I have no wish to win my friends' money and I am sure you have no special wish to win mine. If we play in a casino, we may easily win a large sum of money, but from a stranger ; that is a very different thing from taking money from one's own friends."

This criticism was timed just right ; it had the effect of making the Virginian more than ever keen on the bright idea that had come so suddenly into his head, and he over-ruled the older man's objections. Then Mr. B butted in. He was a venerable old gentleman with snow-white hair and a baby expression that was redolent of everything frank and honest.

"On a matter of principle," he remarked, "I don't like these private games. But if you cannot get a sufficiently large number of people otherwise to make up a game, I will come in."

Eileen definitely sided with the Virginian.

"If I am going to lose my money," she said, "I would much rather lose it to friends who would very likely spend their winnings in my company."

A typically feminine comment, I thought.

When my opinion was asked for, I told my friends that I would be perfectly willing to play, but that they all of them had considerably more money than I had.

All the objections having been overruled by the resolute American, the next obstacle to be surmounted was where the party could be given, as Biarritz was out of the question. With the law in France as strict as it is, it would be sheer suicide to try and run a game of that sort within the confines of that country.

It was ultimately decided that the Hotel Christina at San Sebastian was the best place, and the time was fixed for the following Friday week. The Virginian would take a large suite of rooms at the hotel and give a big dinner party, for which we should all meet at seven o'clock. We proposed to make it a real party and play right through the week-end, because, in Spain, what you do in your own private apart-ments is your own business, so long as you are not depriving the State of any of its revenue.

The affair between Eileen and Campbell was progressing very rapidly, and on the following day I chanced to meet them at La Chaumiére in Biarritz at lunch-time. I noticed immediately that Eileen was wearing a very beautiful solitaire on her engagement finger, and remembering distinctly that it had not been there on the previous day, I asked if I should congratulate them.

"Yes, thanks very much," replied the Virginian, "but please keep this to yourself as I don't want the news made public just at the moment."

On the same afternoon I had to leave Biarritz for Bordeaux, where I had some business to attend to, but I assured them that I should be back in time for the party.

What transpired in my absence I cannot say, but, on arriving at San Sebastian the following Friday week, the Virginian informed me that he had had the most extraordinary luck, and that he had won a little over 15,000 dollars playing poker with his friends.

" Eileen has only lost 500 dollars," he went on to say, " so between us, we are well in."

I gathered from this that he was already making himself responsible for her losses.

I was not as much pleased by his news as I ought to have been, for to my great concern things were beginning to pan out along quite the accepted lines. Everything that had happened to Campbell struck me very forcibly as being part of a scheme to fleece him, and this latest manifestation— allowing him to win, so as to inflame his gambling sense— was one of the oldest tricks in the sharp's technique.

As the discerning reader will see, it encourages a victim immensely when he finds himself winning fairly consistently night after night. In the case of this 15,000 dollars that Campbell won, he did not get it all in one night ; it was the result of playing for a whole week, and after such a run of luck, surely he could not complain if for two or three nights his luck was completely out ? The sharper knows all about the Law of Averages, but he goes one better than the mathematician ; he makes his own law, and kids his victim into thinking that it is just another of the vagaries of fortune.

Now, before describing the incidents that took place during the famous week-end, I had better explain for the benefit of the uninitiated, such mysteries of the game of *chemin de fer* as will enable the ensuing description to be easily followed.

Chemin de fer is a game played with six packs of ordinary cards all shuffled up. These are then placed in what is called, in France, a *sabot*, and in England, a " chemmy " shoe. In the front of the shoe there is a sort of metal gate through an orifice in which it is possible to draw the cards out one at a time. The main object of the game is to get as near to nine as possible in the fewest cards. The court cards—King, Queen, Jack and ten—all count ten, or, if it improves your hand, zero. If you had a queen and a nine, you would count the queen as nought and then you would have what

is called a " natural "—that is to say, two cards adding up
to nine. With this hand you would win. Assuming, in order
to make the explanation quite clear, that you had a six and
a five. These cards add up to eleven—which represents a
court card (ten) and one over. You could count the ten as
zero, and so your hand would add up to one.

The banker slides out one card to the punter, one card
to himself and then repeats the process. If the banker's cards
add up to nine or eight, he wins, but if not, the punter has
the right to ask for another card, and so on.

The banker puts up what sum he pleases in the bank and
the man or woman sitting on his right has the first option of
going what is called " banco." This means simply wagering
the amount of the bank. Assuming the bank is £20 and the
punter having gone " banco," wins, he takes the £20. If, on
the other hand, he loses, the banker wins and the £20 in the
bank becomes £40. The banker has the option of passing
the bank on whenever he likes, and, in an ordinary evening's
play, it is fairly safe to assume that most people at the table
will get a chance of taking the bank.

The important thing to remember is that every time that
some one goes " banco " and loses, the amount in the bank
is doubled. You can understand, therefore, how easy it is to
lose a fortune in a very few minutes.

Having described the game as it is played in an honest
manner, let me explain how the card-sharper fleeces his
victims. Stacked cards are the secret of his swindle, and they
are known in the jargon as " flat coups." These are prepared beforehand, and are secreted on the person of one of
the members of the gang. Just as a new shoe is being prepared,
these cards are dexterously palmed by the man who is
shuffling the cards, and slipped into the shoe so that they will
come out in a sequence that will ensure the " mug " getting
bad cards, and the sharper (who, of course, is holding the
bank) getting the " naturals."

To make the explanation even more simple, we will
assume that five " flat coups " have been inserted into the
shoe, and the game has been pretty high. On receiving the
shoe, all ready to deal, the banker has 10,000 francs in the
bank. The intended victim is sitting on the right side of the
dealer so that he may have the first right of call. Naturally,
the trick is only employed in such circumstances.

Very well, then. On the first hand, the victim goes
" banco " and the cards having been stacked against him,

SECRETS OF THE CARDS

loses. That means to say there are now 20,000 francs in the bank. He goes " banco " again and loses, and keeps on losing until the five crooked coups are exhausted. In the short space of a few minutes that these five hands take to play, the banker finds his bank has grown to 160,000 francs ! After this the banker can please himself whether he takes the ordinary gambler's risk on an honest series of straight cards, or whether he passes the bank. Of course, unless he is crazy, or absent-minded, he naturally gives up the bank as soon as his crooked cards are exhausted.

I think this explanation will enable my readers to follow the principle event in the ensuing story.

The party duly took place, and after a wonderful dinner we all adjourned to the Virginian's suite—a set of rooms veritably palatial in size, decorations and furnishings. Our party had been augmented by the presence of three other people—friends of the Virginian, who were only small gamblers. By " small " I mean those who would lose 50,000 francs maximum. And this is a mere bagatelle to men like Mr. A, who regard 1,000 francs as a tip for a waiter. However, with these three gentlemen added to our party, it made up an excellent game.

We were seated round a large circular table in this order —Mr. A and then on his right, Mr. Campbell, Eileen, the three strangers, myself, and Mr. B in the last chair on the left of Mr. A. The only difference from an ordinary game was that we had no croupier, as we would have had in the casino.

The game started off in an uneventful way. That is always the case with *chemin de fer*. You start off by being careful and saying to yourself that you will continue to be careful, but you forget this excellent precept as soon as the fire of the game enters your blood.

So it was on this occasion. None of us started the banks too big, and caution was the keynote of all our play, but as the night wore on, the cards began to run in a most interesting manner and one of the strangers had an extraordinary run of good luck when holding the bank. Fourteen times he won, and had he started the bank—like the others did—with, say £25 or £30, he would have had a very substantial win. But he was excessively cautious and he started his bank with £2, so that he didn't make as much out of his good luck as he might have done.

I wonder if the discerning reader can see what a heaven-sent blessing this man's luck was to Mr. A? There had already been a run of fourteen in one bank when the game was being conducted in a scrupulously straight manner, so how could anybody be suspicious if five or seven coups went against the Virginian? In the ordinary course of events, such a run of bad luck might be eyed askance by the other players, but the precedent precluded any such suspicion arising.

The first man to start putting up the stakes was Campbell, and his eagerness to make the game interesting resulted in his losing a large amount of money. It was by then getting fairly late, and Mr. A must have decided that this was the psychological moment to introduce his " stacked cards " into the shoe.

At the conclusion of one round of big betting, the Virginian and Eileen had between them won about 25,000 francs, and as is the custom at private games, the players repaired to the sideboard to partake of refreshments while the cards were being shuffled for the next shoe. Mr. A was the dealer, and he called us back to the table when the cards were ready.

I did not see him actually palming the " flat coups " while he was shuffling the cards, but listen to what happened and judge for yourself whether or not he cheated. You have to be a man with eyes like a hawk to detect one of these sharpers palming cards ; he is so skilful that even if you were watching him you would never know that anything was amiss with the pack of cards until it was too late.

On this occasion Mr. A put 20,000 francs in the bank, and the opportunity was given to the Virginian of going " banco." He promptly did so, and lost. The second and the third time he went " banco " and lost each time. On the fourth round Mr. A stopped the proceedings for a moment.

" Look here, my dear fellow," he said kindly, " this is only a friendly game, and I don't want you to do anything that you may be sorry for. Are you going to go ' banco ' again ? "

Before Campbell had time to reply, Eileen chipped in.

" Don't do it, my dear," she enjoined him earnestly. " You are losing a lot of money already."

I am prepared to believe that Eileen meant well in what she said, and that she was quite sincere in trying to dissuade her fiancé from losing any more money, but she did not understand him sufficiently to realise that there was an obstinate streak in his nature which came well to the fore when anybody told him not to do a thing.

Completely losing all sense of proportion, the Virginian went " banco " six times in all, and at last got up from the table having lost no less than 1,000,000 francs (about £10,000).

I must hand it to the Southerner ; he was a good sportsman and he made no complaint about his loss. All he did was to say :

" Well, gentlemen, I think my luck is right out to-night. I am going to take Eileen out for a drive and we will all meet again to-morrow."

After he had gone, Mr. A soon found an excuse to draw the game to a quick conclusion, and I went back to my hotel in a very contented frame of mind, having won a little over 30,000 francs. I couldn't find it in my heart to be sorry for the Virginian even though I knew perfectly well that he had been caught. I had warned him exactly what was going to happen to him, and lo and behold, it had come to pass ! Well, it was his own funeral. And, if he proposed to go on playing, he was nothing more than a fool who deserved sympathy from nobody—least of all myself.

We played again on the Saturday night and the Virginian won a large amount of money—about 275,000 francs, if I remember rightly. This was, from Mr. A's point of view, an excellent move for it whetted Campbell's lagging appetite, and he came back to the fray on the Sunday night looking forward to a really exciting game. Well, he had all the excitement he wanted, for he went down over 500,000 francs, so that in all he lost 1,250,000 francs !

I might say that his winnings on the Saturday night had been as much a swindle as his losing on the other nights. For " flat coups " had been inserted in the pack that would come up in his favour that night.

You can see that Mr. A and his confederates had a good margin of profit on their expenditure, and so astutely had they laid their plans, that when I left him, the Virginian had not the slightest idea that he had been the victim of a cunning sharper. Mr. A was not the type of swindler who, after fleecing his victim, immediately finds some excuse to leave the district as soon as possible after he has collected his money. This frantic behaviour naturally has the effect of making even the most innocent " mug " suspicious, and proves to him that his erstwhile friend was nothing more than a card-sharper.

Mr. A, however, was made of sterner stuff. He carried on the same type of life after he had brought off his coup as he had done before, and he went on consorting with the Virginian as if nothing untoward had happened.

I had to leave Biarritz the following week as I had some urgent business calling me to town, and on arrival in Paris I put up at the Carlton Hotel. I had been there about ten days when I had occasion to go into the Ritz for a cocktail, and to my surprise, who should I see sitting there but Eileen and the Virginian.

They greeted me warmly and we had a very pleasant evening together. On leaving Montmartre, they invited me back to their apartment, a beautiful suite just off the Avenue du Bois. As far as I could see, they were both ideally happy, and even though their relationship did not bear too close scrutiny, it was not my place to judge them. I enquired after Mr. A and was told that he had gone to Carlsbad, where he was taking the waters. The way in which the Virginian supplied this information to me showed me quite conclusively that he still had no idea but that Mr. A was just a charming old gentleman who had been lucky.

This romance must have lasted a good time, for throughout the long period that I spent in Paris, I used to see them quite often. About a year later, however, I had to go to New York again on business and lost touch with them, but when I returned to Paris in the following year, I ran into the Virginian again in Claridge's. I naturally asked after Eileen and he was so off-hand in his reply that I did not press the point ; I sensed immediately that all was not well between them.

A secret is a secret until a man has a few drinks inside him, and in this case the axiom held good. The Virginian opened his heart to me and told me that he and Eileen had agreed to disagree, as it were. He did not like certain things that she had done and they had therefore parted in quite an amicable manner.

" But I tell you what, old man," he went on to say, " I've done a lot of thinking lately, and I now realise that I was definitely caught for a ' mug.' "

It was a golden opportunity for me to say, " I told you so," but I resisted the temptation, and instead, I asked him how he had found out the truth.

" Well," he replied, " I realised it through a letter that I found one day written to Eileen from Mr. A. I don't want you to think—" he added, hastily, "—that I used to read her correspondence, but, you see, one day I was looking for a letter of my own that had been mislaid, and quite by accident I came across this letter to her. Naturally, I can't tell you all that was in it, but I'll just say this—reading between the lines, I realised that all you warned me about was perfectly true."

In the course of the ensuing conversation, I gathered that this letter to Eileen had been written in such an extremely friendly strain that it was the direct cause of the parting.

I could not help, before we went our ways, getting in one little jab.

"Aren't you sorry?" I asked, "that, in the first place when I warned you about Mr. A you didn't take my advice?"

"Certainly not," was his surprising answer. "These last two and a half years have undoubtedly been the happiest time I have ever spent. I have had my fun although, it is true, I have paid for it. Experience such as I have gained is considerably more valuable than anything that has ever happened to me before, and—well, you may think my outlook is funny, but I consider the money I have lost to be a good investment. My lesson will be of invaluable service to me in the future."

Campbell was a first-class sportsman; he would not hear a word against Eileen, or Mr. A, and summed-up his feelings about them in the salient comment:

"If I was fool enough to play with them after what you told me, it is useless for me to cry now over any one taking advantage of my foolishness."

It is seldom that a man, caught for such a large amount of money, can look upon his experience with such a balanced and sporting vision. Campbell had the additional aggravation of knowing that the girl he loved—and his feelings for her were absolutely genuine—was also mixed up in the swindle, but he did not allow even this fact to distort his common sense. He had made a mistake; he had been too trusting and too independent; now he had paid for it, and having only himself to blame, he quite rightly refrained from taking the easy path of the weaker man and laying the blame for his own folly on other people's shoulders.

There are two interesting sequels to this episode. The first took place in Vienna about a year later when, being at a loose end one evening, I went along to that well-known and exclusive cabaret and night club—the Red Mill.

Alone in a strange town, I looked round for somebody

who might be a kindred spirit, and it was with feelings of surprise and a great deal of pleasure that I recognised a charming young lady around whom all the eligible and aristocratic youths of Vienna were fawningly fluttering. Dressed in the height of fashion and even more beautiful than I had ever seen her before, for the vivacious beauty of her face had been tempered and mellowed by some secret sorrow, Eileen held court, and feeling that my company might be more welcome than that of the stiff and precise Austrians, I went over and reintroduced myself.

She was extremely pleased to see me, and when she had managed to shake off the attentions of her admirers, we had a long talk together during the course of which she admitted quite frankly, when I taxed her, that she had been in league with Mr. A for many years.

" I've got to live," she told me wryly, " and conscience is one thing, but a hungry stomach is another. I make no excuse for what I have done, but I do want you to know this, Captain—I really am ashamed of the whole miserable affair which resulted in Campbell losing so much money. It is the only coup I have ever participated in that I have really hated doing, because "—her voice sank and she looked away from me—" I loved him." She looked up at me with a most engaging frankness and gave a twisted smile. " I still do, as a matter of fact," she confessed.

I learned afterwards, in the course of our long conversation that after the affair with the Virginian, she had severed all connections with Mr. A, and was now living on the money that she had made during her association with him, and in other ways that I could only guess at. She told me she was still writing to Campbell and received letters from him three or four times a year.

I asked her about the letter that was the direct cause of their separation, and she told me something that must convince even the most Victorian of my readers that she had a fine streak in her character.

" When I realised how much I cared for him," she said, " I found myself faced with a problem that caused me acute agony. I could not go on deceiving him. He thought me honest and upright and I could not allow myself to sail under these false colours caring for him as I did. So I decided that he must find out for himself all about me, and that knowing the facts, he must judge me. If I had had the nerve, I would have confessed openly to him, but you can understand how

difficult such a task would have been. So I left a letter
from Mr. A lying about where he could not help seeing it,
and when he found it—well ! . . ."

She shrugged her pretty shoulders and stared unseeingly
across the gay room.

It is not my place here to condone her faults, but at the
same time it is not my place to judge her. All I can say is
that she deliberately turned her back on comfort, security,
and a fine love shared between two happy people—all for
the sake of her principles. Admittedly she was rather late in
discovering that she had principles, but there !—there are
many so-called honest women who go throughout their life
blissfully unconscious of the fact that they have no principles
at all !

The second sequel is particularly interesting. It took place
three years afterwards in Los Angeles when I chanced to
walk into the Lankarshine Hotel on Broadway. There I
noticed a man sitting in the lounge, and it struck me immediately that I knew him from somewhere. The feeling
was a particularly strange one inasmuch as his features
awakened no sort of recognition in my mind, but the outline
of his face was definitely familiar.

So certain was I that I knew him, in fact, that I outraged
all the proprieties by staring at him curiously for a long time,
while I cudgelled my brains to think where I could have met
him before. At length, he smiled, got up and came over to
me, saying :

" Well, do you remember me ? "

" No," I confessed. " Your face bears a striking likeness
to somebody I once knew, but I'm hanged if I can place you."

He smiled and made a mock bow as he said :

" I am flattered by the unintentional compliment. Don't
you remember the good times we had together at Biarritz
and San Sebastian ? "

I could hardly believe my ears. It was indeed Mr. A who
confronted me and yet, how completely changed ! Everything about him was different except just one thing, the
suavity and pleasant nature of his bearing and manners.
When I knew him, he had been clean-shaven, his hair had
been jet black, and he had talked with a very distinct American
accent. Now he wore a very neat Vandyke beard, his hair was
iron grey, and he talked like a most cultured Englishman. By
this, I do not mean only that he had changed his accent ; I
mean that he intelligently used English idioms and phrases

with just the right amount of drawl and expression that would have deceived everybody into believing that he had only just come away from one of the most exclusive clubs in St. James's.

He told me that since I had last met him, he had hardly touched a card. He made no pretence of hiding his true profession from me, and was quite frank in admitting that his appearance had become too well known on the transatlantic liners. During the three years, he had buried himself in a secluded county retreat, and had hired a first-class professor to teach him " English as she is spoke " by the Englishman. He had pursued his studies so conscientiously that it was not absolutely impossible for any one to believe that he was really an American. The changes in his hair were, of course, details that had not required such energy, but they had been performed in a most skilful way and he was absolutely a new man.

You will see from this that the card-sharper leaves nothing to chance—not even the run of a pack of cards—and every one of his movements is carefully worked out with an object. Mr. A gambled many hundreds of pounds on the Virginian before he was able to get it back in one fell swoop ; he had gambled three valuable years against the chance that the change in his appearance and in his speech would give him a new lease of life on the liners.

In every sense of the word, he was a gambler, and had he been honest, what a business man he would have made ! For the attributes that he displayed would, in an honest man, have meant the taking of risks, the ability to lay the foundation of an undertaking satisfactorily, the power of being able to see ahead, and—greatest of all, the power of making men obey him.

I admired Mr. A. He was not only a card-sharper. He was an artist.

THE RED INDIANS' DANCE OF DEATH

By

BOB DYKER

The author is a North-West Mounted policeman and he is stationed at Indian Head in Saskatchewan, Canada.

Not far from the Indian Head station there was a Government Indian Reservation occupied both by full-blooded Indians and half-breeds (" breeds " as we used to call them) and a report was received to the effect that there was a great deal of unrest there. I was detailed to carry out a thorough investigation of the cause of the unrest, and accordingly I set out on Paddy early next morning.

I arrived at the Reservation about ten o'clock. There was a lot of singing and dancing going on, interrupted every now and again by ear-splitting yells. I inquired of some of the more sober-looking Indians what the matter was. But I couldn't get a word out of them. There is no more difficult job in the world than trying to get information out of an Indian who doesn't want to give it. He just grunts in reply, and his face remains absolutely inscrutable. It is impossible to tell what he is thinking or whether he is disturbed by your questions, or in fact anything at all.

I felt thoroughly irritable by the time I'd finished questioning them, for I'd got no further than when I'd first arrived. In exasperation I tethered Paddy, and began to make a thorough search of the wigwams. I did this because I was pretty certain that drink was at the bottom of the trouble and probably " fire-water," for whisky is the one drink they crave for and would go to any lengths to get hold of.

I had spent a long time searching and was beginning to think that I would never find anything, when I suddenly came across a half-bottle hidden away in a corner of one of the wigwams. This confirmed my belief, and the next thing to find out was who was responsible for getting the stuff into the Reservation.

Then I began my questioning again. Confronted with the
evidence of the bottle I held in my hand they at last stopped
their monotonous and irritating grunts and admitted that,
unknown to their chief (at the head of the Reservation was an
Indian Chief, a fine old character, and it was to him that I
had gone first to tell him that I was making investigations),
a quantity of " fire-water " had been smuggled in. But more
than that they would not say, and I gave up the unequal
contest without making much effort. I was sick of listening
to their grunting !

It was then that I remembered a notorious "breed" who had
been suspected on other occasions of getting drink into the
Reservation. He was a curious character, very intelligent
and could speak almost perfect English, but he was a bad man
to have in an Indian Reservation for he had a lot of European
blood (of the worst sort) in his veins.

I asked where he was, but no one seemed to know. Eventually I received the reply that he was away from the Reservation and would not be back for some hours. It was now
getting well on into the middle of the day, and I had been
there about four hours, but I decided I could not return
without getting more definite information. Besides, the dancing and shrieking was going on all the time, and indeed
seemed to be gathering strength, which looked as though
they were still drinking steadily from some unknown supply.

" I shall remain," I said, " until he returns."

They made no answer but looked at me steadily with the
cold blank stare that only an Indian can produce and which
has an unpleasant effect even on the most unimaginative
people. It seemed to me that they were saying silently :
" *You dare wait here !* "

For the next hour or so I walked about the Reservation.
There was pandemonium everywhere. There was no doubt
that most of them had been drinking heavily. They were
dancing and chanting, and sometimes uttering blood-
curdling yells that made me shiver. Some of them cast sullen
glances in my direction, but for the most part they took no
notice of me at all. This was definitely disturbing, for as a
general rule the Indian had a great respect for the " red
serge of the Great White Queen " as he called it. It was nine
years since the death of Queen Victoria yet they still talked of
the Great White Queen, and still do, for all I know, to-day.
But, as I mentioned when I was telling you the story of my
fight with Sweaty Morland, " fire-water " makes an Indian

lose his senses. He becomes, more often than not, aggressively drunk, and it is unwise to rub him up the wrong way when he is in that condition. I should have realised this and returned to Indian Head, content with what little I had discovered. But I wanted to get hold of this " breed," who I was certain was at the bottom of the trouble, and, truth to tell, I was anxious to get the whole matter cleared up by myself so that I could return with another feather in my cap. This folly very nearly cost me my life and gave me the worst scare I ever had.

I suspected the " breed " was in the Reservation all the time. The Indians I had spoken to, though apparently quite sober and possibly disapproving the revels that were going on, would never give away a fellow member of the Reservation even if he is only a " breed." It was the same with the Chief. One could never get anything out of him that would incriminate any one belonging to the Reservation he was in charge of, and yet as a rule he kept an iron control over them and there was seldom any trouble up there.

One bunch of Indians and " breeds " I noticed were making even more noise than the rest with their singing and shouting. I went over to investigate, and there I saw, in the middle of the group, the " breed " I had been looking for. I went straight up to him and asked him point-blank where he had got the " fire-water " from. My shot went home. He stared at me open-mouthed for a moment, and the little group around him were sullenly silent. He shrugged his shoulders hesitantly, timidly, and his face changed expressions with such rapidity that it would have been amusing if the occasion had not been so serious. Then he suddenly got control of himself and laughed loudly.

" Me get ' fire-water ' ? That is funny. That is very funny."

He turned back to the others, but I was not going to be out-done, and I questioned him sharply again. For a long time I could get no satisfactory reply from him, but at last he admitted that he had got the drink from a prospector in exchange for skins. While he was giving me this information I saw out of the corner of my eye that the drunken group had silently formed itself into a circle around me. I pretended not to notice, but I felt a sinking feeling deep down inside me. There was some whispering going on behind me, some muttering, ominous and menacing.

I determined to get out of the Reservation as soon as possible for I remembered with an unpleasant pang that a drunken Indian often reverts to primitive desires and customs, and satisfies them, too, if the opportunity is given to him. . . .

But I knew that at all costs I mustn't show my foreboding. Just as a savage dog will bite a timid stranger and not a fearless one, so I felt that as long as I could remain perfectly calm all would be well. But I was wrong. I had already been prowling around the Reservation too long. The drunken group around me set up a low kind of howling noise ; a mournful sound, and one that made me wish I had left the Reservation hours ago before things had begun to look nasty.

I put away the notebook in which I had been jotting down what the " breed " told me and then I curtly asked two or the Indians to move out of the way so that I might pass through the group to get to my horse. They stared coldly at me and did not move. I tried to thrust them aside but they flung me back. Now I was really scared. An Indian must be very drunk before he will lay hands on a white man, and a constable of the North-West Mounted at that. Then I realised that the group had grown to alarming proportions. More and more Indians came to join the others and danced around me with a terrible, silent determination. Once again I tried to force my way through. Once again I was thrust unceremoniously back.

This is fantastic, I told myself ; it can't really be happening. Indians don't behave like this. But then I told myself that it *was* happening, and that an Indian who is drunk on " fire-water " is capable of the most terrible acts, and that I had only myself to blame.

This wasn't very comforting. The silent dancing figures around me got on my nerves. I began to shout and rant at them, but they took not the slightest notice and continued their fantastic dancing. Then I realised that nothing I could say to them would do the slightest good, and I began to consider my best plan of action. I had my revolver and it might be possible to fire my way through them, but I had no sooner considered that idea than I rejected it. My revolver was absolutely useless to me, for I knew that as soon as I fired a shot the enraged Indians would fling themselves upon me and probably lynch me. There was no hope of escaping in that way. No, my only hope of escape was by using guile. I began to talk to them in a steady voice. I knew that most of them would understand at least part of what I said.

" I do not wish you any harm," I told them. " I am here because it is my duty to see that law and order is kept. I

I heard the wild cries and saw their dark gleaming bodies.

have found you drinking 'fire-water,' which is forbidden,
but if you will let me go now I will say nothing of this
matter . . ."

In this level steady tone I spoke for many minutes, but
I might as well have been speaking to a brick wall. There
was no sign that they had heard me, and the moment I stopped
speaking they started dancing and shouting and screeching
in a kind of frenzy and pointing at the sun. It was late in
the day. In a couple of hours it would be dark. At all costs
I must get away from them before then.

The shrieks and caterwauling got louder and louder
until I held my hands to my ears. When I took them away,
the shrieking had died down, and some one was speaking,
slowly and deliberately. Over and over again the same
phrase was uttered. I could understand a little of the language, but it was some minutes before I realised the significance of that monotonously-repeated phrase. The Indians
kept staring at the sun and then at me, and it seemed to me
that their eyes gleamed strangely. Then, in a flash, I understood that terrible phrase.

The earth swayed . . . I heard the wild cries of the
Indians and saw their dark gleaming bodies first above me
and then below me. . . . I heard a hissing sound in my
ears . . . the earth seemed to rise up and hit me in the face.
. . . I slumped down on the ground, but I stayed conscious.
. . . My brain felt soft and fuddled like cotton-wool. . . .
But one hot searing thought stabbed through it like a
needle. . . .

It was one hour from sunset, and at sunset I was to be murdered.

My head cleared and I leapt to my feet quickly, for I
realised suddenly the ludicrousness of my position. I cursed
myself for my weakness in almost fainting. There was a new
note of triumph in the wild cries of the Indians and I knew the
reason why. It was because they had seen me at my weakest
and knew now that they had me at their mercy. The native
always over-estimates the power of a white man, and therefore as long as I could have kept cool and appeared unafraid,
they would still have believed that in some way I had the
better of them and that I was not really in their power. Now
it was too late. They knew their strength, and as their fevered
songs and dances grew louder, so their blood-lust grew greater,
and I knew that there was no hope. I would be murdered
by them in a brutal and savage manner, perhaps sacrificed
according to some ancient pagan rite. . . .

Looking back upon that scene to-day I can hardly bring myself to believe that all this could ever really have happened. In all my experience of the Indians—and as a Mounted man I got to know them pretty well—I never encountered, or got to hear of, a similar case. It was a known fact that the average Indian showed great respect for the Mounted men. I can only think that they must have had a simply unprecedented supply of whisky and had been drinking steadily for some days. I doubt if there was a sober man in the Reservation on that evening and I am certain that, if luck hadn't been on my side, they would have had an ugly murder to account for to the authorities the next day.

The minutes flashed by, and the sun sank lower and lower in the sky. Still the terrible dancing and shouting and screeching went on, and still I stood helpless in the middle of them. Every now and again I tried to force my way out but always I was thrust back.

I felt weak at the knees, and once again my head began to feel dizzy. It was an effort to keep myself upright. I knew that there were only a few more minutes to go. The dancing and prancing went on, but the screeches had died down to a deep monotonous chant that was even more eerie and terrifying.

For some reason my thoughts at this moment turned to Paddy, my horse. He was tethered not far away from where I was trapped. I wondered if the Indians had done anything to him. A ridiculous notion crossed my mind that he might have been cut loose and had cantered riderless back to the depot, in which case help from there might still arrive. But when I told myself that those sort of things never happen in real life, only in Wild West novels, and anyway I knew that Paddy always remained steadfastly where I left him. For the first and last time in my life I cursed Paddy for his faithfulness. Then, when I thought I heard him whinny (for now that the dancing figures had stopped their screeching I could hear other sounds quite plainly), my last hope went and I abandoned myself to my fate. But I clutched my revolver tightly, determined to shoot a few of the devils in a last desperate bid for liberty.

A second or two later I heard Paddy whinny again and I wondered why he was doing it. Suddenly the Indians were silent. They stopped dancing and stood motionless. Again a whinny from Paddy.

It was dusk now. The hour of sunset had come. But

nothing happened. The Indians stood like statues, listening. It was very strange. I listened too, and heard nothing, but evidently the Indians, who have a very acute sense of hearing, heard something they did not like, for they began to mutter uneasily amongst themselves.

Then, all at once, to my unutterable relief, half a dozen horses thundered up to us and rode straight for the Indians. In the dim light I could not see who was riding them ; then I distinguished the familiar red jacket, and once again my head began to swim, but this time through sheer relief and joy. The Indians scattered wildly. One of the horses seemed to be coming straight for me, but the rider checked abruptly when he saw me. He leant out of the saddle and a strong arm helped me up behind him. It was only when we had started off again that I realised it was Jackie Rutherford, the cheerful, ugly little American.

"They nearly killed me," I whispered. I couldn't speak properly, for I was dead beat.

"Sure, it was a near thing," Jackie answered.

"What are you going to do ? "

"I'm taking you right back."

"But my horse. . . . ! "

He yelled to one of the other Mounted men :

"Bring Bob's horse back with you ! "

"O.K."

We galloped out of the Reservation.

.   .   .   .

The five Mounted men who were left behind quietened things down a bit at the Reservation. There were some arrests made, and my information led to the arrest of the " breed " who appeared to be at the bottom of most of the trouble. I asked Jackie how they managed to get to the Reservation at such a critical moment.

"We'd been getting anxious about you for some hours," he answered, " and at last we got permission to come out and look for you. But as to why we arrived in the nick of time, waal "—he grinned broadly—" I guess that's just your usual luck."

MICHAEL COLLINS GAMBLES
WITH DEATH

By

PETULENGRO

SOMEWHERE about 1919–20, I was travelling across the face of Ireland by night, bound from Dublin to Cork. In these days of the Rebellion, Dublin had some ugly sights to show. I had seen men shot out of hand in doorways, in the open street, even in tramcars. I had seen one shot in the alley at the back of the theatre in which I had been performing in a vaudeville act.

I was glad to be out of Dublin, little knowing that the "Troubles" there were being duplicated in Cork—only they were twice as bad. As the train rumbled south, I believed I was leaving the storm-centre. In reality, I was hastening towards it.

I began to realise that even before we reached Cork. We were just coming into Mallow, when the train stopped with a jerk that almost flung me on to the seat opposite. I put my head out of the window, but the night was very dark and I could see nothing.

Along the length of the train, doors were opening and people were demanding to know the cause of the stoppage. Some of them were jumping out and going towards the front of the train. I opened the door of my own compartment and jumped out, and walked in the direction of the engine. Standing about it were a small body of the Royal Irish Constabulary and a few Auxiliaries. Among the passengers also standing about, a great deal of excited talk was going on.

"What's the matter?" I asked an elderly man near me.

"It's Mallow Bridge. It's been blown up. Lucky for us we weren't crossing at the time."

"We can't see what's left of the bridge from here, can we?"

"I don't know. I'm a stranger here. You might."

I moved outward from the track to see ahead, the stranger coming with me. Against the dark sky ahead I saw the

loom of some irregularly shaped object. I pointed to it.
" That isn't it, is—— ? "

I had no time to finish the sentence. There was the crack
of a gun, and a bullet sang close past my head, and went
whining away into the darkness.

Instinctively, I flung myself flat on the ground. The
group of R.I.C. men at the head of the train came running
towards me. One of them hauled me to my feet and dug the
muzzle of a revolver against my stomach.

" Where's that gun ? I saw ye. Come on, hand it over,
or—— ! "

" Got a gun, has he " demanded a man in the uniform of
a sergeant, and began searching me.

" If he had one, he's dropped it. See if ye can find it on
the ground about here, boys," he said after satisfying himself
that I was unharmed.

" Wait a minute ! " I interrupted indignantly. " This
fellow here had a shot at me for no reason at all—and nearly
hit me, too. I haven't got a gun, and I never had a gun."

" Oh, yes ye had," retorted the man who was holding his
revolver to my stomach. " I saw his arm against the sky.
Pointing it this way, he was."

" It was my finger I was pointing. I saw something ahead
that I thought was the broken bridge, and I was pointing to
it. Then you let fly at me."

It was a long time before I could convince them that I
was telling the truth. Even the elderly man I had been talking to was for a while under suspicion of being my accomplice
in attempted assassination. The face of the man who had
fired the shot at me was strained and haggard. His nerves
must have been taut as bowstrings with the strain he and the
other members of the R.I.C. had been undergoing for months
past. At last I convinced them of my pacific intentions.

The sergeant said brusquely

" All right, I believe ye. But take my advice. Don't be
pointing at anything ye see in Ireland these days ! "

I went back to my compartment—and stayed there.
Not for long, however. After a while we were shepherded
out of the train and across country to Mallow, where we
crossed the Blackwater by the footbridge.

On the other side of the river we waited for another train
to take us to Cork. It was the early hours of the morning
before it arrived. During that wait, I thought, for the second
time that night, that my last minute had arrived. A soldier,

wearing the Tam-o'-Shanter of the Black-and-Tans came blundering among the waiting passengers. He was drunk, and from his right hand he was swinging a revolver by its lanyard.

He was in an ugly mood, and he glared from one to another of us as if inviting us to speak so that he might put us in our places for it. He twirled the revolver on its string recklessly. There was a very real danger of its going off and killing somebody.

Among us was a pretty girl. He went up to her and fondled her cheek. As she drew away, he frowned angrily and made to grab her round the waist. She smacked his face. He stood glaring at her, pouring out a flood of filthy words at her, then he jumped forward to grab her again.

I took a step forward. Hearing the movement behind him, he checked himself and turned to face me. For several seconds we stood quite still staring at one another fixedly. The madness of a beast was in his eyes. He began to swing his revolver again. He caught it by the butt and moved towards me.

" This is the end," I thought. " Whether I stand here or jump at him, he'll shoot me. I haven't a chance."

. . . A voice called out a name. A second man in the uniform of the Black-and-Tans with two more behind him was standing behind the first. By his Sam Browne belt, he appeared to be an officer. He walked slowly up to the first man, then, with ferocious suddenness grabbed his revolver and wrenched it completely off its lanyard. The force of the tug sent the drunken man staggering forward. The officer snapped out an order to the two men at his back. They advanced with rifles levelled, and, at a nod from the officer, marched the first man off. . . .

.   .   .   .   .   .

I wandered into the bar of the Palace Court Theatre in Cork. The performance was just starting in the auditorium, and I was due to begin my turn in about an hour.

Standing at one end of the counter was a group of seven or eight men. As I entered, I glanced at them. One I recognised immediately. He was a notorious rebel called Larry O'Lynch. A second later I recognised a second member of the group. It was Michael Collins himself. I knew him at once for I had already been introduced to him by my good friend Mike Nono at a party in Merrion Square, Dublin. There he stood as large as life. There was a large price on his head, and a complete indifference in his demeanour. He leaned against the bar in the brightly-lit public place with as much ease as if he were safe from peril in some mountain cabin. Had the representatives in Ireland of the British Government known he was in the theatre—in Cork even—they would have gone almost hysterical with excitement.

He smiled recognition at me and I walked across to his side. I was talking to him about some mutual friends, when Dick McGrath, the manager of the theatre, entered the bar and came straight across to my side.

" There's a man here looking for you," he said, and handed me a card.

I looked at it. It bore the name of Captain Holbrook.

" He says he knows you."

" I don't know him."

" Then he's not coming in here," said Dick. He nodded towards Collins's men and whispered : " Not with these boys here. It's the ' Captain ' in his name I don't like."

" Wait a minute, though," I said. " There's a Captain Holbrook who used to be friendly with one of my brothers. He may be taking me for my brother."

Dick was silent for a moment, then said dubiously :

" Well, if he's a friend of your brother's, I suppose it's all right. I'll tell him you're here."

I turned to resume my conversation with Collins.

" There's a friend of my brother's coming here to look for me," I said.

A few minutes later Dick McGrath entered with three other men. I heard one word whispered by the group beside me : " *Tans* . . ."

They stared across the room at the three strangers. Their faces were hard and set, and the right hand of each man was in his jacket pocket. It seemed that next moment I should see the three newcomers killed before my eyes.

As to the three, there was none of them whom I recognised as the Holbrook of my brother's acquaintance. Equally, none of them gave any sign of recognising me. They moved to the opposite end of the bar and called for drinks. McGrath came across to our group.

" There's some mistake," I whispered to him urgently. ' This isn't the Holbrook I know."

" Then who the hell are these fellows ! "

" They're Tans, Dicky," said Collins quietly.

" Listen, Mike," McGrath implored him. " Don't start

shooting here. Once you start, it'll mean reprisals, and it'll be the end of this theatre."

Collins had not heard my whispers to McGrath about not knowing the strangers. He glanced round at his men and nodded towards me.

" Keep your guns in your pockets, boys," he ordered. " These fellows are friends of his."

" They're Tans, Mike."

" I know, but you'll have to make it some other time."

Meanwhile the three men at the other end of the bar must have recognised the leader of my group. They stood there silent, unmoving, their drinks waiting untouched on the bar. There was a horrible dumb fear written on their faces. Later I discovered they had heard a rumour that Michael Collins was in the theatre, and had come in mufti to test the rumour, believing him to be alone. They had seen my name on the playbills outside and had used it simply in order to go where they liked about the building. It must have been a nasty shock to find the Rebel leader with half a dozen of his men.

At a nod from Collins, his men began to walk slowly across the floor towards the door. To do so, they had to pass the other group. The latter must have thought their last hour had come, and their relief must have been painful when Collins and his men walked straight past them and out of the bar.

By not shooting these three men out of hand, Collins was taking an almost suicidal risk. Well known as he was in Cork, every Government sympathiser was on the alert to look for him. Yet there he was wandering publicly in the town. To add to that the fact that three of the Auxiliaries had recognised him and had been allowed to remain free to raise the hue-and-cry was almost madness. Yet Collins was the kind of man who did things like that, and I believe that it was his brazen taking of foolhardy risks that kept him safe for so long.

As it was, Holbrook and his two companions waited only long enough to let Collins's men get out of the building, then they rushed out of the bar. Within a few minutes, the hunt would be up for Collins all over Cork. . . . .

McGrath relaxed limply against the bar and let out his breath in a great sigh.

" Two John Jamiesons—doubles," he said weakly to the bartender.

We drank them neat. We needed them. It had not been

pleasant standing between two bodies of armed men, just in the line of fire.

" Our troubles aren't over for the night," he announced fretfully. " There's a crowd of the bright boys downstairs, and God knows what'll happen when we play ' God Save The King.' "

" Then why play it ? "

" We've got to play it. If we don't, the Black-and-Tans'll wreck the place."

" That's hard. Who's the poor devil who's going to play it ? "

" You are," he said simply.

Frankly, the prospect did not appeal to me. I told him so. But he assured me that no danger attached to the mere player of the tune : besides it was unlikely that the Rebel sympathisers would dare to express themselves openly in Cork, with martial law in force and soldiers everywhere. In the end, he persuaded me, and any one who knew Dicky McGrath will know that he had a genius for persuading people to do things against their will and better judgment.

I gave my own performance about the middle of the bill. The show went on and presently the curtain fell on the last turn. Now was my ordeal, and McGrath was at my elbow to see that I did not refuse the fence at the last moment.

The curtain parted again. I came out in front and began to play. I got about as far as the sixth bar, with a third of the audience on their feet and the rest sitting down—and then the riot started. There was a wild yell of indignation, then a solitary shot—then a fusillade. I took one dive off the stage into the orchestra-well and another down the conductor's bolt-hole. Momentarily safe under the stage, I listened to the pandemonium in the auditorium. The crackle of shots went on, intermingled with the unmistakable sounds of a first-class panic. The shooting fell off for a while as the people fought to get out of the exits. It was providential that the exits were open, and that the audience had been a small one.

For a time there was no sound but the uproar of the people battling their way out of the theatre, and there were no more shots. Then, when most of them must have got out, there came muffled from outside the building the vicious yammering of machine-gun fire.

For several minutes rifle and machine-gun fire went on sporadically, then the climax of that eventful evening came.

There was a terrific explosion that rocked the whole building on its foundations.

It was not till several hours later, when the firing had ceased and Cork, for the moment, was a city of calm, that we ventured out of our hiding-places to see what had been happening outside. The explosion had done its work thoroughly. The whole front of the theatre had been blown up and hung in a crazy wreck on its shattered pillars. Poor Dicky McGrath.

AMBUSH

By
"TIGER" O'REILLY

The setting of this story is with the Foreign Legion in French Morocco.

AFTER a bare twenty-four hours in Marrakesh—another pleasant city—our squadron was ordered out again. It was "boot-and-saddle" in the very devil of a hurry, and post-haste out of the city, and then down the road at a gallop.

We men were all keyed up with excitement. We thought that Ab-del-Krim and his wild horsemen must be advancing on the city at the very least ! But the scenes we passed through were peaceful enough, and, after a couple of miles or so, we slowed down to a jog-trot, and finally to a walk. We did some twenty-five kilometres without seeing or hearing anything of a punitive nature, and then we bivouacked for the night.

But the sentries were doubled, and extended vedettes were thrown out on four sides of us. I was one of the men selected for this duty. I was posted at a distance of about four hundred yards from the camp, told to keep my eyes open, and to fire my carbine at the least suspicious sight or sound.

There was no moon, but also there was no real darkness. The skies were full of stars which gave a certain amount of light—just enough, in fact, to make normal things look unpleasantly eerie.

When I was first left alone I felt a trifle nervy, and on two occasions I nearly fired my carbine at what were probably fancied sounds. However, the place seemed about as peaceful as anything well could be, and, with an orange grove on one side of me, and not far off on the other a crop of cultivated barley, with a few huts forming a small, sleeping Arab village on the farther side of it, it seemed ridiculous to think of battle and sudden death. Besides, I had privately decided that all this hurried marching and these extra guard precautions were part of the silly dramatism of which the hysterical French are so fond.

After the first quarter of an hour I quite enjoyed my two hours of lonely duty—especially as I took a chance and smoked a couple of forbidden cigarettes.

I was relieved at the end of two hours, when I returned to the camp and dropped easily to sleep, nor did I wake again until *reveille* sounded.

Rather to our surprise, about ten minutes after the trumpet had gone the Captain gave orders to sound the *reveille* again.

I heard a *Mareshal des Logis* say that this was because the vedettes had not come in. Their instructions were to fall back on the camp when *reveille* sounded.

The trumpet sounded again, but with no result. There was some little excitement, and a consultation amongst the officers. Then they detailed a Brigadier to take two men and go bring the vedettes in. Schmidt and I happening to be handy, the Brigadier ordered us to accompany him. We mounted and rode off—straight to the post which had seen my first guard the previous night.

In the light of morning the place looked quieter and more peaceful than ever—but there was no sign of the vedette !

We all three looked at each other, and discussed the possibility of having passed him on the way. But decided that this couldn't have happened.

The Brigadier, who was an old campaigner, was looking mighty grave. He instructed us to ride out in different directions—like three spokes starting from a central hub—from the place where the vedette should have been standing, and to examine the ground carefully on each side of us as we went.

In my path, about fifty yards or so from the starting point, was a clump of bushes. I could see nothing there, but, as I passed by them, I looked back—and, next moment, I was hallooing excitedly to the others.

They came galloping up, and then we dismounted and pulled from out the bushes the horribly mutilated body of a naked white man.

At first we couldn't be certain that it was what was left of our vedette, for the head had been clumsily hacked off, and there wasn't a stitch of clothing to identify him by ! But on the left forearm there was a tatooed heart, with two sets of initials, which Schmidt recognised—and so that was that !

We left the body while we galloped round to the other

three posts—and at every one of them, within a few yards of where the sentry should have been posted, we found a naked, headless, and otherwise horribly mutilated body !

We surmised that a small detachment of the enemy must have cautiously crept up behind the unsuspecting vedette, contrived to kill him, somehow, without his giving the alarm, and after that had decapitated and mutilated him, and then cleared off with horses, arms, equipment and clothing.

We rode sadly back to camp and made our report.

Our Captain, a fat and particularly fussy little Frenchman, was in a fine taking. He almost danced with rage, and the blasphemies and threats he flung far and wide were terrific. But it was hard to see what we could do, for, no doubt, the murderers had made themselves mighty scarce by that time. But the captain had his own ideas about that !

We had breakfast—I eating mine with no great appetite, for I was still thinking of the risk I had run the previous night, when I was on that vedette, contemptuously certain there was no danger, and calmly smoking my cigarettes ! . . .

The four corpses had been brought in, and, as soon as breakfast was over, we struck camp and got into the saddle. A small party of our men, with the corpses, were sent straight up to the village. The rest of us were ordered to make a cordon round it, which we then drew in, driving the men of the little village who had been working in the fields before us.

Having got the whole population of the village—men women and children—assembled before him, our commander then proceeded to harangue them in their own tongue which he seemed to speak fluently. I gathered, for they were shown the corpses, that he was accusing them of complicity in the foul deed.

Having finished his speech, the Captain then had all the men lined up in single file. He then took some coins out of his pocket and counted them, with the Adjutant looking on.

" Whatever the number is over ten ! " the Captain observed to him. He counted coins, and then said : " There are thirteen coins—every third man, then ! "

The Adjutant saluted, and got busy. Each third man was dragged out of the line, his hands roughly tied behind him, and was then marched, at the point of the bayonet, to one of the huts where he was stood against the wall. There were ten men, altogether, and three huts had to be used as backgrounds.

This having been done, a firing party was lined up before the first batch, and they were incontinently shot—the firing party then passing on to the other two huts and repeating the pleasant operation !

After that the village—a poor enough place—was sacked, the huts burned, and the more personable women forcibly raped (half an hour was allowed for this " amusement," as the Captain called it). After which, we started off on our march again, I, for one, feeling pretty sick—for I did not for one moment believe that the villagers had had anything to do with killing the vedettes ! They would hardly have been so foolish, well knowing, no doubt, the pleasantries the French were likely to indulge in such circumstances !

We left our dead behind us, buried in one grave, with a cairn of stones on top. The men who we had shot were first, by the Captain's orders, decapitated, their heads were stuck on poles amid the ruins of the village, and their bodies burned in the huts when they were fired.

Apart from this childishly inhuman massacre, we made no real attempt at all to pursue or discover the real killers—but that they were still around we soon had evidence.

We were marching along, a rather silent, miserable crowd, when the officer gave an order and the N.C.O.s started shouting :

" *Holà*, there ! Wake up ! What's the matter with you all, eh ? Think this is a sacred funeral march, do you ? Sing, then—let's have a song ! *Allez*, now ! *Chantez, Legionnaires—chantez !* "

So we started to bellow some of those accursed Legion songs as we marched, and Schmidt, riding next me, had just muttered :

" Himmel ! If there's any of the enemy about this noise ought to bring them along, anyway ! "

We never heard the report, it was drowned in the row we were making—but a man three ranks ahead of us suddenly threw up his hands and toppled out of the saddle !

The Brigadier we had been out with in the morning stood up in his stirrups and stared around. Then he pointed to a faint puff of smoke rising in the distance to our left, and shouted :

" *Allez !* Schmidt, Riley—some of you others—come on, *toute suite !* "

He dashed off at the gallop up the steep slope from the top of which, behind a clump of bushes, the smoke had risen.

We searched around and beat about like hounds after the scent, but we never found so much as a trace of the sniper !

During the afternoon, singing again, we had a similar experience, only this time two men went west.

" What damned foolery this is ! " I exclaimed to Schmidt. " We're supposed to be marching through an enemy country, and we're caterwauling at the top of our lungs just to let the Riff know where to find us ! "

I then saw that the captain had overheard the remark, for he gave a sharp glance at me. I fully expected a reprimand, if nothing worse. Instead he looked thoughtful for a moment, and then gave the order to stop singing. After that he looked at me again with what was definitely a glance of approval !

I was amazed. I was more amazed when we finished our day's march that evening and I was informed by the Adjutant that I had been once more promoted to Premier-Class Soldier, to fill the place of one of the men who had been sniped.

I suppose we had about a fortnight of this sort of warfare— marching and counter-marching in what seemed to be the vaguest and most idiotic manner. One day we were heading for Taza, the next doubling on our tracks and apparently making back for Marrakesh, but never getting anywhere and continually being sniped. In that fortnight or so we must have lost some twenty-five or thirty men—and never once did we see an enemy face !

Then one day we came in view of one of the new fortress-wireless-stations, which were springing up all over the place.

We marched up to it and were halted, and our officers went inside to have a pow-wow with the officers there. It seems that a wireless message was awaiting us to the effect that we were to make immediately for Meknes, and report there at the earliest possible moment.

There followed a series of forced marches that became a bit of a nightmare. Our rations were short, and we always had difficulty in getting enough water. The heat was terrific, the flies a torture, and the peril of ambush was with us all the time ! It gave me a taste of why the Legion was known as the finest marching regiment in the world, though !

We reached Meknes, hoping devoutly for a bit of a rest. We arrived about six in the evening, got a fairly decent meal, and, being tired out, turned in and slept like logs. But at *reveille* the following morning we learned it was to be boot-

and-saddle again, and, cursing heartily, we devoured our
coffee and bread, drew a fresh supply of rations for the
march, and were off again before eight o'clock.

We learned that we were to form part of a column going
up into the foothills of the Atlas—right into the heart of old
Ab-del-Krim's country, in other words—on some special duty
or other. The rest of the column, it seemed, had gone ahead,
and it was our job to catch them up !

This filled us with despair, but it wasn't so bad as it
appeared to be. The main body was moving slowly, for it
was largely composed of infantry, and also included a
detachment of the Penal Battalion.

When we finally came up with it we found it consisted
of a whole regiment of infantry—eight companies of 100 men
each—a detachment of the Spahis Moroccan, another of
Ghoubis, and another of Arabs. There was also a detachment
of two hundred men of the Penal Battalion—and a more
miserable, hopeless collection of human beings I have never
set eyes on, as they trailed wearily across the sand, stripped
to the waist, with bent backs and bowed heads, and hardly
any of them with guts enough left to snarl when the whip-
lash found them out, as it all too frequently did !

There were also another two squadrons of our own
regiment, and the whole batch of us were commanded by
a Major.

This was the biggest force I had yet seen all together
during this amazing campaign, and I rightly assumed that
we were rather too big a crowd for the snipers to venture on.
I was right about this, but one morning, soon after we had
started on the day's march, there came a sudden uproar
from the rear, where the P.B. men were marching. They
were out of sight, because the rocky road—if it could be called
that—was twisting and turning around the hills.

Our squadron was hastily turned in its tracks and sent
back to see what was wrong. But it was all over before we
got there !

It seemed that a little band of Krim's wild riders had
suddenly charged out from behind the hills upon the helpless
chained wretched of the Penal Battalion—and, in about
three minutes, they had managed to slaughter about thirty
of the wretched prisoners, and ten of their native guards.
This had started a panic amongst the rest of the prisoners—
for it is a terrible thing for a fighting man to be chained like
an animal, and quite helpless, when there is fighting going on !

The chains were undone, and the dead hastily buried by some of the Arabs. But when it came to making the rest march again, there was nothing doing. They flatly refused to go forward. Most of them had their backs badly cut up with the whips of their guards, and five were actually shot where they stood, before these poor devils could be got on the move again. It was one of the most horrible sights I have ever witnessed, I think.

At length we arrived at our destination—a lone fort and wireless station, badly under-garrisoned and under-rationed, whose defenders had been having the very devil of a time, one way and another. They hailed us with delight, and marched out with greater. But they might have saved their delight—for two days later the poor devils were ambushed and decimated by a large force of Riffs.

Our business was to extend and strengthen the fort, and to build a line of steel and concrete " pill-boxes " out on either side, at about a distance of three *kilometres* from each other. I do not know what the idea was, exactly, but that was the job.

The work was done by the Penal Battalion and the native troops. The infantry were used to garrison the fort, and to act as guards for the working parties. Our (the cavalry) business was to act as a mobile force, and to dash at speed here and there as necessity called. And there was plenty of necessity, for Krim was not letting us alone for very long at any time !

On the morning of our second day in the fort there came a sudden blare of trumpet and bugle, and shouts of " *Aux armes ! Aux armes ! Holà, Cavalerie—aux armes !* "

It was our squadron that was concerned. One of the working parties was being attacked (*vide* wireless message) and we were to get to the rescue !

Away we went, galloping like madmen—with about ten *kilometres* to go. My heart was warmed at the thought of a real fight at last—I was bitterly tired of being continually shot at like a rabbit, without any chance of reprisals, other than the sacking of perfectly innocent villages !

When we arrived on the scene of action things were going pretty badly with our fellows. The party consisted of twenty-five prisoners, with their guards, and a convoy of half a company (fifty men) of the Legion infantry. They were hemmed in by a semi-circle of Riffs, who, firing from behind boulders and scrub, were gradually wearing them down.

Only two things had saved them so far. The spot they had been working on was against the side of a hill, and protected from any attack from above by the overhanging rocks, so that it was impossible to get at them from above in any way at all. And the second point in their favour was that they had a machine-gun with them, and this had effectually aided them in repulsing hand-to-hand attacks.

The attacking Riffs were spread out all over the place, so that a charge *en masse* would have been useless. We charged all the same, but under orders split up into parties of four and six, and drove the Riff from their protective rocks, sabring them as they ran, and chasing them until those who retained their lives disappeared amongst the rocks.

The trumpet sounded the recall, and we galloped back, sweating like pigs, and with our sabres running red, but feeling greatly exhilarated by having at last got to grips with the enemy in a hand-to-hand combat.

We found that we hadn't come too soon ! The defending force had suffered severely. Of the twenty-five prisoners ten had been killed, and another seven wounded, some badly. Of their guards, five had been killed, and eight wounded (the guards were fifteen strong—note the comparison !) Of the Legionnaires, twenty-three would never fire another shot, eleven were badly wounded, and of the rest there was hardly a man who was not bleeding somewhere. It seemed that only their machine-gun had saved them from complete annihilation.

However, we had driven the tribesmen off, and we were all congratulating ourselves and each other, when a sudden shout arose :

" *Prener garde ! Aux armes—aux armes !* "

Instantly on that shout of warning there came a ragged but withering volley, accompanied by the hair-raising war-cry of the Riff, which sounded like :

" *Hi-yar ! Hi-yar ! Ak-hi-yar . . . !* "

It was a terrible sound, and seemed to come from all sides of us. It dawned on me suddenly that we had walked into a pretty trap ! The Riff had never intended to wipe out the first party. They had kept their main body hidden, while the rest made the attack, knowing that a relief force would be sent, and hoping to clean up the lot of us. And they came unpleasantly near to doing it, too !

It wasn't a spot where cavalry, as such, was any use. Rocky ground, loose stones for the horses to slip on, and a

mass of cover such as boulders, scrubby bushes and so on—
and the whole place was literally swarming with the
Riff !

Now it was that our fat little Captain showed his mettle !
No excitement now ! His orders came, sharp and crisp, and
were obeyed on the instant.

Dismount, every one ! Four men to convoy the horses
clear—heaven granting the road was still open ! The four
men remounted, and, yelling like fiends, and driving the
horses before them, went clattering up the narrow road once
more. A little gang of Riffs, firing frantically, tried to stop
them.

Three of the horses were shot down, and one of the men.
Some of the Riffs didn't get out of the way quickly enough,
and were stamped to gory mincemeat under the hooves of
the maddened animals ! . . .

The rest of us form up (the Captain was in command,
now).

Infantry, with their long rifles and bayonets, to the front.
The cavalry, with carbines and sabres, behind and between
them. Small boulders hastily dragged into position to form
shelter, for there was now not enough. A dozen or more men
went down in the manœuvre, but it was accomplished at
last. . . .

Strike off the prisoners' chains. There were rifles and
carbines to spare—let them fight to help save their lives !

The prisoners responded with yells of delight and fury.
It was hard to realise that these were the poor, cowed brutes
of a little while ago. . . .

" *Hi-yar ! Ak-hi-yar ! Hi-yar . . . !* "

In a black mass, like a drove of ants, the Riff came on.
Running from boulder to boulder, crouching at each and
firing into us—and ever drawing closer and closer. The
machine-gun all ready, but under the Captain's order : " Hold
your fire ! "

The Riff massing against the spot where the cover ended—
piling up until there was not enough cover for them. Then,
with another horrible yell, they overflowed like the dark
waters of Death itself, and came pouring down on us—a
black, irresistible mass ! . . .

The Captain yelled an order. The machine-gun spluttered
venomously, its muzzles swinging from side to side, mowing
the tribesmen down like ripe corn, until they lay in shrieking,
struggling, gory piles. Rifles and carbines adding their

rattling to the din—all of us firing as fast as we could empty our magazines.

And still they came on !

My carbine was empty, and hot to the touch. Before me was a sea of black faces—white teeth gleaming, huge, red caverns of mouths as they yelled their war-cry, weapons flashing in their hands.

I reversed my carbine, and whirled it round my head, using it as a club. Oh, the job of it, as I felt heads crushing like soft egg-shells under the blows I dealt right and left ! A sudden burning pain in the left shoulder, but I didn't heed it. . . .

Then my carbine torn from my hand, and something that knocked my feet from under me. I went down on my back with a thud, and a bare brown leg showed itself close to my face. I jerked my head forward, and bit like a mad dog. A yell of pain, and a jerk that loosened some of my teeth, but I held on. The fellow came crashing down as I got my hands free. I rolled over on top of him, and got a grip of his lean buttocks, digging my fingers into the flesh like talons. I dragged myself on to his back, straddled him, and then, with one blow of my fist, I broke his spine.

A heavy, inert body—the body of a man already dead— came slumping down across my back. I gave a mighty heave, and got rid of it. Then I got to my feet, wrenching out my sabre as I did so.

A swarm of black faces still in front of me. I whirled my sabre round my head and slashed and hacked at them like a madman. . . . By God, but they were giving . . . !

" Get your rifles—get your rifles ! Fire into them . . . ! " Vaguely the sound reached my ears. I glared around through the red haze that seemed to be obscuring my vision, and I saw my carbine lying near. I snatched it up, slipped a new clip into the breach, and started firing again—right into the brown.

Others followed suit, and the machine-gun was sputtering its messages of death once more.

The Riffs fell back—slowly at first—then with a wild dash to reach the cover of the nearest boulders.

Our officers were shouting :

" Cover ! Take cover, all of you ! Down, men, down ! "

We crouched behind our boulders, firing like madmen. A sputtering fire came back, and bullets whistled overhead, but the guts seemed to have gone out of the enemy. Peering

from behind my boulder, I saw that the place was a shambles
—corpses piled everywhere, and the blood running like a
network of crimson rivers everywhere.

I looked closer around me—and I looked straight into the
eyes of my old pal Schmidt. But they were staring and glassy,
and they were neatly divided by a crimson edged gap, where
his head had been cleft almost to the chin !

I turned my head hastily away, and then saw that I was
soaked in blood—my own blood, too ! I suddenly became
conscious of a wound in my shoulder—and then I fainted !

TANOY, PRINCE OF POACHERS

By

L. HANDLEY

" These are my people, and this is my land.
　I hear the pulse of her secret soul.
This is the life that I understand,
　Savage and simple and sane and whole."

Laurence Hope.

AT evening, in the smoke of the camp-fire—in the fullness of the moon, silent on a lonely machan—in the hush before a jungle dawn—down the corridors of memory come stalking ghosts of past tragedies that one can never entirely disperse.

There is for me one aspect of a sunset jungle which will ever conjure up such memories : an evening zephyr, herald of the wind which seems to rise always at the dying of the day, ruffling the surface of a swamp ; the hoarse, insistent creak of bamboos fringing a lonely pool ; the suck and gurgle of the waters round the twisted mangrove roots—such sounds, touching the chords of memory, will always find me straining my ears across the water to catch the last imagined, dying gasp of Tanoy, prince of poachers.

　．　　　．　　　．　　　．　　　．

He had come from far across the Pakchan River—from the distant jungles in the southern Siamese Peninsula. Years later I discovered the village of his birth, whence he had set out on the expedition from which there was no return. It lay astride the tracks leading northwards to Bangkok, and eastwards to where the sea laps the shores of the Gulf of Tongking. From early youth he was a mighty hunter—before his cupidity for the closed rhinoceros lands urged him to lead his trained band of poachers into British India, across the distant Pakchan.

　．　　　．　　　．　　　．　　　．

The late spring found me installed in a Malay hut on the outskirts of Maliwun, at the junction of the Maliwun creek and the Pakchan River, which meandered sluggishly west-

268

ward on its eighty-mile course to the Gulf of Martaban. I had a licence to shoot two male elephant and, most coveted of all, a permit for one rhinoceros—the single-horned variety —as rare in British India as the white rhino in the West Nile province of Africa. Apart from the Nepal Terai (an independent Native State), Southern Tenasserim was the sole habitat of this rare species in the whole vast continent of India. The few which had existed south of the Pakchan River in Siam proper had long since disappeared at the hands of poachers. There remained the few in Southern Tenasserim, between the river and the sea, which owed their immunity to the forest laws and the density of the untravelled jungles. Up to date no expedition to exploit these virgin gamelands had been organised from Siam. But at last there were universal signs that a master hand was combing out the jungle for the ultimate extinction of the species.

The forest authorities at Victoria Point, fully aware of this menace, had drawn a net tightly round the authorised firearms in the preserved area. Villages had been limited to one gun only per loogi (or headman)—all other guns became illegal. Special forest guards and patrols had been appointed, and tempting rewards had been offered for the apprehension of all poachers.

Yet in our daily wanderings in search of my one legitimate rhinoceros the jungles cried out the fact that Tanoy was afoot. Although no one had ever set eyes on him this side of the Pakchan, his presence made itself felt at every turn. The trees bore the impress of his axe. Too often we saw the blaze of two vertical and four horizontal cuts—indicating a party of four with two guns (both illegal). The swamps cried out the testimony of his passing. The very torch that he had used for night fishing lay beside a charred heap of sticks where he had eaten his midday meal.

But the most damning testimony to his unlawful depredations was vouchsafed us one evening, after an all-day stalk knee-deep in bog combing out a mid-jungle morass where there were unmistakable signs of rhinoceros. We had been visiting one pool after another, ever hoping to find our quarry ruminating muddily in the midday heat. Alongside one such wallow—the mud piled high upon the undergrowth, where he had been dragged from his midday siesta—lay the fresh carcase, striped bare as the hulk of a derelict ship.

The marauders' tracks led away to the remains of a fire, where, from the débris of bamboo-stems and the charred embers of a gigantic wooden spit, it was obvious that the meat had been boiled down to extract the essential blood and juices.

Herein lies the intrinsic value of the rhinoceros. Peddled in far-away Rangoon to the Chinamen, it is worth almost its weight in gold. Every square inch and fluid ounce spells potency and increased vigour to the sexually debilitated. It is the King of Aphrodisiacs—the very Elixir of Life—compared to which Nervinus and the host of well-advertised restoratives of lost manhood are mere dilutions ! Thus thinks the Chinaman. So, to pander to his Faustian beliefs, no portion of the unfortunate beast is ignored save the bones. Every atom of meat is boiled down to fat to massage his flagging muscles. Each bristle is chopped up and compounded as a love philtre, those of the tail fetching the most exorbitant price. The blood is drained off into hollow bamboos and drunk as a most cherished aphrodisiac. Even the urine and droppings are not excepted, and are despatched to the Rangoon markets for the ultimate exhilaration of devitalised mandarins. The carcass can be sold on the spot for a thousand rupees ; so it needs no great imagination to visualise its enormous value in the far-distant markets of Rangoon and Mandalay. . . . Such is the lure of rhino-hunting ; and as long as there remains a China-man in Burma prepared to pay the price for his libidinous rejuvenation, so long will poaching flourish on the banks of the far-distant Pakchan.

Day after day followed blank. Within a week of my leave terminating I recognised the utter futility of sharing the jungles with Tanoy, and of pitting local Malay wits against all the organisation and untiring energy of his Siamese hunters. He had, moreover, established a reign of terror, and the trackers who had proved invaluable in elephant jungles now showed reluctance in even entering the rhinoceros area which this prince of poachers had claimed for his own.

It was while I was bargaining one evening in the Maliwun bazaar—trading good jungle pork for a bottle of indifferent port (the only obtainable intoxicant)—that a friendly Chinaman broached a course of action which had repeatedly suggested itself to my mind during my last few fruitless wanderings. . . . If competition with Tanoy and his gang merely induced non-co-operation from all the local trackers and villagers, surely the only alternative was to throw in one's lot with the poachers. Rhinoceros spelt to me a veritable El Dorado, and the weeks spent in constant disappointment and unfulfilled hopes had driven me to a total disregard of all moral considerations. I had come over a thousand miles for one of the species—vouchsafed me legitimately by a benevolent government—what mattered the means by which I attained my desire ?

I played with the idea throughout the long hours of the night, and at dawn, after troubled dreams of flight, arrest, gaol and subsequent extradition, I sought out Kai-Loon, my Chinese tempter.

Over a bottle of port—produce of Maliwun—in the chill of a Malayan dawn we came to the following agreement. That night if possible (as time was short) he would try to induce Tanoy—whose confidence he shared ; also his ill-gotten gains—to meet me by the river. In exchange for my influence with the authorities to legalise Tanoy's bastard rifle, he would propose his co-operation to procure my much-coveted rhino. It would be represented that my influence with the powers that be was inestimable.

When dealing with a poacher who had terrorised the district and practically destroyed all game, and was proscribed as a definite outlaw, I decided to play his game—unmoral and unscrupulous though it may have seemed. I hoped to be well out of the country, many leagues distant, ere he realised the futility of my promises. The risk of being placed in the same category as the gang and caught red-handed added relish to the project. Since when I have never ceased to shudder at the sight of the Forest official stamp on my occasional Burmese mail. But I reiterate I had travelled a thousand miles and within a few days must perforce return the way I came.

That night, long after the last twinkle of light had been extinguished in the Maliwun bazaar, I passed through the sleeping village, threading my way between the myriad corpse-like sleepers spread-eagled on the ground. It was a breathless night. A grey veil of evil mist from the swamp was creeping up to take possession of the slumbering village. It was as though a pestilence had passed its hand over the face of the sleepers. They were so quiet, so grave-like, so utterly un-conscious of the creeping miasma.

Down by the river's edge there was the hush of death, disturbed now and again by the ripple of some night saurian in the depths of the creek, or the plop of a fish as it struggled to escape a vicious death. All the world seemed sleeping, yet the jungled were alive with beast hunting beast, and the myriad night prowlers seeking their meat or grazing grounds after the brazen heat of the day. The mangroves crawled with nocturnal-feeding crabs killing among the slime and ooze of the twisted roots.

The trees alone were silent, awaiting the coming of the day, their branches an asylum for countless families of slumbering apes and birds of every hue. . . . It was all primitive—lonely and utterly desirable ; so far from any organised hive of industry and modern civilisation spelling activity, efficiency, and all its attendant horrors of noise, bustle, people.

Here one would never hear in the silence the exhortation to " Come on—we must get to bed, or you'll never be up in the morning ; breakfast's at nine, and you can't disorganise things ! "

Law and Order ! . . . Here, God be praised ! was the emptiness of a non-organised existence, where clocks meant nothing, and one was not haunted by the thought of time ticking ever onward to ultimate extinction at one's very wrist. The movement of the sun and stars told me of the peaceful passage of the blissful hours. The murmur of the stream flowing to the sea beneath the remote Malayan sky emphasised the distance from the nearest port—the focus of civilisation !

Down the misty waters of the Pakchan came the distant sound of paddles. The wavelets rippled at our feet among the decaying mangroves, heralding the approach of our fellow-conspirators. . . .

Tanoy stepped from out his sampan and stood eyeing us distrustfully, with no apparent desire for more intimate acquaintance. In the background hovered his four most trusted hunters, and each was armed with an illegitimate rifle. In the ghostly swamp-light they seemed naught but grey wraiths lurking in deeper velvet shadow, reluctant to disclose their identity to any stranger . . . as wild as the animals they hunted.

I was outwardly unarmed (to establish confidence), but secretly invested with a Colt automatic—as I was not taking too many risks. There was a lengthy conversation between the poacher and Kai-Loon, watched curiously by the sinister shadows in the background. Over these negotiations hung an atmosphere of extreme distrust, reminiscent of the attitude of a herd of sambhur drinking in tiger-frequented waters. One poacher stood gazing intently into the farthest jungle, the sampan rope in hand ready for instant flight.

The moments slipped by. Calm as a Mahatma in suspended animation, I sat gazing across the sleeping river. Really caring little for Tanoy's co-operation or hostility so long as the peace of the jungles—passing all understanding— still vouchsafed me an æon of such lonely, lovely nights. . . . Time flowed as heedlessly as the drifting stream. . . . The strangers vanished into the gloom, and the sound of their paddles was swallowed up in the immensity of the jungle silence.

If Tanoy—chewing the cud of deliberation overnight— regarded my promises favourably, we were to meet the following day and start our nefarious operations. We returned through the glory of the night to bed.

.   .   .   .   .   .

The afternoon of the following day news came to pack sufficient kit for at least two nights in the open, and to be prepared to meet Tanoy in a hut some ten miles away—below the workings of a long-disused Chinese tin mine. So he had accepted our proposal, and I was to be associated with as disreputable a gang of poachers as ever came out of far Siam. I knew that he would definitely resent any hint of even comfort in one's impedimenta, and would refuse the inclusion of any outside tracker in the party.

I decided to take my Mussulman orderly—both travelling light. We were prepared to carry our own comforts, packed in one large haversack, and sacrificed extravagance of bedding and change of clothing to our stomachs, which bitter experience taught must be adequately filled.

Into the haversack we crammed to repletion kettle and cup for the inevitable milkless tea, bread, potted meat, tinned fish, bovril and bully beef; also an electric torch, matches and one blanket. This we took in turns to carry, and with a rifle apiece (·470 and ·318), my automatic and spare ammunition, we were self-contained for several days. Independent of aught save water and a jungle branch for fire.

.   .   .   .

At the foot of the steep ascent to the old tin mines Tanoy and one of his fellow-trackers awaited us. He certainly looked every inch a hunter. Bare, but for a wisp of cloth about his waist enfolding the inevitable leather box for the twist of tobacco, betel nut and some old fish-hooks. Over this hung a cartridge belt for the most evil slugs; also a powder horn from which he occasionally refreshed his fowling-piece. This

latter never left his hand, waking or sleeping. I evinced no
desire for a closer acquaintance, as a more evil, dangerous
matlock—bound with brass wire where the barrel bulged—
it would be hard to imagine.

To my intense relief, during the next few days he had no
occasion to discharge this perambulating nightmare. But
the knowledge that I was walking within a few yards of a
hideous death (if the hammer fell) gave my over-developed
imagination many an uneasy moment. Like the poor, it was
ever with me. My only hope was that the bullet—as generous
as a plover's egg in dimensions—would seek the line of least
resistance, and escape sideways and upwards through a
rift in the barrel. And that at the moment of release I should
be in line with the muzzle—in comparative safety.

Yet the owner, entirely trustful of the vagaries of this super-
culverin, constantly faced death from wild elephant and
crusty rhinoceros with complete equanimity. A charging
elephant ahead, and the assistance of Tanoy and his blunderbuss behind as one's alternative to a sticky end, would have
seemed the choice of two evils. A fitting subject for a more
than usually vivid nightmare.

Tanoy's face and lean figure were as gnarled as a twisted
briar root. He had an extraordinary jutting chin, far-seeing
hunter's eyes, and a strange way of setting his nutcracker
jaw and talking through the gaps in his betel-stained teeth.
During the next few days he spoke hardly half a dozen words—
or rather commands—and they were in guttural Siamese
and wholly unintelligible. Swift and unerring in sight and
movement, the jungle was obviously his home and the forest
ways his second nature.

There were no preliminary peace overtures. He gave our
haversack one searching glance of disapproval, indicative of
extravagance. Followed by his henchman carrying an
equally defunct fowling-piece, he turned to climb the precipitous slopes above the old tin mines. We followed submissively in single file.

Just as I had reached the conclusion that compared to this
the task of Sisyphus was a mere bagatelle, we reached a
deserted hut, well over a thousand feet above our starting-
point in the steaming jungle below. Tanoy motioned to us
to rest or sleep while he looked for tracks.

At our feet lay a vast amphitheatre of virgin forest,
uninhabited and untraversed. Through it meandered the
feeders of the Pakchan River, and in its pools and swamps

we trusted to Tanoy to find us our El Dorado. . . . We were optimists.

We cooked some tea and lay down for an hour or two. From far below came the crashing of bamboo and the organ-like rumble of wild elephant, interspersed with the scream of some truculent tusker.

Our first disappointment was soon forthcoming. The trackers returned with news of no fresh trails. The hands outspread palms uppermost and the click of the tongue conveyed this gloomy fact. So we decided to have a look at the herd in the valley below.

We soon came on the tracks of a large tusker apart from the herd. As darkness was coming on, and the last flush of sunlight already drenched the tips of the feathery bamboo, we pushed on apace.

From our left, close at hand, came the crack of a breaking bamboo. Tanoy crept into the gathering shadows towards the sound. It was full evening, and amongst the giant clumps it was practically night. By crawling down an ever-darkening tunnel of undergrowth we came to within a few yards of where our quarry was standing. He loomed magnificently in the sombre aisle of bamboo—black as ebony. A dull gleam of ivory as he raised his trunk to strip the tender young shoots of their succulent leaves : ivory almost to the ground—a king of tuskers. All my heart cried out for sufficient light to pick out a vulnerable spot. It was far too risky, so we crept away, and stumbled uphill in the pitch darkness to the doubtful comfort of our evil hut. We arranged everything for an early start at dawn—convinced that a big tusker in the hand (or so we hoped) was worth many a rhino in the mythical wallow.

We left the hut before dawn, and with the first light were on the tracks of overnight. These led us through the thickest bamboo and undergrowth, and had we kept to the tracks conscientiously we would have progressed only some half a mile an hour. Tanoy, with his hunter's instinct, left the jungle and took us over the open, casting and cutting in on to the spoor farther on. We thus gained on the tusker, who had a whole night's start of us.

At last the trail grew plainer—fresh droppings and bamboo recently cropped. We strained our ears for any sound of feeding or movement in the solid wall of forest looming ahead. Then in the dim distance we heard the crashing of bamboos, and Tanoy and I went on alone. The tusker was standing almost completely concealed by a gigantic green clump. For the moment he had ceased feeding, and was lazily flicking the flies away with his great ears. Perhaps he was ruminating on the distant sounds of pursuit. Any further movement on our part, however stealthy, was impossible until he recommenced the rending of bamboos.

With just this one generous clump between us (a distance of some twelve feet), I waited, with every pulse drumming, for him to move and offer me a vulnerable spot. Through the interstices of the bamboo stems I glimpsed one massive tusk sweeping towards the ground, heavily encrusted with mud at the extremity ; but of the other I could see no sign. . . Minutes like hours passed with no movement.

From over my shoulder I saw Tanoy walk up a tree and frantically signal to me that the wind would soon be rising, and that I must take a shot. The fowling-piece itched in his hand, and I could see him priming fresh powder from the horn at his belt.

Almost imperceptibly the morning breeze was rising. It only wanted one eddy from us to the tusker to invite a charge or sudden flight—both equally non-conducive to a steady aim. I decided to step from out the kindly shelter of the bamboo into full view, and before he had galvanised into conscious activity, to get the chance of a fatal brain-shot. It *must* be fatal, as any movement in my direction would bring him literally on top of me before I could regain the protection of the friendly clump.

What I dreaded most were facing the recognition of sudden danger in his eyes and the simultaneous step forward in self-defence. If at this moment I missed a vital spot with both barrels, it would be my last hunt.

We moved simultaneously. As I stepped nakedly into the open he turned tail on and started to move slowly away. There was no alternative, and I took the brain shot from behind with both barrels. He screamed once and fell as if poleaxed ; Tanoy fired simultaneously with my ·318. I reloaded and went forward to finish him off. To my intense surprise he rose and made off at a tremendous pace. We followed all out, convinced it was only a matter of moments before he fell.

Tripping over fallen trees, through tangled undergrowth and dripping, evergreen forest, drenched with blood where my ear had been torn by a hanging tendril of thorn. Tanoy, always five hundred yards to the good, constantly raised his rifle to take a killing shot. Momentarily expecting a charge round every corner, I followed in his wake, dripping with perspiration.

Gradually the noise of the pursuit grew fainter and fainter, and was swallowed up in the immensity of the jungle—as a cry dies in the silence of the night.

We halted, dead beat, in a gloomy valley and cooked some tea—the unfailing nerve sedative after moments of great excitement and strain. The outlook was gloomy. I had without doubt missed a vital spot. No animal could recover almost instantaneously from a solid ·470 bullet and get clean away. He probably fell in turning or from the shock of a badly aimed graze, and the scream was of pure fear and not of pain.

Tanoy insisted that he was wounded, and that we would continue the pursuit within an hour. After a muttered conversation, his companion vanished along the tusker's tracks on what we imagined was a preliminary reconnaissance.

After only too short a rest, the sun blazing down almost vertically and the jungles simmering with heat, we started out once more along the trail. After some two miles' monotonous tracking, Tanoy motioned us to rest, while he proceeded to do a complete ring of vast circumference. After another hour or so he returned, and we gathered from his gestures and strange Siamese gurglings that the tracks had not crossed the circle. The tusker was therefore still inside it, and within easy range. This circle embraced a grey and sinister valley, into which we descended to look for our quarry.

In this welter of swamp into which we had plunged, the ground cicatrised with elephant trails, it was impossible to say whether or not we were on the tracks we wanted. We were entirely in the hands of Tanoy—our late inveterate rival.

As is the habit of all sick or wounded animals, he had sought asylum in the thickest and gloomiest of jungle recesses, and was apparently wandering aimlessly, still dizzy from what we hoped was a fatal head wound. Darkness was coming on apace, and we were still wandering within the circle, equally as mazed as our unfortunate victim.

As the last belated bird was composing himself for rest in the tree-tops, we stopped in a gloomy nala beside a sinister pool. Tanoy, throwing down the haversack, indicated our slumber ground for the night. It had been raining throughout the day, and the carpet of leaves was soaking wet. Disconsolately we sat on a fallen tree and watched Tanoy prepare our night's caravanserai : a few armfuls of wet branches, with an upper layer of wetter grass, and a few palm-fronds overhead as protection apparently from the few tender beams of a clouded moon.

The other tracker returned, and with the lighting of a good log fire prospects brightened considerably.

We were unable to remove our sodden clothes, as we had brought no others, but we removed boots and puttees and their attendant leeches, and took stock of our night's resting-place. . . . It was depressingly damp. By the light of our solitary candle we distinguished a long trail of soldier ants already engaged in sampling the remains of our super-annuated loaf. There were ants and leeches everywhere, and we had to burn them out with ashes from our fire.

We had been travelling all day in bamboo and evergreen jungle, the happy hunting-ground of the leech. When hungry and anticipating a meal he has the appearance of an inch of bootlace. But let him scent blood and manage to impinge with his sucker on the human anatomy, and he never releases his grip until inflated with blood to the size of a respectable slug. Thus he insinuates himself before distension into the smallest interstices of the boot, or through the cracks in one's puttees. Leech gaiters worn next the skin well above the thigh are the only protection. Even then I have known him, foiled on the ground (his natural habitat), to drop from the trees on to one's exposed neck ; or on to any bare portion of the anatomy. Once he is established and feeding, it is useless to endeavour to remove him, as in the process he will remove a portion of the epidermis and set up a nasty infection. He must be allowed to drink to satiation ; then he will either fall off or can be picked off after the application of a pinch of salt. In Tenasserim and Siam he literally carpets the ground of all evergreen jungles where there is an abundance of moisture.

Every night on leaving the jungles we used to remove boots and puttees, and " deleech." Outwardly at first one appears to have escaped their attention, but as gradually fold after fold of puttee is unwound, revealing their repulsive bodies gorged on a blood-caked leg, there is a feeling of complete revulsion which takes much acclimatisation. Personally I never overcame the horror of waking with a stream of warm blood flowing down my neck from the atten-tions of a couple of these night-feeders clamped to the brow.

Silent and almost invisible, equally rapacious by night

as by day, as ubiquitous as the house-fly, they ruined all the romance of sleeping *au naturel* in Tenasserim jungles.

This night we threw the swollen bodies into the fire and weeded a few square yards for our communal blanket. It was a dreary outlook, and the ten hours to dawn seemed an interminable prospect. The younger Siamese had returned with a tortoise. Tanoy, producing from the folds at his waist, cotton and a fish-hook—which he bound to a bamboo— proceeded to the gloomy pool, and by the light of an improvised torch (held above his head by his " chela ") plucked forth a couple of protesting fish. These he cleaned and smoked between a couple of pieces of bamboo over the fire. We ate them with rice cooked in a hollow bamboo. The tortoise was next put on the boil, and when cooked was removed from the shell, filleted, and offered me on a green plantain leaf. Fortunately I had wafted it in the process of preparation, and politely but firmly refused this culinary delectation.

Helped out by tea, what the ants had left us of the loaf, and some bully beef, we rolled ourselves closely in the one blanket and wooed the elusive goddess of sleep.

The fire burnt low, and the moon pierced its veil of cloud and gazed benignly down through the trellis of leaves. The Siamese had settled down beneath an overturned tree. I lay with my head pillowed on the root of a tree stump and soliloquised in the light of our solitary candle. The fire was a mere smoulder of wet wood, and the trackers slumbered sonorously. Majid pitched restlessly at my side, flicking off occasional ants and leeches.

My thoughts journeyed the full range of my imagination. . . . Thus slept our ancestors nightly in bygone civilisations— or rather savageries. Thus was born the jungle fear which exists to this day in an inherited distrust of darkness, the fastening of doors and windows at the approach of night, and footsteps hastening homeward on the advent of dusk over some lonely countryside.

We took it in turns to keep awake and rekindle the dying fire. In my rare patches of slumber, imagination people my subconscious mind with wounded tuskers, prowling rhinoceroses, and a Medusa-like welter of leeches, snakes and other night crawlers. Towards dawn, Majid at my side enjoyed the unruffled sleep of twenty—as black and unimaginative as his village cattle.

Dawn broke wet and chilly, and found me wide-eyed

and miserable, my body racked with damp and lack of sleep.
We drank our milkless tea in silence and left the night's
shelter with no regret. I want no meaner, damper resting-
place this side the grave.

The younger tracker was sent ahead as we started out
along the tracks of overnight—a repetition of yesterday's
maze of nightmare swamp and leech-infected bamboo. We
came up with him again after an hour. There was a whispered
consultation, and Tanoy, putting our haversack on the ground,
indicated with upturned palms the futility of further pursuit.
He waved a hand westward and upward signifying the
dissolution into thin air of our much-coveted tusker. One
might almost have visualised an elephantine ascension.

At any rate, Tanoy was through with any further pursuit;
and our efforts to dissuade him were fruitless.

Reluctantly we abandoned the trail and turned for home.

. . . .

We gave ourselves one day's rest, and then sought Kai-
Loon for news of the elusive Tanoy. By our night's pact
at the water's edge he was committed to a partnership. Yet
here it was broken at the very start. He had taken to the
jungle once again and left no trace. For this breach of faith
I nursed a bitter grievance, and determined thenceforth on a
campaign of retaliation.

Mahbir Singh (my original shikari) was restored to favour,
and an appeal made to his professional pride. He had felt
very keenly the transference of my patronage to Tanoy, and
was bursting to restore his reputation as the local hunter.

A mongrel Gurkha from the Assamese hill tracks, he was
out of a job through the closing of the local Chinese tin mines.
He had twice been mauled by tiger, had a passion for crude
alcohol, and was never too trustworthy in the presence of
elephant; but he knew the surrounding jungles by heart and
shared my growing hatred for Tanoy and his evil actions.

We decided to have one more look for the wounded tusker
and ring him close to where we recently abandoned the trail.
I had an idea that Tanoy had marked him down for his own
and would be found somewhere in the vicinity. We always
hoped, in the course of our wanderings, to pick up a stray
rhino in one of the many wallows; but here again we would
be confronted with the active hostility of the poachers.

I ached to lay my hands on them and their illegitimate
rifles. This obsessed me more than my desire for rhinoceros.
. . . Yet but three days remained.

Once again we packed the communal haversack, this time with "swords and staves" (a match for any Siamese raiding party), and took the jungle once again—seven all told.

Our first objective was where we had abandoned the tracks in the sinister valley of swamps. Of the party were two local Malayan trackers, anxious to settle several grievances they had long nursed against Tanoy. These, with Mahbir Singh, soon got on to the tusker's trail of two days ago. As he was considered badly wounded and could not be far away (despite Tanoy's protestations), we decided to do a ring of large diameter. If his tracks crossed its circumference we would abandon the hunt, as he had undoubtedly got his second wind and might cover anything up to fifty miles, and be far beyond our reach.

The ring took to well beyond midday. It proved conclusively that he was still within a radius of some two miles, as nowhere on the circumference of this circle were his tracks to be found. The natural conclusion was that he was lying up nursing his wounds within this prescribed area. This in contradistinction to Tanoy's conclusion, which from the first I had doubted—as I had always doubted his sincerity and genuine co-operation.

The suspicion that he had double-crossed me was now confirmed ; and there was poor comfort in the reflection that it was a case of diamond cut diamond. Yet I honestly believe that, had he played me fair, I would have made every endeavour to improve his status with the local authorities.

Somewhere within the ring lurked Tanoy and his accomplice—also a wounded tusker. The stage was set for a vivid final curtain.

We pushed on along the ever-freshening trail, conscious of impending tragedy. In this steaming maze of dense vegetation, silence hung in the midday air as a cry. From far ahead the jungle rustled with movement. We froze in the shadow of a bamboo clump as a figure detached itself from the shimmer of haze and resolved itself into the " tortoise snarer "— Tanoy's companion of two nights ago. Too good a prize to be left unmolested. As he passed within a foot of where we crouched, I tripped him up and gathered his rifle ere he had collected his wits. We subjected him to a cross-examination— to which the third degree would have appeared anæmic. He collapsed and confessed the bitter truth. Tanoy from the first had marked this elephant down as his own. It was apparently a renowned solitary bull—a single tusker of great purity and weight.

We came on it purely by chance, and he could not prevent my getting a shot, which, fortunately for him, proved unsuccessful. The tracker owned up to having gone on ahead in our frenzied pursuit (acting on Tanoy's instructions), to keep the tusker, who was badly wounded, on the move, to obviate my getting the chance of a finishing shot. The elephant was just ahead all the time, wandering dazed and semi-conscious. Time and again the Siamese had awakened him from an apparent swoon. He was within two hundred yards of our fire the night we slept under the stars. . . . A case of ignorance being truly bliss !

The following dawn he had roused him from his resting-place, and left him exhausted within a hundred yards of where Tanoy had suggested giving up the hunt. . . .

Worse followed !

Tanoy, on leaving us, had doubled straight back on his tracks, and within half an hour of taking up the trail dropped him dead—as he stood nursing his wound among the bamboo clumps. True to tradition, he had sought the most impenetrable forest to nurse his wound, but had been unable to shake off this veritable Siamese scourge as relentless as the leanest bitch that ever led a wolf-pack, killing not for huntings sake or for his whelps, but for pure mercenary gain—to be traded in the nearest market for the best obtainable price.

Thoroughly cowed, the Siamese promised to guide us to the scene of this latest outlawry. At last Fate was propitious and we were hot on the scent. There was no need now to track our prey laboriously. The terrified Siamese—wrists tied behind his back—led the way with unswerving precision. We had taken the liberty to lightly gag him, so as to prevent any warning shout. Thus, in the wake of our snuffling guide, we pressed forward ere our indignation had evaporated in the midday heat.

The leading tracker signalled a halt ; and in the great silence—disturbed only by the drone of myriad insects—from a distance came the muffled sound of jungle axes : a common enough sound on the outskirts of some village or jungle clearing, but of sinister import in the depths of this great solitude of swamp and decay. These were no woodcutters, but poachers plying their nefarious trade—relentless and dangerous as a hungry tiger disturbed on his kill.

Somewhere ahead lay our quarry, this time in human

form. That he would make full use of his evil firearm I had no doubt. I turned to our prisoner ; in reply to Mahbir's inquiry he raised his fingers, indicating a party of four—the principal and full chorus. Whether armed or not, his Siamese companions presented no grave problem. If surprised, they would probably take an appreciable time to kindle the powder which detonated their abortive weapons. But Tanoy presented an entirely different proposition. An outlaw at bay, expecting no quarter if apprehended, faced with years of captivity—a greater punishment to this free jungle savage than a thousand deaths—he would never consent to be taken alive.

A pretty problem, the necessity for a rapid solution growing nearer and nearer with every step. During the next hundred yards of silent approach I had made up my mind. It was useless to trust to luck and a real dog-fight. I had already experience uncontrolled fire under like conditions in a Congolese forest, and distrusted the weapons of my friends even as I feared those of our opponents.

I decided to leave the Malay trackers and the " tortoise slayer " in the offing, to come to our aid if things went awry. Otherwise to remain in intelligent observation well out of the limelight and line of fire. To take Majid, armed with my ·318, in a silent stalk—deadened by the sound of the axes—to within shouting distance ; whence we would hold the party up while Mahbir (who accompanied us as interpreter, unarmed) made known our terms of surrender.

I wanted no indiscriminate shooting ; and hoped with our two rifles to dominate the situation and prevent any bloodshed.

We bore silently down on the unsuspecting Siamese. Now we were within fifty yards—moving invisibly from clump to clump—passing from sunlight to shadow—imperceptibly closer and closer.

Tanoy, ever clasping his murderous weapon, squatted, directing operations—like the sentinel of a pack of wild dogs devouring an unlawful kill. Two of his companions were plying their axes on the solid bone encasing the solid tusk ; while the third sharpened his axe on a near-by stone. None of them was far from his rifle, which stood propped up against a near-by tree.

Tanoy's eyes never left the distant jungle. Fortunately for us, his gaze was directed towards our recent night's bivouac, whence the danger he sensed was to be most probably expected. I had purposely made a détour so as not to approach from this direction. Just as I had always felt a vague presentiment in disturbing dangerous game on a kill, and longed to avoid breaking a perfect jungle silence by a sudden disturbance—the desire to leave well alone—so I dreaded the fatal challenge which would spell danger and obvious strife.

For an appreciable space of time I paused in the shadow of the bamboos, while Mahbir Singh shivered at my side. Well he knew the reputation of this jungle outlaw. Had it not been a byword of lawlessness on both banks of the Pakchan ?

Then I whispered to him to shout (as had been pre-arranged) to Tanoy to stand up and lay his rifle on the ground —likewise his friends.

We moved from out the shadows, and Mahbir Singh shouted his challenge. Even as a tiger, surprised on his kill, remains motionless for the space of a few seconds before bounding off into the jungle, so Tanoy and his accomplices froze in their tracks.

I had always foreseen a complete ignoring of our shouted demand, and had been at a loss to form any plan for such a contingency. I could not shoot them down in cold blood ; yet to let them get possession of their rifles spelled failure to my plans.

It is easy to show wisdom and theorise after an event, with calm reflection ; but things happened so quickly that almost before I had realised the danger of the situation, the Siamese had recovered their rifles and stepped into the kindly shelter of the forest.

In civilised, police-inflicted countries, with all the inherited instinct of unswerving obedience to law and order, there would have been an instantaneous laying down of arms on Mahbir Singh's insistent shout. The movies have gone far to inculcate the masses with the dire results of disobedience of the order " Hands up ! " The mother of eight would instantaneously raise her arms heavenward on the injunction " Stick 'em up ! " This has been one of the British Islander's many great heritages from " God's own country "—the knowledge of the exact procedure whereby to preserve one's life when threatened by gangsters, hoboes, bootleggers and other such maggots crawling in the world's (outwardly most enlightened) inwardly most corrupt and fœtid cheese.

Unfortunately the law of the gun from Chicago had not yet reached the twilit jungles of Tenasserim ; and Tanoy resolutely refused to play the game according to the enlightened dictum of the West. . . . My reveries were interrupted by a deafening discharge and the drone of a heavy piece of metal past my head. From the pall of white smoke which enclosed Tanoy as a cloud, I gathered this was the " shot across the bows, so to speak "—his reply to my summons to surrender. A foolish act—this challenge of a duel between the modern perfection of a high-velocity, smokeless rifle, sighted to 1200 yards, and a cloud-making destructor scarcely effective over fifty yards.

I whistled up the rest of my party, who appeared from Tanoy's rear. At their approach his friends deserted him and fled ere the net drew closer. Taken unawares, I imagine that their rifles were not primed ; and before they could prepare them for slaughter our numbers impressed on them the discretion of a *sauve qui peut*.

Tanoy, crouched in the shadow of a giant bamboo, scorning flight, was thus isolated. While the Malays closed in upon him, Majid and I stepped into the open and walked him up—finger on trigger—even as one approached a badly wounded tiger.

Well might I have known he would never consent to be taken alive. Even up till now I could not grudge him my admiration for his savage and lonely jungle spirit. . . . This was his realm ; we were the intruders on his jungle solitude. We represented law and order—his bitterest enemies. Forsaken by his followers—anxious only for the safety of their own skins—he had refused the ignominy of flight. . . . He stood bloody and unbowed, rifle still in hand ; sublimely conscious that he had not yet been taken.

Impenitent and proud. . . .

How my heart yearned to bind him to serve me : to learn from him the lore and mysteries of these sinister forests ! Never would I meet a finer hunter, a fiercer and more relentless tracker and killer. Yet it would have been more profitable to flirt with the mercenary affections of the leader of a hungry wolf-pack.

Tanoy distrusted civilisation and its fancied advantages ; even as a tiger would fight shy of the banquet of a gastronome.

In a flash he made a bid for his much-coveted freedom. As swift as the tiger's rush he lifted his rifle, and the shot aimed at me caught Mahbir Singh straight in the face. I had been watching his eyes, and caught the glimpse of action telegraphed from brain to hand. As he moved his rifle, subconsciously I stepped aside. Before I could press my trigger, the damage was done. Mahbir Singh, who had moved to screen me, dropped at my side with a gentle grunt of reproach. Tanoy, as swift as the fatal bullet, passed from the sunlight into the shadows of the forest.

Instinctively my finger curved round the trigger of my ·318 (which I was carrying in preference to the ·470, which would blow a hole through an elephant, and was scarcely suitable for human game). I took careful aim below his waist-line and fired. Tanoy staggered, recovered himself, and with one swift look over his shoulder plunged into the depths of the jungle and passed from sight.

Mahbir Singh lay heaped at my feet. He had travelled his last trail. As the Arab says, " This time he had followed the wrong star." Possibly he was already exploring new hunting-grounds—the Gurkha Elysian fields. But he had followed his last rhino, and his hunter's eyes were dimmed to the further sunlight and shadow of his beloved Malayan jungles.

We carried the poor remains into the near-by shade, and covered what Tanoy had left of his head with my handker-chief. Already the flies were swarming. . . . I despatched two men to his home to summon his relations, while the others watched by the body.

Taking Majid and one most tried tracker, I turned—possessed with a cold and relentless hatred—to see if fortune had vouchsafed us aught for the final hunting down of our human quarry. We went straight to where Tanoy had staggered to my shot and had plunged into the forest. That I had winged him I had no doubt. I had aimed between the knee and the waist, and had hoped for a flesh wound which would hamper his movements and eventually bring him to a standstill.

A cry from the leading tracker as he picked up a leaf with just one spot of blood. Enough to tell us all we wanted. My bullet had not been in vain. Where there was one tell-tale spot there must be more to lead us to our journey's end.

Tanoy's sun was setting.

The grass was waist-high beneath the great bamboos which soared skywards like gigantic organ-pipes. Harsh and unyielding, through this the trail read as an open book, where the unwilling grass had yielded to the passage of Tanoy's body. In patches the trampled blades were dyed a vivid red. This increased as we progressed ; and in one place the undergrowth was all pressed down as from the weight of a human form. There were great smears of blood upon the trampled grasses.

The tracker was convinced that he was making for water. We must not give him time to lick his wounds or assuage his thirst, or, like the wounded animals that he hunted, he would recover and make good his escape. With the blood staunched and his second wind, he had the legs of any hunter in the length and breadth of Tenasserim.

The jungles were becoming increasingly familiar. We passed from the belt of dry, cruel elephant-grass into the shade of giant bamboo. A great silent world of endless dim green corridors, down which we sped, ever following the vivid trail on the soft carpet of fallen leaves. It was almost dark. The gigantic stems, interlaced far above our heads, creaked in the light evening breeze with harsh resistence.

Then I realised the familiarity of my surroundings. We were returning along our tracks of two days before ; heading for the old tin mines and the desolation of the leech swamps, beyond which lay the river—Siam—and salvation. Tanoy was following the natural inclination of a wounded animal, and making for home.

With a last desperate bid for freedom, he was taking to the mangrove swamps—the short cut to the creek wherein his sampan swayed to the rising tide of the Pakchan. A " via dolorosa," reeking with quicksand, which, with his intimate knowledge of the locality, he hoped yet to turn to advantage against his less enlightened pursuers. But we had with us his equal—the loogi of Bankichong—as inveterate a poacher as he whom we followed. Had he not, night after night, used these very solitudes to smuggle nefarious goods from over the river for the delectation of the merchants of Maliwun ?

Now far ahead we glimpsed a hurrying figure, which could be none other than Tanoy—whom we hunted— delivered into our hands. . . . No necessity now to follow the dripping, laborious trail. We were running to view.

We raced through gloomy swamps, pulled our feet out of great elephant tracks, clutched at thorns as we tripped over jungle creeper ; and gradually and relentlessly shortened the distance between us and our quarry. The air was salt with the tang of the sea borne on the evening breeze. It was a race for the creek—the sampan—and Siam.

We were now but a hundred yards away, and as he glanced over his shoulder his face showed naught of fear ; only exhaustion and a great bitterness—the shadow of a doubt that he had looked his last on distant Siam. A fugitive in his own realms ; an apt reward for the deepest treachery.

From far ahead came the glint of sunlight on water. A tendril of the main creek where lay the coveted sampan.

He was now almost running, and for the first time I noticed that he had discarded his only loincloth (a possible hindrance), and had reverted to a state of stark nature Yet round his waist was coiled the belt of slugs and from the waist downward the left leg was caking with dried blood. . . . But for the haunting memory of poor Mahbir Singh's featureless head I might yet have given him a chance ; but the horror of his final lawless act stood between me and any consideration of pity.

The sun was almost set, and the arm of the creek lay bathed in an amber glow. The evening breeze ruffled the surface into rosy wavelets, light as the snow-soft plumage of a swan. There was a brooding calm ; a peaceful Malayan dusk descending—sunset dying—as Tanoy stepped into the creek— now so nearly home.

The tracker put out a restraining hand : " Do not follow, Takein, he will never reach the other side." . . . We stood beside the rustling mangroves—rigid with a sense of impending tragedy. With the descent of night the mists were creeping up from the river, and the glow-worms and fire-flies gleamed in the forest's sombre depths.

Tanoy was already nearing the farther shore ; yet he appeared to be making no further progress. Waist-deep in the sunset water, he seemed to be fighting an invisible enemy who was chaining him down.

In a flash I realised the significance of the tracker's prophecy, " He will never reach the other side "—the Siamese was in the toils of a quicksand, and his moments were numbered. Subconsciously I started to his rescue, but my companions, with a wave of the hand, whispered, " It is useless, and 'tis better so."

We could only stand and watch his final torment.

Slowly—even as the sun died—Tanoy sank into the merciless depths of the lagoon. One could almost feel the cloying horror of the slime as it welcomed his tired body and the mangrove roots imprisoned him with their livid grey tentacles. . . . There was one long cry of horror and utter despair as the mud closed over his head ; and the glowing waters regained their unruffled calm.

The Siamese was in the toils of a quicksand.

T

Slowly the last bubble died upon the surface, and night spread its mantle over the unhappy waters of the lagoon.

. . . . . .

I sat on heedless of the passage of time : mindful only of my memories of Tanoy. All the incidents of the past few days processed vividly before my tired eyes—from our first clandestine meeting that dim, ghostly night, with the mists rising from the Pakchan, even as they were now gathering about his awful tomb. Awhile Kai-Loon murmured to me the local superstition that these very swamps were the home of the malevolent forest spirits, and that they who had transgressed the jungle laws were pulled down by chains. Perhaps the " Nats " had claimed a lawful victim ; and he who had waged a merciless war against all jungle life paid the final penalty—ensnared in their relentless chains.

. . . . . .

And thus, in after years—as memory casts its cloud about the spirit—an evening breeze ruffling the sunset surface of a mid-jungle swamp will always bring to mind those last few moments of anguish of Tanoy, prince of poachers.

ROMANCE IN THE UNDERWORLD

By
TREVOR ALLEN

Mr. Trevor Allen has taken this story straight from the lips of a habitual criminal—one Charles Brooks.

THE majority of men living a precarious life find it necessary to have a mate to satisfy the emotional side of their nature just as all other human beings. I have hardly known a crook who was not fond of his wife or woman, and his children, or who did not treat them handsomely and wish to provide them with every comfort and a good education.

To-day there are almost as many women crooks as men ; if anything, they are more systematic and practical in their methods, and invariably possess a sounder insight into the psychology of people. A great many crooks find their mate in this class of woman, and if they do not marry her, live with her and benefit by her advice and sympathy if not by her actual co-operation in graft.

In most of these unions there is an absolute equality between the two which is not always found in normal society. The woman is in every way a help-meet of the man, sharing his risks and usually remaining staunch to him when he is " shopped " and goes to prison. Not in every case, of course. As I tried to explain in an earlier chapter, physical fidelity is not such a rigid condition of unions in the criminal class ; it is the mental companionship which is regarded as of more vital importance. Most criminals are sensible enough to realise that a woman is subject to the same needs as themselves, and if she is segregated from the man during terms of imprisonment, they cannot justly complain when she makes other associations. In cases where this happens, however, the woman will usually return to her man when he comes out. He asks no questions, and the relationship is as strong as before. Their sympathy implies a tacit under- standing that certain things may be necessary owing to the abnormal life they lead. There is tolerance on both sides.

Until I met D. at the age of twenty-six, women had played very little part in my life. I did not consider myself particularly exacting, but felt instinctively that it was not fair to a woman to ask her to share the sort of life I was leading. I preferred to live solo and thus avoid embarrassing explanations or unfair concealment. I suppose you would have called me rather a lonely, sex-starved individual, with none of the warm human attachments which bind most young men.

The truth is that I hardly thought about the matter ; I was too busy existing, scheming, moving from place to place. I had been lonely from boyhood—ever since I could remember. My kind of life intensified that loneliness ; I accepted it as part and parcel of my very unusual career, which left so little room for sentiment. It became in course of time second nature, and I could never imagine myself as otherwise.

Before meeting D. I had formed an association with a girl named Violet, which continued, on and off, for the best part of five years. It did not go very deep, I'm afraid. She was a wilful, erratic creature, about as unstable as an irresponsible young woman can be. During the time I knew her I had several short terms of imprisonment, and on each occasion she found other associations—not, I believe, so much from necessity as from sheer caprice. She was made like that—a light of heart, a will-o'-the-wisp, who never stopped to think twice before skipping off with somebody else.

More than once I decided to leave her ; each time she would behave hysterically and beg me not to go. When matters came to a head, after my meeting with D., she would follow me about the streets, crying, shouting, entreating, creating scenes. Once, I remember, she flung herself, literally, at my feet in the middle of Coventry Street, with a West End crowd looking on, and refused to get up until I promised to take her back.

When I took her back she would be her old self for a time, and then sail off at a tangent with some one else who happened to attract her. She was a camp-follower of the Underworld, never a true member of it. From my first meeting with D. I realised Violet could never be a real mate for a man like myself. I can see her now, her eyes inflamed with weeping, her pretty lips half smiling, half pouting, her hands caressing and cajoling, her waywardness

apparent in every restless movement as she looked at me and
said :

"Do let's go back, Charlie. I know I'm bad, but I can't
help it sometimes. I'll be different—I will, really. We
have been happy, haven't we ? I like you better than any one
else, really. Don't be angry with me, Charlie. We can't
live without each other. You know we can't. If you leave
me I'll go all wrong. There's nothing else for me to do.
Let's go home, Charlie ! "

I tried to be patient, but it was of no use. In a short
time she would be back at her old games, drinking too
much, skipping round town with some fellow who had
more money than sense. The time came when I felt I
should have to be rid of her or go mad. When finally she
formed an attachment which looked like lasting longer
than most, it was an immense relief to me. I let her go
without a pang of regret.

Had I not come to know D., I suppose she would have
cajoled her way back to me even after that. There is a
type of woman who is half a helpless child ; Violet was of
that sort, and she knew it and would count on stirring your
pity. One could never forget that she could be charming
and lovable at times ; on every occasion one thought :
"This time she has changed, she will really keep her word."
When she was following me about the streets creating scenes,
I felt I could murder her. I began to understand how some
men could hang for a woman and be glad of ridding themselves
of her at the price.

I first saw D. in a Soho café I used to frequent, a picturesque, informal place which always had a Bohemian
atmosphere and music of some sort, usually provided by
patrons who were also itinerant musicians or entertainers.
From the first moment I was attracted to her, although I
saw her there several nights before finding the opportunity
of talking to her.

What I liked about her at once was her essential woman-
liness coupled with an unmistakable air of freedom and
independence. She dressed in an artistic, individual way,
and was fond of bright, knotted scarves of the kind ranch-
girls wear in America—an effect which, to my eyes, was
captivating and romantic.

Her hair was blonde ; her features I thought beautiful ;
she had very expressive eyes and a delightful smile. Above
all, I could see at a glance that she had personality. Although

I had encountered attractive women of all kinds and of all classes, she was the first to whom I was strongly drawn from the moment I set eyes on her.

I soon realised that she was to be a deeply disturbing influence in my life. I went to that café night after night hoping she would be there, fearing when she did not happen to turn up that I should never see her again. For the first time in my life I began to feel that I should be pretty badly hurt if anything happened to me, in my precarious life, which would take me away and prevent my seeing her for a long time. I was—I had to admit it—in love ; and head over heels in it at that.

But the old misgivings returned : how could I hope to know her ? What would she say when she found out the manner of life I led, as she was bound to do eventually ? Hadn't I better clear off somewhere and forget all about it ? The love of a worth-while woman was not for such as I. And yet, if for others I knew, why not also for me ? Those evenings of haunting the café solely to see her were disturbing evenings for me.

My chance came one night when a couple of Italian musicians came in with mandolines. I had taught myself to play the instrument, after a fashion, at Ruhleben, and asked one of them to let me have a try—just for the fun of the thing. I forget what I played—probably some German tune I used to strum in the prison camp—but apparently it wasn't too bad, for the others in the café, who knew me, called out :

" Now, Charlie, give us a song ! "

So I gave them a song. I sang them Toselli's *Serenade* ; or, rather, I sang it to *her*. Yes, I caught her eye and smiled and held it and left no doubt in her mind that I was really serenading *her*. She smiled in acknowledgment, and when the song was finished invited me to sit at her table. All my bravado left me when I sat down ; I felt almost too excited to speak. But, at any rate, we had broken the ice. For one thing, we discovered we had both travelled a good deal. We did not become very confidential that evening. Still, we did *talk*, and talking with her thrilled me and made me happy. When the time came for her to leave, she gave me a charming smile and said :

" I hope we'll meet again. I'm here most evenings."

After that I floated about on air, thought of little else but our next meeting. That café for me became as wonderful and romantic as any in Munich or Montmartre. Was I not living

the first real experience of my life in it ? Were not its colours,
its music, just a harmonious background to the thrilling
emotional life which was now mine ?

Nothing mattered until she came ; I took less interest in
the other people, the free-and-easy groups sitting about
talking, drinking, laughing, ragging the other fellows sitting
with their girls and sometimes " necking " them slyly when
they thought they were for a moment unobserved.

But the moment D. arrived the atmosphere of the place
was galvanised for me : the talk was brighter, the music
more carefree, the faces around me seemed happier, hand-
somer. I even dreamt of running a place like that some day,
with her enthroned in the midst of it as hostess and queen.
Perhaps a club . . . . I had not long been out of hospital
after the stabbing affray in the Soho " case," and was therefore in a condition to appreciate to the utmost real companionship and sympathy.

Late one evening when the café clientele had thinned out
and things were quiet, it was suggested that we should go
somewhere else and talk the night out instead of separating
and going home. Already we were sufficiently happy in each
other's company to want to remain together as long as
possible. We went to an all-night café in the vicinity of the
Tottenham Court Road—a place favoured by all manner of
Soho casuals, including prostitutes and crooks. As soon as
we were comfortably settled in a corner she looked me steadily
in the eyes and said :

" You're not looking too well. What have you been doing
with yourself ? "

" Oh," I said, " it's nothing much, really. I got into
a scrap some time ago, and haven't been long out of
hospital."

At mention of the scrap, she smiled. " I guessed as much,"
she said, " I could see you'd been having a rough time."

And then came the question I had been dreading :

" What do you do for a living ? "

I wasn't anxious to answer that. How would she take it ?
I wondered. Would it mean the end of this new-found
happiness ? At the same time, I did not mean to tell her any
lies. I felt instinctively she would understand.

" Me ? " I said. " I didn't want to tell you. I'm living
on my wits. I've been living like that for years now. But "
—anxiously—" you won't let that interfere with our friendship ? I'm happy sitting here with you, talking . . ."

Again she responded with a smile of utter sympathy and understanding.

" I guessed that, too—some time ago," she said. " It happens to be my profession as well . . ."

You can imagine what a great moment that was for me —greater than any other in my life. It meant that our friendship not only could continue, but that it would grow deeper from the sharing of mutual interests. There was no need for awkward explanations ; we were equals, we had had much the same experience of life.

After that she told me a lot about herself, and I discovered that she, too, was self-educated, and had derived her knowledge of life from contact with all manner of people, both in England and abroad. Once the barriers were down, there was utter frankness between us ; I realised that I had indeed met the one person suited to become a true mate to me. We never had to declare our love openly, or make the conventional avowals ; we were both conscious of it deep within us, and went and lived together as if it were the most natural thing in the world to do—which, indeed, it was, in our peculiar circumstances. We never exacted any pledge of faith from each other ; we took that for granted, too.

We were as happy as any two people could be, and remained so for over seven years. I cannot remember one unkind word between us. Although I was capable of feeling jealousy, like any other man deeply in love, she, with her broadmindedness, taught me to regard our relationship from something wider than the narrowly possessive point of view. She wanted us both to remain free, not bound, in our love, and in course of time I saw the wisdom of her ideas. They were the only ones possible in a life like ours, for we each had to move among people freely and without hampering ties. In the Soho " case " and the " procuring house " I had seen too much of the less savoury side of sex from every possible angle to overrate its importance by comparison with comradeship, in which it is but one of many elements.

Just as we were both breadwinners, so we both shared the work of the home—a thing I was always willing to do, for fending for myself from an early age had taught me to be practical and domesticated. In one way I found life easier, and in another more difficult. Separation when I went to prison was a greater hardship now—an almost unbearable one ; on the other hand, I took the beauty of her affection with me to lighten my solitary confinement, and the memory of her face.

My first conviction after I met her was torture, for, knowing the world as I did, I wondered if I might not lose her for good. But she was there in the court ; she came round to the reception-room to bid me good-bye (an almost intolerable leave-taking, that) ; she visited me regularly in prison, and always said, " Don't you worry. I'll be waiting for you when you come back." And always she kept her word. I looked forward to her visits with intense anticipation. The knowledge that she was waiting outside the prison to greet me intensified a thousandfold the thrill of release. There is something too deep for words in the kiss of the woman you love when you have been months in prison ; there is absolute heaven in the first free hours you spend together, shut away from the world—a world which seems to you, after your imprisonment, unreal, uncanny.

I have never met any one who was such a great lover of less fortunate humanity. She worships her mother, who knows the life she leads, and would do anything for her. She is utterly loyal to her friends, and not once has she let them down. She is incapable of the petty envy and back-biting encountered in ordinary suburban life. And yet she has had a hard time of it ; she has had to fight for herself, and has been to prison : experienced the depths and the heights, and kept her womanly emotions intact through it all.

Why did she become a crook ? For the simple reason that so many become crooks : because she wanted a better standard of living than otherwise she could get in the circumstances and environment in which she found herself. Why does she continue that life ? Because it is the only one, so far as she can see, capable of maintaining her at that standard. In knowledge and technique she is equal to any man crook ; in many ways she is far superior, especially in her knowledge of the psychology of human nature.

I owe to her my interest in books and art and kindred things. She is a keen student of economics. Her favourite writers are the realistic novelists, dramatists, poets—Maxim Gorki, Dostoievsky, Upton Sinclair, Jack London, H. G. Wells, Bennet, Galsworthy, Sean O'Casey, Liam O'Flaherty, any one who has written about life as it *is*, people as they *are*. For crime-thrillers of the sensational type she has no use whatever ; few Underworld people have. One of her hobbies is sketching, which she does very well. She has a keen alert mind, and keeps it up to pitch. It would need a clever person to leave her guessing. Like so many of us who live unorthodox lives, she is deeply interested in the new Russia, anxious to see whether a better life for the unfavoured classes come out of its experiment with new social principles.

My great luck in meeting D. was twofold, for I had come to know her mother and found in her just the sort of mother I longed for as a child ; in fact, I think I am better able to appreciate her at her true worth than I would have been had I actually been her child. No man could have greater fortune than to meet two people like that at the same time. She understands me, just as she understands her daughter, and never presumes to preach at either of us, although there is no secrecy between us as to the life we lead. She accepts us both as we are, and leaves us to live our lives according to our lights.

You may wonder why, if I feel as I do, I have never thought of marrying D. and relieving her of the necessity of living that life. If I were in a position to do so, she would not agree. She is far too independent for that ; she cherishes her independence above all things. It is this that makes her such a remarkable woman.

If I went to her to-morrow, or if she came to me, and said : " This is all over, I want to live my life alone," there would be no bitterness, no recriminations, on either side. The only bond between us is the true comradeship we share. If that goes, everything goes. It is a union with equal rights, equal liberty. We believe in love the liberator, not love the tyrant.

THE HUNTING OF NGAGI

By

ASHLEY GIBSON AND H. F. FENN

THE people at South Kensington wanted a father gorilla
for a "scene," one of those picturesque family groups
that are so much more edifying to the young idea,
though probably of less value as object-lessons in practical
hygiene, than the Frightful Flea and his Brobdingnagian
companions. One little boy can be vouched for, and there
must be lots more like him, whose almost nightly dread is of
an encounter adown the glades of dreamland with that
fearful symmetry in tinted wax, the Flea that has eaten the
Food of the Gods.

Gorillas, though? Could they be featured *au naturel* in so
meek and mild a light? It was the full-grown male, the
puissant, herculean, gigantic, irresistible ruler of the arboreal
roost, whose presence was particularly requested. The others
were there already, disunited but accounted for, scattered
about in dusty corners of the show-cases. In the family circle
it was only the chair of paterfamilias that lacked an occupant,
or rather, it was explained, an adequate occupant. Could we
undertake to fill it? And photographs, authentic and plentiful,
of the family's jungle haunts were a very special need.

We said we would try. The photographs, we thought,
we could promise definitely.

There was one very necessary proviso and preliminary :
the Permis de Chasse.

Unlike his western prototype (*Gorilla gorilla*), the Highland
species (*Gorilla beringeri*) is not, so far as is definitely known at
present, to be found in British territory, his only recognised
home being the Belgian Congo. The Belgian Government,
we knew, was getting chary of extending to strangers facilities
for acquiring specimens of its rarer fauna even in the *bona fide*
interests of science ; and who could really blame them, seeing
that not many years ago one party had construed such
requirements as justifying a bag of fourteen gorillas in about
as many weeks?

One permit for one gorilla was all we meant therefore to

try for, and since the Museum appeared so keen about it, it seemed up to them to make a move in the proper direction. But their application, presented through the Foreign Office, brought no reply, or none that reached ourselves.

One of whom was going on that trip was a nephew of the Belgian Ambassador to England—at least the Ambassadress was his aunt. That seemed a string it would be folly not to pull, so we pulled it. Baron Moncheur replied with a letter that we took straight over to Brussels with us. We collected others—one to Millington-Drake, First Secretary of our Legation, who was indefatigable in his attempts to get us what we wanted.

We interviewed the Colonial Secretary and Finance Minister (M. Houtart), who was friendly. Handed on by him to the Directeur Général du Congo (M. Arnold), we had a frostier reception. We suspected from his demeanour in our presence that Mr. Arnold was at least no Anglophile. He did not temporise or deal in diplomatic ambiguities. He told us we could not have the permit.

Undaunted, we sought out others in high places. The Secretary of Agriculture, who was courteous and did his best. Categorically we dealt with all the portfolio-holders in the Belgian Cabinet. Politeness everywhere, but no permit.

A last chance. King Albert?

We meditated our angle of approach, called again upon the Finance Minister's Secretary, collected all our courage and asked if he thought the King would give us a private audience. Perhaps it was the multiplicity of our introductions ; perhaps because Belgium (a fact the King himself was to point out to us) is the only really democratic country that retains a crowned head ; perhaps the stunning effect of our sheer effrontery ; perhaps, and most probably, a combination of all these factors, plus the accident of our luck being well in that day, but the Secretary heard, nodded, left the room, came back and announced that the King would receive us no later than ten o'clock the following morning.

King Albert discoursed to us engagingly. He spoke of gorillas and of the Great War. He made it clear he was not giving us permission now to go after a gorilla. Belgium, we must understand, was a particularly democratic place. It was not his business, but that of others, to sign death-warrants, even of gorillas. He would do what he could.

It looked hopeful, and we left it at that.

But a few days later we received in England a letter from

our Embassy refusing permission, and indicating that further attempts would be useless. The knell of all our hopes, and the Museum's too, as they agreed when we made a final call there before sailing.

Weeks afterwards the mail the post-office handed out to us at Kigona on the shores of Lake Tanganyika simply electrified us.

BRITISH EMBASSY, BRUSSELS,
December 5, 1926.

DEAR COLONEL FENN,—Mr. Knatchbull-Hugessen, who is Chargé d'Affaires in the absence of the Ambassador, asks me to send you herewith copy of a note which we have received from the Belgian Government stating that they have granted you permission to kill one gorilla, provided it is shot outside the limits of the Parc National Albert.

I presume that you already know of this decision, as it is presumably due to your personal efforts, but we think it well to send you a copy of the note.

Yours sincerely,

(Sgd.) E. MILLINGTON-DRAKE.

There were doubts at first whether this was more than an extremely elaborate diplomatic courtesy, whether, in fact, it had much material value. Was there actually and as a matter of fact even that one single gorilla extant for us to locate and, having located, declare authorised war against, outside the forbidden confines of the Parc National Albert?

Nobody had reported one, but we felt he must be there. In camp that night we drank two royal toasts.

It was three months before we were able to put that permit to its use. None of the few Europeans we met had ever seen a gorilla. Many tribes of the natives, having the appearance and habits of the beast described to them, denied its existence. Though we ranged over large tracts of the Belgian Congo, inquiring perpetually for news of our quarry, only the dwellers on the lower mountain slopes around Lake Kivu were able to identify the creature we spoke of. They knew of it, or some of them did, as the almost legendary " Ngagi." Very few had encountered him ; most of those who had not disbelieved in him altogether.

Then we met a Belgian official who gave us good advice. The White Fathers, he said, from whom we could always count on a welcome should we visit Lulenga, their mission at the foot of the Virunga Volcanoes, were learned in gorilla lore. Lulenga was well inside the Reserve, but what of that ? The Fathers had other stations outside it, and were great travellers.

Eventually we did get to Lulenga. Nothing could transcend the courtesy and hospitality which there greeted us. One expects every white man you meet in the African bush to ask you to dinner, unless your camp is nearer, when, of course, you will ask him. But these Belgian padres did more, they insisted on our regarding their excellently equipped house as a hotel. Their establishment was well organised and run in every department, but what we admired most was their wonderful garden. Every useful plant and vegetable, all the palatable and thirst-quenching fruits we ever remembered meeting in the tropics, seemed to grow there.

There was a diversion at dinner the first evening. We had hardly sat down when noises suggestive of a riot in the outer kitchen disturbed us. The butler and his acolytes forgot their training and dashed out to investigate. Cries and screams arose. Then, unmistakably, a roar, a chorus of roars. Pandemonium throughout the mission domain. A lion, some would have it several lions, actually inside the boma, or stockade. There they were, between the padres' quarters and the outhouses. The Fathers jumped for Verey pistols, half a dozen hissing flares lit up the murk and turmoil. We others had snatched rifles and torches, and tumbled already down the verandah steps. No lions could we see, with the light behind us. But there was something padding to and from just beyond the circle of firelight. The roars, resonant and blood-curdling, were only twenty yards away. They shook the house.

" Do come back inside ! " the Fathers shouted.

Morning revealed a break in the boma, and the mission flock minus a brace of goats.

That was a trifle. Lately, two native converts had fallen victims in another such raid.

II

GORILLAS ? Yes, there were plenty. Up above there, in the country of the mist. Very occasionally they came down to the low levels, and more than once in the last decade it had happened that natives had been killed quite close to the mission. Not dangerous if you leave them alone ? That was certainly not true of these gorillas, the males, anyway. They always attack man. They pick him up and pull his arms and legs off, as the nastier kind of little boy would treat a fly.

Before the new game laws were passed, the Fathers had often hunted gorillas on their own account. The females were only aggressive when themselves were cornered or their offspring visibly in danger ; but the old one always, as you say, nine times out of ten, attacks. You must shoot quickly.

One of the Fathers had only lately returned from another station, Katana, at the south-western corner of the lake. Nine months before his departure a big gorilla, he told us, came down from the mountain and made a terrific onslaught on the first party of natives he met. There were three of them, and fortunately they carried spears. Two he killed and dismembered, a lucky spear-thrust from the third revenged them. There were many gorillas still on Katana mountain. Was Katana in the Reserve, the Parc National Albert ? No, well outside.

III

THE month was March (1927), and for weeks we had been wandering, camping and shooting, in the plains between the Rucheru and Ruindi Rivers, our headquarters seldom more than three days' march (fifty miles or less) north of Lake Kivu.

Our base was Kisenyi, the old German station at the north-eastern corner of the lake, and at the foot of the Virunga Volcanoes. Here all our heavy stores were deposited. Also, in trustworthy keeping, a much cherished dog, our Great Dane " Tiger," convalescent, as we hoped, from tick fever.

As the crow flies, Katana, a place now become of great interest to us, was eighty miles south-west of Kisenyi. There were four in our party, and one of the four was a woman. Not all of us could clamber up those cloud-wrapped mountains to try conclusions with that gorilla. Not after the Fathers' report, anyway. We must split up, then. Only two of us would make for Katana. The others could amuse themselves as we had all been doing heretofore, and meet us in a month's time—that is, if we had got the gorilla. If we had not, the junction of our forces would have to be postponed.

This arrangement did not please everybody. Our fair

companion particularly. But how could we possibly have
taken her along? Bill, our big American, was one of the
pair who, plus boys, baggage and many smelly indigenes,
embarked on a steel barge at the Kisenyi jetty. For two and
a half days a small launch kept us in tow, chugging steadily
southwards down the lake. We were dumped out upon a
beach near the Katana mission settlement.

Signs of trouble were already discernible among our
forces. The boys, it seemed, always curious as to our plans,
were dead against this particular adventure, so far as they
could envisage its nature and objective. We heard them
grumbling among themselves, then one or two spokesmen
came forward and laid a complaint—several complaints, in
fact.

Firstly, they averred and solemnly asseverated that there
was no such animal as "Ngagi." The name—yes, that
existed, but that which it pertained to was fabulous, a
chimæra. Secondly, the country ahead was a very bad
country. The people so foolish as to live there were no good.
Thirdly, it was well known that all strangers who ventured
into these parts died of cold. Fourthly, if by miracle preserved from freezing to death, starvation killed them. Anyway, if they were going they must have more money.

These arguments did not surprise us. We had often heard
their like when lesser dangers threatened. We could deal
with this sort of thing, but sensed further and graver troubles
ahead.

Our landing beach, we found, was actually within the
boundaries of a new coffee plantation owned by the Prince
de Ligne. That moment found the Prince on the brink of
home leave and very much tied up with eleventh hour affairs,
but his manager (M. François) offered to do anything he
could. We wanted thirty-four carriers, did we? Well, he
would try to produce them, but his hopes were not roseate.
Two days of hoping left us where we were. Very kindly he
lent us sixteen of his own men, who took us as far as a Government experimental farm four hours away, dumped their
loads and skedaddled without waiting to be paid. That did
not surprise us either.

There was a superintendent here, a former pilot of the
Belgian Flying Corps. A true comrade he proved, and most
hospitable. It was suggested we should wait a little, forty-
eight hours it was, and then he produced ten men. They
looked more reliable than the last bunch.

F.T.S.   U

Misfortune, in the guise of " 'flu," had meanwhile overtaken Bill. The best plan seemed to be a determined dash
ahead without him in case no further carriers arrived (we
had not really far to go now), and then to send the same
men back for Bill.

Luckily we collected here four Batwa pigmies, who were
quite willing to join our hunting party, but not in the least
prepared to carry anything whatsoever, barring their own
or our weapons.

Batwa, it should here be made clear, are not true pigmies,
but rather a taller type, who live on the verge of the forest
belt. The males average about four feet eight inches in
height, their women considerably less. They live almost
entirely by and for hunting, have no villages, but construct
temporary huts of leaves when they wish to use them, which
happens infrequently. Far from eschewing contact with their
neighbours, and thereby displaying their most marked trait
of divergence from true pigmy psychology, they show no
anxiety to keep themselves *to* themselves, have acquired a
taste for luxuries, and barter the spoils of their incessant
hunting with the dwellers of the plains, receiving in exchange
vegetable cloth and other commodities.

They will pursue any and every species of big game for
the meat and the skin, both of which are the accepted currency
of barter. But though they prize gorilla meat beyond all
other food, it is only an occasional female or young one that
falls to their bow and spear, or more usually to the cunningly
laid snares which they are past-masters in contriving. Fearless
enough of any other animal, they let old man gorilla well
alone.

The leader of this quartette appeared incredibly old,
wrinkled and wise. Nimble he was, too, and nonchalant, and
we called him Socrates, which seemed to please him.

We had been climbing steadily since leaving the lake.
Our Belgian friend told us that his farm, where the Batwa
joined us, was 5500 feet above sea-level. Above that the
mountains, swathed in mist, seemed to rise almost perpendicularly.

At once we entered the zone of heavy timber, so heavy
indeed it seemed miraculous that such trees could find foot-
hold on a rock face whose gradient was next door to that
of a precipice. With hours of stiff climbing, though, we
noticed the trees becoming smaller. At 8000 feet they
thinned out rapidly and vanished. We stood on the verge

of the bamboo thickets ; to left, to right, above us, nothing but bamboos, densely set, but not too much so for a low thick-growing undergrowth to warn us that not yet was the going to be made easier.

This was the gorilla country, as all reports agreed, but for the time being we pressed on. We might have to stay here a month, and wanted to get our bearings right, and some approximate notion of landmarks. A thousand feet higher the bamboos petered out, the upper edge of the belt defined as mathematically almost as the lower.

Beyond the vegetation was the oddest mixture of familiar European forms—bracken, heather, honeysuckle, black-berries ; with African montane growths—euphorbias, saxi-frages, sun-dews, bizarre of silhouette, gargantuan in their height and spread. Even homely and recognisable species showed an exotic tendency to overshoot the limits of seemly development.

It was a curious land to sojourn in, as we did for some weeks. Providence did not appear to have intended it for human ocupation. Though a sparse populace inhabited the plateau on the farther side of the range, no natives of any sort lived on these mountains ; few except the pigmies would even venture there.

Nearly always it rained, and on the rare days when the deluge held off a thick white blanket of mist lay over every-thing long after dawn and before dusk. Where we were, it did not actually freeze at night. The thermometer marked a constant 45, but to us it seemed colder. Frequently in camp, when the rain put a stopper on our excursions, we maintained a fire all day merely to keep warmth in our bones. We were as forlorn and miserable as two bank clerks in quest of week-end adventure might feel if marooned in mid-November on the shoulder of Helvellyn. If it was this sort of climate gorillas throve upon, Regent's Park should have no terrors for them. Probably it was more a question of food. But more of that later.

We had been climbing for hours, had left the forest belt behind us and penetrated the bamboo thickets for some distance, when our porters from the farm downed their loads and intimated bluntly that they did not propose going any farther.

The pigmies were ahead, on the gorilla trail somewhere in the higher thickets.

The expedition, now consisting of one white man, his boy

and the cook (Bill, still *hors de combat*, being miles in the rear of the farm), stood scowling at the recalcitrant porters while waiting for the stragglers to come up.

The bamboos above us parted, and two pigmies dropped down from a rock. The trail we sought had been found and followed. There was a gorilla family quite close ahead.

The cook had his orders to pitch camp immediately.

We took the trail. Another pigmy had dropped back to escort us. The three little men carried their spears, the boy the rifle. The white man's weapon was a camera.

The first unusual thing we noticed was a smell. At first a faint half-caught ghost of a smell, just a musky taint that seemed different among the usual and familiar compost of aromatic essences, earthy, vegetable, or recognisably animal. Gradually the taint thickened till the air seemed loaded with it. Rank and musky, like the dug earth of an old dog fox.

The pigmy guide pointed. A huge hand-print in the mud. Right hand, the fingers bent over.

We were scrambling through bracken, very thick and tall. Just ahead something barked, short and sharp, like a terrier. The noise did not suggest a big animal, but the pigmies' attitude told us it was Ngagi that had given tongue.

Clutching the camera to his chest, Ngagi's pursuer tried to worm his way round in a half-circle through the tangle. That bark was so near, he might get his picture. But it was no use, the bracken was impenetrable. In a business-like fashion, one pigmy began to cut away at the tangle with his spear.

There was another bark. Not short and sharp. Deep-throated, angry. Better have the rifle back, so it was grabbed quickly, in exchange for the camera.

Every stroke of the spears told, and in one minute the pigmies had opened a portal in the wall of bracken. Crouching and creeping, we entered almost at once a sort of tunnel through the bamboos, not open to the sky, its roof perhaps four feet six inches above the ground. That moment was not auspicious, though, for taking measurements or notes.

We had not even decided which way it was expedient to turn, right or left, when the doubt was decided for us in no uncertain fashion. An infernal yell seemed to blast our ear-drums, to set every leaf and twig of the green smother through which we strove to peer aquiver. Shambling and scrambling down the accursedly dark passage, a full-grown male gorilla projected himself upon us like a hairy thunder-bolt. He seemed to bowl and lollop along the ground like a ham-strung Hercules, "leading" like a prizefighter with a huge left paw outflung, while the knuckles of his right hand helped the bowed legs to lever along his huge top-heavy bulk. That suggests a not too speedy progress, a deduction not borne out by the facts. He was on the top of us, seemed towering over us, in a couple of seconds, when one of us fired, from the hip—no time to get up the rifle, and there was not room anyway. Yelling still, he checked, lumbered round and hurtled back the way he came.

Some one produced a measuring tape. Three yards had separated us, no more ; it had, indeed, looked less. The pigmies had stood like rocks, their spear-points advanced bayonet fashion. In the rear, the boy still clutched the camera. His teeth chattered, but he spoke. Only one comment, many times repeated. "Funya picture wapi ! " he said, " Funya picture wapi ! " The English of that is, " Take pictures ? I don't think ! "

Two minutes' start was all our further preparations gave him. Whether he was badly or lightly hit we had no real means of judging, but we assumed not very seriously, as the blood trail was slight, and when the tunnel forked (we ran into a perfect maze of them) the pigmies picked up his traces merely by the freshly bent leaves and bamboo shoots. Heads almost on the ground, working like setters, they scuttled along at a pace we could hardly keep up with. One was thankful that weeks of jungle travel had tanned knees and forearms to the toughness of leather, for our progress was mostly on all fours. Trailing a rifle that way along those confounded tunnels was the devil, but we kept it up for four hours.

Soon the thicket became a labyrinth of these corridors, with here and there a clearing marking a sort of Clapham Junction of them. There were thrills when the pursuit halted at such spots. True, we were chasing Ngagi, but he might so easily have turned the tables on us, and who could say by which of these approaches he might not at any moment turn, outflanking us, surprising us perhaps from the rear ? Up hill and down, sometimes almost perpendicularly, the tunnels ran, but our pigmies never gave us a real rest. At the junctions they had to cast round for the trail, and not seldom at such times they pointed out to us rough nests in the bamboo and bracken. Usually there were indications that Ngagi, whom report recommended as a cleanly beast, intended to sleep elsewhere in future, and the pigmies said it was so ; he never used a nest, or one of this type, more than one night.

What mystified us were the large balls or pads of crumpled bracken that we sometimes stumbled upon in the corners of these lairs. With gestures, the pigmies explained. Ngagi had manufactured those to sit on. We disbelieved this at the time, but later had ocular demonstration of its truth. Here and there were flung down handfuls of chewed bamboo, a diet to which Ngagi is prone, but varies with other vegetable delicacies that we identified later.

From time to time, at various distances ahead or abreast of us as we struggled to catch him up, Ngagi roared his anger, and we would catch glimpses through the bamboo lattice of some solid and quite decent-sized tree shaken like an aspen. The pigmies told us he always did this when annoyed.

But we never saw him.

By signs, Socrates intimated that he would try a new dodge. Squatting on his haunches, he barked. Then his lips emitted a stream of animal sounds, a species of monkey chatter. It sounded derisive and insulting, and he told us afterwards it was meant to be. After a time Ngagi answered, in a language somewhat similar. But he kept himself hidden, swallowing all the pigmy's insults.

We thought we saw him. No, a much smaller beast, one of his wives. The challenge of Socrates had ceased ; our crawling progress was being silently conducted. Clearly she knew nothing of the alarms and excursions of the earlier afternoon, continuing unconcernedly to munch bamboo shoots. For a minute we kept her in good view. Still without catching our scent, she ambled leisurely into obscurity.

Raindrops fell pattering, and thickened to the usual steady drizzle. The pigmies ceased work automatically. Rain always had that effect upon them, we found.

It was nightfall when we made camp. But a note, an urgent one, had to go back to Bill, and braving the night terrors of the bush, a porter went loping down the track with it. An hour or so after daybreak Bill staggered up, shaky but eager.

Socrates and his minions took up the trail again where we had dropped it. But we saw no more of our first gorilla, nor heard of him. Crawling all day through those vile tunnels, we drew an utter blank.

For a week we hunted, seldom without striking some trail the pigmies pronounced fairly fresh. Many times we heard gorillas. On the third day we saw some, three or four females and several baby gorillas, but no head of the family. Clearly he was in the offing somewhere, and the pigmies went off down a trail that proved to be his. We stuck to this for hours.

At last we saw him. The bamboos grew more thinly here than was usual. Twenty yards ahead of us there was Ngagi, lurching irresolute in the shadows, grumbling and snarling, sensing pursuit, his great head turning this way and that.

Spotting us, he launched himself straight upon us at full gallop, raising that ghastly battle yell. He was not our old enemy, a shade less ponderous in height and build. A possible shot, but not yet a good one ; as he came on we could only see bits of him through the tangle. With ten yards covered, some premonition of special danger seemed to halt him. We had not moved, but he lumbered round and the bamboos swallowed him up.

Hot on his tracks we followed. But it was no good. " Gone away," was the pigmies' report. On the morrow, it became clear that wives and babies, the entire family, had gone too. For days we cast round, and neither saw nor heard a trace of gorilla. Even the gorilla odour seemed lifting from these abandoned haunts of theirs.

We saw nothing for it but to break camp and renew our operations from a fresh centre, and Socrates and his fellow-gnomes confirmed this view. Our last lot of porters had decamped. Socrates volunteered to get over this difficulty, and was as good as his word, collecting a carrying squad from a village on the other side of the range. These were all women.

His idea, we found, was that we should make the village they came from, Kalongi, our next camp. It was hardly, indeed, a village, as we found on getting there after a climb, down and up, of six hours, only a tiny cluster of huts. It stood on the top of a sort of table mountain considerably lower than the peaks of the main ridge. At this height (9000 feet) the tangle of bamboo and bracken we had got so used to formed the only vegetation. We could perceive that it was likely gorilla country. Colder, though, and wetter than our last camp, or so it seemed to us.

IV

WE repeated the old procedure. On the trail at six, and sticking to it till dusk. But it was heart-breaking work. scrambling and slithering in the cold and the wet, continuous grumbles threatening mutiny from the boys, increasing doubts as to whether that permit was ever going to be much use to us. There were gorilla runs in plenty, but never a fresh scent along them for the Batwa to pick up. If there had been, they would have found it.

But on the third night, just as we were about to turn in, Socrates arrived and demanded immediate audience. Quite excited, for him, so we guessed his news was good.

One of his men had located another whole family of Ngagi. We could catch up with them to-morrow morning easily.

At 6 a.m. we were off again, marching and climbing. Three or four hours of this began to get on our nerves. For we found nothing. Were these little devils fooling us ? Some Africans, if they perceive you want a thing very badly, promise it to you, knowing perfectly well you will not get it.

It was almost the last straw when Socrates, without any suggestion from us, halted his party. All squatted deliberately at their ease. Dinner-time, said Socrates. This had not happened before, and we expostulated ; dinner, we urged, could wait.

But they said no, and munched their cold sweet potatoes. Why hurry ? The gorilla were quite close. We decided to be philosophic and have our own lunch.

In twenty minutes the little men were on the move again. We struck a tremendously thick patch of bamboos, where the pigmies used their spears. We saw daylight through the fronds. The edge of the thicket won, Socrates stopped and pointed.

Below us, in a kind of dell of more open bush, the black shapes of two female gorillas moved slowly among the tangle. Obviously they neither saw, heard, nor smelt us, but quietly browsed, mainly on all fours, occasionally reaching up to gather, abstractedly, some tender shoot among the higher foliage. Another joined the party from the thicket beyond, a fourth. Their leisurely rolling gait suggested bears rather than apes.

With his spear Socrates pointed again.

Two balls of black fur rolled into the field of vision. Baby gorillas—males, he said. They fought like puppies, buffeting and scratching, squeaked, barked in a puppyish fashion.

Unseen and unsuspected, we watched this scene for twenty minutes. If only we had had the camera ! But the wretched Ramasan was skulking a full mile behind us.

He was five yards away.

Cautiously we worked round for a nearer view. Then we saw that one of the females, glimpses of whose silhouette had puzzled us, bore on her shaggy back a still younger family, not one but two much smaller infants. We could see their so human small fingers clutching her fur, their little eyes blinking even.

The bigger gorilla children were still at their skylarking. One of them lost his temper and bit his brother in the shoulder as if he meant it. The joy-squeaks became shrill and angry cries. Their mother dropped the shred of bark she was nibbling and scrambled over to her offspring, pulled them apart and actually boxed the aggressor's ears.

That was too much for the equanimity of an audience that had crouched as still as statues for half an hour. Somebody moved, and the female who had been steadily munching her way towards us looked up, got our wind probably at the same moment, and throwing round her head gave one short sharp bark.

There was instant commotion, a chorus of grunts and squeals, and the whole family scrambled to cover in the thicket. From that retreat the warning bark was once or twice repeated.

Out of the bush at the other end of the glade came an answering roar. No mistake about that signal. It was the old man's.

A hundred yards away the bamboos parted, and there he was. He could probably see us, but we were not sure. Anyway, he made straight for us for twenty-five yards, then reared up, erect on his bowed legs, and with one colossal arm against a tree-trunk kept his balance. He saw us now all right. Balefully he glared at us with his little red eyes, bared huge yellow fangs, snarled horribly, roared his defiance.

We had to shoot now, if we were going to, but we could have wished the range a little closer. It was Bill's turn, and he took a double ·475 Express. It was a heavy weapon for an accurate standing shot, especially with one's wrist unsteadied after four hours' mountaineering. Obstinately, though, he would not take the lighter Mannlicher.

Bill fired, and the gorilla crashed to earth. But in two seconds he was up again, had turned, vanished. We tore our way to the tree, but it took us ten minutes to reach it.

There was a lot of blood. Frothy, a lung shot ; pity Bill had not taken the Mannlicher. The chase might be long. For an hour and a half we followed it. Every few minutes the mountain echoed with his roars, but we saw no glimpse of Ngagi.

Then he nearly got us. We were in a tunnel maze again, and at a junction we were just deciding which line he had taken when the battle-yell was raised—*behind us*. Down another tunnel he came like an express train, screaming. No time to sight on that target; he was five yards away when Bill let off at him anyhow. It turned him. Once more we followed.

Another hour, and Socrates checked. There was the gorilla, climbing laboriously up a half-fallen tree. His huge left arm dangled useless; Bill's last shot had broken it. Poor old Ngagi, he was clearly done for. Blood still oozed from his side. He peered at us, his little eyes dull now, no longer red and fiery. His snarl was half-hearted.

What brutes we felt! That Mannlicher bullet to his heart was a relief.

He toppled, started to roll downhill, met, luckily, a tree strong enough to hold up his enormous bulk.

For the first time since they had been in our company the pigmies, when the gorilla's huge black body came tumbling and crashing down the slope, vanished. They were not so sure he was dead as we were, and better than ourselves, no doubt, knew Ngagi's potentialities for last-minute mischief in his death flurry, if any imprudent or excited enemy chanced within the immense reach of his arms.

He never moved again, however. Two minutes passed, and the little men crept out of their hiding-places. They were vastly excited, gabbling and chuckling, as they helped us lever Ngagi's tremendous frame up into a sitting position against a tree—no light task, even for our combined forces. We photographed him, supine and then upright. Weight-taking and height measurements were most difficult, but with much trouble and many shifts we established the weight of the complete carcase as 450 pounds, and height as five feet eight inches—it would have been far more, of course, if his leg-stretch had not been negligible in comparison with the tremendous arm-reach and chest dimensions. The span of his outstretched arms proved to be eight feet three inches, his chest measurement five feet two inches, biceps eighteen inches, circumference of fingers four inches.

DEAD MEN TELL NO TALES

By

J. MILLIGAN

ON the dirty little coaster that took me up from Vancouver to Skagway, I met Sacrament. Red. He must have been packing a wad himself on the run across the Rockies, for he was toting pick, shovel, pan, etc., just as I was ; and these tools had cost me plenty in Vancouver at that time.

The boat was packed so tight with gold-seekers that I thought it was sure to sink if it ran into anything of a sea. Most of them were the real old prospectors, fellows who had chased the yellow stuff in every part of the world, fellows who had never made a big strike but were all convinced that they were just going to. There were others too ; crooks, tin-horns, clerks, labourers, down-and-outs, merchants. There were even some cracked mugs who were taking their wives and families along with them ; and there were more than a few hard-bitten dames who aimed to make *their* fortune in the oldest way in the world.

Sacramento and I quite naturally hitched up together. We'd both lost our side-kicks, and we'd both a few dollars in hand, so we made a pact to hit the Klondyke as partners.

Skagway was like Madison Square Garden just before a big fight. Everybody was charging about trying to find some quick way of pushing on to Dawson City, and precious few were getting it. Dog-teams were hitting it out over the Chilcoot Pass, but it was only folks who could afford to pay something like a thousand dollars who could hire them. The rest had to make it on foot, and we were among the rest.

That Pass about fits my private idea of what Hell is like. The big freeze-up was expected any day, and everybody was hurrying like mad to get to the Yukon before the river froze. Otherwise, they'd have to mush over the ice to Dawson City, and that was six hundred miles—not so long by water but a hell of a distance to walk. They hurried so much that dozens of them burst their lungs with the cold hitting it, and nearly as many froze to death. Going over the Pass we came on bodies by the side of the trail as regularly as milestones.

Once we found a whole family of stiffs laid out—father, mother, and two half-grown boys. . . .

Maybe Sacramento and I had been more inured to cold than most of the others through hoboing and riding in ice-boxes. Anyway, we crossed the Pass and reached Lake Linderman in about as good shape as any.

There was still free-water about, but it seemed like the last water of the season. There was thick ice on the lake and ice in the creeks of the river. The snow was coming down hard, and it got colder and colder every day. It was certain that it could not be many days before the river froze—maybe a week, maybe only one day.

The boats doing down were weighed down nearly to their gunwales with the packed crowds of people on them. There was no hope of getting a passage on any of them. Fellows were working like madmen chopping down trees to build rafts, but they hadn't much hope of even getting the rafts finished before the freeze-up, far less making Dawson in the time.

Sacramento and I mooched along the beach of the Lake, wondering if we were going to be stuck in this God-forgotten spot all winter. Then we got a break. We came on an Indian with a canoe. He was paddling a little way from shore, when Sacramento hailed him. The Indian came nearer.

"It's our only chance of making Dawson City," Sacramento Red whispered to me. "That big freeze-up's right on us, and I figure a canoe's about the only thing that could get there in the time."

"What you want?" the Indian called out, when he got within shouting distance.

"A passage on that there canoe down to Dawson," Red shouted back. "We'll pay you five hundred bucks to take us."

The Indian shook his head.

"Not too much," he answered. "I get a thousand easy from some of the others along the beach."

He wouldn't come closer to us than a certain distance, though Sacramento kept motioning him to come nearer.

"I'll make it seven hundred," said Sacramento.

"Make it seven thousand," I said to him under my breath. "It's all the same once we get 'way up there among the dollars."

"I in hurry," the fellow in the canoe retorted. "Make it a thousand, or I go on."

"Oh, all right then!" Sacramento capitulated. "A thousand it is then. . . ."

Cautiously, the Indian paddled nearer. A few yards from the shore, however, he back-watered.

"Lemme see your money!"

Sacramento growled. Then he took off his right glove and stuck it into the breast of his fur jacket. But it wasn't a wad of dollar-bills he brought out of his breast. It was a revolver, a big Colt ·44 that I remembered him showing me on the boat and telling me he'd bought in Vancouver.

"You God-damn swindler!" he snarled. "You just paddle that l'il birch-bark of yours right into the beach here. or there'll be a dead Indian sitting where you are now!"

The man's face registered the most complete contempt I've ever seen expressed on a human countenance. Slowly, he paddled towards us.

"Fling our kit in," Sacramento told me. "Then get in yourself. We're moving for Klondyke—right now!"

I got in at the stern, with Sacramento facing the Indian at the bow.

"Get going, you!" Sacramento ordered, and the Indian put up a small sail, and we swung off through the thick blanket of the falling snow across the lake.

It was slow work hitting it across the lakes, for the ice was forming at a fearful lick. Once we struck the Yukon, however, we got along faster. Every day, though—almost every hour—it got colder and the ice became more of a trial. Some places we were stuck for hours.

When we camped, Sacramento and I took it in turns to guard the Indian with the Colt to see he didn't try any funny games on us. Neither of us could manage the canoe, and we would have been helpless if the Indian had dodged away from us.

The strain was pretty grim. The run down the river was an uninterrupted race with the oncoming winter, and, during the last part of it, with more and more ice forming all the time, it seemed certain that it was going to be a losing race for us. Not only that, but the Indian got me worried. He never opened his mouth to say a single word to us, and he didn't even look at us if he could help it. When he did, he made it plain that he thought we were pretty low. It kept me wondering whether he didn't have something up his sleeve.

At last the end of the race came. We found ourselves one day in the middle of a completely frozen stream, packed

solid in a great unbroken sheet of ice. The big freeze-up had
come, and the canoe was useless from now on.

For the first time since he had haggled with us on Lake
Linderman, the Indian spoke :

" Free-water finished now. We must walk to Dawson
City—half a day's walk only—maybe less."

" That's swell," said Sacramento quietly, fumbling inside
his jacket.

Then, before I could grasp what he was doing, I saw his
right hand flash out, and I heard the crash of his Colt.

He emptied all six chambers into the Indian's body. The
man had been staring at him with his usual contemptuous
expression, when he fired. His body jerked and shuddered
and the bullets thudded into it, but his face didn't alter its
look. There was still a sneer of superiority on it as his eyes
glazed and he slumped sideways where he sat.

" My God ! . . ." I whispered, numb with the shock of
the sight.

" Take it as it comes," Sacramento growled at me. " He
had to get it before we hit the town. I've heard about them
miners' meetin's in the Klondyke to string up guys for doin'
things like stealin' canoes. It was him or us."

There was nôthing to be done. We left the dead man in
the ice-locked canoe, and took to the ice. I guess the canoe
would take the riddled corpse downstream when the ice
melted next season, and maybe some folks in Dawson City
would find it and wonder how it all came about. . . . Or
maybe they wouldn't waste time wondering : dead men
weren't so unusual in the Yukon.

THE TIMBER DROGHER

By

"SHALIMAR"

IT happened about a year before I finally "swallowed the anchor." I was still quite a youngster, only a few months out of sail, and was fourth officer of a large "bull-boat" which belonged to a Scottish firm, and ran between various ports in Eastern Canada and the east coast of Scotland. I remember that it was our last voyage from Montreal for the season, for the ice would have closed the St. Lawrence before we got back. For some reason we had no cattle on board that trip, with the effect that, with all the weight of her cargo below, she was pretty stiff and inclined to roll heavily. We had experienced a south-west gale and thick weather all the way from Cape Race, with the result that we had had few opportunities to get decent observation. The wind had, however, gone round to the north-west during the night, and it was clearing up, but there was a heavy sea rolling up on the port quarter which caused the old boat to lurch about a good deal. We had still another day to put in on the open ocean, but expected to sight the group-flashing light on Flannan Island, or the Butt of Lewis, early the next morning prior to proceeding through the Pentland Firth.

I was on the watch with the chief officer from 4 a.m. until eight, and about half-past five daylight came in and revealed a most uninteresting sight. From the high bridge to the horizon on all sides there was nothing to be seen but a grey waste of white-capped ridges. It was bitterly cold too. Presently the officers' steward, a hospitable lad and a very welcome visitor at that moment, came up the bridge ladder on the starboard side and made his way across to the weather side, where, under the lee of the dodger, he let down a temporary table which had been stopped up to the rails. He then left the bridge, but a few minutes later reappeared, this time carrying a tray, on which there was a large pile of hot buttered toast, a big jug of coffee and two mugs. We got grand coffee on that ship. I was standing beside the binnacle when the steward passed me on his way to windward and got a whiff

of it. By jove ! the smell was fragrant. The chief officer was
already sheltering behind the dodger, and after a good look
round I joined him, smacking my lips in anticipation. The
steward paused for a moment, gazing forward over the top
of the dodger before going below again. Suddenly he pointed
over the bow and ejaculated—

" Good God, sir ! what's that ? "

Considerably startled, the chief and I left our coffee and
gazed toward where he was pointing, but for a moment we
could see nothing. Then just as a shout of " Broken water
right ahead " came from the look-out man up in the crow's-
nest, we picked up something. It was a black irregular-
shaped object less than half a mile ahead. The same idea
struck the chief officer that struck me, for we exclaimed
simultaneously—

" Rockall ! "

That rock which rears its head seventy feet out of the
Atlantic lies about 260 miles to the westward of the Outer
Hebrides. It stands almost in the centre of a large bank
which runs roughly north and south, and is about sixty
miles long by thirty-five miles wide. Close to the rock there
is a depth of about forty-two fathoms, and the average depth
over the whole of the bank would be about seventy-five.
All round it is much deeper water, averaging hundreds of
fathoms. The great circle track which we were following
runs from a position due east of Cape Race to the Butt of
Lewis, and passes thirty miles north of the rock itself, so
apparently we had got well off our course. The chief officer
ordered the quartermaster at the wheel to port a couple of
points, then he addressed me—

" By heavens ! " he said, " it's a blessing that it's daylight.
How could we have got so far to the south'ard ? Call the old
man and tell him that we sighted Rockall dead ahead, and
that I am passing to the south of it."

As I went off the bridge to go to the captain's cabin,
which lay beneath it, I also was wondering how we could
have got so far off our course. I remembered reading on the
chart the evening before that " an area of magnetic disturbance is reported to exist two or three miles to the N. and N.E.
of Rockall," but I could not imagine that our compasses
could have been affected to the extent of taking us thirty
miles off our course. The captain's cabin was dark, the door
was shut and the curtains of every port drawn. He was a
man who really loved his bunk. When we were in open water,

clear of the land, he would go to it about 9 p.m., and it would take something decidedly serious to get him out of it before eight o'clock the next morning. I switched on one of the electric lights in his cabin, woke him up and gave him the chief officer's message. He yawned and stretched himself, then answered me.

" Rockall right ahead, did you say? How the devil did it manage to get there? Right, tell the chief officer to pass to the south of it. It's steep-to, but don't run it too fine. He'll want to lay off a new course for the Butt of Lewis, too, and you had better get an azimuth as soon as you can and see what the error of the compass is."

With that the old man turned over, and, feeling myself dismissed, I left his cabin and regained the bridge. The chief officer was gazing through his binoculars out on the port bow. I got hold of mine, after giving him the captain's orders, and did the same.

" That's not Rockall," he exclaimed presently ; " it's a large piece of wreckage—quite big enough to damage a ship all the same. Better call the old man again and tell him about it."

I sought the captain's cabin, and once more he yawned and stretched.

"All right," he replied patiently in answer to my information. " Tell the chief officer to get a sight as soon as he can. We will have to report the position of the wreckage if it's big enough to be a menace to navigation."

Back on the bridge, I studied the wreckage through my glasses, the chief officer having hauled our vessel up so as to pass close to leeward of it. It looked like the whole of the after-end of a wooden vessel sticking above the surface of the water at an angle of about thirty degrees. Her wheel appeared above the level of the bulwark, otherwise her deck seemed to be bare. Her rudder was jolting to and fro, and as we got under her stern we read in white letters on her counter—

Marion of Belfast.

As the piece of wreckage drew abeam on the weather side we rather lost interest in it. We had got our steamer back on her proper course again, and were looking around to see if there were any other pieces of wreckage floating about, when suddenly a strange sound fell upon our ears. It had come along with the wind.

" *Wuf—wuf.*"

"What the devil's that?" exclaimed the chief officer nervously.

"Sounded like a dog, sir," I replied.

"I know damned well that it sounded like a dog," he said irritably, "but there's no dog on board the ship."

"*Wuf—wuf.*"

One of the deck-hands came running up the bridge ladder.

"There's some one on board o' that there wreck, sir," he cried. "I see him wavin' somethin' white."

I stepped clear of the dodger and got my glasses on to the wreckage the best way I could, for it was now right in the wind's eye, and it was a bitterly cold wind to try to look into. Sure enough, I saw something white being feebly dangled, and presently made out a man lying alongside of the port bulwark. We had been unable to see him before owing to the way that the stern of his vessel was sticking out of the water. Abaft the skylight, which we could now see, on the only part of the sloping deck to which it could possibly cling, was a large yellow dog.

"Call the captain again," said the chief officer.

Once more I descended from the bridge and switched on the captain's light. He was clearly annoyed, and little wonder; this was the third time that I had disturbed him in less than five minutes.

"You again!" he exclaimed sharply "What the devil do you want now?"

"There's some one alive on board of that wreckage, sir," I replied.

His demeanour changed instantly. "Eh? Somebody alive!" he said. "Right, I'll be up in a moment."

Before I left the cabin he was out of his bunk and pulling on his clothes. In an incredibly short time he was on the bridge fully clad and buttoning up his heavy bridge coat. His feet were encased in gum-boots. He seemed to take in the wreck, the weather and the sea in one comprehensive glance.

"Hard a-starboard, quartermaster," he ordered.

Then he turned to the chief officer. "There's a very heavy sea running, mister," he pronounced gravely. "I don't know if I can risk lowering a boat. Could we get volunteers, do you think?"

I stepped up to where he stood beside the wheel.

"I'll go for one, sir," I said eagerly.

"You would," he replied. "You haven't got the sense to know any better"

I fell back rather abashed The vessel was now beam on to the sea and rolling very heavily. The captain called me to him again.

"Look here, Norris," he said kindly, "there's a heavy sea running, isn't there?"

"Yes, sir," I replied.

"Yes, even from this high bridge it looks heavy, doesn't it? Well, let me tell you that from a boat it will look twice as high—in fact it will look terrifying. Now do you still want to go?"

I realised that I had spoken out of my turn, but felt that I could not draw back then—not if the sea was as high as St. Paul's.

"Yes, I'll go, sir," I said.

"Well," he replied slowly, "if you can get two men to go with you—they must be volunteers, remember—you can go."

"Two men, sir," I said in surprise.

"Yes, two," he replied sharply. "That will be quite enough the way that I'll work it. You had better hurry up and try to get them while I manœuvre to get to windward of the wreck."

He staggered across to the port side of the bridge. The steamer, with her helm hard a-starboard, was swinging up into the wind. I was making for the bridge ladder on the starboard side on my way down to the next deck in quest of volunteers, when the quartermaster at the wheel spoke to me.

"Sir," he said, "I'll be one o' them."

The quartermaster was a tall, dark, powerfully built man of a saturnine nature, named Malone. He hailed from County Cork, and I strongly suspected him of having Fenian tendencies. Apart from giving him helm orders, I had hardly spoken two words to him the whole voyage, but in some subtle way he had managed to convey to me the impression that there were two impediments in the way of my being a good officer—I was too young and I was an Englishman.

"An' there's another, sir," he continued; "ask him."

A young able seaman named Driscoll had just come up on the bridge to do some job; he was carrying a bucket of water and a swab. He was, I imagine, a "townee" of

Malone's. He was a much smaller man that the quarter-master, and I looked at him doubtfully.

"He'll do, sir," urged Malone ; "sure he has the guts."

I approached Driscoll, told him what we proposed to do, and said that, of course, he was quite free to decline, as it was a volunteer that I wanted. He never even troubled to look at the sea or the wreck.

"If it's good enough for you an' Malone, sir," he said indifferently, "well, it's good enough for me."

I sought the captain, who, having steadied the steamer head to wind and put the engines to slow, was now in the chart-room, and told him that I had secured my two volunteers.

"You've been damned smart about it," he said. "Who are they ?"

"Malone and Driscoll, sir."

"Splendid," the captain replied cheerfully ; "you couldn't have done better. Malone is as strong as a dray-horse, and Driscoll is as active as a kitten. Get another quartermaster to relieve the wheel, then bring the two of them in here."

When we were gathered in the chart-room the captain explained his plan, and we learned why only three of us were going in a lifeboat, which ordinarily would require at least double the number. He was going to place the steamer to windward of the wreck, and slack the boat down to it by means of a long line. When we had rescued whoever was on the wreckage, he would then heave the boat back to the steamer, drifting down toward it the while. We would thus not be required to use oars at all, with the exception of one, and in that one there lay a bit of a snag.

"Can you use a steering oar ?" he asked me suddenly. "A rudder is useless for keeping a lifeboat head to sea when she has no headway on her."

That would have stumped a good many deep-water seamen, but fortunately I had had a good deal of experience with a steering oar in Western Australia, where we had to bring off a lot of the cargo through the surf in our own boats—and I was able to assure him that I could use one.

"Good," he said. "Now the whole thing depends on a small code of signals. Malone, who will be in the bow of the boat, will make them, but you have all got to know them in case of—well, you never know what may happen."

The code was simple. If we wished the line slacked

away on board, Malone would stretch out his right arm horizontally ; if we wished the line hove in, he would stretch his left arm in the same way ; when we wanted the line held on, he would raise one of his arms above his head. An officer would be stationed at the taffrail aft with his glasses glued on the boat. The captain made us repeat the code until he was certain that we knew it ; then we went out on to the bridge. All hands had in the meantime been called. The third officer was on the bridge standing by the telegraph and watching the steering ; the second, with one watch, was swinging out one of the lifeboats on the starboard side ; while the chief had got up from the forepeak a coil of new 3-inch Manilla rope, and was stretching it along the deck. We put on lifebelts, then made our way along to the boat, which was now swung out, and got into her. The end of the Manilla rope had been rove through the ringbolt in the bow of the boat, a few fathoms of it had been hauled through, and the bight of it had been hitched round one of the forward thwarts. A new heaving line and a lifebuoy had been placed in the boat, and all the oars save two had been taken out. The steamer being now to windward of the wreckage, her head was canted to starboard so as to make a lee for the boat on that side, and the engines stopped. It was still blowing hard from the nor'-west—a keen, clear, cutting wind.

" Lower away."

The order came through a megaphone from the bridge. While one of the hands forward poured oil from a five-gallon drum into the sea, the boat slid slowly down the side into a comparative calm. A wave, its crest smoothed by the oil, rose up to meet her and, water-borne, she subsided with it. The davit-fall blocks were unhooked, and save for the Manilla rope we were free from the ship. I shipped the steering oar. The steamer's engines were put ahead again, and rising and falling with the swell the boat slowly drifted aft.

II

I STILL sheltered from the weather by the protecting wall of the steamer's hull, we passed aft under her counter, and in another moment we were clear. Then we got it. A huge wave came surging past the steamer's stern, caught hold of the boat and seemed to throw her yards upwards. As we perched dizzily on its crest, the flying spray lashed me across the face like a whip, and for the moment blinded me, then the boat seemed to fall like a stone and I felt as if the pit of my stomach had dropped out. The Manilla rope tightened with a jerk, and the boat surged up as the crest of the next wave rushed at her. Almost stunned by the force of the wind, the driving spray and the tremendous surge of the waves, I struggled with the steering oar to keep the boat head on to the sea. As the captain had predicted, the sea looked terrifying, and for a moment I *was* almost terrified; certainly I was completely confused. I did not think just then that the boat could possibly live. I got my eyes clear of water, collected my thoughts and took stock of my companions. Malone stood upright in the bows, a leg on each side of the forward thwart, which he was gripping with his knees. Occasionally he stretched out his right arm horizontally as if to show that we still required the line to be slacked away, the action, I expect, being subconscious, for the officer at the steamer's taffrail could see that we were still some distance off the wreck. Driscoll, crouching in the bottom of the boat, was hitching the bight of the heaving line to the lifebuoy, and when he had completed that he made one end of the line fast round his waist and the other end fast to a thwart.

The most sickening feeling of all was when we dropped down into the trough between the waves, where we could see nothing but a wall of water ahead of us and another wall behind. I soon noticed, however, that when the boat was in that position I could recover my breath, and as I got more used to the thing I grasped the opportunity when up on the crest of a wave to notice the relative positions of the steamer and the wreckage. The former had been beautifully handled, and was now head to wind, with the boat-rope with which we were being slacked down leading over her stern, and she was dead to windward of the wreck. All that I had to do was to keep the boat head on to the sea, and give the order to hold on the line when she had been slacked down far enough. Some one had been pouring oil copiously over the steamer's stern, and the crests of the waves were, in consequence, becoming rather smoother. Occasionally, in an endeavour to judge the distance we were still off the wreckage, I would glance over my shoulder. Not a word had been spoken in the boat since we had left the steamer until suddenly Driscoll, who was facing aft, shouted—

" Look out, sir. We're on top o' the wreck."

Considerably startled, for I thought that we were still some distance off, I looked round, to see the ragged stump of a mast with the fife-rail attached and several belaying-pins sticking out from it like teeth, almost level with the water and only about ten feet off the boat's port quarter. Somehow or other I had formed the opinion that the wreckage, about twenty feet long, which we had sighted from the steamer was only a part of a vessel, and I had imagined vaguely that she might have been cut in two by some fast liner, and that the after-part had been left floating. Now, however, I realised that the whole ship was here, and that her bow must be floating about thirty feet below the mean level of the waves. Her deck was like a sloping beach, up which the waves were rushing and frothing, high-water mark being represented by the small part of the vessel which was showing above the sea. Other things were now occa-sionally visible upon the deck—the stump of another mast and the iron wheels of the pumps. With a wrench of the steering oar I sheered the boat off to starboard just in time to avoid having her stove in on the deck of the derelict. We were soon close enough for our purpose.

" Hold on, Malone," I shouted.

Malone's right hand shot straight up above his head ; the boat-rope tightened up, and we were, as I thought, in a good position just slightly to windward of the wreckage. The dog still lay across the after-part of the skylight ; the man—an old chap, bareheaded, with white whiskers, evidently very exhausted and thoroughly soaked—was lashed to a ringbolt alongside the bulwark on the port side, the yellow-white of the rope lashing round his waist showing vividly against his tattered black oilskin coat. Besides being down by the head the derelict was listed to starboard heavily, which was the reason why I had chosen to go on that side, and in some mysterious way, although continually rising and falling, she was lying head on to the wind and sea. To my horror the boat, instead of remaining in position, was drifting rapidly past the wreck—evidently I had not been quick enough in ordering Malone to signal to hold on the line. I declare that I could feel myself blushing with shame. What an incompetent ass ! they must all be thinking. The captain of our steamer, whose binoculars would be fixed on the boat, the boat's crew, even the old chap whom we were trying to rescue. He, poor old fellow, was apparently trying to tell me something as we surged past, but, although his lips moved, no sound came from them ; with his right hand, which still held the handkerchief with which he had been waving to us, he was pointing toward the position of the submerged bow. There was nothing for it but to get to windward again.

"Heave in, Malone," I ordered.

Malone's left arm was extended horizontally, and the boat began to creep to windward over the crests and down into the hollows, until we were again a little bit ahead of where the old man was lying. I told Malone to signal to hold on and Driscoll to get ready, but again the boat began to surge to leeward past the wreck. The old man was now trying harder than ever to draw my attention to something forward. Suddenly, without any fresh orders from me, the boat-rope tightened up again ; the boat got into position, and was held there, as I afterwards learned, by the steamer's engines being kept turning slowly ahead. The captain had divined our difficulty.

I was now to learn why it was well that Driscoll was as active as a kitten. I sheered the boat as near to the wreck as I could safely go, then, first balancing for an instant on the boat's gunwale, the able seaman made a flying leap and landed on the sloping deck of the derelict. Desperately struggling to hold on, he was sliding back into the sea when a wave came along and washed him almost up to where the old man lay along the bulwark, quite unable to help him. Driscoll grabbed the lashing which was round him, manœuvred himself into a position with his feet between the bulwark and the old chap's body, and then commenced by means of the heaving line to haul toward him the lifebuoy which Malone had just dropped overboard. He slipped the buoy round the old man's feet and gradually worked it up toward his waist, then drew his sheath-knife, severed the lashing and worked the buoy up under the old man's armpits.

"Haul away, Malone," he yelled.

While Driscoll was cutting the lashing I had ordered the boat to be slacked down a bit, so that she was now to lee-ward, and it was an easy matter for Malone to haul the old chap off the sloping deck of the derelict into the water and alongside the boat. Then it became evident to me why it was necessary that Malone should be as strong as a dray-horse—he had to get the rescued man into the boat. Leaning over the gunwale he got both hands under the lifebuoy,

The able seaman made a flying leap.

and with a tremendous heave he raised the old man right out of the water and deposited him, as tenderly as if he were a child, in the bottom of the boat. Again Malone leant over the gunwale, and for the first time since we left the steamer he spoke—

"Come away thin, owld fella me lad," he said.

I looked over the side. The dog, swimming strongly, was making for the boat, his handsome yellow head—he was a golden retriever—steering straight for Malone. The quartermaster laid hold of him well up on the forelegs ; there was another heave, and the heavy animal was deposited in the boat as tenderly as his master had been. The dog licked the old man's face, and was rewarded by a feeble pat ; then the two lay very still on the bottom boards between the thwarts. We had now to recover Driscoll, but that was easy. The end of the heaving line was still fast round his waist ; he plunged into the sea, and Malone soon hauled him alongside and lifted him into the boat.

"Right," I shouted to Malone as I sheered the boat away from the wreck ; "heave in."

From the crest of each successive wave which we climbed I watched the steamer. Her helm had evidently been put hard a-port, for her head gradually fell off in our direction until she was lying beam on to the seas. The lead for the boat-rope had also been shifted—it was now rove through one of the mooring ports amidships. Very slowly they hove on it ; indeed I fancy that they only took in the slack as the steamer drifted down toward us. The sea grew calmer as we drew under her lee, and before long we were rising and falling on the well-oiled waves against her rusty side. The blocks of the davit-tackle falls were hooked on, and the boat hoisted up level with her rail ; the old man and the dog were lifted out, and I can assure you that I breathed a silent prayer of thankfulness as I stepped once more on to the steamer's deck.

"Go below and get into dry clothes, you men," the captain shouted from the bridge.

It was a very welcome order, for we were all soaked to the skin, and now that the excitement was over I was shivering in the cutting wind. I went to my cabin, smoked a cigarette while I changed, and returned to the bridge. Quick as I thought I had been, Malone was before me. When I reached the bridge his hands were gripping the spokes of the wheel, and his eyes were glued on the compass card.

III

Two days afterwards in the late afternoon we arrived at our port, and when we were fast alongside the quay wall and the work was over, I sought my cabin. The chief officer's wife, who had arrived from her home by train, had been waiting on the quay, and was now on board ; that meant that he would keep ship that evening and that we juniors would be free. I was thinking of visiting the third officer, who lived in the next cabin, to propose an excursion uptown in search of a theatre with a decent show in it, when there was a knock on my door. I opened it, and found Malone standing in the alley-way.

" The owld fella from the wreck would like to see ye, sir," he said.

It was the first chance that I had had to speak to Malone since the rescue, and I thought it a fitting time to thank him for having gone in the boat with me. I tried to improve the occasion by a modest reference to our comrades in distress and the brotherhood of the sea, and thought that I had made quite a nice little speech. Malone listened in silence until I had finished.

" Ah, not another word, Mr. Norris," he said. " If I can say so without givin' ye offence, sir, ye handled that boat well—far better than ever I expected ye would do. But when it comes to the brotherhood of the sea, sir—there's no such thing ever existed betwixt me an' annythin' that ever sailed out o' Belfast."

" But," I exclaimed in astonishment, " you knew that the wreck belonged to Belfast before you volunteered to go in the boat."

" 'Tis true, sir, I did," he replied with dignity, " but I wouldn't have it on me conscience that I'd left a dog to dhrown."

That finished me. I proceeded along to the saloon to visit the " owld fella from the wreck." Incidentally I had discovered that she had been a timber-laden brig and that the " owld fella " had been the master of her. I knocked at the door of the stateroom in which he had been put to bed, with hot bottles all round him and a stiff peg of brandy inside after a hot bath. He shouted to me to enter. I opened the door and found him sitting up on a settee fully clad in some clothes that our old man had given him. The dog was lying on the floor at his feet, its head resting on its paws ; its tail flapped once or twice in welcome as I entered. Both of them were looking less the worse for wear than they did when I had seen them last. The dog had also had a hot bath and he had been groomed—it did not surprise me to hear that Malone had been looking after him—and the old man in his borrowed clothes looked quite smart, although still rather exhausted.

" Good-evening, Mr. Norris. Please sit down," he said.

I opened out a camp-stool which was part of the furniture of the stateroom, and sat down beside him.

" I didn't send for you to thank you for what you did for me, for I know that you don't want thanks," the old man said, " but I wished to explain something which I could see was worrying you at the time and probably still is, for I imagine that you are a keen young officer. It wasn't your fault that you twice drifted past the brig with your boat, for both the boat and the steamer were drifting to leeward, whereas the brig was stationary. She was anchored, as I tried to tell you at the time."

" Anchored ! " I exclaimed. " How could she be anchored in the middle of the ocean ? "

The old man replied. " She *was* in the middle of the ocean," he replied, " but she was anchored all the same. She was on the northern edge of Rockall Bank. Your captain took a cast of the lead while you were away in the boat, so he told me, and he got bottom at sixty-four fathoms."

" But even then," I muttered in a bewildered sort of way.

" It seems strange," he conceded, " but I'll explain it. When the brig was overwhelmed and the deck load was washed away, anchors, cables and windlass all went with it. As is the fashion in those little vessels, the cables were stowed in troughs on the deck, but the ends were shackled to the keelson below, and they held. So there was the brig with both anchors hanging plumb down, and a hundred and twenty fathoms of cable out on each. The brig was then in very deep water, of course, and it was the weight of the anchors and cables that took her head down so low in the water ; also it was that that kept her head-on to wind and sea, otherwise what was left above the water would have fallen off into the trough and been swamped."

It took some little time for this information to soak in ; then I asked him how the accident had happened.

" I had overrun my little brig, I'll not deny it," he said.
" I reckon that I know the Western Ocean as well as any
one ; man and boy I've sailed it, winter and summer, for
forty years. I've never been off it since I first went to sea,
never served in a South Spainer and never crossed the Line.
Yet the Western Ocean plays curious pranks at times on
those that know it best, and this was one of them. The brig
was homeward-bound from Quebec to the Clyde with a full
cargo of timber below and a heavy deck load besides. We
had had fair sou'-westerly winds all the way and were
making a good passage ; and although it was blowing half
a gale at eight o'clock on that awful night, the glass was
steady and there was no sign of a change. At that time she
was running along at about nine knots, with both fore and
main upper and lower top-sails on her and a full foresail,
and I thought that she would do nicely like that for the
night. I was mistaken.

" By half-past eight the wind had freshened almost to a
full gale, and the glass was dropping fast. I had to call all
hands to get the canvas off her, and at midnight the wind was
terrific and the seas were running like mountains. It was
never properly dark that night. There was almost a full
moon, although, of course, we never saw it, as it was obscured
by clouds, but its light made the night seem more weird
than ever. It helped the men with their work, but it also
revealed to them the height of the tremendous waves and
the inky-black scud racing at furious speed across the sky.
By that time the brig had been shortened down, and was
now under the main lower top-sail and a reefed foresail,
and I also had the fore-topmast stay-sail set with the weather
sheet well flat as well as the lee one, to pay her head off if
she were caught by the lee, or commenced to broach-to.
I still had all hands on deck, and as you may imagine they
hadn't been idle, for sail after sail had been clewed up and
furled since half-past eight, and the hands were pretty well
played out. A gust of hurricane force exceeding anything
that had preceded it showed me that I had run the brig
too long, and that, if any of us were to see the dawn, she
must at all costs be hove-to. The first job was to get the reefed
foresail off her, and after a terrible struggle, during which
I took the wheel myself and sent the helmsman to help the
others, it was hauled up and furled. The brig was running
with the wind on the starboard quarter, and I determined
to try and heave her to on the starboard tack—which in

any case was the right one—under a goose-winged main topsail, for I did not believe that she would stand up to a full one.

"I was relieved from the wheel, and while the mate was hauling up the weather clew of the top-sail preparatory to goose-winging it, I went below into the little cabin. There was a locker off it in which we kept new coils of rope for the running rigging, and I wanted to cut a good length of inch-and-half rope for a lashing for the top-sail. The first thing that I noticed in the rays of the lamp, which was swinging crazily, was that the cabin floor was littered with ship's biscuits. The man who was doing the combined job of cook and steward—he was now on deck in his oilskins toiling alongside of his shipmates—had opened a large tin that evening, and had carelessly left it on the table, from which it had rolled off. I remember feeling irritated about it—I never dreamt that his carelessness would result in providing me with the necessary food to keep me alive. I had just cut off the length of rope which I required when I felt the shock of a tremendous wave striking the vessel, and heard a succession of crashes above the roar of the gale. At the same time the door of the companion-way was burst open, I became enveloped in water and the light went out.

"I managed to find my way to the foot of the companion-way, for there was a faint square of light showing in the inky darkness of the cabin, and fought my way up the stairs against the rushing water until I reached the deck. I looked forward. My God! Mr. Norris, there was nothing to be seen but sea and sky; my brig seemed to have completely disappeared. Where the masts and yards and straining main top-sail and fore-topmast stay-sail had been, there was nothing but black flying clouds. I looked aft—there was nothing there but the deserted wheel, from which the man must have been washed away. I soon found out that not a thing remained above the water but about twenty feet of the after-deck, and that my men had all gone. I staggered to the wheel, not that I thought of steering, but I could see nothing else to hang on to, then something brushed against my legs; it was the dog. He must have been washed out of his kennel forward, and had probably been overboard too, but he is a powerful swimmer. All night I hung on to that wheel, which was jolting so much, in spite of the relieving tackles, that it nearly tore the arms out of me. I never, of course, expected to see daylight, but thought every moment that the brig would founder under my feet.

"The dawn took a long, long time to break, but at last daylight came and I saw the brig just as she was when you saw her. During part of the night masts and spars still secured to her by the rigging had been hanging alongside and bumping into her, but by this time they had all been swept away. I collected my thoughts and tried to puzzle out how the thing had happened. The fore-topmast stay-sail must have carried away, and the brig had broached-to with a terrific swerve; the deck load had gone overboard, carrying the lower masts and rigging with it. I couldn't understand at first why she was keeping head to wind and floating so deep forward until I thought of the anchors and chains. Of course, with any other cargo but timber she would have sunk like a stone, but she had just sufficient reserve buoyancy left to keep the after-part of her floating above the waves. I felt that I could hang on to the wheel no longer, and although I considered that my case was hopeless, I lashed myself to a ringbolt in the covering board alongside the port bulwark with the length of rope which I had cut. The dog took up his position abaft the cabin skylight, the after-end of which was standing above the water.

"I began to feel hungry, and presently noticed a couple of biscuits floating up from the direction of the companion-way. One floated close to me, and I grabbed it; the dog got the other. A few more floated up, which the dog at my bidding retrieved and brought to me. How many days I lived like that I cannot at present tell. When I feel stronger I'll reckon them up, but we must have drifted to the eastward a long way, and it was only the evening before you took me off the brig that I felt that the anchors had brought her up somewhere. They dragged for some considerable time before they held, and I had, of course, no idea where we were. I hardly ever felt thirsty, for I was wet through the whole time, but when I did I soaked my handkerchief when it rained and sucked it. I suffered a lot from cramp, but, strangely enough, I slept a good deal; in fact, I was asleep when your steamer was passing, until the dog woke me up with its barking. It wasn't until your boat was alongside that I found that—for the time being—I had lost my power of speech."

Completely fascinated, I had listened to the old chap's tale, and I marvelled how he had lived and preserved his reason through all his hardships. He did not look at all robust, even allowing for the fact that he had not yet recovered from his partial fasting and exhaustion, but he must have had the heart of a lion. I hardly knew what to say to him, but fell back on a question which between seamen is quite a common one, but which might have been considered impertinent as between landsmen.

"What will you do now?" I asked. "Get another ship?"

"God knows, Mr. Norris," he replied quietly. "I fully expect that my owners will offer me one, but after twenty years in command of the *Marion* . . . She was a fine vessel, Mr. Norris. You didn't see her quite at her best."

A faint smile flitted across the old chap's face. I believe that under different circumstances I would have found that he possessed a keen sense of humour.

"But," he continued, "you ought to have seen her with every stitch of canvas on her, belting through the Gut of Canso, outward-bound for Miramichi. A lovely ship, Mr. Norris. She would go to windward like a yacht, and she was as strongly built as a whaler."

I probably *had* seen her. If not, I had seen dozens of her sisters of all sizes, beating up the Gulf of St. Lawrence in ballast or rolling home across the Western Ocean with deck loads half-way up to the lower yards ; and to be perfectly candid there was not a fine ship amongst them. Most of them leaked like sieves, so that they would not have been trusted with any other cargo but timber, and all of them had their bows disfigured by having square ports. ports cut in them for the loading and discharging of logs. And yet . . .

THE FOREST OF ILLUSION

By

ROGER COURTNEY

IN the course of my roamings I often thought about the place where the boundaries of four territories meet—Kenya, Uganda, the Sudan, and Abyssinia, and even pictured to myself the actual spot I wished to go to—a spot just over the border of Abyssinia. Hence a great feeling of expectancy and gratification was mine when I found that my second *safari* with a client was taking me away up towards this mysterious region.

It was not long before I heard something which greatly heightened my interest in the whole thing.

It was a legend, a very, very old one, concerning a man who lived two thousand years ago and more, an Egyptian, or perhaps a Nordic blond ; and I had it from some natives I met at a place called Kitgum, Uganda, which is near the far upper reaches of the Nile, and about 150 miles in a straight line from that spot across the border in Abyssinia to which I felt so strangely drawn.

Here at Kitgum I was on the border, so to speak, of the Negroid African peoples of the south and the Nilotic and Semitic peoples of the north. About the natives who came into the Kitgum markets from the districts to the north were hints of Egypt. While retaining many of their Negroid characteristics, numbers of them had the long noses, narrow eyes, high cheek-bones, and curved lips of the Egyptian. Some had a habit of resting by standing on one leg, a habit which belonged definitely to dwellers among the papyrus swamps by the side of the Nile. Others carried with them ancient Egyptian neck-rests, made of wood, beautifully carved and polished, which they used as pillows in such fashion that their head-dresses would not be disturbed. They were like a faint echo of the decorative Egypt of centuries ago.

It was from one of these natives who were so suggestive of the long-ago past that I had the legend. The man who told it to me was of a tribe called the Lango, and had himself got it, he said, from the Banyoro folk, who live in the Nile valley.

It was *kale za kale*, he said—that is, long, long ago—and

the strange man came not from the Nile, but from the direction of the unknown country of Habash—Abyssinia. He
was not of the Abyssinians, though, for he was a white man,
and the Abyssinians are black. He had come through their
country from his own land. It was indeed long ago. It was
before there were any *bakabaka* (kings) of Uganda, even
before the first king of that country, who was Wamba, the
Great Snake. The man had a bronze spear and a copper
bowl, and with him was a woman, whose hair had the creamy-
gold colour of ripe mealies. For many years he stayed with
the Lango and Banyoro, and became a great witch-doctor
and soothsayer among them. One day the woman with the
hair the colour of ripe mealies went into the forest and failed
to return. The heart of the man died within him, and his
powers waned, and a black rival with four sons rose in his
place. The strange white man was cast from the country,
never to be heard of more. The Banyoro say that the forest is
still haunted by the ghost of the woman, and her tall figure in
white robes may be seen flitting among the trees at evening,
and the sound of her voice heard calling for one who will
never return.

That is the legend, simple and undramatic, though thousands of years old ; but it impressed me tremendously. I had
a queer feeling that I knew something more about that man.
I felt that the whole matter was more personal to me than
just a simple legend. I wondered much about him. I tried to
think what was his idea in leaving his own land and coming
away down through Abyssinia. Was he on some quest—a
deathless quest ? I wondered and wondered. In the quiet of
my camp in the evenings I sat alone for long spells thinking
about him. He might have been an Egyptian, or even a Greek.
He might have been any one of a number of things ; but I
liked to think of him as a Nordic adventurer who had set
forth to bring to fruition some idea which possessed him, and
that he was a man very much like myself, with my aims,
ambitions, and urges. I wondered a great deal what that idea
of his might have been, and if it had been brought to fruition.
I had a feeling that it had not—and a feeling also that some
day it would have to be. Often I looked away across towards
the country through which those thousands of years ago he
had come, and wished intensely to go there. Here at Kitgum
on a clear morning I could see a suggestion of the Karamoja
escarpment—just a hint of the blue outline of the hills—
which was the first part of a gateway, as it were, into mysteri-

ous lands beyond. It was through this gateway that that white man, with the woman and the bowl and spear, must have come. I should have liked to set out for that region right away on this trip.

But, although so near, I was not to make that journey just yet. The *safari* which had brought me to Kitgum ended a couple of days later, and I was immediately called away south to Nairobi, to take charge of a fresh client. Taking out clients was the way I earned my living, and earning my living had to come before other considerations.

This new client was a splendid fellow, the sort of man to make a White Hunter feel that his occupation was not such a bad one after all. A Philadelphia lawyer who had once been an officer in the U.S. Navy, he had come to Africa for a month's hunting, for which experience he had put aside his savings for years. His one great ambition was to bag a lion ; it was an ambition he had treasured since early youth. He knew very little about hunting, and said so, but I saw at once that he was what I call an instinctive hunter, and it was a pleasure to show him round and teach him. It seemed natural that I should want to give the very best that was in me in order that he might see his ambition realised, might get his lion. He could afford only the one short month in the country, but I am happy to say he got his lion, a rhino, and many other things besides.

His lion was a fine specimen, and provided him with a thrilling adventure, which happened in this way. .

As the lion in the particular district we hunted were exceedingly shy I decided to kill a zebra, put it down for bait near a water-hole, and build a little screen of grass round a neighbouring tree, behind which we could hide all night, until the lion came to the meat.

This we did, and towards evening my client, a gun-bearer, and I took up positions behind the screen, or " blind," as we call such structures, and settled down. The gun-bearer and I took turn and turn about to watch.

Visibility was good, as a lovely moon was at the full, and the whole of the clearing before us, in the midst of which showed the striped carcass of the zebra, was bathed in soft white light.

There was no settling down for my client, however. Our shelter was less than six paces from the bait, and hour after hour he sat there, expectantly " wiggling " his gun-barrel through the leaves and twigs of the " blind." I have never seen any one more eager. He was like a small boy who had been promised something wonderful, and was darn' well going to sit there till he got it.

The night was full of sounds. Far away in the thorn-scrub a herd of elephant trumpeted shrilly, with a sound not unlike that of the sirens of a fleet of small steamers—tug-boats in a fairway, for example. Down in the *spruit* a hunting leopard coughed, and made a kind of sawing noise, as though he were talking to himself. From behind a near-by patch of scrub came a thudding of hooves and a clinking of horns under the branches—a herd of impala, frightened by we knew not what, stampeded off. And, thrill of thrills, we heard, three miles away, the reverberating roar of a lion challenging the night. At every fresh sound my client, whose name was Forrester, quivered with joy, and mouthed : " Oh, boy ! Oh, boy ! " and I would mouth back at him : " Glad you're enjoying yourself, Forrester ! "

About two in the morning the gun-bearer took my watch, and I curled up in a corner of the shelter and dropped off to sleep. Some time later I was awakened by a frantic tapping on my knee, which was followed immediately by a terrific explosion—the roar of Forrester's rifle reverberating in the enclosed space of the shelter—and a cry from Forrester : " My gad, he's coming ! "

My next impression was of a heavy body crashing up against the " blind " from outside, and an enormous paw breaking through the leaves and twigs of the screen above my head—an enormous paw that swung and groped fiercely for a victim. I promptly thrust the muzzle of my rifle up against the body and fired. There was a choking grunt, and the animal bounded away.

What had happened was that there, in the clearness of the moonlight, the lion had come forth from the scrub and gone straight to the bait. Hurriedly tapping my knee to wake me, Forrester fired ; but he only wounded the animal, which at once leapt straight at the shelter, to fight it out with his aggressor. The whole thing—Forrester's hurried awaken-ing of me, his shot, the charging of the lion, and his paw coming through the " blind "—had been only a matter of a second. It was a well-filled second.

Forrester, almost delirious with excitement, was all for pursuing the wounded lion there and then, but after a cautious reconnaissance with the aid of an electric torch we decided it was too risky, and had better wait till morning. As soon as it was daylight we went out, and after a short search found the body of the lion—a big animal—about two hundred yards from the " blind." He had been hit through the stomach and heart. Forrester gave a college yell, and did a dance of his own invention around him.

A great lad was Forrester, one of the best clients I ever had! An idea of his quality may be gathered from the fact that when, half-way through the *safari*, I was taken ill with malaria he was all for giving up the rest of the trip, cutting in half those few weeks in Africa for which he had saved so long. There were not many who in such circumstances would have suggested a thing like that—and as cheerfully as he did! I am glad to say the fever was of very short duration, and the *safari* was not interrupted. In any case, I just could not have allowed such a sacrifice. I am also glad to say that when at length his month was finished and he departed for home this eager young sportsman had acquired a very decent "bag," including, besides his lion, rhino, buffalo, eland, leopard, koodoo, and other heads and skins, all of them good stuff.

It was at Mombasa that I finally said good-bye to him, and as my next client was not to arrive for a week or more I had a bit of a wander on my own, taking in Mombasa and the district round about, and also going up the coast to an extraordinary place called Gedi.

A wonderful place is that east coast of Equatorial Africa! From Zanzibar to Lamu it is saturated with historical romance. Adventurers right through the dim ages past have fought there and bled, bought slaves and ivory, or been themselves sold into slavery. During the sixteenth century the old fighting Portuguese, in morion and corselet, conquered the advancing hordes of the Imam of Oman and the Sultans of Muscat, who strove to get possession of this stretch of glorious coast, the key position of which was Mombasa. Indeed, the name for Mombasa in those days was Mvita, which means " war." On Mombasa Island is a fort called Fort Jesus, which commands the harbour, at the foot of whose walls I often spent hours looking up at the tall ramparts, imagining I could see the glint of steel, hear the tramping of feet, as the harquebusiers and pikemen marched to the various guard-points.

The ancient city of Gedi, a few hours' journey up the coast from Mombasa, is a sizable place, some miles around, and encircled by the ruins of four walls. Little seems to be known about the people who inhabited this strange city in the long ago ; but the place is haunted, as any one in the district, black or white, will tell you.

I myself have been very close to the ghosts. On my visit to this ruined city I had with me as a kind of unofficial guide an old Giryama herdsman, who knew the place very well. All the time, as we wandered through the ruins of the temples and dwellings, he talked in a low, soft tone, not to me nor to himself, but to unseen beings all around us. They seemed to crowd about us as we went along the path, as though seeking to bar our entrance to the temples. At least, that is what I gathered from the things that my old herdsman-guide said to them. " Peace be on you, friends ! " was what he said. " All is well. I do but show the white man the marvels that have been. Make way—make way ! " To my eyes there was no one present but the herdsman and myself, nothing around us but the tangle of baobab-trees and the heaps of tumbled stone. But I had, none the less, a sense of the presence of other beings, and of being jostled a little. I had an awareness of resistance to my progress, a subtle, half-formed, resentful resistance. I was glad to get out of the depths of those ruins.

That the haunting is very real is shown by the way the local Swahili—a very level-headed people—avoid the place. There are all kinds of stories of mysterious happenings. One grim story, stuttered out by a frantic native cook-boy to his master, who immediately reported it to the Government, was as follows.

The cook-boy, whose name was Ali, had two round-shaped huts in a small camp that his master had made near to the Gedi ruins. One evening Ali sat peeling potatoes in the doorway of one of the huts, and incidentally playing with his two-year-old son, a naked little toddler. In the doorway of the other hut, which was about fifteen feet distant, sat Fatima, his wife, also peeling potatoes, but out of sight of her husband, because of the round bulge of the wall. Presently the wife called to her husband : " Ali, send the little one to me that he may drink a *kibuyu* of goat's milk and grow strong." Always obedient to the voice of his better half, Ali gave the infant a gentle love-spank, and sent him staggering on his way across that short space of fifteen feet, round the bulge of the other hut, and so (as he thought) into his mother's arms.

There were a few moments' silence as Ali went on with his work, then came again the voice of Fatima :

" Ali, why dost thou delay in sending me our child ? "

" But, Fatima, he went on to thee some moments since," answered Ali, and sprang up.

But the child had disappeared—completely disappeared in the course of that short journey of five paces from the one hut to the other. It was astonishing, unbelievable. From the moment the child had left Ali's side he had been in Ali's full sight till he reached the bulge in the other hut, when he should have been in full sight of his mother. But he was gone, vanished into thin air. They searched frantically, high and low, but the country round the camp was as bare as a board for three hundred yards or more, and there was no place where the child could have hidden, or from which any animal, for instance, could have come forth and seized him. Nor were there any signs of the tracks of any such animal. Further, it was impossible that in the moment or two since leaving his father's side the little toddler could have crossed these three hundred yards of open space and disappeared into the brush. There was no doubt about it—the child had vanished completely right there between the two huts, in the little journey from his father to his mother. The actual point of the disappearance must have been within three feet of his mother. The child has never been seen since.

Again, to the westward of Gedi there is a certain dark forest which has been called the Forest of Illusion. An account of an experience in this strange forest was given to me by a Government official who was stationed in the region for a time, and who prefers to remain anonymous. His story went something like this :

" Ever since I came to this district I had been hearing tales about this forest—native stories, you know. They said the trees were not real, but came and went like shadows, were mere illusions, and that travellers were often confused by them, and accordingly went hopelessly astray. I didn't pay much attention to the tales at first, thought it was just some silly native yarn or other. But one day Miss R."—a white lady who has lived in East Africa since she was a small child, and is extraordinarily well informed in all matters concerning native customs and lore—" put a different complexion on the matter. Finding herself near this mysterious forest one day, and having heard the story of the illusory nature of the trees, she determined to test the matter there and then. With the hunting-knife of one of her boys she sliced away a portion of the bark of one of the trees, leaving a large, clear mark. She then walked away a hundred yards or so, and turned and went back. There was no sign of the marked tree. There was not even a sign of the path along which she had originally gone up to the tree in order to make the mark.

" That was the story Miss R. told me, and my first reaction to it was that she must have made a mistake, had in some way become confused as to the position of the tree, and gone to look for it in another direction. I decided to try the thing for myself, and one day went to the forest for this purpose. I must say that at first glance it looked just like any other forest, and I was quite unhopeful of any queer results from the experiment. It was in a most sceptical frame of mind that I took a sheet of paper, torn from a large memo-book, and fastened it to a big, curiously twisted baobab-tree that stood well out from its fellows. Making sure that the paper was so securely fixed that it could not fall off or be blown off, I turned and walked back a hundred yards or so, as Miss R. had done. Then I turned again and went back.

" Now I want you to get it quite clearly that I hadn't made any mistake as to the position of that tree. I went right back to the spot where it should have been. I'm as certain of it as I could be of anything.

" But there was no sign of the tree, nor of the piece of paper. They had disappeared as completely as though they had never been there at all.

" Not only that, but the whole character of that part of the forest seemed to have altered, the individual trees to have changed their position. There was a queerly shimmering effect about them, not unlike that of a mirage. There was a threatening effect about it all, and I left the place as soon as possible."

That is the story of the Forest of Illusion as told me by the Government official. Later I met Miss R., and she confirmed the story of her experiment of marking the tree. During my sojourn at Gedi I had no opportunity to visit this mysterious forest and try for myself the illusory nature of the trees, but I hope that some day my wanderings will lead me there again, when I will most certainly make the test.

So active are the allegedly occult or dark forces at work in Gedi that the natives are being compelled to abandon the district ; the day will come—it is really not very far off now—when the place will be left completely alone to brood on its mysteries, and its ghosts will be left to walk undisturbed in the moonlight. Only recently—only a few months ago, as a matter of fact—reports came in that numbers of Gedi fishermen were leaving the district because of the frequent repetition of a certain mysterious visitation from the sea. The fishermen declared that first there shows out to sea a brilliant flickering blue light. Presently it comes in towards the harbour. When close to the land the light vanishes, and a boat appears, a strange boat, like none they have ever seen, say the awestricken natives. The boat grounds, and out of it steps an aged man, with flowing white hair, and wrapped in a white garment, and wearing a high conical hat which flashes, as though encrusted with jewels, and gives forth a strange lustre. This man, say these fishermen, is like no man they know. He is neither Ingresa nor Mahindi—that is, neither English nor Hindu—and when he alights on the sand he kneels in strange prayer, making gestures towards heaven, and then as though to embrace the wideness of the earth. But his knees leave no mark in the sand. Finally man and ship melt into the moonlight and are gone, and the beach is left empty to the surf and the screams of rock-rabbits in the dim blue ruins behind.

The last appearance of this mysterious stranger from the sea caused such a stir among the natives that the attention of the East African Press was drawn to it, and accounts of the visitation appeared in the papers. Coming on top of all the other mysterious happenings at Gedi—the resentful ghosts in the ruins, the illusory trees, and the rest—it is not to be wondered at that a visitation such as this should be driving the fishermen away.

DOPE IN CHINATOWN

By
ALEC DIXON

The author spent four years as a detective officer in Singapore. Bennett was the chief detective officer, and Blount, Ainley and Henderson were other detectives at the same bureau.

MY second day at the Detective Bureau was distinguished by three murders (two by shooting, a third by stabbing) and three armed-gang robberies. Four of these crimes were attributed by our native detectives to Cantonese secret societies.

Our morning newspaper reported these events with grim relish, and described Singapore as the " Chicago of the East." An afternoon journal, not to be outdone in scare tactics, told in half-inch type of the " Chinese Gunmen's Reign of Terror," and concluded the story with an allusion to " indescribable carnage."

I marvel that, faced with such problems, Bennett should have found time to give more than a passing thought to my professional education. Most Europeans in the colony looked upon the Chief Detective Officer as a convenient information bureau. His telephone rang every few minutes from dawn until dusk, and reminded him of his duties at frequent intervals during the night. His opinion was sought on every subject from extradition to obstetrics, and it was invariably given with patience and the utmost courtesy.

Despite his many and urgent duties, Bennett supervised my activities with the greatest care. The standard he set was high, for he was recognised as the cleverest detective of his day. Half a dozen visits to court in his company taught me more of the Penal Code than I had learned in all my weeks of " study " at the Depot. I noticed that when talking to the Chinese Bennett used a kind of simplified Malay. I lost no time in mastering this *argot*, for the men understood scarcely a word of the bookish language which Haji Allam had taught me.

Meanwhile the gunmen fought and robbed at all hours of the day and night. Some of them commandeered Ford buses as transport for the gangs, while others drove private cars which were fitted with duplicate number-plates. The newspapers were overwhelmed with copy, and daily grew more abusive of the police force and its methods. Yet a European, wandering the city streets in search of excitement, would have been disappointed. The " reign of terror " which moved the Press to eloquence was confined to the darker alleys of Chinatown and to remote hamlets of the country districts.

Nevertheless, the situation was serious, and it was not improved by the continued absence of reliable information. Bennett was unwilling to press his informers to risk their lives for the sake of a few dollars. Only the week before one of them had been shot dead within half a mile of the station. Of the detectives' courage there could be no question, and one hesitated to blame them for their caution in shadowing men who were known to shoot at sight.

This state of deadlock lasted nearly three weeks, during which period many unsuccessful attempts were made to get news of the criminal gangs. Patrols were doubled throughout the Chinese city. Brothels, coolie-houses, coffee-shops, and opium dens were raided night after night without useful results. Every officer and man of the Bureau was impressed for special duty in the night patrols. But information—reliable or unreliable—was not to be had.

When the crime wave was at its worst an incident occurred which put new life into our detectives. With dramatic suddenness our luck (perhaps the greatest factor in successful police work) changed for the better.

While patrolling Chinatown with two detectives Blount stopped to search a suspicious-looking coolie who was loitering outside a coffee-shop. Two Chinese, dressed in black from head to foot, watched the search furtively from a nearby table. When Blount turned his head they sidled out of the coffee-shop and took to their heels. The narrow street was crowded, and the Chinese had a good start. Blount and his men followed as fast as they could, literally fighting their way through the throng of the street. Everything was against the detectives, and it seemed that the fugitives must escape. Then, at the corner of the street, the Chinese slowed to a walk. Producing automatics, they turned to face their pursuers. But Blount and his men moved quickly, and, rushing in upon the gunmen, rolled them over in the gutter. Not a shot was fired, and after a tussle in the roadway both men were handcuffed.

When Blount returned to the Bureau one of his prisoners was recognised by the detectives as a notorious gangster, said to be the best marksman in Chinatown. Bennett talked to the gunmen for over an hour, but they answered all his questions with an oyster-like silence. Then detectives were sent out to fetch those who had been held up in the recent gang robberies. Identification parades were held and further statements taken. After being identified by eight witnesses the gunmen were charged with armed gang-robbery. When the last witnesses had gone Blount came into my office, puffing contentedly at a black and venomous cheroot.

" No mistake about it this time," he remarked happily. " If those two birds don't go down for ten years I'll sign the pledge ! "

This arrest raised Bennett's hopes, and inspired new confidence in our informers. Although, as yet, there was no definite information about the gangs the atmosphere of the Bureau underwent a sudden change ; it became brittle with anticipation. The detectives regarded the capture in the light of good " joss," and prophesied further successes. We shared their optimism, for the gods of ancient China seemed benevolently disposed towards detectives.

One morning a day or two later I found Bennett in his office scribbling away on a memo pad. A Cantonese detective was talking in low tones to a tattered coolie who squatted on the floor near the desk. Bennett laid down his pencil and smiled. Here, he said, was something to interest me. Would I close the door and sit down ? His bedraggled visitor was an old and trusted informer with a long tale to tell, and it was worth hearing.

Society spies watched the Bureau offices by day and by night. So my respect for the informer increased when I heard that he had escaped their vigilance by crawling along the wide drain which passed within a few feet of the station door. The office windows were tightly shut, and a senior detective stood at each of the closed doors to deal with intruders. Switching on the ceiling fan, I sat down and listened while the informer told his story in a husky, dispassionate undertone.

He related how he had gained admittance to the cabala of the Sun Wei Kuan secret society, the most powerful and dangerous organisation of its kind in Singapore. Its leaders, he reported, were exchanging diplomatic notes with the headmen of two rival societies, the Heng and the Kuan Yi. Of these two societies the Heng was the stronger. Allied with the Kuan Yi it would be formidable enough to challenge the authority of the Sun Wei Kuan. But at that time the relations between the Heng and Kuan Yi societies were strained, and the Sun Wei Kuan headmen were doing all in their power to prevent a reconciliation.

At the first opportunity, our informer predicted, the Sun Wei Kuan proposed to invite the Kuan Yi officials to a tea-meeting (the Chinese version of a round-table conference), of which the issue could not be doubted. Once allied to the Kuan Yi the already powerful Sun Wei Kuan would be able to crush the Heng and dominate the Chinese city. Having thus gained a good deal of " face," the gangs of Sun Wei Kuan gunmen would be free to operate over a wide area, and the reign of terror might become a reality.

As I understood it, the position of the Kuan Yi was analagous to that of England in sixteenth-century Europe ; the two rival societies stood for Spain and France respectively. So far the balance of power had been preserved ; but it was doubtful whether the Kuan Yi leaders would have the courage—or the " face "—to play the high hand of an Elizabeth.

The informer also revealed the whereabouts of many " lodges," and named fifty or sixty Cantonese all of whom were either members or officials of secret societies. When asked about Blount's prisoners the fellow described them as " Five-Tiger-Generals " (gunmen) of the Sun Wei Kuan, and said that their arrest had prompted the society's officials to convene a special tea-meeting of the fighting members.

This was news of the first importance, for it enabled Bennett to organise a surprise attack which would put the societies on the defensive and so check the further increase of serious crime. The information took nearly two hours to record, and while Bennett checked his notes the exhausted informer sipped hot black coffee which had been well laced with brandy.

To me it seemed that the stage was set for a thrilling and spectacular melodrama ; but the Chief Detective Officer knew better. His attitude suggested that it might be little more than a curtain-raiser, or at best a one-act comedy. He pointed out that before criminals could be paraded for identification they must be hunted down ; and that was but one degree less difficult than producing conclusive evidence of their guilt.

Nevertheless he lost no time in launching his attack, and during the next few days I saw but little of him. As a 'prentice hand I could not hope to take part in the hunting, for experience and a practised eye were essential when raiding Cantonese haunts. So Bennett was usually partnered either by Henderson or Blount, and his raiding parties were made up of senior detectives.

Already I was feeling my feet as a detective, and when Bennett began his Cantonese round-up I was allotted a desk in the large office next door. This room I shared with Ainley, a tall, boisterous fellow who had escaped from the stool of a London office only a year previously. His ready wit had a Gallic flavour which relieved the tedium of office work and shortened the heat-drenched hours of afternoon.

Ainley's days were divided between flying visits to court, planning dramatic raids (most of which were successful), and writing elaborate reports on his more recent investigations. He was assisted and frequently criticised in his dealings with Teochiu criminals by a sturdy but garrulous detective named Bak Soon.

Raiding was food and drink to Ainley, who combined a chess-player's cunning and forethought with the dash of a cavalryman. Under the watchful eye of Bak Soon his squad of detectives provided a steady flow of reliable information. Thus Ainley was able, if he so desired, to organise a man-hunt every day of the week. These raids covered a wide area ; and Bennett suggested that by taking part in them I should learn some tricks of the trade and become familiar with the topography of the remote country districts. Our first raid stands out in my memory as a unique experience although it was neither difficult, dangerous, nor very fruitful. Ainley expected a good capture, for his information came from a reliable source, and promised, in addition to four automatic pistols, a large quantity of cocaine.

Accompanied by three native detectives, we set off at four o'clock in the morning to raid the house, which lay within half a mile of the station. Ainley led the way down a narrow street and halted before the door of a closely shuttered house. A moment later Bak Soon joined us, and by the light of a torch set to work on the door fastenings with his penknife.

No word was spoken as we stood there. The two detectives who waited in the shadow of a nearby wall looked very like the gunmen captured by Blount a few days before. A string of chattering hawkers trotted down the road, with baskets of vegetables swung from their carrying-poles. Their conversation ceased abruptly when they caught sight of us. Quickening their pace, they scuttled down a side street.

Then the door opened to reveal the gloom of the pit. On the threshold we were overwhelmed by the heavy, funereal odour of China, a stench compounded of garlic, stale urine, opium dross, and fermenting rice. Like all Chinese dwellings the house had been hermetically sealed overnight, and its atmosphere, enfolding us like a greasy blanket, contrasted rudely with the cool morning air of the streets.

Ainley plunged boldly into the fuggy darkness, and with the utmost difficulty I followed him up a stairway which creaked alarmingly beneath our cautious tread. Believing that this noise must surely wake the household, I fingered the trigger of my Webley and peered nervously into the darkness ahead. If there were arms in the house, I argued, its inmates would not hesitate to use them.

But when Ainley pushed open the door at the top of the stairs the beam of his torch revealed only three half-naked Chinese snoring with porcine vigour on the floor of an unfurnished room. Opium pipes, two lamps shaped like milk bottles, and a pot of treacly *chandu* (prepared opium) stood on a wooden tray near the sleepers' heads. When roused by gentle kicks they stared at us with vacant eyes, grunted their disgust, and stretched themselves lazily. This indifference to authority was too much for Bak Soon. Growling like a mastiff, he dragged them to their feet and marched them off to a far corner of the room, where they were subjected to an Oriental variation of the third degree.

Leaving the detectives in charge of the upper room, Ainley and I began our search of the house. It was like playing hunt the thimble in a pigsty. For nearly an hour we wandered from room to room without a friendly soul to tell us when we were getting " warm." In his anxiety to discover the promised pistols Ainley did not shrink from a careful search of the lavatory ; he emptied bowls of wet rice, raked over baskets of decaying vegetables, and even probed among the yet warm ashes of the kitchen fire.

We were about to abandon the search when my companion flashed his torch on a pile of rubbish under the staircase which had hitherto escaped our attention. After groping and swearing among the litter for some moments Ainley emerged, dirty and dishevelled, with a wooden box. It was carefully packed with small bottles. Uncorking one of the phials, he decanted some of its contents into the palm of his hand ; the stuff sparkled like snow-crystals in the beam of the torch. Ainley sniffed the white powder suspiciously, and after a moment's hesitation tasted it with the tip of his tongue. A slow smile of triumph spread over his grimy face.

" Cocaine ! " he pronounced. " That box must be worth a pretty penny—but I'd willingly exchange it for a sight of one pistol."

Nevertheless, our capture was important (or so we imagined), and we hurried upstairs to discover which of the three Chinese was the culprit. Bak Soon pointed out a tall, emaciated fellow as the chief tenant of the house. When Ainley accused him of dealing in cocaine he denied all knowledge of the stuff, and was loud in protest all the way to the station.

After breakfast Ainley sent for his prisoner and questioned him about the drugs. The fellow answered every question with a broad grin and a shake of his bullet-head. Then Bak Soon's globular face appeared in the doorway, and the prisoner began to talk at the top of his voice. Not only did he admit ownership of the drug, but confessed to having bought it from a sailor friend at a stiff price.

In court that morning our prisoner pleaded guilty to a charge of trafficking in deleterious drugs. Judgment was withheld, however, until a report on the cocaine had been received from the Government analyst. Two days before the trial Ainley received the analyst's report. The " cocaine " was nothing·more harmful than salicylic acid. In due course the case for the prosecution was withdrawn ; but the prisoner, having been discharged, refused to leave the dock.

In vain did the court usher and two sweating interpreters seek to persuade the Chinese that he was a free man. He demanded justice, and complained that after making a plea of " guilty " he had not been allowed to tell his story to the judge. Worse still, it was said that the drugs for which he had paid so dearly were worthless. Now, after he had lost both " face " and money, the police denied him the joy of a holiday in prison. Did not the worthy judge understand that a term of imprisonment would save his supplicant's face ?

One raid was very like another, and nine out of ten were

fruitless. Sometimes we went out in search of arms rewarded with opium, or to arrest a gunman who turned out to be a harmless brothel-tout. Other excursions which began as pleasant country walks ended as chases in the true Wild West manner.

At two o'clock one wet morning we set off on a ten-mile walk through rubber estates and jungle to arrest the headman of a secret society. Our guide on this occasion was a weasel-faced Hokkien informer whose thin body was bent nearly double with constant prying into the affairs of other people. After we had wandered for two hours through a belt of virgin jungle the fellow brought us to a palm-thatched hut which stood on the edge of a narrow clearing. There, he asserted, we should find our man.

The shack was occupied by a Chinese squatter, his nun-like wife and two golliwog children, and all protested loudly when we declared our intention of searching their house. It was contemptible work, and at such times one blushed for the crimes committed in the name of justice. Although one of Walt Disney's sprightly animals might have found a hiding-place in those three tiny rooms they offered little cover for an Asiatic mouse, much less for a grown man. When the unfortunate squatter's belongings had been turned upside-down our informer spat noisily into the ashes of the cooking-fire and remarked that we were searching the wrong house.

He blamed the darkness for his mistake, and said that the house he had in mind lay half a mile farther down the track. To my surprise Ainley abandoned the search without comment, and our detectives did what they could to restore order in the shabby dwelling. Silently we followed our uncertain guide through the jungle to a yet more remote homestead. Here again the fellow confessed to an error of judgment only when the detectives had all but finished their search. So to a third house and yet another interrupted investigation.

Although Ainley took his informer's tactics very much for granted there was a dangerous glint in his blue eye. Good informers are seldom willing to accompany a raiding party even as guides ; yet Weasel-face appeared to be making the most of his opportunity, and openly declared himself a friend of the police. One imagined his visiting that district again on the following morning, alone, with arrogant words on his lips. " Give me five dollars," he would say to the wretched squatters, " or I will bring the police to your house to-morrow as I did last night."

When we came to a fifth house I felt that the joke had worn thin ; also I was dead tired. But Ainley was optimistic, and still hoped for a capture. With the patience of a true detective he turned to the search as though for the first time that morning.

The house was as large as an English barn, and I stared stupidly at a large black pig which, it seemed, was the only inhabitant. While the detectives ran in and out of the box-like rooms I claimed a spectator's privilege and sat down. From a bench just inside the door I watched their antics with a drowsy eye. Behind me was a small cubicle, and through its open door I saw a Chinese youth sleeping soundly under a large mosquito-net. How I envied that fellow !

My eyes were closed and I was beginning to feel at home when I heard Ainley's voice belabouring the informer. On the instant I sat up and assumed a bellicose expression. From a corner of my eye I saw the Chinese youth was still sound asleep.

" What about that fellow ? " I asked innocently, nodding in the direction of the cubicle.

" Haven't you searched him ? " Ainley demanded in a surprised voice.

I was about to make an appropriate excuse when our informer tiptoed past me and peered anxiously into the little room. He glanced curiously at the man on the bed, then, throwing up his hands in astonishment, he took to his heels and shot through the door like a startled hare. Before we could utter a word he had disappeared among the surrounding trees.

Believing that the hunt was up, we hurried into the room. When one of the detectives lifted the mosquito-net the sleeper opened his eyes and slipped his right hand under the pillow. Bak Soon grabbed at a bare leg, but the fellow squirmed out of his grip like an eel, and before we could lay hands on him was thrusting at us with a long and serviceable dagger. He held us off for some moments, and nearly escaped by using the mosquito-net as an entanglement. But when he jumped to the edge of the mattress Ainley caught his dagger arm and we all joined in the scrum on the bed.

Our captive fought like a tiger, and seemed to possess the strength of ten men. Presently the dagger fell from his fingers, and I seized the hand which was thrust under my nose. While I twisted the yellow wrist, schoolboy fashion, Bak Soon crawled over me and straddled the fellow's chest.

Then Ainley, who held the other wrist, reached over and slipped on the handcuffs.

When the struggle was over we found that our prisoner was a mere stripling, less than five feet in height. He proved to be a cheerful soul, and after refreshing himself with egg sandwiches, coffee, and a cigarette entertained us with colourful but highly improbable stories of his adventures as a " bad man."

At the station later that morning Ainley endeavoured to establish the identity of his prisoner by searching through a file of police circulars. I was not surprised to hear that our youthful captive was a homicidal lunatic who had escaped from the mental hospital only ten days before.

A MODERN TREASURE HUNT

By
" SINBAD "

" Sinbad " has decided to sail alone with the well-known character "Red" Saunders from Singapore to the Crozets—small islands in the Indian Ocean. Their objective is a wreck which was said to have gone down with a chest of money. The boat in which they sail is "The Black Pearl," little bigger than a Brixham smack.

WITH gold over the bows who cares for hardship ? Our chief problem was fresh water. The navigation kept us both on the alert until we passed the Sunda Strait, between Java and Sumatra, but after that there would be a stretch of some four thousand miles of ocean in which ran few steamer tracks. We estimated an average of a hundred miles a day for the sea passage, thirty days at the islands, and about forty days to return to whatever port we selected, which would be decided by our luck. We must carry water for a hundred days, because we knew that though we could find the Crozets easily enough, we might by no means so easily land there. It might prove impossible to land at all. So we watered at Anjer, and again at Keeling, and at last set out on our lonely traverse feeling fairly hopeful.

" We'll catch all the rain we can," said Saunders, and I agreed with him. I have heard many tales about rainwater at sea—how it stinks, goes rotten, and becomes good again after so many days. Such yarns may or may not be true, for I can't know all there is to know about rainwater. This, however, I do know : for a period of seven years I caught and used exclusively rainwater, and never had it go bad or cause me the least distress ; during four years of residence in Bermuda my family and I drank nothing but rainwater, and did not suffer in any degree. My own experience may have been due to the fact that in my yacht I stored water in lime-washed metal tanks, while in Bermuda my house roof and water tank were also limewashed regularly. It may be that rainwater goes bad in wooden containers only. Whatever the reason, my experience has been all against the yarns and in favour of rainwater to drink. In the *Black Pearl* we caught rain whenever possible, and came to no harm from it.

The voyage was easy until we drew south of the latitude of the Cape of Good Hope, and then we met the big seas, and, farther south, blusterous winds that were all too powerful for our small ship. But she was nicely trimmed, not overloaded with heavy cargo, and we always snugged her down in good time when the weather was too fierce.

We went skittling across the big westerlies, and kept a good look-out for ships. The sailing-ships and steamers of the Shaw, Savill Line, the New Zealand Shipping Company, the Aberdeen White Star, and other lines ran their easting down well to the southward, but we saw only one glint of sail, one streak of smoke until our estimated forty days were up. We had sighted no islands, but were hourly expecting to, when a thick fog came down and we hove-to.

"We're thereabouts, Skimps," the skipper announced after working up the distance from the last sight. "While the fog hangs about, we'll get our ground-tackle and diving-gear ready. We shan't want to mess about once we sight the island."

Our only navigating timepiece was nothing better than an old Connecticut kitchen clock, and our longitude was of necessity something of a guess. The Crozets are notorious for fog, as they are for gales, so I for one kept a keen look-out while working at the anchors, and wished desperately that my vision had been better.

Our wreck was supposed to have sunk alongside the Apostles, but whether it was completely submerged or not we had to discover. The available records had it that the survivors of the disaster had landed on North-east Island, existing precariously until rescued by a whaler seven months later; and since they had suffered much from privation we assumed that the ship had sunk at least beyond all access to stores. If we hoped that might prove to be true, it was not because we were callous concerning the sufferings of others, but simply because it increased the chance that the gold had never been recovered, and likewise our chance of finding it with our diving-gear.

Treasure hunters are ever sanguine.

The fog lasted for three days, and during that time we laid out all our anchors and warps on deck and prepared our one boat. Saunders had patched up his ancient diving-suit, put new washers in the pump, and parcelled some places in the pipes which were leaky. Much as I liked my shipmate, I was glad I was too small to use that diving-suit ; but he seemed entirely happy in the prospect. The fog bothered him much more than did the possibility of risking his life in what was little better than a suicide's uniform.

We sighted high land while hove-to, but the sound of seas bursting about its base warned us against nearer approach and we squared away and ran off at once. There was something terribly forbidding in that shadowy glimpse of the islets. Above the crash of seas, and the whine of the wind, the cries of penguins came trickling through the murk like the wailing of castaways.

The weather was bitterly cold. As soon as we hove-to again well to leeward of the danger, Saunders broached a bottle of square-face gin. Next to American prohibition liquor, trade gin is perhaps the most unpleasant drench the human stomach will tackle. It has the kick of a jealous *boomah* kangaroo in rutting season. Saunders was used to it, and he made me swallow half a tumbler of the stuff to keep out the chill. I was so cold that I never tasted it until it landed inside me, but then I saw sparks in the fog, and gasped for ten minutes before I could draw a normal breath. But it did warm me, and I felt ready and willing to tackle anything —except that diving job. Had I taken one more drink like that, I would have fought Red for even that privilege.

The fog cleared, and a strong westerly breeze settled in. We beat up for the islands again, and sighted them after four days. Luck was kind to us, for the sea fell almost calm, and the wind dropped to only a pleasant air as we drew near, so that it was fairly comfortable in the lee of the Apostles.

We lost no time. Two anchors were let go to windward, with springs on the cables ; two kedges were carried ashore in the boat and secured in the rocks. Then we sounded all round the schooner with the boat. It was no trouble to locate the wreck, but it was no simple matter to work our vessel into position. Two men may easily sail such a vessel as ours over all kinds of wide ocean, but when it comes to handling ground-tackle beef is required. Saunders had it to spare—I was still only Skimps. It took us all day to moor the schooner, and as night fell the fickle weather showed signs of changing again.

We slept all standing, and turned out before dawn to swallow scalding coffee well laced with gin. Abominable muck as it was, it drove out the appalling chill of morning ;

and before the sun dawdled up in the east I was pumping air
down to my shipmate, keeping an eye on the weather, and
watching the mooring lines as well. I saw the bubbles rising,
following them in fascination as Red moved about below.
When he signalled at last I sent down a bundle of crowbars
and mentally counted our salvage. When no more signals
came for what seemed to be a long time, I grew uneasy. The
western horizon looked foul, and I felt tremendously alone.
The bubbles continued to rise, but only in one spot now, and
hope fought against fear.

After nearly an hour Red signalled furiously for more line.
The line hung slack, and so I signalled him. The line ran
through my hands, but the air-pipes hung down in a bight.
Then I got really scared, for Saunders had obviously fouled
something. I pulled hard, signalling my frantic question, and
back came the order :

" Haul up ! "

I let go the pump and set my back to hauling. Red was
stuck. I hauled until my nose bled, then up he came, upside
down, his lead-soled boots missing, and a knot tied in his
air-pipe, which had parted. Whipping the line over a snatch-
block rigged for the hoisting of our treasure, I laid back and
slowly dragged my mate over the rail. My fingers fumbled
at his fastenings, and his own fingers sought the nuts of his
face-glass. At long last he sat up free, and sucked in great
draughts of air.

" The damned pipe fouled a broken iron plate," he
panted. " I dropped my knife, and had to pull the pipe apart.
Give me a hooker of squareface, Skimps ; I've looked a sticky
end right in the eye."

I wanted to hear about the gold, but Red proceeded to
get out of his gear altogether, which did not seem hopeful.
Then he gave one glance at the weather, and sprang into
the boat.

" You blind bat ! " he yelled at me. " Didn't you see that
coming ? "

He flung an arm towards the west, and sculled furiously
to the rocks. He was like a gorilla for strength, in spite of
his recent ordeal. Those kedges came out of the rocks and
into the boat as if they were no heavier than grapnels ; then
he hauled the boat back to the schooner by means of the
warps. I had already started to tie down a double reef in
the mainsail, and when we had hauled kedges and warps
aboard he tackled the foresail. We had her reefed down in

fifteen minutes, but we could not get our big anchors ; we slipped one, and the schooner dragged the other out of the ground as she ranged about.

Then we got sail on her and let the hook drag, for was had no time to fool with it. It would soon be in deep water anyhow. I stood by the headsails, ready to let the chain run if the anchor caught the bottom again ; but the wind came in a fierce squall, and then we had enough to do to keep clear of that line of savage reefs to leeward. Saunders stood bare-headed at the helm, steering coolly ; but he was whistling, which was always a bad sign in him. I crouched with my head below the foot of the fore staysail, watching the thunder-ing surf, until I got panicky, certain that we could never win clear. I felt the thrum of the dragging cable, and feared the anchor had taken hold. Knocking up the windlass pawl with my boot, I let the chain go and leapt clear of the flying end. Red had seen to it that all cable-ends were free before we moored over the wreck, and I now realised how wise he had been. I felt a bit stuck up on my own account too, for I believed that only my action had saved us from destruction.

" You silly awss ! " roared Red, as the cable-end shot over-board. I saw the vessel's head swing, and heard the main-sheet whizz through the blocks as he rolled the wheel up. We were clear. We shot down wind, past the roaring crags, travelling like steam before a rising gale that already had painted the sky hell-colour.

" You silly sheep," the skipper bawled, " you've lost me a good anchor and chain. What did you do it for, you fool ? '

I went aft in fury, but Red met me laughing, his momen-tary anger gone along with the peril.

" You did right, Skimps," he said. " You're a better man than you'll ever look. Take the wheel while I put on some boots."

We hove her to again, and ate some food, while Red told me about the wreck.

" That ship's in a mess, Skimp. I bent those crowbars into horseshoes breaking away twisted frames. If there's anything in her strong-box, or even a strong-box at all, it'll need dynamite to get it." Red ate silently for a while, then remarked with a grin : " We need a better diving outfit too. I had you scared, didn't I ? "

" I don't scare so easily," I retorted. " I knew you were never born to be drowned. Where are we bound for now, though ? We're still broke."

" We're going to get out of these damned cold seas as
quick as we can drive her ; then we'll have a try on the
Western Australian pearling grounds. We'll be short of grub
pretty soon."

So we drove her across the heavy quartering seas, making
north with a little easting. As she raised her latitude the sun
gave heat, and we caught some fish sometimes to eke out our
provisions. When we agreed that we were far enough to the
north, we swung off due east, and grumbled because we had
both forgotten to check our clock while at the Crozets. Our
longitude was very uncertain, but I believed, as he did, that
we were to the eastward of the meridian of Amsterdam
Island ; therefore we trimmed her to steer herself, and let
her ramble, catching up on sleep while we felt certain we had
a whole ocean ahead of us.

The night after we turned east, however, we struck with
terrific force in the darkest hour, and the sea rolled us out
among the splinters of our little ship. A bit of wreckage
broke my cheekbone, and knocked me completely out ; when
I came to, I lay on a heap of sand, my head bandaged in a
bit of shirt, and Red was kneeling over me with anxiety in his
strong face. Dawn was just breaking.

" Shamming, eh ? " growled Red when I opened my eyes,
but I knew that he growled to hide his real concern.

" Where are we ? What struck us ? " I bleated.

" St. Paul, I think it must be," he answered, peering into
my face. " The schooner's busted to hell, and I can't see
enough left of her to build a fire with. Can't you stand up,
you poor apology of a man ? "

I scrambled to my feet, the world spinning around, and
the earth leaping madly beneath my feet. Red's great arm
slipped about me, and he led me up the shore.

" That's the stuff, Skimps," he said gently. " Got to make
the effort, you know. I've been trying to stir you up with
kindness for hours. I thought sure enough you had sailed for
Fiddler's Green, laddie." Then he laughed. " You're a hot-
headed pup when a fellow gets under your hide. How d'ye
feel now ? "

" Thirsty."

" That, Skimps, is going to be our trouble, I'm afraid,"
he said gravely.

When full daylight came, I tottered after him and we
scanned the shore for wreckage. Of the schooner we saw
nothing. Something bobbed about in the surf a hundred

yards out and Saunders waded and swam after it. He came back swearing, dragging the white canvas wheel-cover on which the schooner's name was painted.

" If this got washed out of where I stowed it, she must have busted all to bits," he announced gloomily. " We'll have to try another tack, Skimps. There ought to be a store hut somewhere about the crater. I'm hungry, as well as sore. Come on, laddie."

In the middle of the island was a crater lake or lagoon, about three-quarters of a mile wide. That fixed the place for us. St. Paul it was. The island was craggy, volcanic, with no trees or even heavy bushes. Only a tangle of grass, among which we started a horde of rats, rabbits, and goats. Red tried to catch a rabbit, but it had the speed of an electric hare, and Red grinned at his failure. We scrambled round the crater, seeking water, but all we found were pools in the rocks, and the water was hot and tasted as if sewer-cleaners' boots had been boiled in it. On the northern side of the crater, however, we spied a small stone hut, which had been thatched, but the winds had ripped the thatch partly off. We made for the shelter hungrily.

The door hung from one hinge, and on the door was a board with some French words painted into chiselled grooves. Saunders said it stated that here were food and clothing for shipwrecked mariners. I couldn't guarantee that, the only languages I ever got a smattering of, besides my own, being Coastwise Hindustani and seagoing Italian. We entered the hut. A ripped tarpaulin partly covered two or three barrels, broken and coated with tar and sand. We pulled the stuff about, but somebody had visited St. Paul and made a main-sail haul of the grub. A broken hatchet lay in the sand, and Saunders handled that ominously as he completed the search.

" Sealers or whalers, they were no seamen ! " he muttered.

We went from the hut. On the board inside, which was a duplicate of the one on the door, was a direction for finding water. We followed it, north-west by the sun, and soon came upon a hot-water spring which had less of the foul taste of the pools. Hot as it was, we drank it gladly. With the hatchet, and water, we hoped for the best.

When I could make my legs behave, we searched the island narrowly. There was a flagstaff, placed there by the French vessel which established the store hut. On that we lashed Red's outer shirt. We sought salvage from our wreck, but she had struck on the weather side and had vanished.

Except for the broken barrels in the hut we saw not one stick of wood. We found wild cats, living comfortably with rats and rabbits ; the goats we chased took to the crags, and travelled like chamois. For our first meal we perforce ate penguin, and vowed to eat no more until forced by hunger and exhaustion to do so. Towards night I caught a big cray-fish in a rocky crevice, and we boiled it in a steaming pool. We were sick during the night, and the penguins ruined our sleep.

We sat on the sand looking at each other, when day broke. " This is all on account of a blooming Yankee dollar clock ! " said Saunders. " It must have been twenty minutes out."

" It's all because I forgot to check it at the Apostles," I retorted. " You had enough to think about. I've kidded myself I'd make a navigator. Let's stop belly-aching, and do something sensible."

I was beginning to feel proud of my nautical knowledge, and to resent my mistakes. I have made plenty since that day ; and I have not forgotten one. Sometimes I have camouflaged them under an awning of assurance, but in my heart I know them and don't feel at all proud about my success in hiding them from the world.

First of all we made an inventory of our possessions. We had no cutting tools besides that broken hatchet ; no twine, or canvas from which to twist it. We tried to draw threads from the ripped tarpaulin, but the tar had made them brittle. We had clothes enough for our persons, but from none could we get threads long enough in fibre to spin into fishlines or rabbit snares. We tried to make snares from the grass, and we caught rabbits, but the rabbits ate their way out. A rabbit which I knocked over with a rock was stolen from under my hands by a big wild-cat. Of stores there were none. Our first need was a regular food supply, for we baulked at crayfish, of which there were swarms.

The island was distinctly volcanic ; the earth was warm, but the nights were cool. Red had a pocket matchbox with watertight lid, and there were several matches in it ; but of fuel there was only the woodwork of the hut and the broken barrels inside it. We made a fire of some barrel wood, hoping to keep it going always ; but the sand that had been stuck into the tar while wet, to help preserve the contents, killed the fire. We gathered piles of grass, and by keeping short watches during the night contrived to keep a smoulder going.

" We must catch a goat, Skimps," said my comrade.
" We'll try to corner one among the crags."

For hours we drove goats. Towards dusk we separated
a big Billy from two companions and got between him and
the lower land. He had to climb. With rocks and howls we
scared him into taking a craggy pinnacle.

" Now, Skimps," said Saunders, spitting on his hands,
" you go ahead and drive him upwards. I'll stand by to
head him off if he jumps over you. Go on ! What're you
afraid of ? "

It was not fear so much as a sinking sensation at my
stomach. That old billy-goat turned to look at me a dozen
times, and in his eyes I saw stony callousness which was
doubtless equalled by his stony skull. When he had climbed
almost to the peak, and I still followed, Billy put down his
head, uttered a warning " Ba-aa-aahh ! " and began to scuff
the rock with his hind feet.

" Go on ! He's ours ! " growled Saunders, pinching my
stern. I was between devil and deep sea, for if that devil in
front ever hit me, I'd go sailing clear over Red's head into
the thirty-fathom depths of the crater. And behind me was
Red Saunders himself, who could pick me up with one hand
and boot my rear end without taking a hurried breath.

I crept upwards. Twice when the goat made as if to butt
me I made a grab for his beard, and he drew back. Again
I felt a merciless pinch behind, and heard Saunders curse at
me to go on, so up I went, breathing a hope that if I were
not utterly destroyed by the billy-goat I might land softly
when I fell. The goat stood on the pinnacle, and his eye was
red. I shuddered, and shut my own eyes to the terror before.
Something happened. I opened them. The great right arm
of my shipmate flashed over my shoulder, his great right fist
grabbed the billy-goat's forelegs, and with a snatch and a
whirl the beast was swung backwards over me, to crash
against the rock on which he stood.

That goat was old and high and tough, but he was the
beginning of much better things. His hide and sinews, bones
and hair, made us snares and fishing gear and covering for
our feet, which were badly broken and infected by the sharp
rocks. We stored our meat in the hut, and the rats stole it.
We placed it on rocks, and the cats ate it. In the end we
took the door from the hut, laid it on a pile of stones raised
in the centre of a wide pool, and placed our meat upon that.

Eleven weeks ! In one week our diet of parboiled goat

and fish and medicinal warm water reacted upon our dispositions. In two weeks we were not speaking to each other,
but, after eating, each took his lonely way and wandered over
the island seeking for anything which might be made into
a floatable raft. The loneliness was terrific. Even the penguins departed, and the goats' vocal noises sounded like
sardonic laughter.

Saunders had read much about all the islands of the sea
on which a freelance skipper might perchance find profit ;
but he had scarcely given a second thought to St. Paul or
Amsterdam Islands. He had told me a little : that Réunion
fishermen had once frequented St. Paul ; that whalers had
used it for watering ; that many ships had come to grief
there. Surely there must be left some trace of these. If only
we found a broken, half-buried boat we might work out our
own salvation. It was about the end of the seventh week that
Saunders sent a yell pealing around the crater that awoke
the echoes and reached me on the far side.

"Hey, Skimps ! Here's a find ! "

I went scuttling around like a crab, my heart thumping
at the sound of his voice again, regardless of the words. I
found him tugging at a piece of rotten wood in which was
a copper spike. The wood broke off in his hand as I reached
him.

"Dig ! " he grunted, and continued scraping away sand
from the jagged timber. With bits of the wood we uncovered
we dug until our hands were raw. By evening, our nails
broken to the quick, we had bared a row of timbers and
some copper sheathing. Most of the night was spent in
forming rough shovels from pieces of copper hammered round
split and rotten planking.

"We'll get enough wood out of it to make a raft, if not
a boat," Saunders said as we lay down to rest.

The job seemed hopeless from the beginning. Most of the
wood was rotten ; a piece of teak which would not crumble
sank when we tested its floating power in the crater. We
dug for two weeks, for hope lay at the bottom of the pit we
made. By the time we reached what seemed to be the hold
or saloon of a sizeable craft, we had collected half a ton of
nails and spikes, and a heap of wood as big as a small hay-
rick. But our great need was a rope. The wood split under
the nails when it didn't crumble in our hands. But we made
fishhooks and spears and traps ; our food problem was no
longer exciting.

He staggered out of the knee-deep sand with his find.

We made clothes of goatskins; and Saunders fashioned a dainty little needle from a fishbone, with which he sewed a lot of goatskin bags.

"We'll need 'em to carry water, Skimps, if we ever float away from here," he smiled.

At the end of the tenth week we faced our daily labour with nausea. Everything seemed futile. Saunders urged on the work, believing we might still find sound wood. Whatever the vessel had been, she was thoroughly broken apart, for her interior was full of sand and stones. Then one morning, starting to dig in the sand, our shovels struck something solid in the shifting heap. We had got beyond surprises; but still we shovelled, and presently I was hurled aside, Saunders flung down his shovel, and I could see his broad back straining as he lifted something with his hands.

"It's a box!" I gasped, scrambling to my feet.

"What eyesight!" grunted Red, and staggered out of the knee-deep sand to the open air with his find.

"Can't say what the old hooker was," he muttered, "but this looks like a cash-box to me, Skimps. Strong as the *Strachmore's* safe, too. Let's burn it open!"

We built a fire and tended it for hours, watching that little box as if it contained the riddle of life itself. Day was nearly done when the hard wood and metal of the box burst open; then we both ran into the embers and kicked madly at the pieces, for the dull gleam of gold was there. We kicked fire all over the place, and scraped a clear spot around the gold. All hot and yellow it lay, and when it grew cool we counted it—two thousand Australian sovereigns! I stared at Saunders in awe. It was my first—and only—treasure find. To me it looked like steam yachts and racehorses. Saunders uttered a queer laugh, and kicked the coin into a shower.

"I'd swap it all for a ten-foot dinghy!" he said. The thought was like a douche of icy water upon my enthusiasm.

In three days more we had fallen back into our wearisome routine. The coin was put into two of the water-bags and sunk in the crater near the shore. We fell into silences again, each plodding his own road, hoping against hope now to find rafting materials.

On the first morning of the twelfth week we rose from uneasy sleep. A little barque lay hove-to at a safe distance from shore, and a boat was on its way in.

"Skimps! Run like hell!" cried Saunders, and the boat's crew must have stared at the spectacle of two ragged castaways dashing madly from their rescuers. But Red Saunders was not mad. We reached the crater and lifted the coin bags. With speed we divided the gold into four smaller lots and tied up the bags. We tied two bags apiece around us, beneath our rags, already shapeless enough.

"Don't say a word!" he warned me. "If anybody's earned it, we have."

We went to meet the boat. The officer believed us when we said we had been startled. The barque was the *Actœan*, of Port Louis, and it was to Port Louis we went, to be made much of by the good people of Mauritius. It was all I could do to keep our secret. We divided the money in what I considered to be a very fair manner : Saunders took one half to pay for his schooner, and we took half each of the remainder. It gave me more money, in solid gold coin, than I had ever hoped to see in one pile in my life. We were too utterly destitute for the authorities to bother us.

HE LAUGHED AT DEATH

By

WILLIAM G. JOHNSON

WHEN the 321 V.C.'s sat down to dine with the Prince of Wales on November 9th, 1929, one man present, Lieut.-Colonel Arthur Drummond Borton, V.C., D.S.O., might possibly have experienced just one tinge of regret. For had the great function taken place two days earlier it would have coincided with the twelfth anniversary of his winning the coveted honour.

I know just a little about the winning of that V.C., and the man who won it, but I doubt whether the colonel would recall the fellow he swore at during that most critical moment of his career.

It happened in Palestine on November 7th, 1917. The day is Wednesday. We are hard on the heels of the Turk. Gaza has fallen, we have taken Beersheba, and are now on the way to Sheria. There are wells at Sheria, and we are very thirsty !

From dawn all Tuesday we have ploughed through sand and sun, no food to speak of—a nibble of bully and biscuit ; and, though warned at the start to hang on to our water, there isn't a man with a fly's bath in his bottle when we come to a halt in the evening. The grit on my teeth ! The mud on my tongue ! Lord ! I can taste it now ! Trekking the best part of a month, we are tired, ragged, verminous, and itchy with septic sores. Now we have halted and know we are close to the Turk. Petulantly through the twilight half-spent bullets whine out their last breath overhead. Nobody cares ; we are too fagged out to heed them. Dropping our packs, we unload the mules and feed the poor brutes a mouthful of corn.

We stretch our backs on the warm sand. Our aching backs ! Oh, for a little green apple to quench this blistering thirst ! Our spirits are low with fatigue and thirst and dirt. This hopeless, unending misery, this madness, this ultimate futility ! Would I could sleep for ever. Would I could wake in the morning and know all this for a nightmare. Ah me, have we not dreamed thus a thousand times through twenty unthinkable months !

I sleep. The four hours seem but a minute before I am awakened with the toe of a corporal's boot.

" Get dressed ! "

I rise and shiver, hating that corporal. I dress as a dog might shake himself. It is dark, but away to the left the sky glows red. I hear faint crackling sounds. The air is full of whistling lead.

" What's up ? "

" Moving off."

I groan and drag my stiff legs over to my mule and tug and punch him into his harness. Taking his cue from me, he shows his teeth in a succession of mighty yawns.

Shadowy forms are everywhere moving to and fro in the darkness ; tired and expressionless faces show palely out of the gloom, and pass.

" Stack packs ! "

Ah, we're in for it now. Grimly I smile as I hump my clobber to the pile and pitch it with the rest. I meet Silburn on the way.

" Another stunt, Sunbeam ? "

" Dunno, Gunga. Looks like it."

" What's that light over there ? "

" Johnny getting breezy. Blowing up his ammunition dumps."

" Best thing he can do with 'em," I grumble. " Why not let him get on with it ! "

" Fall in for rum ! "

" That's about corpsed it ! " mutters Tich Webster, divining that not for nothing is he to get a noggin of rum in the Plain of Sharon.

But the rum's good—dashed good it is ! It stings our leathery tongues and stops our shivering. It calms my damnable nerves. I join a little group ; Baker is there, the Welsh miner, our last remaining tenor, the red-headed, unquenchable " Scrounger."

" What's doing, Scrounger ? "

" Oh, nothing much. Clearing snipers. Colonel can't sleep."

I smile sceptically. " Who told you that ? "

" Harold," says Baker.

" I thought as much."

" A knowing bird, that mule of yours, Scrounger ! " sneers Holland.

" He is," replies Baker. " Fed on bully and four-by-two, is Harold. In return for which he tells me things."

" He's a b-blatant liar," growls Durrant. " That's w-what he is. It's b-bullets 'e wants, not b-bully ! "

Then Durrant is ashamed of himself. " Sorry, Baker. M-my nerves," he says, and turns away.

" I suppose you didn't ask him if we're getting any water to-night ? " inquires Evans.

" I did," answers Scrounger. " And he kicked me in the —— ! "

I go. Yes, as always, the officers will know all there is to be known when we start. We shall know nothing. We batten on rumours. Rumours ! And are led like lambs to the slaughter. My blood boils. Are we such cowards we may not be told ?

" Fall in ! No noise ! No talking ! "

We line up. Bombs and additional bandoliers of ammunition are served out. Ten rounds are loaded into the rifle magazines. Things look bad. Contrary to orders, I slip a cartridge " up the spout," adjusting the safety-catch.

Now we are shuffling out over the plain. Some one coughs ; entrenching tools, haversacks, empty water-bottles clatter and rattle ; here and there an iron-shod heel strikes a flint, igniting a shower of sparks ; a man stumbles—and that man surely curses.

Rob and I march side by side. We talk little. A York-shireman is Rob. His calmness reassures me. His sturdy bulk is a tower of strength to me. *Vive le* rum !

We trudge on in silence. I think of those at home—all warm and clean in bed. Perhaps they turn restlessly now and then and think of me. May they sleep deep and long to-night. *We* have work to do. Keep your eyes skinned, lad. Steady and cool ! Don't fumble. Strike—swift as the lightning ! I feel braced up and fit. God bless the distillers of rum !

I glance at Rob. His face in the dark is bloodless and dirty ; there are streaks of grime on the cheeks where sweat has dried in the night ; and a four-day growth of beard gives him a strangely spiritual expression. I think : This might be the face of Christ ! A distant look in his eyes, has Rob. *I* know. He's away and playing on his old violin. " How feeling, Rob ? " But Rob makes no reply.

Then the silvery voice of Baker, just behind me, breaks the silence, singing :

How lovely are the Messengers
That preach us the gospel of Peace ! . . .

" Put a sock in it, Baker ! " says a sergeant irritably.

The roar of the burning dumps grows louder ; and flames, leaping into view, send out cascades of sparks ; we hear the crack of the rifles ; bullets whistle shriller, filling the night with little spiteful devils. We stop to unload the mules. I strap on my chest and back the two wallets of spare Lewis gun magazines. The weight of them ! We are leaving the mules behind. *I* am the mule—a proper soldier now !

And now, suddenly, we enter a world writhing in its last agony. . . . Deafening crashes, flames and smoke, unearthly boomings and rumblings ! Above this din comes the splutter of machine-guns ; and, from a towering structure to the left, massive fragments of masonry are being pitchforked into the night ! It is grand ! The Turk is blowing up the world !

" Shiverin' saints ! " comes a voice.

" Strike me pink ! " says another ; and I catch a glimpse of an illuminated face uplifted for a moment in the glare.

Now we are off at the double. We zigzag about ; then, swinging to the right, plunge over the edge of a deep but narrow *wady*, and fall into dust and darkness. We regain our feet, bewildered, shaken. Officers dart hither and thither, shouting orders. " Steady now, boys ! Steady ! Lock-up, lock-up ! Keep together ! . . . For God's sake, don't bunch up ! "

Then out of the gloom and the confused medley of men emerges the colonel. I see him in the light of the conflagration. Like the rest, he has a steel helmet on his head ; but he wears no tunic, his shirt-sleeves are rolled up past his elbows. How clean and neat and fresh he looks ! His hair, sleek and parted, shines in the glare. He is lean and tall ; his face is red. He carries his head as though his neck was stiff. His gait seems a shade unsteady. He waves a cane in his hand, and in the crook of his other arm he hugs a football ! Borton is laughing !

" Twenty-second Queen's ! " he bellows. " It's your turn now to cover yourselves with glory ! Follow me ! "

" Stone me paralytic ! " gasps Tich.

He leads us along the *wady*, every gun in creation going mad at us. In that dusty inferno we are merely shadows. We come to an opening in the *wady*. Borton gets across, but not so others following ; they seem to stagger and wilt and crumple up and fade away into the gloom. A murderous fire from concealed machine guns sprays death along that alley. . . .

"Stand fast!" cries the colonel. "Now quickly . . . in twos and threes!"

Rob and I plunge into the abyss. I hear a cry and Rob sinks into the dust. A momentary halt. I see heaving breasts all round me, and drawn, white faces. I hear curses unmentionable. I curse unmentionably too. But there's one man as cool as a water-melon—a man with a stiff neck, and a football under his arm!

"Fix bayonets!" yells the colonel. And the shining things leap from the scabbards and flash in the light as they click on the standards. They seem alive and joyous; they turn us into fiends, thirsty for slaughter. We scramble out of the *wady*.

"Charge!" And away goes the colonel, flourishing his ludicrous cane!

The hail of lead! We greet it with a blood-curdling shout, ripping our throats; and, as surely as I have eyes, there's Borton driving ahead, taking the hill at a bound, and kicking the football!

Breathless, we gain the top. The Turks have bolted. Torn tents flat in the wind; pots and pans are about our feet. Away now from the flaming dumps we pick our way at a walk, peering into the dark, bayonets ready to stab. Then I go sprawling over a vessel of porridge standing among the remains of a weed fire. I rip out an oath as an ember burns me. Scrambling up, a sticky mess, I flounder over something that is warm and groans as I clutch it. Again I stagger forward, and a strand of barbed wire catches me in the leg. I tear myself out of its grip. Near me, Scrounger Baker trips over a tent rope, and, attempting to rise, is shot. A raking fire sweeps the darkness, but still we advance. The ground is rough and treacherous. Men are falling. Where's the colonel? Has he also stopped one? I hear his voice! God save Borton! *We* know him. The mad major of Gallipoli! He'll fetch us through, this man with a broken neck!

Suddenly the darkness lifts, paling to grey, and a ridge looms out ahead. "Down! Down! Down!" and flat as a sack I go. Men are moving on the skyline. What use to take aim! I blaze away madly, striving to silence those swine on the ridge. I sweat. I gibber with glee when a form flings up its arms, dances a second between earth and sky, and vanishes.

A little ahead of me, on rising ground, lie two pals working a Lewis gun ; its bark, its spiteful rat-tat-tat, is music to me.

Spells of the tensest concentration are followed by moments of terrible fatigue. My strength ebbs away ; I feel unutterably weak ; I could sleep. There succeed intervals when my senses seem to stalk abroad, icily alert and alive ; periods when my mind is a whirling wheel, my brain a furnace white-hot, my pulse a sledge-hammer. When my nerves seem about to snap there comes instants of exquisite calm. Death ! What does it matter ? I am alone. Surrounded by friend and foe, I am alone in the world ! But the will to live wells up—the desire to live is a torment, a torture, a devilish, damnable agony !

A man near by groans and rolls over. A yard or so away an officer lies quiet as though sleeping. I see a friend writhe and twist. I hear a man scream. A sergeant rising from the ground, staggers forward, shot in the back ! I hear sobbing. No stretcher bearers here. Vaguely, as in a dream, I am conscious of flashes and rumblings overhead and regular crashes and slams to our rear. Where's *our* artillery ? Where are the guns ? Bring up the guns, O God !

The barrel of my rifle blisters my fingers ; then the bolt sticks fast, fouled with grit. I tear and swear at it, and my hands goes stiff with cramp. The reeking breech sickens me.

Now I become aware that the gun ahead is silent, and motionless the men beside it : one on his back with his eyes open, his hand outstretched as though beckoning ; the other, his head on his arm. I look at the thing in a daze. It is getting lighter. A clammy sweat breaks out on me. *I* am a Lewis gunner ! Turning my head, I gaze at the ridge. My hand shakes as I grip my rifle and take aim ; but the bolt is jammed, the trigger limp. I lie there panting. . . . " You're a coward—a dirty, crawling coward ! That one gun . . . that one gun might stop those . . . curs ! "

A stone, struck by a bullet, jumps from the ground and hits me on the knuckle. It stings me to terrible anger. Next to me, Tom Rolls gives a yell as blood spurts from his wrist and splashes me in the face. I spring to my feet and race to the gun, heaving aside a corpse to get to it. I lie down to the gun, between the two dead men, and . . . I feel fine !

But the magazine will not rotate. I strain and strain at it. The cocking handle is stuck fast. I squeeze the trigger. I change the magazine. I talk to it, swear at it, do impossible things to it. Then, glancing down the barrel casing to the sights, I see that the muzzle is frayed and torn and broken, and the gas-regulator blown clean away. The gun is as dead as the men beside it.

At this moment the colonel appears. His face is black and sweaty ; his shirt is torn to ribbons. " Don't lie here ! " he roars. " Come on ! . . . With me ! "

We scramble to our feet and follow him down a long, rocky slope in the half-light, but heavy fire breaks out anew. We cannot stand it, and are forced into the dust again. Ripping out the bolt of my rifle, I lick it clean, spitting out the grit. It is hot and scorches my tongue. Now a worse enemy attacks. Shells scream about us, exploding overhead, on the ground, everywhere ; they tear up the dust ; they cover us with stones ; the air is a hell of whizzing shrapnel. I see Harman with his back ripped open. We bite into the earth. Our mouths are full of muck. Not so Borton. He's on his feet (has he yet been off his feet ?) ; he crouches, his neck thrust outward. His grey-blue eyes are searching, searching. . . .

" Ah, good ! " he cries, and, tossing away his cane, pulls out his revolver. " Now I have them ! Follow me ! "

I go staggering after him down the slope. Had every man been shot he would have gone alone. Dimly ahead I see a hedge of stunted cactus swathed in smoke from which come flashes—white, knife-like flashes. Then I see figures moving, and, pausing, fire from my hip.

" Don't stand there like a palsied idiot ! " shouts the colonel. " Come on ! "

I go on. Something warm is coursing down my face and trickles into my eyes, half-blinding me. I stumble on—my head is bursting. . . .

" *Camarade ! Camarade !* " Men in grey-coloured uniforms and " pork-pie " caps are coming forward, their arms above their heads.

" Austrians ! " The colonel's voice is hoarse and husky. He rams his revolver into a man's ear.

Beyond—across the open—men run for their lives ; and I, breathless, land up against the smoking nozzle of an artillery field gun, the point of my bayonet stuck into the tunic-button of a burly Austrian bombardier ; while the colonel, with a man or two, strives desperately—but without success —to get another gunner to turn his gun and fire on his fleeing comrades !

Daybreak ! I stand panting before my prisoner, a breath

from whose smoke-blackened mouth could bowl me over. He towers above me, smiling. I am trembling.

"Mercy, Johnny," says he quietly, dropping a sooty hand and holding it out to me. "You brave feller. You haf face all bloody ! Have mercy ! "

He smiles. He looks a decent sort. His glasses and ginger hair remind me of Baker. Scrounger Baker ! Rob ! It is touch and go with the Austrian. Blood for blood ! He smiles. *Camarade !* I cannot kill him. . . .

Next to me on my right, little Sid Avery has a similar problem confronting him, and quickly he solves it, as well as mine :

"Cigarettes . . . or yer life ! " puffs Sid.

THE CROSSING OF THE
CASITAS PASS

By
DARE DU BOIS PHILLIPS

AT that time in California there was a tremendous craze for record-breaking in the motoring world. Principally the attempts on the various records were made on the roads, to the excitement, and often peril, of ordinary travellers, and measured stretches on certain roads had become recognised as something like unofficial race-tracks.

The competition in the struggle to establish new records was kept alive by the agents for the various makes of cars. Most of these agents were racing-drivers, and their fights to outdo their rivals over measured distances, and thus establish their particular brand as definitely superior to all others, were intense.

That stretch of road between Los Angeles and San Francisco had come to be accepted as a standard one, along which the agents regularly vied with one another. For road records, it became the most famous in all California.

Its popularity among record-seekers had been due to the battles which had taken place there between the agents for two different makes of cars : the Pope-Hartford and the Cadillac. " Wild Bill " Ruess was the Pope-Hartford agent, and the brothers Lee (Kyler and Don) were the Cadillac representatives.

They were an energetic trio. One fine morning Ruess would set out in his Pope-Hartford, and set up some amazing new time for the 'Frisco run. Kyler and Don would promptly get busy with the tuning of their racing Cadillac, and one fine morning (fine days are not rare in California) would roar up the mountains and down the valleys of the same run, knocking the new record sideways. Wild Bill, undismayed, would get to work on his Pope-Hartford again : smash ! would go the Lees' record. Then Kyler and Don would start off again. . . .

They were every one of them superb drivers, and the

performances they put up, over difficult roads, were amazing. They undoubtedly succeeded in demonstrating what was what in motor-car manufacture, and made Pope-Hartfords and Cadillacs the most popular cars in the State.

I, myself, was agent for the Haynes car, and naturally, this brilliant record-making, though exciting my admiration, did not make me very pleased. The public could not be expected to buy many Haynes cars, when they were already buying Pope-Hartfords and Cadillacs like hot cakes.

Besides the successful competition of these rival makes, I found myself at yet another disadvantage in endeavouring to sell the Haynes car. At the time the repute of the brand was under a cloud, owing to the unwary introduction in the past of a semi-floating rear-axle, which, in the wet season, would keep breaking, if the car got stuck in the limpet-like Californian mud. Since the failure of this type, the company had scrapped the semi-floating and substituted a full-floating (" Timkin ") axle, which was a complete success.

But the unfortunate semi-floating axle was still remembered by the public, and they shied clear of the Haynes in distrust. I decided it was up to me to restore confidence in my wares. The other agents were always up to some stunt or other to advertise their special makes, and I made up my mind that it was time I started a little stunting too.

At length I fixed on the lowering of the famous Los Angeles-San Francisco record as what was to be an excellent start for my campaign ; that, at least, was my intention !

My first requirement was a good mechanic for my record-attempts. Accordingly I inserted advertisements in the Santa Barbara Press, and received various applicants for the post in my garage on State Street. None of them, however, satisfied me sufficiently to give him the job.

Then one day a tough-looking *peon* appeared, armed with excellent references. I had the usual distrust of half-breeds, and didn't fancy the idea of having one with me, but the man's references were good, and, on looking him over, I found I rather took to him.

He was short and disproportionately broad for his inches, obviously powerful. He was certainly a hard-bitten specimen, but his black eyes were bright and attractive, and he had a charming smile, when he *did* smile, which was rarely. He seemed eager for the job, when I warned him that I meant to do some hard racing ; and thereupon I took him on as my mechanic.

I was never to regret it. His loyalty was such as I have never encountered, before or since, and he was as honest as the day. His name was Machado, and he became my friend, as well as my faithful follower. During our association he went through a number of exceedingly tough spots with me— as you shall hear—but he never once complained or shied from sharing danger with me.

At the time I had a splendid racing Haynes with me, which Machado and I promptly got to work on in preparation for our attempt on the Los Angeles-'Frisco record. As a mechanic, Machado turned out to be as good as his references, and soon we had our auto tuned up to concert pitch.

We had little time in which to make our attempt, before the rainy season arrived and made the roads impassable. Accordingly we drove to Los Angeles, from which we set out almost immediately again on our gruelling run to San Francisco. From Los Angeles to Ventura, over the barrier of the Casitas Mountains into Santa Barbara, up the long stretch into San Jose, we made good time, and were, indeed, a little ahead of the record, when we reached San Jose.

Here we were within sixty miles of our goal, and, having merely to cross the San Jose Mountains into 'Frisco, we were already beginning to congratulate ourselves on smashing the record—which stood at the moment, if I remember rightly, to Wild Bill. Optimistically and impatiently, we roared up the steep San Juan grade through the mountains.

It was between ten o'clock and ten-thirty at night when we made out two red lights waving to-and-fro about half-way up the grade we were climbing. Concluding we were approaching a section along which road-repairs were being carried out, we cursed our luck in being held up, and slackened our pace. We could not know that we were to be held up in more ways than one !

As we drew nearer we saw that the red lights were situated in the very middle of the highway, and we reduced our movement to a snail's pace. No sooner had we done so, than three men appeared like magic from the tangled hillside alongside the road, and Machado and I found ourselves staring into the muzzles of two large, old-fashioned Colt 45's. The wielders of these ponderous firearms were a wild-looking, ragged pair of powerful build, and their companion was equally fierce and down-at-heel in his aspect. The latter went over our pockets with practised deftness and thoroughness as we sat with our hands up, closely covered by his two confederates.

Presently two more ragamuffins appeared—probably these two had been waving the red lights we had seen, and they aided in the search, which did not exclude the interior of the car. They collected, among other belongings, a gold watch and chain and about $100 from me and $25 from poor old Machado. Eventually, they appeared to realise that there was no more to be got out of us.

" Well—can we clear off now ? " I asked.

" Yeah," said one, scowling portentously, " but *don't get gay* ! "

As mysteriously as they had come, our five assailants then disappeared into the dark hillside, but small, furtive sounds told us that they were still hanging about nearby : it was an eerie sensation.

Puzzling over the meaning behind the last cryptic remark, I was in the act of letting out my clutch, when we heard a series of shots—the unmistakable explosions of big Colts— and we felt the car shudder, as if to a succession of blows. We heard a crashing sound from the dark underbrush into which the footpads had gone ; then silence.

We climbed out, and examined our unfortunate car, and found that its tyres were perforated and slashed with bullet-holes. The bandits had made certain that they would have time for a clear get-away, before we could raise the alarm against them.

I turned ruefully to Machado.

" Well, this looks like the end of the day's run. We're not beating any records this trip."

We managed to get the car turned. 'Frisco lay just over the range, but there was no hope of reaching the city on such tyres. Disconsolately we coasted down the grade back to San Jose. . . .

By the time we got our car back to Santa Barbara, and tuned up, ready for a second attempt (we would not make the mistake of going unarmed this time !) we found that the rainy season had already arrived, and we were told that the roads were hopeless now for ordinary traffic, far less record-breaking.

" What do they mean—' hopeless ' ? " I demanded of Machado, who knew the route like the back of his hand. I was still fuming at the way in which the 'Frisco record had been snatched from our grasp, and this fresh snag was making me irritable.

Machado explained : the Californian mud, landslides, etc.

"It is hopeless to try for a record in the rainy season. We could not even cover the distance."

"But there must be some way of making the run," I said impatiently. "What's the particular reason why we shouldn't?"

Machado shrugged expressively.

"The Casitas Pass. Landslides all the way—and mud. No one has ever crossed the Casitas Mountains in the rainy season. It is closed even to a horse and buggy."

"Right-o," I said rashly. "We'll cross the Casitas, if we can't smash the 'Frisco record. I don't much care what we do, but we must pull some sort of stunt if we want to put Haynes cars on the map. We'll have a shot at that pass. . . what do you say?"

Machado smiled, and his eyes gleamed eagerly.

"If the Captain says so. . . ."

The Casitas Mountains are those fingers of the Sierra Nevada which push their way between the towns of Ventura and Santa Barbara. The road between the two towns passes through the wild Casitas Pass, whose bed is a bouldery creek, and whose tree-clad sides rise up almost sheer to the summits of the mountain-ridges. The road is cut through one of these sides, and in some places runs nearly two thousand feet above the level of the creek.

We had some notions of what we might be expected to face in crossing the Pass, and we prepared ourselves for most eventualities we could think of by taking aboard rations, spares, block-and-tackle, spades, and other stores, in the little town of Ventura, before setting off up the Pass.

The word had gone round the town that a crazy Englishman and a half-witted Dago were going to try the Pass, and half the town turned out to gibe or warn us—mostly to gibe! The Deputy Sheriff also appeared at our departure, and solemnly warned us that we made our attempt on our own responsibility and that he would not trouble to send out search-parties if we should not turn up again, as he would take it for granted that we had met our deaths!

This was not a cheerful farewell, but, combined with the jeers of the rest, it made us all the more determined to get through to Santa Barbara somehow.

The road runs up from Ventura, in the manner described, till it reaches a point some 2,000 feet above the valley-bed, then drops down towards Santa Barbara. We attained the crest with relative ease, although several times we were forced to remove boulders and masses of earth from the road-way, and squeeze past others, too massive to shift.

We had just passed the crest and were picking our way downhill, when we found ourselves face to face with a terrify-ing barrier. We jammed on our brakes in horror, for, just in front of us, we saw the brink of a sickening chasm, made by a landslide of vast dimensions. The mountain-side, washed away by the rains, had here simply crumpled away, taking with it nearly two hundred yards of the road. The rocks, trees and earth dislodged by the avalanche were strewn in thousands of tons down the precipitous slope and heaped up in the creek 1,500 feet below.

We looked at each other, white-faced at the sight of the results of this awful cataclysm, appalled at the prospect of lowering our car with block-and-tackle that frightful distance into the creek. . . .

At that same moment a terrible thing happened. We heard a horrible sound of grinding and rending; then we saw half the hillside behind us trembling—moving. . . . The roadway was moving . . . the ground under our feet seemed to be shifting gently in the direction of the cañon's brink. . . . I do not think I have experienced, before or since, the sensation of overwhelming panic which took me by the throat, in the face of that gigantic upheaval of Nature.

We saw loose stones rolling, shooting out into space. Then the hillside crumbled, and great tracts of the roadway to our rear simply dropped away into nothing. There was a frightful grinding roar, as the avalanche gained momentum. . . . Great trees thundered down the slope, huge boulders bounced like giants' footballs. The whole valley echoed and re-echoed with the thunder of the slipping mountainside, then gradually the roaring diminished, until only sullen shifting sounds were left on the air, and earth poured down-hill in dour, slow trickles. . . .

We stood on a narrow platform, formed by the only small stretch of road for several hundred yards. Above us towered the insecure hillside, and below swept that terrible slope. Looking down, one saw the tree-tops piled in tiers, as if growing outwards from what seemed a vertical wall.

Advance and retreat were both denied to us. Now we had no choice but to make the attempt to lower our car to the far-distant creek.

Seeking for an object to which we might moor our tackle, we were forced to fall back on a pine-tree, whose position, on

We jammed on our brakes in horror.

the very lip of the chasm, had struck us before as insecure for our purpose. However, there being nothing else at hand, we had no option but to use it. Having tested its strength and solidity to the best of our ability, we moored our tackle round the trunk, then, climbing cautiously down the almost sheer slope to a position some fifty feet below, we took hold of the rope and, together, began lowering our gallant conveyance into space.

We had let it down scarcely twenty yards from the road when we felt a sudden give in the resistance to our pulling. Our eyes, straining fearfully upwards, saw the tree, to which our tackle was fixed, give a sudden cant forwards and out-wards, as its roots tugged through the crumbled earth. The sudden give in the resistance to our heaving was fatal to our balance. We had been pulling forwards, with the rope braced over our shoulders. Now we were precipitated abruptly backwards, and reacting involuntarily to the sudden sense of instability, let go the rope and flung out our hands for some-thing to steady our toppling bodies.

The moment we released it, the rope flicked upwards like a whip. We had no time to observe what took place after that, for we were hurtling down that frightful slope, rolling and bumping ; sometimes dropping clear through space.

Fortunately there was a tree trunk to pull us up, before our momentum increased more than it did ; otherwise, there is no doubt whatever but that we would have been dashed to pieces before we reached the foot of that fearful slope. As it was, our flying bodies, shooting downwards in a cloud of loose earth and stones—a small avalanche of our own making —met the tree trunk with a sickening crash.

As a matter of fact, that impact broke three of my ribs, and dislocated Machado's right shoulder ; but it saved our lives. Strangely enough, although I was conscious of sudden spasms immediately afterwards, it was not until two days later that the pain grew severe enough to make me sure that I had broken bones. From the first, of course, there was no doubt as to the nature of Machado's injury.

The less said about our descent of that 1,500 feet of slope to the valley-bed the better. Ill and weak and winded, we slid painfully from the refuge of one tree-trunk to another, until, at last, we found ourselves on a clean bed of shingle.

About a score of yards away lay a shapeless heap of what looked like scrap-metal. Surely no one but Machado or I could have recognised our familiar racing Haynes ! The sight of her was enough to make us weep. In our battered condition, we had no heart to examine this pile of apparently worthless metal, to ascertain the extent of the frightful damage caused by its transit, in a series of ever-quickening jerks and bumps and crashes, from the road so many feet above.

It seemed as if ill-luck, so unpleasantly in evidence on the occasion of our attempt on the 'Frisco record, was dogging us persistently during this effort as well. Yet, in the midst of our gloom, we saw something which inclined us to believe that good luck was being fairly well distributed among the bad.

This was the sight, a little way down the valley, of smoke rising in the air, and the tip of a roof beneath the smoke. At this point in the Pass, the opposite mountain-side took on a gentler slope, and its great height dwindled away into a series of undulating foothills. It was among the dales of these less harsh hills that the building, to which the scrap of roof visible belonged, lay. We slogged wearily in the direction of the smoke.

At length we found ourselves approaching a small fruit-farm. The farmer, a decent old fellow who had immigrated to these parts from England many years before, was very friendly and hospitable. We patched Machado's shoulder up as best we could, and after that we settled down to a heavenly sleep, before deciding what our next step was to be.

In the morning Machado, the farmer and I returned to the scene of our adventures, and examined the wreck.

The four wheels were crumpled and useless, the petrol and oil-tanks were completely wrenched off; so was the radiator. The chassis, in fact, was almost stripped bare. The chassis itself, however, seemed sound, though much bent; the front-axle was bent like a bow. The chassis was our hope.

" By George, Machado ! " I declared, " we'll ride into Santa Barbara on this old 'bus yet ! "

The farmer's sons were dispatched to Santa Barbara with a note from me to our spares-department in East Corilla Street. They brought back, among a collection of odd spare-parts, four wheels, four tyres, two basket-seats for testing, a radiator, and oil and petrol-tanks

We set to work, building a car of sorts on the old chassis. The front-axle we straightened out by building a fire, heating the axle, and hammering it out well enough to serve our purpose, on an anvil formed by a large, flat-topped boulder.

At long last we got our astonishing conveyance to go. But, if we thought we could now bowl easily down the creek to Santa Barbara, we reckoned without the famous mud of the country, which is cousin to the *adobe* of which the Mexicans build their walls and houses. We had no sooner left the shingle than we were stuck fast. The adhesive qualities of this kind of mud will be understood, when it is pointed out that cars, which are caught in it during the rainy season, are abandoned if the mud begins to harden, and are often allowed to remain permanently where they have become embedded, like joists in hardened concrete. In some parts these derelict cars may be found lodged immovably, many of which have lain for years.

I begged the farmer to lend me a team of horses to pull us out. He had no horses on his farm capable of draught-work, but he obligingly borrowed a couple from a neighbouring farm.

In laborious fashion, alternately making ground over patches of shingle and being hauled out of the mud by the horse-team, we made our slow way down the base of the Pass towards Santa Barbara.

Our entry into the town caused a sensation of the first order. We were accorded a triumphal welcome, and were made a tremendous fuss of. For days we were fêted, and almost smothered with honours, among which not the least pleasing was the concession, granted by the municipal authorities, to drive about the town for a week with an open exhaust, as an advertisement for our make of car, travelling about Santa Barbara with open exhaust being strictly against the regulations and sternly denied to all our rivals.

For my own part, I was unable to enjoy these tokens of honour to our feat to the fullest extent, as, on the second day, the pain in my side sent me inquiringly to a doctor, who told me of my three broken ribs.

The Californians had hitherto believed that, in the rainy season, the Casitas Pass was utterly impassable, and they could not shower enough praise on us for our success in crossing it. They more than made up for their former mocking doubts with a terrific generosity of acclamation. In the dry season, one hour and ten minutes is a fair time to take, crossing the Pass. We had taken four heart-breaking days in the rainy season, but we had done it, which was more than any one else could say.

The press, of course, made the most of our exploit.

Machado and I found ourselves the centre of a dazzling flare of publicity. We were nearly swamped with interviewers and cameramen. In every self-respecting journal appeared our photographs under some such screaming headline as : " CASITAS PASS CONQUERED ! " For some days we attained a fame almost equal to that of movie-stars or murderers.

AN ATTACK ON PIRATES

By
E. J. TRELAWNY

The life of Edward John Trelawny has a ring of old-time fiction about it. At school he became the ringleader of a revolt and tried to set fire to the building. He was dispatched home under guard and his father placed him immediately in the Royal Navy. Within a few years he had rebelled and deserted and thrown in his lot with a Dutch American called De Ruyter, who commanded a privateer under the French flag. The following is one of their adventures in the Eastern seas, and it takes place about 1810.

ONE day we descried a strange sail to the westward. She bore down on us, and we, finding we outran her, shortened sail, till she came near enough for us to make her out. De Ruyter then knew her to be a French corvette. We hoisted a private signal, which they answered. We hove to. At sunset she came under our quarters ; and after some conversation with the captain, De Ruyter went on board, where he had a long conference. On his return we altered our course for the island of Madagascar.

We then understood from De Ruyter that the corvette had been sent to examine into an act of piracy, committed, it was supposed, by the Maratti, a formidable nest of brigands, on the north point of the island of Madagascar.

We continued in company. The weather being particularly fine, with little wind stirring, we passed our time very pleasantly, in giving parties alternately on board the corvette and the grab. Aston, who had been a prisoner in France when a midshipman, spoke French as perfectly as De Ruyter. At daylight we used to separate, and keep a look out to windward ; and towards sunset we bore down, and remained together during the night.

Soon after we fell in with and boarded some Arab trading-vessels. They had been plundered ; the greater part of their cargoes and crews were taken out, leaving merely a few old men to work the vessels, with a little water and rice. This was committed by a fleet of eighteen Maratti proas, each

393

having from eighteen to forty men on board. It appeared that this fleet was bound to some of the islands in the Mozambique Channel.

De Ruyter now conferred with the French commander; and his advice was that we should, in the absence of the greatest part of the pirates, effect a landing at St. Sebastian, surprise them during the night, plunder and destroy their fortifications, burn their town, and rescue their prisoners; for doubtless they were loaded there, as they had kept possession of two of the largest of the Arab traders. This was agreed to; and the corvette supplied us with two of her brass guns, and lent us fifteen of her soldiers.

Without anything particular happening, we got into 15° 20' South latitude, ran on till we saw the high land of Madagascar, and kept to the north-east side of the island till we had run well inshore, when we sent a boat, and brought off some fishermen, who gave us information. We then crept round the land, to the north, at night, De Ruyter piloting, being in sight of the north point of Cape St. Sebastian, which stretches far out to sea, in the form of an estuary. Taking advantage of the twilight, De Ruyter piloted us through a narrow channel in the recess; and, before midnight, we brought to as close to the rocks as we could on the east side, having the cape between us and the town, by which means we were unobserved.

It was a cloudy night, with frequent showers of rain. We got out our boats, and landed a hundred and twenty officers and men well armed: eighty from the corvette, and forty from the grab. To do the Frenchman justice, he felt no envy of De Ruyter's superior knowledge; on the contrary, he insisted on his taking the command, and gave his officers orders to implicitly obey De Ruyter in every particular, he himself staying on board the corvette.

On landing, De Ruyter divided the men into three parties, retaining to himself and the first officer the strongest, consisting of fifty men, armed with muskets and bayonets; a French lieutenant commanded thirty-five, and I thirty. I had a part of De Ruyter's favourite band of Arabs, armed with their lances and short carbines. We kept on together, till we got round the cape; then De Ruyter ordered me to ascend the rocks, and keep round the hill, nearly at the foot of which the pirates' town was situated, till I arrived immediately above it. The lieutenant was directed to keep along the beach, till he was in line with me; while De Ruyter, with the main body, went directly forward. We were all to march as near as possible, and by every precaution to avoid discovery. When we had taken up our respective positions, we were to conceal ourselves till just before he dawn of day, when the main body would fire a rocket, which, on being answered by us, was to be the signal for a simultaneous advance and attack. We were to make what observations we could, under cover of the night, as to the readiest means of getting into the town, which was defended by low mud walls, having three entrance ports. On taking possession of these entrances, we were each to leave a party to keep them, who were to kill or make prisoners all who attempted to escape, whilst the remainder attacked those within. If any of us should be previously discovered, or if we should be attacked, we were to retreat to the main body. After some other instructions, De Ruyter commanded us to kill none, at our peril, but those with arms in their hands ; and particularly to avoid doing injury to the women, children and prisoners.

My party had some distance to go, and up a rugged and precipitous path, where we were suddenly stopped by a black and deep ravine, or chasm, at the bottom of which we heard the dashing of water. It would have been folly to attempt to cross here ; for a couple of men, on the other side, might have perhaps opposed us with success. We therefore went lower down the mountain ; and it was with great toil, and loss of time, that we crossed to the opposite side. My impetuosity spurred me on ; and, when it wanted little more than half an hour to dawn, our scouts in advance gave us the welcome intelligence of being near our destination. I now halted our party, and advanced with two men. We descended a narrow sheep-path, amidst broken and stony ground, overgrown with prickly pears, low shrubs, and clumps of the palm cocoa. We heard distinctly the surf breaking on the beach with the monotonous regularity of the ticking of a clock at night. The ground became smoother, and we discerned, close under us, the low huts of the town, huddled together, and looking like a multitude of large white ant-hills, or bee-hives. We then came to some ruins, on a conical hill, up which one of the Arabs climbed on all fours, like a jackal, and found it was deserted. I sent the other man back, to bring up our party, as this was a capital post to occupy, in case of surprise. With great caution I then descended to the wall of the town— it was low, and in a crumbling state—till I came to two or three palm trees, where a mud hut was built on the wall, like a swallow's nest. Below there was an entrance, or rather a hole, which evidently led to the interior. Having examined the place well, we hastily returned. The clouds gave indications of breaking in the east. The rain was still falling. I crept down with ten men, and advanced under the shadow of the wall, till within pistol-shot of the entrance. There taking our position, we impatiently awaited the concerted signal from De Ruyter.

The night was tardily withdrawing her dusky canopy, and the morning advanced gloomily. The hushed stillness was ominously broken by the whizzing noise of the rocket signal, flying like a meteor over the devoted Maratti town. It evidently came, not as it should have done, from De Ruyter, but from the lieutenant, being exactly opposite to my position, which showed that the lieutenant's party was discovered, or anticipated discovery. I replied to it ; and nearly at the same moment another rocket ascended from De Ruyter. This commanded an immediate attack ; and scarcely had it risen to the height of the lance I held in my hand, ere I had forced the trifling impediments at the entrance ; and, in my haste, stumbled over something on the ground. The man, for such it was, essayed to rise. I dropped my lance, and grappled him by the throat. The greater part of my Arabs rushed in. I called out to force open the inner entrance ; which done, the faint light showed us four or five of the Maratti rising from the ground, commencing their war-cry. These were despatched quickly. The man I held scarcely needed the aid of the creese, which I forced through his breast into the sandy floor.

A commotion was now raised within. We got through the rude outworks into the interior. The remainder of my men were dropping down inside the wall, which, with the aid of their lances, they had scaled. A noise of the assault on the other side was growing high ; and presently we heard the sharp report of firearms. I left a portion of my men to guard the entrance, and advanced, as previously arranged, to the centre of the habitations ; the inmates of which—for the surprise was complete—came out in twos and threes, in great confusion and terror. Those who crossed our path we speared ; and those seeking to save themselves by flight we fired at. We gave them not an instant to rally, till we arrived at the ruins of a considerable building in the centre, which had been erected as a magazine and court of guard by the Portuguese or Dutch. Here having taken possession, we halted. Presently

the lieutenant, and then De Ruyter, came up ; he said,
" Well done, my lad ! always first in danger." Then leaving
an officer and twenty men to keep this place, we advanced
in three parties, dividing the men equally, with strict
injunctions to make all the prisoners we could, and send them
in to this post.

De Ruyter told me to go round to the port I had entered,
as there would be an attempt to escape that way to the
mountains ; and while he was speaking, a sharp fire was
opened from that quarter. I hastened thither, amidst a
scattering fire of muskets and matchlocks, and the yells and
shrieks of men, women and children, running about in all
directions. The war-cry of the Arabs, and the *Allons !* and
Vive ! of the French were so loud, that I could not hear either
my own voice, or distinguish the report of my own carbine.
On nearing the place at which we had entered, we saw a
mingled heap of naked savages, of all ages, men and women,
armed with creeses, guns, knives, and bamboo spears ; others
with their children, and many loaded with their goods, all
rushing on. I stopped my men, and gave them a volley ; and
as they were facing about, we charged them with our lances.
They stood on their defence with the fierceness of desperation,
and a few of our men dropped ; but they resisted without
method, impeded by their own numbers, and a panic seizing
on them, they separated to escape. A great many were
butchered, and no prisoners made ; for blood is like wine,
the more we have the more we crave, till, excited to madness,
one excess leads to another ; and it is easier to persuade a
drunken man to desist from drinking whilst he can hold his
glass, than a man, whose hands are reeking with blood, to
desist from shedding more.

My fellows rushed about in ungovernable disorder,
destroying all whom they met ; and I was obliged to remain
myself at the outlet, until I had enforced ten or twelve of them
to keep that post. As the light grew clearer, objects became
distinct, and I beheld the confusion and slaughter going on
within. My senses were dizzy with the blood I had shed,
and seen shed. The Maratti, environed in their own walls,
essayed every outlet, sought every means to provide for the
escape of their women and their children, and, finding none,
they fought with the fearlessness or heedlessness of ensnared
tigers. They ran from gate to gate with blind fury, and threw
themselves headlong on the bayonets and lances. They had
never heard of mercy, yielding, or asking for quarter. There

were no such words in their language. They had been
accustomed to shed blood from their childhood, whether of
men or monkeys, with equal indifference ; and they believed
all the world to be of the self-same nature. As for Europeans,
they were always treated by them, if they fell into their hands,
like fish—hanged up in the sun to dry. Old men, women, and
children, therefore, preferred to die fighting ; and, thus far,
we had not a single prisoner. They would have succeeded in
forcing my position had not De Ruyter come to my aid.
I feel extreme pain and shame at remembering the horrible
ferocity with which I slaughtered these besotted barbarians,
and more at the savage and inhuman delight with which I
did so. It would have ended in their total extermination, had
they not effected several outlets in their mouldering walls.

The only wound I received was in the leg, from a woman,
who attempted to hamstring me as, in hurrying along, I
stepped on her body ; and the first symptom of my returning
reason was, on discovering her sex, instead of crushing her
with my uplifted foot, to have her carried to the main guard ;
this was the first prisoner we had taken. It was then De
Ruyter came to me, and said, " We have had blood enough.
Call our people off, and let the poor devils go. Seize what
prisoners you can, but take no more lives : and lead your
men to the huts on that sandhill ; there you will find their
Arab and other prisoners ; take care they are not sacrificed
in the fray ; and send them to the guard. Bandage your leg
—you are bleeding fast."

I did so and went, as directed, to the sandhill. It was
well I did, or we should not have had a prisoner to release ;
for the women were killing them, as they lay bound hand
and foot on the ground in heaps. These dark hags were
despatched. Then entering a small matted tent, affixed to
a larger one, the first object which struck me was a naked
gaunt Arab, bound and fastened to a short stake driven into
the earth. He was covered with stabs, weltering in his own
blood ; yet though bound, helpless, and dying, his unsub-
dued spirit still shone like a chieftain's. An aged, a decrepit
she-devil was lying on his prostrate body, she having slipped
in the gore, and with a coco-nut knife in her hand, was
hacking at him with feeble blows. Her fallen victim held
fast her left hand in his teeth ; and at his feet, huddled up in
a corner, was a young girl, almost naked, screaming in affright,
" Oh, father, father, let me get up "—with her bound hands
stretched out, struggling to rise, but pressed down by the

strong limbs of the man, who thus sheltered her from the fiendish old woman. I seized on the cloth band round the Hecate's loins, and, lifting her withered carcass up in the air, I dashed her down with such force that she never stirred more, but lay sprawling like a crushed toad, the faint sparks of life being extinguished without even a groan escaping her.

This scene exhibited to my view the worst of cruelty, in its most diabolical shape, and filled me with horror and pity. I bade an Arab unbind the father, who lay motionless watching me, as I proceeded to liberate his daughter. He seemed perfectly reckless of himself, and hesitating how to act, doubting my designs. In vain he endeavoured to sit up, for the ground was slippery with his blood. I saw his fears, and, to dispel them, instantly placed him in a sitting posture, and drew my creese from my belt. His eyes glared ferociously. I put the weapon into his hand, and said, " We are friends, father—fear not ! " He tried to speak, but the blood oozed from his mouth, and the words died on his lips.

His child, now unbound, over whom I threw a mantle, crawled to her father's side, and kissing his encrimsoned hands and eyes, bent over him in speechless and indescribable anguish. The old man's desperate look relaxed ; his eye lost its fierceness, then became clouded and dim. I knelt, subdued by the scene, on the side opposite his child, supporting him. He, with an effort, took my hand in his ; I felt its clammy moisture ; he put it to his lips, then, with great difficulty, he removed a ring from his finger, and placed it on mine ; and, laying my hand on his child's he alternately looked at us both, and convulsively squeezed our hands together, muttering some words. My eyes were wet with tears, which dropped on his bosom. His head and frame shook as with an ague-fit ; his fingers grew cold as ice, his eye stony, fixed, and glazed, and his limbs rigid. I could no longer uphold his increasing weight. His spirit fled its earthly tenement. Yet still our hands were bound together so fixedly in his, that I could not release them ; and he still seemed to gaze on us both with intense anxiety.

Motionless as a form of marble, his child bent over him. She neither wept, nor even appeared to breathe. This recalled me to my senses. I thought she was dead too ; and unclenching his death-grip, I freed myself, arose, and went to her. She appeared to awaken, when I tried gently to remove her, as from a trance, threw her arms round her father's neck, and clung to him with convulsive strength. I cleared the tent of the gazers-on, who were not unmoved, for they gave vent to their feelings in vows of vengeance ; then placing two Arabs, in whom I could confide, at the entrance, to let no one pass, I went into the open air, to recover from the faintness that was creeping over me.

I slung my carbine over my shoulder, and now used all my efforts to stop the slaughter. A general pillage was going on. The grab's and the corvette's long-boats were attending on the beach, the vessels themselves not being able to get round the reef, as it was perfectly calm. These boats, therefore, and some canoes lying on the beach we commenced loading with the booty, which was considerable ; gold, spices, bales of Chinese silk, the muslins of India, cloths and shawls from the Persian Gulf, bags of armlets and anklets, silver and gold ornaments, maize, corn, rice, salt fish, turtle, rackee, and an infinity of arms and apparel, besides slaves, male and female, of all ages and countries. Every eye glistened, and every back was bent with a costly burden.

Yet so greedy and insatiable were our men, who were at first fastidious in their selection, that at last they regarded everything with a jealous eye, and became so gross in their avaricious desires, that they would fain have born off garbage which the wild dog would have passed heedless by ; rotten fish, mouldy rice, rancid ghee, broken pots and pans, cast-off apparel, mats and tents, nothing so villainously worthless or nauseous but had some value in their inordinate avidity for plunder. What they could not carry on their backs they did in their bellies ; they gorged themselves, like the ostrich, till they could scarcely move.

Van Scolpvelt and the steward now appeared in the field, and took their ground, intent on very different objects. Van seemed distracted with the rich variety of patients before him. As he hurried about the encampment, with his shirt sleeves tucked up, his skinny arms bare, bony, and hairy, a case of glittering and appalling instruments in one hand, and in the other a monstrous pair of scissors, rounded into the form of a crescent ; he realised, in his appearance, the most damnable picture of an avenging demon that was ever conceived by saintly painter or poet. Some, not quite dead, feebly shook their creeses at him, others screamed with horror as he stopped to examine their wounds, and a few actually gave up the ghost as he approached.

The steward, on the other hand, grinned from ear to ear as he contemplated the huge mass of plunder, and the destruction of the pirates, whom he hated, because they had repeatedly intercepted the cattle trade to the Mauritius. But his joy was presently checked, and he said to me in sadness, and in worse English than I give him, " Oh, Captain, can you let these improvident savages waste so much ? Look, the earth is covered with grain and flour as if it had snowed ! And do you see these lively turtles ? They are of the most delicious kind, and the most beautiful kind, and the most beautiful creatures I ever saw ; what beastly savages to leave them here ! Make the men throw away the lumber they are carrying on board ; we don't want it ; do you ? and load the boats with these. Of what use are those black savages you are sending in the boats ? One of these "—(pointing to a turtle) " is worth an island of them. Nobody can eat them ; can you ? Bah ! I hate savages, and dote on turtle ; don't you ? We have enough of the one sort on board ; but where have you ever seen such lovely creatures as these ? I have not for years ; have you ? "

Intent on this, which now solely occupied him, by threats and entreaties he endeavoured to induce the men to assist him in bearing off the turtle. At last growing desperate at the Arabs, who loathe them (which Louis said proved they were without human palates), he set about loading the slaves and women with them, the latter of whom he declared he never saw usefully employed before ; then turning to me, asked, in his peculiar voice, which began in the deep hollow tones of a muffled drum and ended with the tinkling jingle of a matin bell, " Have you ? "

De Ruyter now came up, accompanied by Aston, who had just come on shore to see the place. I told them of the scene I had witnessed in the slave tent, when Aston's gentle heart was moved, and he reproved me for having left the girl. My reply was, that I had done so, thinking it was better she should be left alone, to give vent to the first burst of sorrow.

" But," said Du Ruyter, " there is not now an instant to lose. We must hasten aboard ; for these fellows outside will assuredly rally, and, aided by the Madagascarenes, assault us in our turn. So call the stragglers together. The prisoners are embarked, and we must embark forthwith."

" Come, Aston," I said, " assist me in getting this poor orphan girl on board."

We proceeded together to the tent, where we found her making loud wailings. Then she would break off and cry, " Father, arise—we are free ! The strangers are good ; and see ! they have come to free us. The old woman has not killed me ; I am well, and she herself is dead. Oh, father, get up !—look, I have bound up your wounds—you don't bleed now ! " And indeed she had carefully bandaged him with the only remaining rag on her person.

Taking her hand, I said, " Come, dear sister ; you are free. We must leave these cruel Maratti."

Without looking at me, she went on, " See how my father sleeps ! They would not let him sleep or eat, and he is weary and hungry."

" Come, dear," I said, " we must go."

" Go ! " she replied, " how can we ?—our father sleeps ! —and I cannot awake him ! Oh, awake him, that I may feed him ! See, I have got some beautiful fruit, and his lips are dry. Oh, these cruel Maratti will come again when you are gone, and kill him ! Awake, my father ! His eyes are open, but he can't move. He is old, and feeble from hunger ; he wants food ; his lips are cold with hunger ! " At this she kissed him, and rubbed his head, and squeezed pomegranate juice in his mouth.

" Come ! " said Aston, " they are calling you. We must be off. I cannot bear this sight. I'll take her to the boat."

I entreated him to do so ; then gently loosed her hands, covered her with my abbah, and told her I would take care of her father. Aston snatched her up, and bore her off. Her screams were appalling. She called on the name of her father to save her ; and Aston shook, but not with his light burden. I was in little better trim. Sending some Arabs down to the beach with Aston, I returned to De Ruyter, who was drawing-off the men with great difficulty.

Louis, whose bad English I must continue to make better, as Aston passed him, exclaimed to me, " What is he carrying away ? What ! a girl ! What use is she ? Why, he could carry this great turtle, which else must be abandoned, for no one here can lift him—can you ? And she might carry that little one—it will make very good soup ; and is very pretty— much more so than a little girl ! "

I passed on, ordering him instantly to come on board, or the Maratti would soupify him. " What ! " he ejaculated, " leave that turtle, worth all the rest we have taken ! " and he wrung his hands in anguish.

Armed men were now appearing on the hills ; and De Ruyter grew furious at the tardy movements of his men. Many of the Frenchmen were drunk, and could not be got out of the tents. The shouts on the hills augmented, and we were obliged to move. De Ruyter went out of the gate, and I stayed some time longer with the Arabs, to collect stragglers, and then followed him. I omitted to mention that we had fired the town in many places and burnt two Arab vessels which were grounded, with seven or eight canoes on the beach.

The natives were hurrying towards the town; and soon after we saw bodies of them armed, skirting along the side of the river we had to cross, and descending as if to attack us there. We hastened on, preparing our arms. When we arrived there, keeping as near the sea as possible, we heard a firing, and saw De Ruyter crossing the river. He left a party to keep the opposite bank, went on to the boats, fearing they might be attacked, and sent a messenger to me, to hasten me on. But before I could arrive there, being detained by the difficulty in getting on the drunken Frenchmen, the natives had increased till their numbers were formidable. They grew bold, and attacked the party on the opposite bank; then wading down the stream, and closing on our rear, they became troublesome. We kept our ground firmly, and I continued on the bank till our party had crossed. Just as I was following with my Arabs, I heard some shots in our rear, and now appeared, emerging from behind a sandbank, a monstrous figure, a Patagonian, in (what I thought, as the sun shone on him) bright scaled armour. It was the steward, with the turtle on his shoulders, accompanied by a Dutch soldier. I roared out to them to come on quickly, for every moment became more perilous. As they staggered towards us, I could hardly refrain from laughing. Louis, whom I could with difficulty make out to be a human figure, looked like a hippopotamus, as reeling like a drunken man, he bent under the weight of the huge fish, which I thought he had left behind. The other fellow, the Dutchman, who came staggering on in his wake, was bulged out into preposterous proportions; his red guernsey frock and ample Dutch trousers, secured at the wrists and knees, were crammed with stowage of gold and jewels, which he had discovered after one of the houses had been pulled down. He looked like a wool-sack, and moved like a Dutch dogger, which his broad beam resembled, labouring in a head sea. I told them to cast their slough, if they valued their lives, and commenced crossing the river by a sandbank thrown up by the tide, the only passable ford.

The natives pressed more closely on our rear ; the difficulty in using our arms in the water made them bold ; and but for our men stationed on the opposite bank, we should have had little chance of escape ; for they, in a great degree, checked their advance, and kept the space clear before us. Still we were compelled to hurry on. At this moment I heard something flounder in the water, and a savage yell, as of triumph, from the natives. I looked round, and the Dutch soldier, who was in my rear, was missing. Overballasted by his treasure, he lost his footing on the ford and sank in the stream, borne down by the weight about his body, which it was impossible for him to shake off. I only got a glimpse of his person, when my attention was called off by the steward, who, either from fear, or from having been caught hold of by his fallen countryman, who was close to him, had also fallen. I ran back, and holding the shaft of a spear to him, he grasped it tight, while the huge monster he had been carrying tumbled into the water, and flapped his heavy fins in triumph as he regained his native element.

When Louis had recovered himself on the bank, he exclaimed, with a rueful look. "But where is my turtle? Oh, don't mind me, Captain !—save the turtle ! "

" Hang the turtle ! I wish he was down your throat ! "

" Oh, so do I, Captain !—that's all I want ! Oh, where's my turtle ? " As he vociferated this demand, up it rose to the surface, in mockery of its enemy ; and the instant its bright shell glistened in the sun, Louis seemed inclined to rush down the stream after it, bawling out, " There he is ! Oh, save him ! "

Thinking he meant the soldier, I looked, and inquired, " Where ? "

" Why, there ! " he replied, pointing to the turtle. " Oh, Captain, I told you how lively he was ! I cut his throat two hours ago ; but he won't die till sunset ; they never do ; and then he will be lost—won't he ? "

I had ordered two of my men to drag him along ; and so loath was he to leave the turtle, that with his eyes strained down the stream, he came reluctantly in a sidelong motion, like a crab.

Once or twice I was compelled to turn round on our pursuers, and drive them off, before we reached the other side. We hastened to regain our boats. Four of our men were slightly wounded in this retreat ; beside the loss of the Dutch soldier, and the deeply lamented turtle. Wherever the ground was broken, or where there was a cover of rocks or shrubs, the Madagascarenes closed in on our flank and rear. I therefore retired close to the sea and skirted its margin. There was one very dangerous pass ; it was the rough abutment of ragged rocks jutting out into the sea, half a mile on the other side of which were our boats. The natives were ranged along the ridges in files, and there was already a sharp firing going on there. While wondering that De Ruyter should have deserted me under such circumstances, and hesitating as to the best mode of proceeding, I espied on the extreme point his swallow-tailed flag. We now ran on, and were hailed by our shipmates ; who seeing this post was possessed by the enemy, had driven them up, and opened a passage for us. Yet every inch was obstinately disputed, and here three of our men were left dead ; for the natives, under cover of the rocks and lying down with their long matchlocks, had a great advantage, while we could not get a shot at them. The boats approached ; and the French soldiers were drawn up on the beach, which being open, the natives dared not advance, though they kept up a scattering fire. We embarked amidst the wild yells of the savages, who, the moment we shoved off, came down like a countless flock of crows ; and with as much noise and din they even followed us into the water, and their arrows, stones, and balls fell about us like a hailstorm.

All of us, I believe, were glad to regain our ships. We then towed them out, it being a dead calm ; awaited the land breeze at night ; and ran directly from the land, shaping our course for the island of Bourbon.

On computing our loss on board the two ships, the killed and missing amounted to only fourteen, but we had twenty-eight wounded, most of them, however, slightly. I observed to De Ruyter, as I was entering these particulars in the log-book, " It appears to me, considering the service we were on, and the numbers against us, this is a very small loss."

" No, it was a very large one ! " cried out Louis, who had just come down the ladder, " you'll never see so fine a one again. I'd rather have lost every man and thing than that—would not you ? "

" What do you mean, Louis ? "

" Mean !—why, the turtle, to be sure. You saw it, sir, and might have saved it—could you not ? But you think of nothing but little girls—my turtle was worth all the girls in the world—was it not ? "—turning, as he always did, at his repeated interrogations, sharp round, and shoving his expanded nostrils right in one's face.

" This fellow," said De Ruyter, " is a Hindoo, and believes the whole world is supported on the back of an enormous turtle."

" And I should not wonder," I added, " if he makes a voyage to the Pole, not for the benefit of navigation, but to extract its calliopash and calliopee. What luxury, Louis, to let your entire carcass wallow in such a sea of green fat !— would it not ? "—mimicking him.

" Yes," he replied ; " but there is no turtle there ; nothing but walruses, white bears, and whales."

Soon after, under the superintendence of Louis, a feast that might well be termed a turtle one was served up. A huge tub of soup, where a fleet of canoes might have almost fought a battle, the steward himself put on the table ; and mopping his reeky brows, said, " Taste that, and you'll live for ever ! Why the odour itself is a feast for a burgomaster, or a king ! I never smelt anything so beautiful—did you ? "

Then came calipash and calipee, and stewed, and steaked, and minced, and balled, and grilled ; and when all these were cleared away, leaving us well-nigh surfeited, quoth Louis le Grand, " Now, here are two dishes which I have invented, and no one has the secret of them ; though burgomasters and foreign ambassadors have been sent to me with great offers to discover it. But I never would ; because this secret makes me greater than all the kings in the world, for they cannot purchase them with a kingdom, nor would I give them in exchange for a kingdom—would you ? All I shall tell you is this—and it is more than I ever told any one before—the soft eggs, and head, and heart, and entrails, are all there !— but there are many other things, which I shall not, must not, speak of."

Casting his eye on my plate, and seeing the green fat left, he inquired in astonishment why I did not eat it. I answered him, " I can't ; I don't like it." " Can't ! " he exclaimed— " why, if I were dying, and had but strength enough to open my mouth, I would devour that divine food ! And not like it !—then you are no Christian !—is he ? But it is impossible— I don't believe him—do you ? "

The evening was singularly beautiful, the sea calm and clear as a mirror, and our crew sinking into rest, outworn by the unwonted toil of this busy day. De Ruyter was in the cabin ; I was keeping the watch, and Aston bore me company. He lay along the raised stern, and I leant over the taffrail, gazing on the land. The forms in the distant range of mountains were growing dark and indistinct. The transparent, glassy, and deep blue of the sea faded into a dusky olive, sub-divided by an infinity of mazy, glimmering bars, as if embroidered with diamond heads, traced by the varied, wandering airs, and sporting like a lion's whelps on their mother's quiet bosom ; while he, their mighty parent, lay hushed within his cavernous lair, torpid from toil and devastation. Over the land the glowing sun hastened to his cool sea-couch : his expiring rays stained the lucid sky with bright, faded colours—deep ruby tints changing to purple ; then emerald green, barred and streaked with azure, white, and yellow ; and as the sun was dipping, the whole firmament was dyed in crimson, and blazed, they left the western sky brighter than molten gold, till the sun's last rays were extinguished. When the moon came forth with her silvery, gleaming light, all the gay colours faded, leaving a few fleecy and dappled specks, like lambs grazing on the hills in heaven. The change was like life in youth and beauty suddenly extinguished ; white and misty death, with his pallid winding-sheet, enveloped all around. As the grab's stern swung round, and as my eye caught our companion, the corvette, her black hull and white wings alone broke the line of the moonlit horizon, like a sea-sprite reposing on the boundless waters. Enwrapped in our contemplation of the wonderful beauty of an eastern night, we remained hours in silence ; and after the turmoil of the day, this stillness had a preternatural or magic effect on the mind, more soothing than sleep. The helmsman, in his sleep, from habit, called out—" Steady ! steady ! " and even the customary forms of changing the watches had been neglected ; while the sentinels, unconscious that their time of duty was expired, dozed on their posts of guard over the prisoners ; and the balm of sleep medicined the wounded, and made free the captive, who, perhaps, dreaming of hunting on his native mountains, or fondling with his young barbarians, or their mother, was destined to awake, fettered and bound with festering manacles, chained, like a wild beast, in the worst of dungeons, under the sea, in a ship's hold, doomed to death or slavery.

TRADING IN DEATH

By
DOUGLAS McHARDIE

The author has arrived in Kabul to consider, on behalf of his employer in Bombay, the possibilities of gun-running into Afghanistan.

I BEGAN to assemble my information for transmission to Mukerjee. In the first place I had discovered that the Amir really had a small number of white engineers in his arsenal in Kabul, probably Russians, but lack of modern equipment restricted the potential output to under 20,000 cartridges per diem and the number of rifles was barely 75 per week. This was further complicated by the fact that there was no standard type of rifle, several patterns being used and, of course, cartridges of different calibre. This was not nearly enough for the demands of his own " regular " army, quite apart from the rest of the male population which did not consider a man worth his salt unless he was the possessor of at least one rifle and a marksman's eye with it. In consequence the Lee-Enfield British service magazine rifle or a modern Mauser was worth a good deal of money. Among certain border tribes the price had risen to the equivalent *weight* in silver rupees, and was certainly never less than Rs. 800 apiece.

Most of the manufactured arms from Europe, whole or in parts for assembling, were run into Bushire in the Persian Gulf and brought thence to Kabul by camel. As this had to be done carefully to avoid any seizure *en route* by marauding tribesmen, it was a hazardous undertaking, and all travelling was done at night. However, there was undoubtedly money in it for any one who got through—a profit of a good few hundred per cent, and I wrote to Mukerjee that if he thought it worth while financing, I would take the risk.

The only reply was a summons, sent through Sherif Ali, to return to Bombay immediately, which I did, wondering whether my little scheme had appealed to my employer.

After establishing myself at the Taj Mahal Hotel I went straight to his office where we immediately began to discuss my various consignments and how I had acted in Peshawar.

No word of the other matter was breathed until that evening when I went round to his house on the Malabar Hill for dinner. When we had eaten an excellent meal he drew me aside and said in English : " I was very interested in your letter from Peshawar, and I must thank you for going to such lengths to collect your data. I'm not sure, though, that a journey to Bushire and back to Kabul won't be too risky an affair if we are going to buy in any quantity. Have you any notion of the price this material fetches at the port ? "

I told him, and he began to make calculations on a piece of paper. At length he looked up, and still addressing me in English, said : " If you care to make a little more for yourself, I have another idea. It will mean a trip to Europe."

I suppose my expression must have betrayed my utter surprise, for he laughed and went on : " While you have been away I have had certain information from other sources respecting the price at which these goods can be purchased at the fountain-head. Now I have a proposition to make."

I do not propose here to acquaint the reader with just what terms he made me to carry out his plan, but will merely state that his suggestions were more than generous and I accepted them instantly.

" Very well, then," he concluded, " in ten days' time you will take a boat from Karachi to Bushire, assuming your identity as an up-country Pathan. I will arrange that you pick up money there—it is inviting suicide to carry it with you—and you must then get in touch with the officer of the boat which runs in the next consignment and arrange a passage to Hamburg with him. Reaching there, you will communicate with an address I shall give you, and effect a meeting with an individual whose name I shall also give you. He is in a position to supply you with all the goods we can safely negotiate between Bushire and Kabul. I leave it to you to arrange the freightage and, of course, you will travel back with the consignment."

After he had said this, we immediately changed the subject and reverted to speech in Hindustani. I was not a great deal wiser for what he had told me, and certainly no eavesdropper could have realised what on earth we were talking about. It was another example of the veil of secrecy with which all things are shrouded in India and I knew it was not until the last minute before I sailed that he would give me any definite names and places.

I was pretty pleased with the idea, not alone because it

would be my first trip to Europe, but because the financial inducement was extremely inviting. Also, I was flattered to see how implicitly Mukerjee trusted me. But I had given my word, and now that I had become a Muslim, I realised that the hand of every other Muslim in the world would be against me if I was " not true to my salt "—*nimuk halal*. In that respect Mahommedanism is one vast brotherhood—a sort of freemasonry, and if the true believer fails he is cast out to become a pariah among men. Sometimes an even worse fate awaits him. . . .

For the next ten days I was largely occupied in preparing myself for my journey. I had already a pretty shrewd idea that guns were not run into Bushire itself—the Anglo-Persian Oil Company had already made the place a hive of British officialdom and as far as I knew the freighter lay a couple of miles off the port itself, and that to avoid the excise patrols the arms were put in at night by row-boat to a cove about ten miles north of Bushire near a collection of fishermen's huts called Khor. All this, of course, was not even hearsay ; it was for the most part conclusions I had drawn from conversation concerning (apparently) something entirely different. It would all need careful confirmation, and until I reached Bushire I was completely fogged as to how to go about it. Mukerjee afforded no assistance and I doubt whether he knew, either. People who are directly concerned with the practical end of gun-running are apt to find a little knowledge a dangerous thing. It was far safer, from his own point of view, that he should remain in ignorance.

I saw Haynes, the I.C.S. man, once or twice before I left, and he asked me how I had got on up in the North. I did not dare to tell him of my experiences, although I do not think he would have been anything but highly amused. He asked me if the tribesmen were still up to their tricks gun-pinching, and I was able to satisfy his curiosity with a number of tales which had been the talk of European Peshawar while I was up there. Almost every day horses would mysteriously disappear from locked stables, soldiers sleeping in barracks locked and guarded would miss their rifles in the morning, and a certain major sleeping under canvas in the compound of his bungalow with two sentries posted had woken one morning to find himself staring at the sky. Tent, mosquito nets, clothes and equipment had disappeared into thin air overnight ! The father of cunning, the Afridi, had been at work again while he slept.

Before we parted Haynes said to me : " Mac, when I leave the Service, I'm damned if I don't have a crack at getting to Kabul. If they need guns all that bad, I think I might be useful up there myself."

" Not a bad idea," I told him and wondered what he'd have said if he knew.

II

THE trip from Karachi would probably have been a night-mare to most people—in fact, to myself a couple of years previously. But I was in Afridi clothing and became myself part and parcel of the throng of natives which lined the decks of the vessels going up the gulf.

The night before I left Bombay, Mukerjee had told me that I should find what I wanted at the house of a certain Ya'qub ul Hamdani, a merchant of silks in Bushire. After that, all arrangements were left to myself. Just how much money he had forwarded I did not know, and it was out of the question to ask. I had to wait and see. The name of my assignation in Hamburg also awaited me there. The likelihood of any " trouble " on the boat was therefore reduced to a minimum as I scarcely knew myself just what I was going for !

III

ON the appointed day I took the train from Bombay to Karachi—once more as Yusuf Khan, Afridi of the Zakka Khel.

A rather amusing incident occurred at this point. I went to the booking office on the station, laid down the money and asked for my " tikkut " to Karachi. The smart looking half-caste clerk grabbed the money and slung me a ticket, not for Karachi but a couple of stations up the line. He'd thought to himself that a miserable peasant from the hills like myself couldn't read, and the balance of the fare would go into his pocket. He'd probably done it every day for years. But, of course, he struck the wrong man at last. I examined his forebears verbally in some detail, found them all rotten, threw doubts on his paternity in the well-known Indian way, and eventually demanded the right " tikkut." His face was a picture ! *And* I got the ticket immediately !

At about this time I was growing more and more conscious of the fact that by merely changing my clothes I assumed native identity not in appearance only but in—how shall I describe it ?—actual fact. My mind seemed to lose track of westernised modes of thought and standards of values, and become in tune with those of the people among whom I was moving. The metamorphosis was not yet complete, but later I was to lose my identity as Douglas McHardie so thoroughly that even my native tongue was spoken with difficulty.

However, to continue my story, I boarded an old tin can of a gulf steamer, one of those 500-ton boats carrying cargo and a complement of native deck-passengers. There were perhaps forty or fifty of us, and as we arrived on board the Serang of the lascar crew showed us the space allotted to us. On these boats the travelling native is expected to bring and prepare his own food and, of course, we slept on deck.

Each of us carried our clothing and food for the journey tied up in corners, and took turns at cooking in the sheet iron place provided on the deck. Rugs and blankets were spread wherever we could find room, and I settled down to a week's eating, sleeping, cooking and praying all in the same restricted place.

The heat was terrific for those seven days, but if the boat was officered by white men, then surely I could withstand it. Most of us were small merchants, and as is the way with such men in the East, uncommunicative enough about business.

Most of the time in the Arabian Sea we kept in sight of land, though whether this was from nautical considerations or the age and decrepitude of the boat I never discovered, but by the end of a week we had made Bushire in the Persian Gulf, and after we had dropped anchor a mile or so outside in the roadstead, we were rowed ashore by the lascar crew.

Bushire itself I found to be quite a sizable town, but like most Eastern cities a maze of narrow, evil-smelling streets, unpaved and dirty, whose only peculiarity in this instance was the fact that all the buildings were of a kind of white coral which I suppose is a local product. I walked to the extremity of the town, eventually discovering Ya'qub ul Hamdani living close to one of the massive round towers which once composed its fortifications on the land side of the city.

He was a little old man with a wispy white beard, whose clothing, though simple, was of fine quality, and I judged him to be an individual of some importance. His rather distant manner changed immediately I mentioned Mukerjee's name, and after we had exchanged the usual courtesies, he invited me to wash and take coffee with him in order to discuss our business at leisure. I explained my mission with some diffidence until he put me at my ease by pointing to the rich rug on which we were sitting and saying : " Such trifles as these are not always earned by selling silk, O, my son. These old eyes have sometimes sought other merchandise."

It was a plain hint that he also was mysteriously " in the know " and part of the great unorganised " racket " in which I was now playing a dangerous part.

I pointed out that I wanted to get to Europe if possible on one of the boats which brought the contraband into the Gulf. Where should I seek them and how could I get in contact with one of the officers ?

" A boat is expected," he told me, " within three days. I think I shall be able to arrange a meeting with the first officer on the night she arrives. Come to my house at dusk and we shall see what I have arranged. In the meanwhile dost thou desire the money I have received from Bombay to remain here, or wilt thou take it with thee ? "

" A stranger in a strange city would be ill-advised to carry such a purse, O, my father," I said. " Grant me the favour of retaining it in thy house until such time as all arrangements are made."

" Even so." The old man smiled. " God be with thee then until dusk in the space of three days when we meet again."

I spent the three days in the city of Bushire endeavouring to learn, from what I thought seemed likely sources, what I could of where the guns were run in and how disposed of. I had heard one story while I was in Afghanistan and was anxious to confirm it on the spot for future use.

The method used was safe enough, although it involved the use of considerable nerve. However, the policing of Eastern ports can scarcely be compared with those of Europe and the States—as we all saw in the exploits of the German cruiser *Emden* in the Great War—and provided you are suitably equipped for emergencies, any skipper with a know-ledge of the coast in the Gulf could get away with it. To begin with, the guns were rarely landed in the same place and always at night.

The word would go round when she was expected, and several boatloads run in to a cove some way up the coast from the city, from the ship which lay anchored perhaps five miles out. There were no special consignees. Business was done there and then for cash on the shore. There was never any lack of purchasers waiting there with their camels and Arabs. The transactions would be made and by daybreak they were away into the hills on the start of the long trek to Afghanistan.

After that the ship would sometimes proceed to Bushire—supposedly in ballast—and pick up a legitimate cargo for return to Europe, or sometimes put about and clear for Europe right away.

If any questions were asked there was always plenty of documentary excuse for her presence in the Gulf !

Being a stranger in Bushire and without any introduction to that particular underworld I didn't manage to learn much except my way about the city in those three days, and I was glad enough when the time came for me to call once more upon Ya'qub ul Hamdani.

A young Arab received me whom I took to be a servant. When I announced my name he said gravely : " My master hath a message for thee, Yusuf Khan. Go now to the bazaar and in the shop of the seller of coffee calling himself Ali Ben Sabah thou wilt find what is sought. He prays that thou wilt accept this rug too, and that the All-merciful may lighten thy task."

He handed me a rug folded in a neat package, which I took and thanked him. It contained the money the old man had left for me.

The shop I had to find in the bazaar was easily identifiable by its smell and my arrival was evidently expected, for I was immediately asked to go to an upper room.

Here I found the man I had been wanting. I guessed he was the first officer of the gun-runner, a great bull-necked Heinie, and he rose from the table where he was drinking coffee and saluted me in bad Hindustani which I scarcely understood. He nearly fell over when I said : " I guess we'd better talk English, if you can manage that better."

" You speak Englisch very good ? " he asked when he had recovered. I decided I had better take a chance.

" I'm a citizen of the United States," I said.

At that he roared with laughter and shook my hand heartily. " Ach ! ploody good for you, Yankee ! " he roared. I told him not to make so much noise or we should attract attention, but it seemed to tickle him so much it was some time before we could get to talk business. I don't think he believed me even then.

He said eventually that he thought he could fix a passage for me if I had the money, but that I must be ready to leave the next morning when he would take me to the boat in the ship's launch. As far as I was concerned the sooner I got away the better and I made arrangements to meet him as he suggested. What he was doing in Bushire itself I never discovered, but in that business you don't ask too many questions.

I decided to mail the bulk of the money through to Hamburg and pick it up on arrival, as I imagined it would reach there by the mail boat some time before we arrived. Most of it was in Bank of India notes, but I had enough rupee silver to pay cash for my passage and see me through emergencies. I was still rather nervous about carrying much money on my person, even on a European-owned boat. Persons of scrupulous honesty don't usually interest themselves in the gun-running game !

I thanked the officer after fixing a meeting place for the morning and left the coffee-merchant for my sleeping quarters farther down the bazaar. In spite of his amazement when I was obliged to disclose my identity he had asked nothing of my reasons for going to Hamburg, but I suppose he was used to queer customers and only looked at the money end, anyway.

A month later I arrived in Hamburg, with papers in order as a member of the ship's crew, at a cost of rather more than half a first-class passage from Bombay on a P. & O. liner.

IV

As soon as I had picked up my money and exchanged the bulk of it into German currency I began to get my business done. The name which I had been given by Mukerjee was Theodor Mendelsohn with an address in the Hermannstrasse, and having never been in Hamburg or even Europe before I naturally anticipated some beer-dive on the waterfront similar to the places in 'Frisco where I remembered most arrangements for contraband took place. Attired in dungarees and boots from the ship's stores, I found myself the object of some attention as, by general inquiry, I got farther from the docks up into what was evidently a superior business quarter. I wondered if after all I had got the wrong address and the long journey had been futile. But Hermann-strasse 74 was what I had written down and Mendelsohn was the name, and sure enough when I reached the entrance of a palatial office building there it was :

> *T. Mendelsohn u. Sohne*
> *Teppische, Mobeldamask, usw :*

The offices were on the third floor.

The last dirty look I got was from the lift man, since, in spite of my clothes, the clerk who answered my summons betrayed no surprise. I circumvented the language difficulty in a moment.

" Herr Mendelsohn ? " I said trying to look like a question mark, and seizing the pencil from behind his ear wrote Mukerjee's name and address on a piece of paper and prayed for good luck.

The clerk's face remained devoid of emotion and with a remark which I took to mean " wait a minute " disappeared with the improvised visiting card.

A moment later and I was closeted with the Herr Direktor, a typical bullet-headed German with about three chins and the back of his neck like a concertina. We shook hands, and he said :

" You do not speak Cherman, so we speak Englisch. But not too much, hein ? " I took this to be a joke and laughed, wondering at the same time if I should have to do a lot of explaining.

" Now then, my friend, you are prepared to pay cash for dese goods ? "

I breathed a sigh of relief. It was evident that he had been expecting me (possibly Mukerjee had advised him by mail) and knew the object of my visit.

" Sure," I told him. " Good German marks which I'm carrying with me right here." I tapped the parcel I was holding.

He nodded and went to a file from which he produced a sheet of paper and placed it before me.

" I must haf three days to procure," he said.

I looked at the typewritten figures before me. It was a list of the manufactures of about a dozen small-arms firms with prices marked against each !

" But what about packing and freight ? " I asked him. " How do I get them aboard ? "

Herr Mendelsohn laughed. " If you will please let me know what ship they are to travel on, I will see to all that. You must make your own terms with the master, but I will guarantee to see them aboard."

" Very well," I replied, " I shall want 1500 multiple-loading approved-pattern Mausers. How much will that cost ? "

He made a rough calculation on the blotter and told me. It amounted to just over £1 apiece. I paid him and he stood up once more.

" You will communicate by letter the name of the ship to which these goods are to be consigned," he snapped. " Good-day, *mein Herr !* "

Never once had he mentioned the word gun, and indeed, for all the excitement he betrayed he might have been talking about barnyard roosters. I didn't like parting with so much money without so much as a receipt, but I was obliged to presume that Mukerjee knew that " cash without documents " was one of the rules of the game.

I went back to the ship and found the officer with whom I had arranged my passage.

" When do you return to the Gulf ? " I asked him.

He shook his head. " I cannot tell. Maybe in vun week, maybe two. If you wish to talk about it, please to meet me to-night in Schmidt's Weinstube on the Chemnitzstrasse near the Binnenhafen."

Schmidt's was a place more after my own heart. Indeed, except for the language it might have been on the Barbary Coast. It was full of sailors, mostly three parts drunk, smoke, noise and booze. I saw my friend sitting with a girl at a table in the corner and went over to him. He sent the girl away and I explained what I wanted, only to receive my first disappointment. The boat I had travelled in from Bushire was going to be laid up for probably a month.

" Any suggestions ? " I asked.

He shook his head. " I haf heard," he said, " of one boat leaving at the end of dis veek, but I t'ink she already has a full cargo. You might ask der capitan. He iss here now."

He pointed to a grizzled old man sitting by himself with a large jug of wine in front of him listening to the girl playing a concertina at the next table.

The mate left me and brought him over into the corner where, after we had been introduced with an exchange of drinks, I was obliged to listen to ten minutes of rapid German.

From the head-shaking and pointing that went on, I guessed my friend was having some difficulty about establishing my bona-fides. It is a well-known fact in the " trade " that you never know when the next man's a Government agent, or a spy from the arms factories.

However, at last the mate turned to me and said : " He'll do it if you can agree a goot price. How many cases are going aboard ? "

I told him, and they started in again. Finally the old man turned to me himself and to my surprise, in much better English than my friend, the mate, said : " You'll have to get them aboard yourself. I can't undertake to do that as my business is running the ship. We can get them unloaded on shore with the rest, but, of course, you understand I take no responsibility for seizure."

" Sure I understand," I told him, feeling pretty pleased at my good luck. " How much do you want for the job ? I'll see they're put aboard."

He mentioned a figure which put the price of the guns up by twenty per cent. But they were cheap even at that, reckoning what price they would fetch at the other end, and, rather than start dickering, with the chance he might refuse altogether, I agreed.

" What's the name of your ship ? " I asked him, when we had shaken on it.

" *Magdeburg*," he said. " She's lying in the India Hafen now and we expect to sail on Saturday."

I jotted the name down and ordered some more wine. The three of us got very friendly as the evening drew on, and after visiting half the sailors' haunts in Hamburg we adjourned to a café for breakfast where I wrote a letter to Mendelsohns' informing them of my arrangements.

Everything was working out very nicely, as the Saturday the *Magdeburg* was due to sail gave one clear day over the three that Mendelsohn required to procure what he termed " the goods." I imagine, of course, that he was only an intermediary. Where the guns came from and how they were procured to sell at that price I don't know to this day. There is necessarily so much secretiveness about those sort of undertakings that production and disposal units act quite independently and their identity is never revealed to each other, all business being done through a third party who is obliged to keep his mouth shut for fear of " reprisals " from either end.

I went aboard a few hours before the boat sailed and found to my regret I had missed witnessing her cargo loaded. I saw the manifest later and was amused to discover that we were carrying bicycle parts ! For the Shah of Persia's Cavalry, I suppose !

The voyage out was uneventful enough, the *Magdeburg* being a vessel of about 3000 tons burthen not unlike the one which had brought me from Bushire, and the only excitement I remember was wondering whether our cargo of " bicycles " would blow up in the Red Sea, where the temperature turned our iron plates into what felt like molten metal.

Nothing untoward occurred, however, and as we neared our destination the old familiar smells and occasional glimpses of the coast made me glad enough that I should soon be back in the type of country I had come to regard as my own. The brief interlude of a European city with tall buildings and hard-paved streets had brought me no sort of nostalgia for a return to " civilisation " or Occidental living. I felt positively strange and out of place, and longed to be once more among the tall, guttural-spoken peoples of the hills.

At dawn one morning I heard the engines stop and the anchor cable run out. We had arrived. I went on deck to discover that we were still out of sight of land and I concluded that there we were likely to remain and the cargo would be brought off that night in boats, as usual. I had arranged with the skipper to go ashore into Bushire with the first officer at the earliest opportunity so that I could make arrangements about a convoy of camels and a guide, although I guessed the latter would not be necessary since my own shipment would be run in with the rest of the stuff sold on shore and form part of the general caravan right across Persia and Afghanistan. Accordingly I dumped my clothes —dungarees, shirt, boots and socks—over the side with a certain thankfulness and assumed my identity once more as the Afridi Yusuf Khan.

When we parted on the quay after I had given the officer my thanks, I spoke my last word of English for nearly five years. The stench, the heat, the sand, the cruelty of the Northern Hills of India was in my blood and under my skin again until it became part of me.

V

FIFTEEN HUNDRED guns meant thirty camels to be bought and driven to the point on the coast about sixteen miles to the north-west of the city, where I knew the boat-load would be run in at dead of night. The average palang load of a good camel is between four and five hundred pounds, but loading to capacity is inadvisable when there is a fair chance of losing one or more by sickness or theft on a journey of about fifteen hundred miles !

I had to act quickly if I was to get there in time. I knew I need not worry about Arabs for drovers or guides since the word would have gone round among those concerned some time before and there were always a number waiting to offer their services to prospective purchasers at the point of departure. But there were provisions to be bought as well, blankets, food and all the accompaniments to a long journey across mountains and desert.

It was pretty tough going the whole of that day, and when at the end of it all, in a maze of camels (I managed to buy a number of the famous Khorassan Long-hairs), blankets, food, heat, dust and stench, I left the city, I had made up my mind that I was going to ride. On my previous excursions with caravans, you will remember I had never essayed the difficult task of camel-riding, having always walked alongside in the usual fashion. However, tired as I was, I felt I could endure any discomfort rather than a swift sixteen-mile trek which I knew would be followed immediately by a forced march into the hills before dawn with our contraband.

Unfortunately, however, I omitted the preliminary precaution of binding my stomach with a *pugri* before mounting, and it was not until the Arab I had picked up to help drive the beasts noticed my distress that this was remedied and I made the rest of the trip feeling a little easier. Until this was done I really felt as if my insides were being painfully removed. That was my first experience with the camel as a beast of burden. When I came to know him better I had still less admiration for him. A more stupid beast would be hard to find, which I suppose is not surprising seeing his skull's so thick it can turn a .45 bullet.

When we arrived, it was well after nightfall and I was amazed at the scene which presented itself. In the darkness a crowd of white-clad figures was gathered on the foreshore—

there must have been fifty or sixty men besides myself—moving about conversing in low tones. Some way behind them I could just discern the shapes of the camels which were to form the caravan, lying motionless and silent. I sent my boy to see to the beasts and joined the other " merchants." The boats, it seemed, were late, and there was a good deal of apprehension as to whether the right information had been received. I was able to correct this impression, of course, having travelled with the cargo myself, but it seemed that unless things began to happen fairly soon it would be too late as a certain point had to be reached by daybreak which would put us out of harm's way in the form of detection by the Persian authorities.

After about half an hour, however, a light winking for a split second some way out at sea assured us that all was well, and immediately a movement took place to get the camels prepared to receive the purchases.

Having been to some trouble to do my own buying in Europe I was naturally not concerned with any haggling which might take place before our departure, but I was surprised to notice, for the one and only time I was in the East, that these transactions for arms took place without any of the bartering which is such a necessary feature of any sort of negotiation out there. It was done in this way. The boats put in, each in charge of a white officer who announced the price per case of whatever he was carrying, Mausers, like my own shipment, Lee-Enfields, Martinis, or sometimes just " *jezail*," guns of old pattern and calibre, which nevertheless find a ready market among the raiders of the hills. Ammunition was rarely bought, although unloaded cartridge cases could always find a buyer. The price fluctuated on each voyage, but was usually a fair one, seeing the risks run, and as time was an essential factor in the whole business, it was " take or leave it." Those who felt there was a worth-while profit took what they wanted, while the others waited patiently until the next consignment, perhaps two or three months later, when they might buy at a better price.

In a very short time the camels were loaded, the boats had put back and the beach was innocent and deserted. Buyers, guns, camels and Arab guides had vanished into the hills. It was, as I say, the only example I ever encountered of efficient business methods in the East.

By dawn we had crossed the Khist River and were in the hills outside Kazerun. We lay there all day, and in fact practically the whole of the journey moved only during the night, especially as we got farther from the coast into the interior where any sort of policing or judicial administration only exists in the form of the annual tax gathering. It was the strangest journey I have ever made, avoiding even the smallest villages in case word should be spread that a caravan was on the move and some band of professional marauders smell easy money. Occasionally parties would be sent forward to procure water or a few sheep for food while we slept during the day, every man taking a few hours turn to keep watch.

As the long procession moved forward at nightfall, occasionally a shot would ring out and a camel fall. The caravan did not halt. The beast was left there—sometimes with its owner, since if we stopped we might discover the marksman to be a member of a large party and the whole caravan would be annihilated. As it was, one would be picked off from time to time—I counted eight between Bushire and Kabul, although there may have been more. Each member of the caravan remained as an independent unit and there was never a check-up on numbers. We travelled together in silence, only conversing with neighbours when there was food to be found or water to be bought.

Our way lay through the mountains for the most part, across the great desert called Dasht-i-Lut (which itself lies at a great height) dropping only when we came to the vast tracts of salt-marsh and swamp formed by river with no outlet. Half the time I did not know where we were or in what direction we were travelling ; I became, as day monotonously followed day, a little more inured to the intense cold at night in the hills, especially as I had managed to procure at one village an evil-smelling *abba*, a voluminous cloak made of camel-hair which despite its age and former ownership, I found very welcome on the march. But it was only when I heard the name Sabzawar mentioned that I knew we must be once again in Afghan territory. Before we reached the outskirts of Kabul we had been on the road ninety-seven days !

VI

SOME hours before we reached the city business began. Our arrival had been anticipated in certain quarters, I suppose, and invisible look-out men posted along the route had borne tidings to the villages and the city of our approach.

Instead, as was usual with caravans of other commodities, of halting at one of the serais on the outskirts of Kabul and setting about business in an orderly fashion, a number of hill-men and city merchants joined us hours before and " the market " opened *en route*.

A white-bearded old man walked along beside me for some time before I realised that he was going to make me an offer. After we had exchanged the usual pleasantries, he said :

" That she-camel " (pointing to one of my beasts) " she is old and broken-kneed ; this is undoubtedly her last journey. For how much dost thou value her and her load ? "

I told him twice what I wanted and we began to haggle.

" Dost thou think that I have here a load of useless *jezail*, fit only for children and the smith's hammer ? " I asked him. " The sword of Azrael himself can strike death with no more certainty than these rifles for which I have risked my life."

" Aye," he nodded and continued to walk beside me in silence. At length he asked again to examine the one which I had been carrying on the journey for my own purposes. He appraised it with the eye of an expert and announced that although it would mean starvation to his wife and children, since even that fact would not soften my heart, it was Allah's will that I should be paid five hundred rupees apiece for the load, provided I would include the " *oont* " which, although worthless, might have sufficient hair on her to make the sleeve of a small coat.

And so it went on. By the time we had reached the city I had disposed of my shipment at a very handsome profit.

Out of this I procured for myself a house outside the city, where I soon became known as " a buyer of rugs," and then turned my thoughts towards again communicating with Mukerjee (who, of course, had not heard of me directly since my departure from Bombay), and informing him of the results of our enterprise.

A month later I was back in Bombay once more. I had by now drawn so completely apart from all my western associations that even the idea of assuming European clothes was absolutely repulsive and I made no attempt to do so, nor while I was in the city did I attempt to renew any of the acquaintances I had made as Douglas McHardie. As I have explained elsewhere, I was Yusuf Khan as much in mind as in speech and appearance.

I gave Mukerjee some account of my activities since we had parted and he seemed amazed to think that I was still alive. I also told him that I had installed myself permanently in Kabul and that now I had my own resources I was going to continue making the Bushire-Kabul run with as much as I could afford to buy when the stuff came off the boats. I did not contemplate another trip to Europe, since if I was acting independently the loss of time would not counterbalance the profit I could make with a limited capital.

He agreed with my suggestion and told me that whenever I found that aspect of " business " quiet, I had *carte blanche* to act as his agent in the north, making purchases on the same arrangement as we had had before. For some reason he would not disclose, he had washed his hands for the moment of any further activity connected with arms smuggling. For a man in his established position, it was (apart from the physical element) a great deal more dangerous for him than for myself. I thanked him for what he had done for me and left for Karachi once more, this time on my own initiative.

That was the first of four trips I made like this, Kabul-Karachi-Bushire-Kabul, picking up guns at Bushire and selling them at a substantial profit at the other end. I do not propose to plague the reader with descriptions of these journeys since even if they were hazardous at all times, I always managed to escape with my life. Only once did I come near to losing it, when we were attacked on the Persian-Afghanistan border by a body of tribesmen. We had just got on to the move after lying up all day, when we were surprised by a fusillade of shots which put four of the camels down and the man in front of me coughed his life out with a bullet in the lungs. I had only a vague idea as to the direction from which we were being attacked, as no one was visible, but I unslung my rifle and got down behind my kneeling camel, praying I was facing in the right direction. All at once I caught the silhouette of a horseman for a moment against the sky a few hundred yards from us. I shifted my position slightly so as to face him. We might, of course, be surrounded, in which case there was small hope for any of us with the valuable burden we were carrying. The caravan had come to a ragged halt this time, the leader presumably sensing that this was no solitary raider. After what seemed an age of waiting for the concerted rush I judged would be made, the air was suddenly rent with a series of sharp reports, not, apparently, directed at us all. A few shouts echoed down to

us, and further rifle-shots. As far as we could tell the raiders
had themselves been raided !

Either it was the settlement of a blood-feud, or else some
neighbouring tribe had got wind of our attackers' intention
and were carrying out a somewhat premature attempt to
" hi-jack " them. In any case, the front of the caravan
evidently realised what was happening and we goaded our
beasts into a swift run. For over an hour we left the caravan
route and made swift and tortuous progress through the rocky
foothill country. Fortunately we saw no more of our pursuers.
The two bands had probably succeeded in annihilating each
other.

Apart from such incidents as these I pursued the normal
life of a peaceful Kabuli merchant, occupying my time
between these long trips with a certain amount of legitimate
general trading, chiefly in Bokhara rugs. On several occasions
I went down into Peshawar city, scarcely remembering the
time when I had first made the journey in fear and trepidation.
Everything seemed to be going well. I was making money,
the life suited me, my whole personality seemed to have
changed and I had lost all desire to return to so-called
civilisation. I had begun to think it would last indefinitely
until one day something happened which was to throw my
whole life out of gear again.

One morning, in one of the principal bazaars inside the
city, I was suddenly set upon by half a dozen men and man-
handled into unconsciousness !

VII

WHEN I came to, I found myself lying on the roadside to
the city which I recognised as about a mile away, my
clothes torn to shreds and soaked with my own blood. I tried
painfully to move, only to feel that something heavy seemed
to be weighing down my legs. When I at last manœuvred
myself into a sitting position I saw my ankles were shackled
with about two hundred pounds of iron-linked chains !

I had often seen notorious criminals and malefactors thus
publicly " imprisoned " along the roadside during my stay
in Kabul, but it had certainly never entered my head that
I should ever be in that position myself. I was pretty sure I
should die, and prayed that it might be soon. To become one
of those wretches whose only sign of life was a mass of festering

sores and a pitiful mumble for water, was worse than any death. My mind groped blindly for some reason which could have placed me in such a position. I could think of nothing I had done which would have merited this sort of punishment, which was usually reserved for aggravated cases of wrong-doing. A small begging-bowl had been placed at my side, and with that I was supposed to support such life as was left in me for as long as I felt it worth while. Presently, the dogs would come and eat me. . . .

In addition to this revolting prospect I felt horribly ill. Whoever my assailants had been had given me a beating within an inch of my life, and I wondered if I had a sound bone left in my body. Worse than that, I had a raging thirst. How long I had lain there insensible I don't know, for I had been attacked in the morning, and yet judging from the sun, it was not yet midday. I supposed it was the day after.

The instinct of self-preservation was still strong enough in me to make me moan feebly to passers-by :

" Water, for the love of Allah ! Water, in God's name ! " I had heard that cry often enough. It is one no true believer may refuse, even to his deadliest enemy.

My swollen tongue would hardly articulate any more when at last a *bhistie* (water carrier) with his goatskin water-bag slung over his back came along. I drank greedily, which I suppose was a foolish thing to do, for either I became un-conscious again or went into delirium. At all events, I remember little more until I was again crying repeatedly : " Water ! Food ! Allah have mercy on all givers ! Food for the love of the All-merciful ! "

Day followed day interminably. I suffered agonies from the heat of the burning sun, only to endure worse torture from intense cold at night. How I kept alive, I do not know to this day. My diet (of such scraps as were thrown to me and the water I begged) began to show itself in horrible rashes and sores on my body. I became so enfeebled that I could no longer drag the weight of my shackles a few yards to change my position, and for long spells I seemed to remember nothing. I suppose I should be thankful that my lucid moments were few enough in which to reflect on my miserable fate. There was no single person to whom I could appeal, while I did not even know the crime I was supposed to have committed which merited this inhuman treatment. Compared with this a prison would have been the height of luxury !

In spite of my filthy condition—or perhaps because of it
—I excited little enough attention from passers-by. I must
have presented a revolting spectacle. My torn rags had left
me all but naked, my body emaciated to a skeleton and covered
with festers, while the whole of my face and head was a mass
of filthy matted hair. During that time I believe I was
scarcely alive. I can recall none of my thoughts, hardly any
of my feelings. Yet in some strange manner the feeble spark
of life refused to flicker out. I can only suppose that I must,
at the time I was assaulted and flung out on the roadside,
have possessed a constitution a little harder than iron.

I was even more astonished when I discovered later that
I had been lying there for over eight months !

My wretched plight was at last terminated in a strange
manner. There was no hairbreadth escape of good samaritan
rescue about it. I was released eventually by personal inter-
cession with the Amir himself !

VIII

IN case the reader should consider that to sound a little too
grandiose to be possible, let me explain the circumstances.

One morning, when I had long ceased to imagine that I
should ever be freed of my gyves, a party of horsemen
appeared along the road—evidently persons of some importance since a detachment of soldiers was following at a
discreet distance. I was not particularly curious—curiosity
had long ago died in me—but in accordance with my usual
practice I set up my cry of " Food, in the name of the All-
Merciful ! " hoping perhaps for a small coin, when the party
drew rein just opposite me.

One of the horsemen pointed at me and although I could
not hear what was being said, it was evident that I had aroused
some interest. Thinking perhaps this elevated personage
might possibly be a *naib*[1] or a *kazi*[2], I redoubled my wailing
and changed the tune a little. I should perhaps explain that
nominally all Afghan subjects have the right of appeal to the
Amir for trial, and he is supposedly accessible at all times to
hear complaints. Knowing this I wailed that I was condemned without trial, that in the name of Allah my case
might be brought to the notice of the Great Amir, that the
All-Merciful would shower his blessing on those who took
pity on a poor believer.

[1] Provincial governor.   [2] District judge.

To my surprise my howls took effect. One of the men dismounted and came over to me. I grovelled at his feet crying " *Pa makha de khar*, lord." (May light be upon your face.) " Thou hast heard thy servant ! "

He looked at me in disgust for a minute and then said : " Thou sayest thou art condemned without trial ? "

" Even so, lord."

" Thou hast cried and the Amir has heard thee, spawn of a dog. Thou shalt be brought before him ! "

With my remaining strength I shrieked my blessing upon the beneficent Amir as the cavalcade moved slowly off. It was the Amir himself and his party who had ridden by ! The attendant courtier who had spoken to me I recognised subsequently when I was brought before the Amir in Durbar.

Sure enough some hours later, two soldiers came to fetch me into the city. I was slung on an ass, since my chains were welded on my legs, and taken into Kabul where I was fed, remaining in custody for the four days before the Durbar was held. I realised later that I had probably been part of a sort of annual round-up of such wretches as myself so that in theory at least, the idea of the Amir being supreme judicial head, court of appeal and everything else (except for commercial cases) might be said to have foundation in fact.

My spirits revived considerably at the prospect of my release and I felt signs of returning sanity, although my poor body did not respond so quickly. My chains were removed on arrival in the city and it is surprising what a few good meals can do for something that for months has been only half-alive. It's psychological, I guess, but at the end of those four days I began to feel interested in remaining alive again.

Had I any idea of what the Amir of Afghanistan's Durbar was like I might have preferred to remain at the roadside. But I'm getting too far ahead.

This Durbar was not to be held in the Durbar Hall which adjoins the Palace on the edge of the city, but in an enclosure on the north-east of the town beyond the Sherpur Cantonment, and there we were taken under strong military escort. I say we, since there must have been a dozen other pitiful wretches looking very like myself who were taken along at the same time.

Apparently on these occasions it was customary to combine business and pleasure, for before " cases " were heard and often between them, a sort of gymkhana was in progress. The Amir was seated on a raised and canopied dais (I recognised him from my encounter a few days before) surrounded by khans, sirdars, mullahs and the rest of the various officials who formed the Khilwat, which more or less corresponds to a permanent cabinet. However, as the Amir is an absolute despot, cabinet—or even advisers—is scarcely the correct term, for no member of the council may give advice unless he is expressly asked for it.

Persons awaiting trial, including myself, were assembled in a corner under armed guards, and obliged to witness the day's sport before hearing what their fate might be.

Some distance away, a huge bull elephant was shackled by all four feet to the ground. It was not harnessed and from its loud trumpetings and squeals seemed to be somewhat ill at ease, and I wondered what it was for. I supposed it had some connection with the sports to be held until I later discovered it had a much more sinister purpose.

The first day of the Durbar only two " cases " were heard, but they were eye-openers, to say the least. I had hitherto harboured a vague idea that there might be some sort of justice to be expected even of a country where the whole judicial system is centred in one individual, since, after all, the law was the Law of Islam, which in itself is just and equable. I soon discovered, however, that it was capable of the most horrible misinterpretations.

After a long display of horsemanship the first poor devil of our group was summoned and thrown before the Amir by two soldiers. He was not, it seemed, entitled to speak for himself. He lay there, quivering, while the Amir inquired loudly what he had done. It was the business of a tall, grave-faced official at one side of the dais, whom I took to be some sort of Chief of Police, to announce a list of crimes, real or suspected, after which the Amir would either pronounce sentence directly or put it to the vote among members of the Khilwat.

It was as I witnessed this first case that I realised with horrible suddenness that we were all predestined to receive one sentence—to be administered in varying forms.

Death !

But not death by decapitation, or by a rifle bullet, or by hanging. Such methods of execution were evidently too straightforward. The Amir wished to be amused at his Durbar. And so it came about that I was the witness of some of the most fiendish refinements of capital punishment which the mind of man can have devised.

Not only that, but a witness with the certainty that just such a fate was in store for me presently. I soon realised the purpose for which the shackled elephant was required. The huge beast had gone *musth*, and the first man to be condemned was taken over and thrown down in front of it ! Out flung the long trunk, seized him, held him ; then, with one huge forefoot placed on him, the beast's trunk wound round his body and tore him slowly apart. . . . His screams mingled horribly with the enraged trumpetings of the elephant. In my weakened condition I was physically sick as I watched it. Some loathsome fascination kept my eyes open as I saw the next unfortunate wretch bound by his four limbs to four bent saplings whose tops were pegged into the earth. At a given signal the taut ropes holding them were severed simultaneously and the screaming body disgustingly quartered. . . .

After this edifying spectacle the remainder of us were taken back to the mud-wall " prison " that night and fed again. My agony of mind and the screams of broken men still echoing in my ears rendered me incapable of either eating or sleeping, and the next day we were taken out once more. On this occasion I was forced to see a man put to death in a huge jar of oil beneath which a brazier was lit and the liquid boiled. In my half-frantic state I remember being stupidly reminded of Ali Baba and the Forty Thieves, and I expect I joined in the laughter with the rest of the company. Even that day I was not to hear my own fate, although I received a tiny sop of comfort in seeing one of the unfortunates go free. It had pleased the Amir to temper his justice with mercy !

The third day my turn arrived and I was hauled before the dais as the usual questions were called. I can hear now as I think of it the slow gutturals of the voice of the man on the dais.

" *What hath this man done ?* "

The words I had heard so often fell on my ears like a clap of thunder.

" The dog is a *jasoos* (spy), lord. Many men have brought tales concerning him."

So I was a spy ! And that was the first time I had heard even of what crime I was accused. I faced the dais and in defiance of all rules shouted my protest.

" Hear me, merciful prince, as Allah is a witness ! I am no spy but a respectable trader. Spying requires brains which I have not. My house stands without the city, as many will testify, and I have a poor business as a merchant of rugs from Bokhara and the northern cities of Turkestan ! "

I rambled on, protesting my innocence until my mouth was stopped by one of the guards who held me. As I spoke I saw the Amir lean over and address one of the company beside him. I supposed they were discussing which of the beastly deaths I had witnessed was bad enough for a *jasoos*. There was a good deal of laughter and at length an official was summoned.

I thought the end had come when at length the Amir spoke in a loud voice, delivering sentence. But I was mistaken.

" Take this fellow," he said, " give him a purse of two hundred rupees and a safe conduct to the Khyber with six men. It is better that his trading be done in the bazaars of Peshawar and Lahore."

I could hardly believe my ears when I heard this. Was this just another piece of exhibition " mercy " for the benefit of his loyal subjects or was I in fact suspected of spying ? I neither knew nor, at that moment, cared, and as I was led away, accompanied by the important person (whom I gathered to be an officer in the Amir's personal bodyguard) back to the city, I merely felt a tremendous sense of relief !

THRILLS ON A WINDJAMMER

By

A. C. COLLODON

I was born on a barge, and I served my apprenticehip to life in a hard school where kicks, and not kisses, were the order of the day. My father and mother came from a family of bargees who for years had run the lime barges on the old Warple Canal, through Cheshire and Derbyshire, and I was born somewhere on this stretch of water. Exactly where, nobody knew, certainly not my father or my mother, for bearing a child was an ordinary sort of business that hardly interfered with the day's work, and I haven't a doubt that my mother was leading the old horse on the towing-path until a few hours before my birth, and within a few hours after it.

Life on a barge has always been a hard business for a child, and always will be, but now, at least, some sort of organisation has been put into effect, and a child gets a proper schooling. In 1854, when I was born, there was, of course, no such organisation, and the only schooling I ever got was in how to help run a barge, and in swearing. I couldn't read or write until I was nearly twenty, and I was a grown-up man before I could tell the time.

In a way, though, I was lucky because I was an only child. On other barges there were large families who ran about wild in dreadful conditions, but, in my case, all the love and affection of my parents (which was very, very little) was, at least, undivided and I got all of it.

As soon as I could run about, my parents made me work. My father was a thinker, and he had a theory that all men and women should work twice as much as they slept. When I say that he was a thinker, I mean that, while my mother used to lead the old nag on the towing-path, he would sit in the barge, smoking and ruminating, so I suppose that it was in such circumstances that he evolved his theory.

I shan't say much about my early upbringing. It was squalid and, judged by modern standards, appalling. I remember vividly, for instance, how, almost as soon as I could walk, my mother would tie a rope round my chest and heave me over the side into the canal while the barge was moving. A few minutes' agony in the ice-cold water, and she would draw me in again.

That was my bath !

Nowadays, I suppose, some well-meaning association would have people like mine up for cruelty ; and nowadays, too, I suppose, a modern child would catch pneumonia twenty times over under such treatment—so there is one thing I do thank my people for, and that is for hardening me and fitting me for an adventurous life.

When I was ten years of age, my mother died. She had gone off the barge in the early evening to enjoy herself with some friends, and my father and I both fell fast asleep in her absence. I fell asleep because I was dog-tired after a hard day's work ; but my father's sound sleep was as much due to the beer that I had seen him imbibing as to natural causes.

During the evening, a slight shower of rain came down, and made slippery the plank on which we entered the barge from the towing-path. When my mother returned, I will be kind to her memory and say that she missed her footing on the greasy plank, fell into the canal, and was drowned. Neither my father nor I knew anything about the tragedy until the next morning.

All I will add, though, is that I have seen my mother walk up that plank when the frost of a winter's day had made it as slippery as a skating-rink, and, furthermore, that, in ordinary circumstances, she could swim like a fish. . . .

After her death, Fate rattled the dice for me, and changed my whole life. Quite conceivably, I might have spent all my remaining days as a humdrum bargee had it not been for that tragedy.

II

THERE is little time for sentiment in the life of a bargee, and, after the funeral of my mother, work went on just the same as ever. My father continued to sit in the barge and ruminate, while I took my mother's place and led the horse on the towing-path, but, whether he was mourning my mother's death, or whether he was ruminating over the same subjects that had occupied his idle attention when she was alive, I don't know.

F.T.S.   2 E

Anyway, he apparently decided that I couldn't lead the horse with the same skill as my mother, or, to give him his due, perhaps, on her death, he lost interest in barge life, for one day, soon after the tragedy, he brusquely told me to pack up my goods, and go ashore with him. He had sold the barge.

We came to Liverpool, and, if I thought that I was going to share my father's retirement, I was much mistaken, for we had no sooner arrived than he took me to the docks, where I met a man who was indirectly responsible for my leading the adventurous life that is the subject of this book.

His name was Jonathan Scratch, and that was also the name of the windjammer that he skippered. I learned afterwards that nobody knew his real name (rumour had it that he had never been christened), and the name of Jonathan Scratch, by which everybody knew him, had been given to him by some clever member of his crew long before I met him. I say " clever member " advisedly, for I've never in all my life met a man whose name fitted him so well.

The " Scratch " part of his name came from the fact that he was forever scratching his red goatee beard, and the " Jonathan " because he looked ever inch a Jonathan. The poet says something about a rose by any other name smelling as sweet, but, in the case of Scratch, he would have lost half his formidability under any other name. Jonathan Scratch ; I shall always remember him.

He looked like the popular representation of the Devil, and, in his character, he maintained the resemblance. Standing well over six feet, and broad in proportion, he had a thin, hawk-like face, and grey eyes that bored through you like bradawls. He had busy red eyebrows, and a beard that jutted out aggressively. You could always tell when there was trouble ahead by watching his beard, because, when he was angry, it stuck outwards and upwards as he pursed his lips and tightened his jaw. There was a saying among his crew that, one day, he would have such a fit of temper that his beard would find its way into his mouth and choke him. I'll go as far as to say that there were many men who longed to be present on that occasion !

How my father came to know this truculent, weather-bitten sailor, I don't know, but they seemed to be on very good terms, and, down in the cabin of the creaking ship, they fortified themselves with raw spirit and yarned intimately on all manner of subjects. I remember Scratch telling my father that he had just come into Liverpool with a cargo of grain and pickled spices from Australia and the East, and that the journey had taken him altogether two years ! When people fly to Australia in a week or so these days, facts like these sound unbelievable, but it was a slow world sixty-eight years ago.

The stuffy atmosphere of the cabin didn't please me a bit, and, seeing that the two men were much too interested in each other to worry about me, I quietly stole out on deck, and roamed the ship, drinking in everything with real boyish curiosity.

Though I had been born and bred on the water, I felt on board this boat just like an urchin from the East End slums would feel on being transported into an elegant Mayfair mansion, and at first I was too scared of my surroundings to pry closely into the equipment and construction of the ship. Everything looked so clean and smart that I felt quite out of place, but that feeling didn't last long.

Very soon I was exploring with zest and, at last, I determined to climb a sail-mast, and see what it was like up there. It was fine ! I scampered up like a born sailor, hung precariously on the guide-ropes and imagined that I was furling the mainsail with a gale blowing up, until a raucous bellow from below turned my attention to more mundane things.

Looking down, I saw my father and Captain Scratch standing on deck and, sheepishly, I clambered down, and ran to my father.

Strange to say he didn't upbraid me for taking liberties when his back was turned ; he just gripped me by the shoulder and looked hard at me. There was an enigmatic expression on his face—whether of pride, or joy, or sorrow, I shall never know.

" Well, 'Gustus," he said, slowly, " you aren't mine any longer. *I've just sold you to Captain Scratch for a pound !* "

I stared at him, open-mouthed.

" What a chance for you, son ! " he went on. " You'll sail round the world, see places you've never heard of ; you'll have the time of your life ! Eh, Scratch ? "

The Captain concurred.

" I'll show him a thing or two," he said, jovially, in his deep, rumbling voice. " Why, I'll even show you a real, live King—old Raf Sera, when we get to Lagos in a few months' time ! "

I was very silent. I didn't know whether to be pleased

at becoming a part of this beautiful ship, or sorry at leaving England, my father and the barge ; but it didn't seem to make any difference what I felt, for the deal was concluded without my being consulted.

While I stood, wondering what to say, my father took my hand and pressed it hard. Then he shook hands with the Captain, and left us.

I ran to the side and waved to him as he walked briskly along the dock, but he never turned back, and, when he had gone from my sight, I was left forlorn and frightened.

I never saw my father again.

.   .   .   .   .   .

While I was standing by the side, trying to grasp the significance of the great change that had so suddenly taken place in my life, an old salt tapped me on the shoulder. I turned round and he was looking ruminatively in the direction my father had taken.

"Well, son," he said, gruffly, " you haven't got a father now ; only a Father in Heaven, and you'll need Him, too, before this journey's over."

Pleasant words to be greeted with ! They sent a shudder through me, and my fears were not allayed when Captain Jonathan Scratch came up to me, and conducted me to my quarters—a low, evil-smelling bunk close to his cabin.

"Make yourself at home here," he said, " and in a few days you can cough your belly up in the Bay of Biscay."

"Y-yes, sir," I stammered, my childish imagination running riot at his ominous words.

"Your job will be to wait on me," he went on, " and be generally useful in the ship. I'll teach you to sew me a pair of pants and a ship-suit ; and maybe I'll teach you to read the deck-prayers on Sunday." He beamed at me. " And in addition to that, my lad," he said, in a tone of voice that suggested that he was doing me a favour, " you'll get plenty to eat, and a silver shilling at the end of every voyage."

Young as I was I realised that this was not a particularly princely rate of pay, but I knew it was useless to argue, and I consoled myself with the thought that seeing the world was an experience that many people willingly paid for, while I was going to get it free. *And* a silver shilling, which was quite a useful coin in those days.

We sailed for tropical ports a week later, and, by that time, my early fears had been, to a certain extent, allayed. The novelty of being an essential part of this beautiful ship pleased me mightily, and the way I swaggered round the deck when I saw anybody watching the ship from the dock might reasonably had led them to assume that, if I was not the owner, I was at least the skipper of the *Jonathan Scratch*.

But my bumptiousness disappeared as soon as we reached the Bay of Biscay. The Captain, in his own sweet way, had predicted that I would be sea-sick, but he had mercifully not told me that I would be so ill as to crave for death and release from my torture. Heavy seas were running, and the old ship creaked from one end to the other, while the wind whistled tunes through the rigging like a *kwama's* pipe.

Scratch came to me as I lay groaning in my bunk, and all he did was smile and tell me that, after six months of it, I would get used to the sea. Had I been able to talk, I would have replied that, within six months, I would be dead.

Mind you, I can only realise now what splendid schooling this was, but it was hard. After a fortnight, we made calmer seas, and I found my sea legs. Then, weak and pale, I tottered up on deck, and, as soon as I smelt the tang of the sea air, I felt hungry. That was my baptism, and I was only sea-sick once again in all my life. That was off the coast of South America, many years later.

The *Jonathan Scratch* was manned by a crew of forty, including some of the biggest toughs it has ever been my misfortune to meet. I will give credit to the Skipper in this connection and say that he warned me early on about the sort of men that I would have to work with on board, and, in his own rough way, he gave me some useful advice. He told me not to listen to their deck-stories, and no sooner had the voyage started than he summoned the crew and asked them to respect my age, but I am afraid that neither I nor the crew took much notice of his well-meant requests.

It was when we were three weeks out and were becalmed for two days, that I forgot my avowals to the Captain, and went and listened to the crew yarning in the fo'c'sle. There, I learned more in an hour than I could have ever learned otherwise in a year.

I don't think this knowledge did me any harm. Experience has since taught me that it is just as dangerous to hide vital knowledge from a boy as it is to tell it to him too early, and, if the sailors' yarns were uncouth and crude, all I can say is that the mind of a bargee's son is also uncouth and crude, so I learnt what I had to learn in the language that I understood most easily.

The worst man on board was the bo'sun, known to us only by the name of "Slicer." I learned that his name had been given to him by reason of his murderous nature, for his usual trick was to slash his splicing-knife across the face of anybody he disliked. In appearance, he was like a Cameroons' gorilla, with a scarred, evil face, and great hairy arms that hung forward when he walked. When he was angry—and he seldom seemed to be anything else—he had a roar that outdid any modern syren, and was invaluable on a foggy night.

Then there was "Hurricane" Joe, the mate, so called because he only came out of his shell when a gale was blowing ; and the second mate, "Bear" Huggins, another brute of a man, who had earned his nickname by his unpleasant habit of squeezing his enemies to his bosom, with fatal results to his enemies, and no effect at all on his bosom.

As for Jonathan Scratch, he was a hard, dangerous man, but he had a kind heart, and to me he was always good. Every man on board feared him, and yet they loved him for his bravery and his fairness. Although I hated him many times during my voyages with him, I know now that I was lucky to have such a man to guide me when I was on the threshold of life.

Well, we were becalmed two days, and on the third we blew up a north-speeder and sailed merrily for Lisbon, in Portugal, our first port of call. There we had to unload 200 barrels of liquor, and, as it was my first real glimpse of a foreign country, it is easy to understand how excited I was when we docked.

But I was disappointed when the Skipper called me over to him as soon as we arrived.

"Listen, nipper," he said, "don't go ashore with any one but me. There are some filthy places in Lisbon, and even my own crew would trade you for a gallon of wine. Understand ? "

I didn't believe what he said, but I had learnt by then that a command from Scratch was a command to be obeyed, so I refused to accompany any of the crew on shore, and spent the day moping miserably round the ship.

In the evening Scratch went on shore and took me with him, but I don't for a moment think that he took me because he liked my company. Probably he thought I would be safer with him than I would be left on board.

We went into a dingy little tavern by the docks, where Scratch seemed to be well known, for all sorts of queer-looking people greeted him effusively. In a curtained alcove, we sat down and the Skipper ordered me some food and coffee, while he drank a tankard of port wine.

He seemed to be waiting for somebody, and, sure enough, we hadn't been seated long before a sallow, smart-looking young fellow lifted the curtain and came to sit by us. He and Scratch talked seriously together in low, mysterious tones, and the only word I could hear was " ivory "—a fine stimulant to fire my boyish imagination.

At last, Scratch seemed to forget my presence, for he leaned back in his chair, and drummed his fingers restlessly on the table. When he spoke, it was in conversational tones that I could not help overhearing.

" It's hard to get," he said doubtfully, " and 50,000 is a hell of a lot. You know what'll happen if I'm found out ? "

The younger man shrugged his shoulders philosophically.

" It means the finish for all of us," said Scratch.

The conversation then relapsed into whispers, and I could hear no more.

Soon afterwards, Scratch concluded the interview, and went off to talk to the proprietor of the place. He ordered a large consignment of wines, cigars and other necessities, and we went back to the ship.

On the way, Scratch said to me :

" Tell me, son, did you hear much of what I was saying ? "

" I only heard that you were talking about ivory," I answered.

" Anything else ? " he asked.

" No."

" Perhaps it's as well. In time, you'll know all about it." And I did.

.   .   .   .   .   .

From Lisbon, we set a straight course for the West coast of Africa, and, by the time we were within sight of Lagos, I was a hard-bitten, strong little animal, inured to the sea and the hardships of life upon it. There are many aspects of my sailing-ship experience that I must gloss over, but, on the whole, I was better off than when I had been on the barge.

When we were a day out from Lagos, Scratch called me to him in his cabin, and I had to give only one look at his tell-tale beard to know that there was trouble brewing.

" Well, son," he said icily, " we've gone half-way across the world, and you've made a good start. I've watched you work, and I'm satisfied. But "—he stood up and towered over me,—" you've been talking too much with the crew, when I told you not to. What have they been saying to you ? "

" N-nothing," I stammered.

He seized me roughly by the shoulder, and his face was terrible to look at.

" They told you something that I want to know," he hissed. " What was it ? "

I was petrified with fear, all the more because there was a great deal of justice in what the Skipper was asking me, and, at the risk of getting murdered for disclosing secrets, I stuttered out what I knew.

" They say, sir," I said, haltingly, " that you never use a Bank."

" Well ? " rapped Scratch.

" And—and that somewhere in the ship lie piles of gold that you've hoarded."

" Is that all ? "

" Y-yes."

" You're lying to me," thundered Scratch. " What else do they say ? "

I decided to make a clean breast of all I knew.

" They say," I answered, " that you carry all sorts of illegal cargo, and that you make ever such a lot of money. They asked me if I'd ever seen you looking in any secret panel or drawer in your cabin, and I said I hadn't. Then they told me not to tell you what they'd asked me."

" Who told you all this ? " asked Scratch, his red brows drawn together in a blazing line.

" Slicer," I answered in a low, frightened voice.

" Uh-huh," snorted the enraged Skipper. " Well, you're coming aloft with me, and you're going to repeat what you've just said in the presence of Slicer himself. Come on ! "

I was too terrified to move, and the Captain half-dragged, half-carried me up the companionway. On deck, he summoned the crew, and roundly abused them for putting bad ideas into my head. One and all, they virtuously denied the indictment, but Scratch—although he did not mention the specific charges I had made—dressed them down with his tongue, and many black looks were cast at me during his outburst. Then he dismissed them, and the men went back to their work, all except the evil Slicer who was asked by Scratch to remain.

I can't repeat the language that flew between these two enraged men once the Skipper had made known his accusations, and the names that Slicer called me in the course of the argument make me blush even now when I think of them.

In the end Scratch told him that, when they made Mexico, he could take his papers and clear out. Naturally that did not please Slicer, and he made a lightning grab at his hip, where he kept the knife that had given him his name. Fortunately for Scratch, though, two seamen, who had been attracted to the scene by the noise, saw the action and pounced on the maddened bo'sun before he could draw his knife.

They led him away, but not before he had hissed a nasty threat into my face.

" You'll be greasing the belly of a shark before I've finished with you," he said, and I was by no means pacified when Scratch, who had overheard the remark, said to me :

" Don't you worry, my lad ; that fellow will be swinging from the tops'l for mutiny before this trip's over ! "

I had a nasty feeling in my stomach that Slicer's end would follow mine, and I was not a bit happy about him. He was the first enemy I ever made, and he was destined to play a great part in my life.

We stayed sixteen days in Lagos, unloading a mixed cargo hold and taking on another, and, naturally, I was intrigued by everything I saw—although the little, ramshackle trading-port was actually nothing much to get excited about. Even so, the novelty of seeing so many black men all at once did not wear off very quickly, and my joy knew no bounds when, for the first time in my life, I saw a lion and an elephant. These, I found to my apprehensive delight, were part of the cargo we were to take away with us to Buenos Aires—six lions, twelve elephants and a few more assorted wild beasts, for some menagerie or other.

During the first week we were in Lagos, I was really too busy to get more than a superficial glimpse of the town, for I had to help the carpenters make suitable accommodation for our ferocious passengers. I bet that " Chips " and his assistants never worked harder and more carefully in all their experience than they did over that job, for one insecure plank, or one loose nail might mean a lion joining us for breakfast one morning ! Even our skill was not sufficient to keep the lions in, as I'll tell you later when we get on the high seas again, but, fortunately, we didn't know it then.

While we were in Lagos, though, a rather frightening

experience did befall me in this very connection, and, all because of a piece of bad carpentry on board another ship in the port, this book might never have been written.

Captain Scratch, I should explain, was like a real father to me when we touched port, and he kept me very much under his wing, while the crew, united on my side by their common hatred of Slicer, also looked after me. They told me, with many rolling oaths and bloodcurdling threats, that, if Slicer did anything to me, they would " run him up the sail "— a picturesque phrase that needs no explanation. Retribution of this kind was all very well, but I didn't like the thought of the crime that would inspire such rough justice ; still, I was glad to have the crew on my side, and still more glad to see that Slicer sedulously avoided me.

Well, on our third day in port, the crew had some rough work on hand, and Captain Scratch had some business to transact on shore, so he left " Hurricane " Joe in charge of the ship, and took me off with him. The tropical heat was something I had neither experienced before nor imagined I ever would experience, so my clothes were rough, thick and patched—the same clothes that my father had carried on board for me at Liverpool ; to be perfectly frank, they were the only clothes I had, and had ever had. When I began to walk on African soil, I felt as if I were wearing a leaden diving-suit, but, unless I followed the example of the natives, there seemed to be nothing I could do.

Captain Scratch, however, had observed my discomfort, and, without saying anything to me, he led me to a second-hand dealer and fitted me up with a more suitable rig-out. When I tried to thank him, he stuck up his beard and snorted. In his way, he was a great and kindly man.

Frankly, I must have been an infernal nuisance to the Captain, for, although he was on business bent, he had to take me with him wherever he went. I didn't realise then how much he was inconveniencing himself by having me trail after him, or that he was deliberately doing so because he was afraid that harm would befall me elsewhere.

Ultimately, we landed up at a traders' restaurant kept by a negro called Kwama Hoot. Once again, I noticed that Scratch was a popular favourite, for yells of welcome greeted us from all sides of the shack, and one of the negroes behind the bar dashed off in search of the proprietor.

Kwama Hoot came out immediately, and greeted my skipper affectionately. I learned afterwards that, in a port where it was unwise to enquire too deeply into the lives of the men one met, this negro was one of the few men who retained an unblemished reputation and character. He was an elderly man, with woolly hair almost white, and he had spent most of his life at sea. I suppose that was why he and Scratch were such good friends.

The saloon was crowded with sailors, traders, tramps, and white woman. I was horrified to see women in a place like this, but I have no doubt now that they were traders' wives, or passengers from the ships in port, spending an evening at what was then the counterpart of a present-day European Club. Or, perhaps, I may still be wrong . . . !

The place buzzed with conversation, and I listened to as much as I could. Everybody seemed to be talking about ivory, or gold, or precious stones, and I was so excited by the thoughts that these magic words inspired that I could hardly answer when Scratch asked me whether I felt hungry. The worthy Skipper, acting on the quite correct assumption that a boy can always eat something, didn't trouble to make me interpret my stammering answer, and ordered some food, which was set out at a table in the corner.

We sat down there, and mysterious-looking men came up and conversed with Scratch. I couldn't hear what they were saying, because the hubbub in the saloon completely veiled their conversation, but I guessed, from the serious and worried expression on the Skipper's face, that he was talking business. I have often wondered why he didn't transact his business affairs in the privacy of his cabin on board the ship, but he never did ; he always chose a corner of a bar or café in the ports that we called at.

Well, there I was, excited and cheerful, enjoying a good cup of coffee, and feeling that a sailor's life was the only life for a boy like me, when the air was split by a woman's shriek, and then another shriek, and shouts, and yells—and commotion !

I looked up, and standing at the door of the saloon were two intruders—animals I had never seen before in my life, two man-sized apes, snarling and chattering with rage.

As we started to our feet, they bounded swiftly over to where the throng was thickest, and charged in, clawing and biting in their fury. I saw one of them lift a man over his head, and throw him on to the floor ; I saw another bite a woman's arm . . . then I waited to see no more. . . .

The saloon was one struggling mass of maddened people

striving to break through to the entrances, but I was small, and fear lent cunning to my agility. How I wriggled my way through the throng, I've no idea, but, when my abject panic subsided, I found myself cowering with a handful of other people in a tiny, dimly-lit room that I afterwards found to be an attic. Downstairs, the noise of the scampering, frightened people reached us, and I was further scared out of my life by the whirring of wings and a hoarse cawing in the room where I was.

Looking round, I saw a large wire cage in which a gorgeously-plumed cockatoo was giving vent to the anger he felt at having his privacy so rudely disturbed, and I have no doubt that it was his lively squawking that put the apes on our track, for we were soon conscious of a shuffling and snarling that came nearer and nearer, and then we smelt a fœtid odour . . . and the apes were in the room, their teeth gleaming, and their eyes glinting evilly. . . . Sometimes, even now, in nightmares, I see those man-eaters again, with the human blood matting the hair round their mouths. . . .

What would have happened to us if not for the cockatoo, I dare not think, for the apes were out for blood, and we had no means of escape ; but, as they began to advance upon us, they caught sight of the unfortunate bird. That diverted them, and one of the beasts seized the cage like a child might seize a new toy. With hardly any effort at all, he twisted it into a shapeless mess, then tore it to pieces, and grabbed the fluttering polly. All the while, the other ape was squatting on its haunches watching the proceedings and snarling, but there was no chance of our escaping, for he blocked our way to the door. Slowly, deliberately, they choked the life out of the bird, and then began to strip her of her raiment. . . .

How long we were confined within sight of death, I do not know ; it seemed to me like hours, but it was probably about half an hour, and at the end of that time, the alarm had gone round and we heard stealthy movements coming from outside. The apes heard them, too, and started up towards the door, but, as they reached it, a volley of rifle and revolver-fire greeted them, and their brief experience of liberty was over.

I have a hazy recollection of people coming into the room, and of Jonathan Scratch bursting in and hugging me like a long-lost son, then I fainted, and, when I woke up, I was back in my cabin on board ship.

I learned afterwards that these two apes had been caught by a German expedition, and had been lying on board a ship in the harbour when they escaped from their cages. They were being taken to Germany to be shown to the Emperor and then deposited in the Berlin Zoo, but the Emperor never saw them, and their remains were deposited in an improvised cemetery in Lagos.

We didn't go ashore again after that, and I spent the days watching hundreds of negroes filling up our holds. On the day before we sailed we took on our live cargo without any mishap or excitement.

Then we stretched sail for more adventures, our next call being Sierra Leone.

III

I HAVE purposely refrained from describing at any length my impressions of the town of Lagos, for, as it later on turned out to be my jumping-off ground for those African adventures that gave me my nickname of " Congo Jake," I propose to leave any detailed description of the place until I come to that part of my narrative.

Suffice it to say, for the moment, that we spent sixteen days over the bar (as they called lying in Lagos Harbour then) and then set sail for Sierra Leone, which we reached uneventfully. The weather was kind to us, and a fair breeze sped us merrily on our way, but, when we entered the old channel road off Sierra Leone, we found an uncomfortable welcome awaiting us.

I have never been to Sierra Leone since that day, and I do not know much about the place, so I cannot say whether the natural phenomenon that I am about to describe was a regular visitation, or something unusual and unprecedented. All I know is that we ran into a fine curtain of sandy dust that completely enveloped the ship and gave us a troublesome time. It had been blowing in, I understood later, for some two or three days from the Sahara Desert, and it got into our food, into our clothes, into our mouths and nostrils, and into our eyes. As for poor Captain Scratch, no more cunning form of torture could possibly have been devised for his benefit, for the powdery sand settled in his beard—and he *did* scratch !

The food tasted terrible and gritty, but we had to eat

it or starve, and there was no relief from the torment that the sand caused us until something happened on board the *Jonathan Scratch* of such a serious nature that it completely overshadowed such a comparatively minor worry as a sandstorm.

Our cargo consisted, in addition to commodities, etc., of six lions and twelve elephants, all of which, we fondly believed, had been securely caged up down below. We were taking them to South America, and it is a remarkable commentary on the old-time sailing-ships and sailors that we should so blithely have taken aboard animals like these for a voyage that might last any number of months. Nowadays, you can run your steamships to schedule, and you would know that you've got to put up with these unpleasant beasts for a couple of weeks, or whatever it is ; but, back in the 1860's, the time taken for a voyage was purely a matter of wind and luck. Imagine being becalmed for a long time with hungry lions on board ! I marvel, now at the nerves of our crew—or perhaps it wasn't so much nerves as lack of imagination.

Anyway, we were lying off Sierre Leone with our sails down and flares on our port and stern, when wild roars broke the peaceful silence of the night. I was on deck, looking over the side, but I didn't need to be told what had happened. I gave one yell and started running—where I knew not, nor did the rest of the crew, who also started to dash about like madmen.

" The lions have broken loose ! "

I shall never forget that cry as it rose from a panic-stricken seaman, nor the sight of " Junky," our cook (so called because he was a wizard with the salt-junk) trying to scramble up the rigging with his meat-chopper still in his hand, nor the sound of that ominous roaring that seemed to set every board in the old ship vibrating. . . .

As I was running, I felt a hand grab my shoulder, and flashed round to find " Beacon," our lamp-man, shouting at me to follow him. I did. My heart was in my mouth, and I was so frightened that a sickly haze in front of my eyes almost blinded me, but somehow I managed to grope my stumbling way down two flights of iron steps, clinging to the rails, missing my footing every now and then, and hearing with terror the dread sounds of panic above me.

We got right down to the ship's bottom, and tore along a narrow passage-way that led to a store where we kept all sorts of junk—paint, rope, oil, canvas, anything ! Beacon pushed open the door, and in we dashed.

The heat and stench of this tiny room were appalling, but we felt we were safe there, for it was impossible for the lions to get to us. Although we could scarcely breathe the foetid air and the darkness was terrifying, we were prepared to endure these discomforts rather than face the worse danger outside, but, just as we were congratulating ourselves on our security, I noticed something that froze the blood in my veins for the second time that evening.

Eyes . . . green pinpoints of light that stared at us malignantly, unwinkingly from out of the wall of darkness . . . eyes that seemed to appear like magic on all sides of us as we became accustomed to our surroundings . . . eyes around us, baleful, threatening, wherever we turned. . . .

" My God ! " I gasped. " What are those ? "

" Quiet ! " hissed Beacon.

In the darkness, I could feel him by my side, his body tense with apprehension, watching those eyes. I did not know what they were, but my teeth were chattering at this new terror.

I heard a whisper from my companion.

" *Rats !* "

At this terrifying information, I could not repress a shriek, and that was the signal for the rats to charge at us. As we stood, paralysed, we heard pattering and squeakings from all around us . . . then we were surrounded by soft, squashy demons that bit at us with teeth of razor sharpness. . . .

They sprang at us from the shelves of the store, fastening on to our shoulders, clawing and biting at our faces ; they ran across the floor and scrambled up our trouser-legs, biting through the cloth into the flesh ; as we tried to beat them off, they bit at our fingers and hands, and, though we struggled and kicked and fought madly, they clung tenaciously to us . . . hundreds and hundreds of them. . . .

We shrieked and screamed as we blindly struggled to find the door, and it seemed hours before we could make our way out of the death-trap. Then it was only because we heard answering shouts from outside from sailors who came rushing down to help us in our fight against what they thought were the escaped lions, that we were able to find our way to the invisible door. Their voices guided us in the right direction, and, when we at last broke out, we fell into our comrades' arms, blood-bespattered, bitten and pain-wracked, and almost unconscious from the horror of our experience.

We were taken aloft to the ship's doctor, a man who was only known as " Senna," because he invariably administered senna-tea and oil to cure our ills. I still wonder how on earth he came to be on the ship as a doctor ; he did not seem to know much about medicine or surgery, and God help the wretched man upon whom he had to use a knife !

Senna smeared our wounds with some vile-smelling ointment that hurt just as much as the bites, and bandaged us up. I was badly bitten on the hands and legs, but my companion, Beacon, was in a worse state than I was, for the rats had got at his face.

Afterwards, the doctor gave us both a very large dose of rum to make us sleep, and it acted like a charm. The sound sleep that we enjoyed after our adventure did us much more good than his ointment, I'm certain !

But, in the meantime, what of the lions ? Unfortunately, I was otherwise engaged when they were recaptured, but I had the full story told to me afterwards, and I now set it down as yet another tribute to the memory of that brave old sea-dog—Captain Jonathan Scratch.

When Beacon and I dashed down to our cubby-hole among the rats, the other members of the crew scattered in all directions. Some climbed the rigging, others hid in the lifeboats, those below locked themselves in their cabins and prayed hard that the doors were stoutly-built.

Captain Scratch was on the navigator's poop at the time, and also dashed into hiding. I have no doubt that, for all his magnificent courage, he feared for his life as the hungry beasts bounded about the deck, and his conscience must have pricked him at the thought of the irregular feeding that had maddened them sufficiently to break their cages. Actually, the beasts were supposed to get 10 lbs. of meat a day, but a good three-quarters of this consisted of dry, meatless bones, and I don't wonder that they were hungry.

Anyway, the lions went exploring below, but that didn't encourage the men to come out of their hiding-places, although they called across to each other to take their bearings.

" Hi ! " called a voice from a lifeboat.

" Hi ! " came an answering voice from up the mast.

" Who are you ? " asked the first voice.

" ' Hurricane ' Joe. Who are you ? "

" Huggins. Where's the Skipper ? "

" Here," boomed Scratch from his hiding-place. " Who's up there by the wind-chute ? "

" Bandy, sir."

" Attract his attention, Huggins, can you ? "

" Yessir," and the second-mate began to make signals to the man up aloft.

The wind-chute, I ought to explain at this stage, is a canvas ventilating-shaft that used to go through the old sailing-ships and send a current of fresh air to the lower decks. It was a primitive affair, but effective, for it caught the breeze and circulated it.

The Skipper's mind had been working rapidly since the lions escaped, and he had at first intended to make a dash for the " quelling-room," where the arms were kept. But he had remembered, just in time, that, in the first place, the lions were precious cargo if brought to Buenos Aires alive, but were of no use at all if they were dead ; and, in the second place, the quelling-room was some distance away from where he was hiding, so he stood a good chance of getting mauled on the way. Scratch always carried the key of the armoury slung on a chain round his neck, and nobody else could get to the guns.

He therefore had to resort to strategy, and the wind-chute gave him a brilliant idea.

On the first deck, a strong pen surrounded a hundred or so live goats and sheep which supplied us (and the lions) with our fresh meat, and the wind-chute communicated with this deck.

" Slide down the chute," yelled Scratch to Bandy, the sailor sheltering nearest to its opening, " and get in the animals' pen. Stir up the goats and the sheep, and make 'em bleat. Then, maybe, the lions will go down there."

" What do I do if the lions *do* go down there ? " asked Bandy, who obviously didn't relish the job.

" Never you mind," retorted Scratch. " Do as I say."

Bandy had no alternative but to obey, and he took a dive through the opening and slithered down the canvas to the pen, where the goats and sheep needed no stirring up, for his presence made them bleat quickly enough.

But, imagine his horror when, arrriving in the middle of the pen, he looked up and found himself being watched by *six lions !*

They had obviously smelt out the domestic animals, and were now trying to get into the pen. Some of them were reared on their hind-legs, clawing at the bars of the cage ; others were stalking restlessly backwards and forwards like sentinels ; the rest were squatting, and watching the proceedings with ferocious interest.

" Eh ! " shouted Bandy up the chute. " The lions are here already ! "

Scratch's voice came back to him with a note of intense satisfaction.

" Fine," it said. " Open the door and let 'em in."

" *What !* " screamed Bandy. " They'll kill me ! "

" No," yelled Scratch. " They'll jump for the sheep and goats, and, while they're doing that, you can skip."

" Can I ? " roared the sailor sarcastically. " If there's anything like that to be done, you can come and do it yourself ! "

And Scratch did ! The words were hardly out of the frightened sailor's mouth before the Captain himself came tumbling headlong into the pen. He picked himself up, looked at the lions for a few seconds, and then began to herd all the animals, except a few, into one corner of the pen. Then he stationed himself by the door, with Bandy behind him.

It must have been a tense moment. Even though there was a counter-attraction in the sheep and the goats, Scratch could not say for certain that the lions would go for these. They might quite conceivably prefer human flesh, and then it would be all up with Captain Scratch and the bandy-legged seaman.

However, he took the risk, and, pulling back the bolt, jerked open the door. In bounded the lions, roaring and snarling, toppling over one another to get at the meat, and the frenzied goats and sheep ran hither and thither trying to get away from their enemies. But six of them fell to the lions, and others were trampled and killed or wounded in the crush.

As soon as the lions were safely inside, Scratch and Bandy struggled to get out, and they *had* a struggle, too ! The panic-stricken animals were piling themselves up into an immovable barricade at the door, and the two men had to fight their way through.

But at last it was done, and they were out of the pen. Even then, though, the danger was not past, for the crush of the animals prevented the door being shut, and it was only by superhuman exertion that they were able to stem the stampede and, at long last, lock the now-happy lions in their new prison.

Until we could round them up, the sheep and the goats ran free round the decks, but we rigged up some sort of enclosure for them aft the " walk " (the centre of the ship-deck, where we used to spend our leisure time), and, considering everything, it was surprising how many of these animals came out of their adventure alive.

Scratch and Bandy were badly knocked about during their fight for freedom, but they soon recovered ; so did Beacon and I from the effects of our simultaneous excitement.

I shall never forget even the smallest details of the things that I lived through in the *Jonathan Scratch* for they were so out of the run of anything I had ever experienced, or even heard of, before, that they made an impression on my receptive mind that time cannot erase.

I remember clearly, for instance (although, as I said, I have never been to Sierra Leone since) how Captain Scratch and I watched the hands unloading the 300 tons of cargo that we had to put off in that port, and how he pointed out features of the town to me. Particularly do I remember him pointing to the sky-line, and showing me odd little mountains that were silhouetted on the horizon.

" Those are ' sugar-humps,' " he told me, " and the country beyond them is not healthy for white men to visit."

" Why ? " I asked naïvely.

" You'd be eaten there, my lad," he answered, " either by the wild beasts, or by the savages. And, even if you weren't, the diseases of the jungle 'ud get you."

Then he pointed out French Guinea and Liberia to me, and told me some exciting tales of the country.

" It must have been about fifteen years ago, son," he said, reminiscently, " when all the tribes went mad in these parts. 'Way up in Lagos and all along the coast, they revolted and killed hundreds of poor, innocent settlers and traders, and, of course, rival tribes. There was trouble—lots of it.

" I was in Lagos then, not in this tub, but in a fine rigger called *The Blue Pig*, and I remember how, one night, when most of us were on shore, the ship was attacked and raided by a number of tribesmen. The poor fellows left on board didn't have a chance, and, when we got back, they were past our help. And the damn' niggers had stolen all our provisions, *and* turned our sails overboard."

"But why?" I asked.

"To stop us trading in these parts. They wanted to keep the white men away from their country."

"Do they still want to?" I interjected, fearfully.

"I shouldn't be surprised," answered Scratch indifferently. "But white men are here, and they'll stay here. You needn't worry, my lad; things aren't as bad here now as they were in my day."

I brooded a bit over what he said, and then changed the subject.

"How long are we here for?" I asked.

"Four days," he answered, readily enough, although I still don't know why he should have been on such terms of easy familiarity with an urchin like me whom he had bought for a sovereign. "Then we sail across the Atlantic, and, after that, round to Liverpool again. When we get there, you'll have to decide whether you'll do another trip with me, or stay in England. I'll only do one more voyage after this one," he added wistfully. "I'm sixty-three now, and I'm *tired*."

He said this in a heavy sort of way that made me feel sad, and I remembered this conversation afterwards when I saw him go to his last resting-place.

Well, I thought that the escape of the lions was quite enough excitement to last us the four days that we were spending in Sierra Leone, but I was wrong.

On the day before we were due to sail, we were all on deck swabbing down the paintwork and making everything spick and span for our departure. Little scrubbing was being done because Scratch didn't like it; he said it wore away the woodwork! Still, we were doing our best, when a fine old rigger suddenly appeared off our starboard bow. We could see her name clearly—*Louise*, a French boat—and, as we watched, we began to see it rather *too* clearly, for her navigator seemed to lose his head and his ship winged us, crushing our lifeboats and setting the old *Jonathan Scratch* rocking like a hammock.

Not very much real damage was done, but quite enough to rouse the short tempers of our crew, and the air was blue as Scratch and his subordinates hurled choice profanities at the French ship.

Looking at the *Louise*, I noticed that her decks swarmed

with men, most of them in irons, and chained up to stanchions, but the significance of this did not strike me until I heard Scratch shout :

" You damned Frenchies ! Go to hell, and take your miserable slave-ship there, too ! "

Then he relapsed into a fluent stream of words in a foreign language that I guessed was French. I don't know French, but I can recognise bad language in any tongue, and this sounded like real, first-class profanity.

The Captain of the *Louise* apparently thought so, too, for his face grew redder and redder as he listened, and his plump little frame seemed to swell until I felt sure that he would go *pop !* before my Skipper had finished. But he didn't, unfortunately. What he did was to make an objectionable gesture that is well known as an international insult.

Now, we had a surly devil on board whom we called " Grunty." He was a powerful brute of a man, well over six feet high, and he had a vicious temper. He got his name because of his habit of grumbling about everything and anything.

Grunty saw the Frenchman's insult, and replied in a more ominous way by drawing his knife and passing it in front of his throat. That is another international signal, and it indicates a bloodthirsty threat.

The Frenchman knew the meaning of it all right, for he snarled something nasty and dived into his cabin. Shortly afterwards, the *Louise* lowered a boat which came over to us. There were two men in it, and they brought us a challenge from their Captain to a duel with sabres !

" Now you've done it ! " rasped Scratch, when he had read the message. He was speaking to Grunty, whom he had been reprimanding for his gesture to the French captain. " These dirty pirates demand blood, and they can have it. You threatened the Captain, so you can fight him."

He sent back a message to the *Louise* that our man would accept the challenge if the Frenchman agreed to fight in the open, and in the presence of white men only.

Our terms having been agreed to, a party from our ship put ashore at six o'clock the next morning. Scratch and Grunty were there, of course, and eight other men—and myself. I had been pushed into the dinghy by Scratch just as she was being cast off, and I well remember him saying that he might as well take me along, too, to " see the fun " !

I am afraid I could see nothing funny about the subsequent proceedings, though. We met the party from the *Louise* and reconnoitred until we found a quiet, flat patch away from any chance of interference, then we all began to argue together about the way in which the duel should be conducted. As only Scratch, from our bunch, could speak French, and as none of the Frenchmen could speak English, it was difficult to make headway on this point, even though Scratch tried hard to interpret the heated demands on each side.

At first the Frenchmen insisted on sabres, but we couldn't agree to that. We never used those weapons, and we had heard how adept the Continentals were in duelling with them, so it would have been quite unfair to pit a novice in sabre-warfare like Grunty against an expert like the French Captain.

Ultimately, a compromise was reached, and both parties agreed on the use of ship's knives, the wicked little daggers with which sailors are so handy. Accordingly, the combatants were armed with these knives, and were then placed back to back. At the command, they had to walk three paces forward, turn round, and rush at each other. A ghastly way of avenging honour !

I shuddered as I saw those men walk away from each other, and then charge, brandishing their murderous knives, and out to kill each other. They slashed madly, and, if our man was the taller and stronger, the Frenchman had all the agility and cunning of his race, so the battle was even enough.

The foreigner drew first blood. As Grunty lunged at him, he eluded the lumbering rush, pivoted neatly, and buried his knife in our man's shoulder. Grunty gave a roar of rage, turned, and charged like a bull. His opponent, still off his balance, tried to slither out of the way, but Grunty was mad with pain and anger. I saw his hand uplifted . . . I saw the Captain wriggle like an eel . . . I saw the hand fall . . . and the blood spurt. . . .

The Frenchman fell with Grunty's knife in his throat.

We hurried our shipmate back to the dinghy, while the other men rallied round their Captain, and, as we were being rowed back to the *Jonathan Scratch*, I summed up my opinion of the proceedings in two puzzled words.

" Funny work ! " I said.

" Aye, lad," added the Skipper, " and it's a funny world, too. God made it, but the devil rules it."

" What'll happen if that man dies ? " I asked.

" Nothing, except that he'll give up a good job to some one else."

And that was the end of that. Grunty was badly hurt, but recovered later. What happened to the French captain we never knew, but we could guess. If he lived after that last stab of Grunty's knife, it was only by a miracle.

IV

ALTHOUGH we men of the *Jonathan Scratch* didn't mind meeting trouble when it confronted us, we saw no sense in deliberately walking into it, so we didn't stay to see what the men of the *Louise* thought about Grunty's treatment of their Captain. As soon as we got back to the ship, we hoisted all sail and took advantage of a light breeze to leave Sierra Leone. I hope this action will not be construed as " funk " on our part, because it certainly wasn't. We were due to sail when we did ; that was all. Still, perhaps it was just as well that we got out while the going was good.

A day or so out on the open sea, we were becalmed in a real heat-wave. The sun poured down until I honestly thought the sea would boil, and there wasn't a breath of air to take the sting off the sweltering heat. We just had to stay where we were, and, as is usual in such circumstances, tempers became short until the whole crew seemed to be doing nothing but sweat and swear.

I was lounging about on the walk, clad in my trousers and nothing else, when the villainous Slicer came rolling up to me, his thick lips twisted into a horrible expression. I backed away, because I thought he looked really murderous, but I found that that look was supposed to be a smile !

" Say, son," he said thickly, " I want you and me should be pals."

I could scarcely believe my ears, and, when he saw the expression on my face, he looked pained.

" You think I'm joking ? " he queried gravely. " No, I mean it." He became intimate. " You see, son, I been doing a lot o' thinking lately, and I can see that I've been in the wrong. None of us got no right to pry into the Captain's affairs, 'specially when the Captain's such a fine, brave old sea-dog like Scratch."

I nodded. I was an affectionate little soul, and I would rather have been a friend than an enemy of anybody, so Slicer's words fell on receptive ground.

"Twenty years I've known Scratch," continued Slicer, sentimentally, "and a better man never sailed the seas. I want you to tell him that I'm real sorry I acted like I did, and I'll never do it no more. As for you, 'Gustus, I want to apologise for all what I said about you."

"That's all right," I said. "I hope we'll be friends now."

"Of course," he answered, and, patting me cheerfully on the shoulder, off he went.

Full of my good tidings, I ran off to find the Skipper, and came across him talking to the man at the helm. When he was free I poured my tale excitedly into his ears, and was disappointed to find that he didn't seem half as pleased about Slicer's reformation as I did.

When I had finished, he shook his head.

"Be civil to him, my lad," he enjoined me, "as to everyone that you meet, but *don't trust him*. I've known him too long to take much notice of his apologies. He's a bad man, my lad, and don't you forget it."

I was disappointed at the time, but Scratch was right, as I soon found out.

Now, I propose to tell this next story exactly as it happened first, and then to put my own construction on it. We had no proof of our conclusions, so nothing was ever done about it ; otherwise one of our yard-arms might have been used for some different purpose from hanging sail.

The weather, as I have said, was cruelly hot, and most of us who were not on duty were lounging about on the walk, when Slicer came along carrying a curious burden. It consisted of a hunk of raw meat attached to a coiled length of tow-line, and a peculiar feature of the meat was that it was studded with innumerable shining dots that I afterwards found out were pins and needles.

"What's that ? " I asked.

"Just been hunting for ' spikers,' " answered Slicer. "Thought some of the boys might like a swim." He held up the meat. "I threw this over the side, and nothing jumped for it, so the sea's quite safe."

"Spikers," I knew, were the dreaded sharks, and I gathered that Slicer had thrown the meat overboard to see whether any of these nasty fish were about. He had studded it full of pins and needles so that, if a shark *did* grab it, it would have chronic indigestion as a memento of its greed.

When the "runners" (sail-hands) heard that it was safe to have a dip, they immediately approached the Skipper and told him of Slicer's test, whereupon he gave ready permission for the men to go overboard, a few at a time.

"You can never tell about 'spikers' in these waters," he said cautiously, "so each man must have a tow-rope and a belt on him."

Even if there were no "spikers" about, this was a wise precaution, for the wind has a habit of springing up without any warning, and, if that happened when the men were swimming, we'd have a lot of trouble getting them back to the ship.

The tow-ropes were thrown over the side and secured firmly to the rail, then six men stripped naked and dived into the cool, blue water. Up they came, and gripped the belts on the trailing ropes, then they splashed about like children.

"Send over another six," said Scratch to Hurrican Joe, who was supervising the picnic.

Scarcely were the words out of his mouth than I had wriggled out of my trousers and was in the water. In spite of my age, I can modestly claim to have been the best swimmer on board ; so much so, that my nickname among the crew was "Fins"—a name that stuck to me until I left the sea.

How cool the water was ! And how white and bird-like the old ship looked when I gazed up at it after my first, exhilarating dive ! I was deliriously happy as I felt my arms cleaving through the water, and, being only a boy, after all, I could not be bothered with such encumbrances as tow-ropes and belts.

As I was swimming about, a stalwart figure bobbed up next to me. It was Grunty, hero of the famous duel.

"Don't take any risks, 'Gustus," he said to me. "These seas are always dangerous. Grab your rope, and stick to it."

Rather crossly, I did so, and I am convinced that that advice saved my life, for, only a minute or so later, a cry went up from the watching men left on board—a cry that sent us in the water scampering panic-stricken up our tow-ropes.

"'Spikers' !'" was the cry. "For God's sake, get back !"

What a splashing of water there was, what an excitement and a scurrying as we swam for the ship ! I was, fortunately, quite near her, so I was one of the first to be hauled aboard, but two of the rest of the dozen were not so lucky.

As I stood dripping on the deck, giving a hand on the tow-ropes, I saw them go. Poor old Grunty, he was one of them ; and the other was a seaman that we called Candy, because he was always in trouble through stealing the cook's sugar.

They had swum out a bit farther than the rest of us, and, as I watched them scrambling back to safety, I saw suddenly a shadow on the water near them . . . and then a fin that cut like a knife-thrust towards them . . . and then I saw more fins and more shadows . . . and I heard the shrieks as the two sailors were swept away. And the sea ran red with their blood.

Poor fellows ! They didn't have a chance. The waters were shark-infested, and we had blithely been splashing about within sight of death.

We were shocked and horrified at the disastrous end to our pleasure-jaunt, and poor Scratch was more upset than I have ever seen him. Apparently, he felt that he was indirectly responsible for the death of his two men by having given permission for them to go over the side, and there and then he swore a mighty oath never to allow any of us to do the same thing again. He could have saved his breath ; none of us would ever want to.

Slicer, who was not one of the swimming-party, was unpleasantly interrogated by the Skipper, but no satisfaction resulted that way, for it is a fact—as the bo'sun pointed out—that you can hang a rib of beef over the ship's side all day without a shark going for it, and yet the sea might be full of the creatures. He said that the meat was in the water for half an hour, on a 60-ft. towing-rope, and Scratch had to agree that that test was thorough enough.

So the matter was closed, and we went about sad and quiet for some days after that.

But I still have my doubts, and I am not the only one. We argued about it in the fo'c'sle for a long time, and, although we had no proof, we were not satisfied that Slicer was as blameless as he made out. If he was, why didn't he come in for a swim, like the rest of us ? He was a magnificent swimmer, fond of the water, and he had been taking the heat badly. Yet, although he went to the trouble of testing the water to find out whether it was safe to swim in, he had remained on board. But there was another piece of evidence against him, and that came from Junky, the Cook, who, being a timid sort of man, didn't relish the idea of getting into trouble, and, therefore, said nothing for a long time. But, when the dreadful business had almost passed from my mind, he told me in the strictest confidence that the piece of meat that Slicer showed Scratch wasn't the whole piece of meat that was given to him. Junky concluded that Slicer had cut the meat in half, and had thrown both pieces overboard—one piece into the water (where it was snapped up by sharks) and the other piece (which had been produced as evidence of the safety of the water) not quite into the sea.

These may or may not have been the true facts of the case ; only Slicer knew, and he wouldn't say. But he was a dangerous man, and he was not above murder when people were concerned who hated him and whom he hated—like the crew of the *Jonathan Scratch*.

Well, the elements seemed to know that we were in a hurry to get away from the scene of the tragedy for, on the day after it happened, a fresh breeze sprang up and carried us speedily on our way.

Throughout the voyage, by the way, Captain Scratch was giving me two lessons every day in reading and writing, and often he would talk to me about my future. With that fairness that was one of his many virtues, he would paint very accurately for me the many hardships and the few joys of following a sailor's life ; then he would describe the advantages and disadvantages of living on land. It was up to me to make up my own mind.

We reached Buenos Aires (or " Bones and hair," as the sailors called it) without any further happenings that are worth recording, and we were to stay there a week or two.

Our first job was to unload the animals, and, as we enlisted the help of the keepers from the menagerie to which our living cargo was consigned, there was no trouble about getting the lions out of the sheep-pen. Although, remembering the trouble they had caused, I was glad to see them go, I was also sorry, in a way, for these fine beasts had exercised a peculiar kind of fascination for me. Maybe it was the first awakening of an instinct that I would be brought into closer contact with them later on in my life ; or perhaps it was just that I was a boy, and that they impressed me very much.

The twelve elephants on board had given us no trouble during the voyage, except in regard to the prodigious quantities of food that they ate. Had the trip lasted much longer, we would have had to decide with the elephants which of us should starve, for their appetites were colossal, and our stores were quite depleted by the time we put into port. Apart from this, the elephants were splendid. Except for a daily wash with a salt-water hose, they needed (or, should I say, had) no attention, yet they were as docile and quiet as pussy-cats. And they were just as well-behaved when they were taken ashore at Buenos Aires.

I cannot for the life of me understand even now how these elephants could walk after being cooped up for so many weeks on end in quite inadequate accommodation. They had been chained by their near hind and forelegs so that they were unable to move from one spot, yet they seemed to be quite all right when they left us. " Chips," the carpenter, told me after they had gone that, had they liked, those beasts could have broken their bonds and wrecked the whole ship without exerting themselves very much ! It is lucky he told me that when the elephants had gone ashore ; otherwise I would have had no sleep that trip.

Buenos Aires was a squalid, dirty place in those days. It was full of what I can only call " no-goods," and the women there were mostly the scum of the red-lamp districts of the world. I did not then know, of course, how bad the people were, but I know now.

On our third day in Buenos Aires, Scratch had some of his mysterious business to transact in places that he did not want me to visit, so, for the first time since I had known him, he put me in the charge of somebody else, the first mate, " Hurricane " Joe, with instructions to take me round and let me see such respectable sights as there were to see.

Joe was a rattling good fellow; a quiet, honest, pious, seafaring man, miles above the rest of the crew. He took me under his wing, and we went ashore, like a couple of tourists, looking at places and people. I am afraid Joe had his work cut out to keep me interested and, at the same time, to stop me asking awkward questions, for there were many places on our route that he hurried by, and many things that I wanted to know that he would not tell me.

At last he took me to the Espana Hotel for some food. This was quite a high-class place in which most of the business of the city seemed to be conducted, so there was no time for that gaiety and debauchery that characterised nearly every other hotel in the town. It was full of traders and rough-looking men of all nationalities, and I was intrigued to see that there was a counter at the far end of the big lounge where pieces of dull-looking stone were bought and sold.

"What are they handling over there?" I asked Joe, pointing out this counter.

"Gold," he said.

My interest was aroused, and I watched men who were obviously miners and traders pouring the dirty-looking but precious metal on the counter, and receiving money for it. There were arguments over the price, of course, but the man behind the counter was a fierce-looking individual whose motto seemed to be : "Take it or leave it," and, although the customers grumbled, in the end they always took the money that he offered.

Hurrican Joe ordered some food and two bottles of wine. "Don't drink too much, 'Gustus," he warned me. "It's only because you can't trust the water in these parts that I'm letting you drink at all."

My attention was still on the counter and the brown nuggets that were changing hands.

"It must be wonderful to trade in gold," I murmured, wistfully.

"Why?" asked Joe. "If you knew the horrible stories that surround man's greed for gold, you wouldn't want to be mixed up in it. Anyway, gold-bartering isn't much of a business ; ivory is better."

"Ivory? Where do they get ivory, Joe?"

"From elephants, of course."

"Yes, I know that, but *where*?"

"East Africa—Congo—anywhere round there."

"I'd like to go there and deal in ivory, Joe."

"Would you? Well, if you can learn to shoot, hunt, sleep with one eye open, and face risks and dangers of appalling dimensions—you'll be fitted for the job. But how you're going to learn all this while you're a cabin-boy in the *Jonathan Scratch* I don't know."

At that moment there was a diversion.

Loud voices were raised in the region of the gold-counter, and, looking round, we saw that a fine scuffle was going on there. The lounge in which we were sitting was crowded with men eating and drinking (mostly drinking), and they all crowded round the scufflers, while voices were raised in a manner that was not nice to hear.

Joe and I left our table to see what the excitement was

about, and we managed to push our way through the crowd until we came on to the scene of the trouble. There we saw a little, shivering Spaniard squirming in the iron grip of two men, while another man searched his pockets and produced gold-nuggets.

"There you are, boss," he said to the man behind the counter, "my nuggets."

"I saw him take 'em from your pocket, Josh," answered the "Boss," "while you was drinking." He turned to the captive, and a hush settled over the excited assembly, as he said in a loud, judicial voice :

"What have you got to say, Dago? You stole these nuggets from Josh's pocket, and I saw you."

The Spaniard flung himself forward, grovelling on the floor, and pleading for mercy, but the Boss had his own ideas about the seriousness of stealing gold, and he cut him short.

"Take him out into the yard," he commanded the two men standing on each side of the prisoner, "and give him three minutes to pray." He paused solemnly. "And may God have mercy on his soul ! "

Three minutes later we all trooped into the yard, and there the man was hanged from a tree by a lariat lent by a cowpuncher.

That was justice as meted out in South America in the middle of the nineteenth century. Rough, it certainly was, but effective, for it acted as a deterrent to crime, and was the means of cleaning up the country within a short time.

I may be an old fogey with queer ideas, but it's my opinion that that kind of justice would do a lot of good to-day. Not so much with thieves, mind you, but with the worst people who make mischief with their tongues. We've got too many of them roaming loose in England, to-day, and we've got too many people listening to them. Largely through that sort of thing, this country is developing a race of people who talk and think, but don't *do*.

In my day, the survival of the fittest was the maxim that ruled our destinies. A man would take a risk, venture into the unknown with courage and a stout heart as his only weapons, stake his all on a plan of action and never depart from it while there was breath in his body. . . . That was the spirit of the pioneers and the heroes. It didn't matter how much money a man had, or what his social position was like, so long as he had the will and the *guts* to do something. The British Empire itself is a monument to the spirit that ruled among men in those days ; our world-trade is a monument to the humble men who plodded their way into danger, breaking down the hostility of savages so that they might barter and trade with them ; and some of our biggest businesses are monuments to ordinary men who had an idea and the will to put that idea into practice.

Nowadays we associate courage too much with mechanical thrills. Men hurtle through the air at impossible speeds, and outdo each other in driving along a strip of sand or speeding through a stretch of water (for no useful purpose, so far as I can see), and we call them heroes. Certainly they are daredevils all right, but that's not quite the same thing, and I can't see for the life of me how their record-breaking dashes are going to improve the spirit of the race.

After all, man invented machines for certain, specified purposes, but he didn't intend that they should sap the individuality or weaken the character of his fellow-men. That is what is happening, though, and it will go on happening while the young men of to-day continue to think that the height of achievement and courage is reached by going fast in an aeroplane. Bodies and brains are still, and will always be, the only worth-while engines in the race of life.

V

CONSIDERING how short, comparatively, was the time that I spent at sea, I am surprised to find that I have written so much of this book without having yet wound up my adventures as a schoolboy-sailor. In this chapter, though, I start telling of my travels and troubles in Africa—that dark, mysterious continent where most of my wandering life has been spent.

After leaving Buenos Aires, we traded among the South American ports for a matter of some seven months, without anything exciting happening to us, and then we overhauled and refitted the old ship, preparatory to scudding across the Atlantic to our home-port—Liverpool.

When we reached England again, I was no longer the ragged little urchin who had been sold to Scratch for a sovereign ; I had grown muscular and tall, and I looked (and *was*, in experience) a man. The open-air hard life had wrought wonders with my physique, while the sights

I had seen and the odd happenings I had participated in had broadened my mind correspondingly. I think Captain Scratch was proud of his *protégé* and the way in which I pulled my weight like a full-grown, long-experienced sailor, during our voyage, for, when we made Liverpool, he called me into his cabin, where he was paying-off some of his crew.

"Your wages, 'Gustus," he said to me, and thrust something into my hand.

"You've made a mistake, Captain," I said, looking down wonderingly at the two coins that sparkled so entrancingly in my palm.

Captain Scratch chuckled in his beard.

"No, I haven't," he replied. "I'm giving you back the price I paid for you, with 100 per cent. interest. You've earned it, my boy, and I'm pleased with your work."

"But, Captain," I expostulated, while the two golden sovereigns seemed to burn my hand, "I can't take this. You said——"

"Go on with you," interrupted old Scratch, bustling me in a kindly manner out of the cabin. "I wouldn't give it to you if you weren't worth it. Now hop it!"

So I hopped, feeling like a millionaire. That £2 was the first money I ever earned in my life.

After the usual end-of-the-voyage formalities had been undergone, and Scratch had cleared up all his business, he went ashore to see the shipowners. Incidentally, I had thought up to that time that Scratch was the owner, as well as the Skipper, of the ship that bore his name, but I found out, at Liverpool, that this was not the case.

When he returned, he told me that the *Jonathan Scratch* was to be run dry (i.e., dry docked) for cleaning and general overhauling of the timbers, and we would have to leave her for a little time. I thought, with dismay, of my plight, for I had no home to go to, and my two sovereigns would not keep me very long; but I stiffened my upper lip and hoped for the best.

That night Scratch called me into his cabin. Like me, he did not relish the idea of living on shore, and the thought of leaving the ship that he loved, even though it was only for a little while, depressed him. In the dim light of the oil-lamp, he looked tired and old, and I could see that he was in one of those miserable moods when he needed somebody to talk to.

"Well, 'Gustus," he asked me, "what are you going to do with yourself now?"

"Oh, I'll manage, Captain," I answered cockily, although my heart was heavy. "I'll find a room somewhere, and——"

"No, I don't mean that," interrupted Scratch. "You needn't worry about what you'll do while the ship is lying up. What I want to know is—are you making the voyage with me again?"

"Sure!" I answered readily, and I saw a slight smile flicker round his mouth at the hearty sincerity of my reply.

"I'm glad, 'Gustus," he said simply, and then fell brooding, while I waited uncomfortably.

When he next spoke, his eyes had a far-away look in them, and his words came slow and heavy.

"My last voyage, son," he said. "Funny, I don't know whether to be pleased or sorry. Lately I've been getting more and more anxious to leave the sea and settle down ; but now, when I'm on the point of retiring, I find it's going to be more of a wrench than I thought. Still, I'm an old, old man, and the sea is a hard mistress, so perhaps I'll be happier on land."

His tone belied his last words, and I made conversation in order to keep him from his gloomy thoughts.

"What are you going to do when you retire?" I prattled.

"I'll settle down on the Kent coast, lad," he answered.

"Why Kent? Were you born there?"

There was silence, strained and tense. Captain Scratch cleared his throat noisily, and, when he spoke, his voice was thick and choking. I was afraid to look at him.

"I was born on the high seas," he answered, "but Kent is where I want to die. You won't understand why, my lad, until you're older. There's—there's a girl buried there ; she was the Captain's daughter, and I was the first mate. We—were to have been married"—his voice sank to a hollow whisper—"but she fell ill, and—and my life died with her." I felt the table shake as his elbows banged on it, and I stole a glance at him. His head was bowed in his hands, and his shoulders were heaving. I felt my eyes going misty in sympathy, and, fearing that I should break down, too, I rose and stumbled out of the cabin.

Wrapped in the sorrow of his memories, he did not hear me go.

. . . . . .

When I saw Captain Scratch again next morning, neither

of us mentioned his momentary weakness. I am prepared to believe that he did not really know how much he had told me, and I, for my part, respected his confidence to such an extent that these are the first words I have ever breathed about the matter since the conversation took place, over sixty years ago.

"Come on, 'Gustus," was his greeting, "we're going ashore."

We went, and, on the way through the streets of Liverpool, he told me that he had made arrangements for me to stay at the house of a friend of his, a Mr. John Pringle, while the ship was in dock.

"He's an educated man, 'Gustus," he explained, "and he'll see that you go on with your schoolwork. You'll be happy there."

Scratch was quite right in his first two particulars, but wrong in his third. Mr. Pringle *was* an educated man, and he certainly *did* keep my nose to the grindstone in regard to my schoolwork, but I was definitely *not* happy.

It was only then that I realised what a true affection I had conceived for the rough old Captain. As soon as he patted my shoulder and left me to the tender mercies of his educated friend, I missed him, and I counted the days until I would see him again.

When, at long last, I saw him roll up the garden-path to collect me and take me back to the ship, I was happier than I had ever been before, and the way I rushed up to him and welcomed him pleased him, too.

We made our way to the docks, and there we found the *Jonathan Scratch* all ready for another voyage—her last, and an ill-fated one, although nobody knew it then.

She had been repainted, and completely refitted with new sails and new gear, and at first I was afraid to board her for I could hardly believe that this was the same *Jonathan Scratch* that I knew. Except for the chief officers, she carried a new crew, too.

Well, we had all been fretting about on land too long, so we did not delay about getting out to sea again, and soon we were making our way merrily to Lisbon. I felt a real "old-stager" when I saw the Portuguese port looming ahead of us, for I had been there before, and I was still boy enough to brag about my knowledge of foreign countries.

At Lisbon I was amazed to find us unloading 20,000 lb.

weight of ivory, which, I discovered, we had taken on at Lagos and had hawked all round the American ports.

I say " I was amazed " because, although I knew we were carrying plenty of cargo, I had no idea what it consisted of, and the very fact that such close secrecy had been maintained all along about the contents of our hold, made me suspect immediately that there was something " fishy " about the whole business.

Accordingly, I made inquiries, and I found that we were actually smuggling ivory, to avoid the heavy duty, from Lagos (where there was a secret collecting-depôt) to Lisbon (where there was an equally secret market in which no questions were asked). What happened to our cargo while the ship was in dry-dock is a problem that has never failed to puzzle me, and only the ghost of Captain Scratch can answer it satisfactorily. Another problem to which I cannot supply the answer is whether the owners of the *Jonathan Scratch* knew that she was " running " ivory ; I should say they did, for it was a profitable game.

At that time the demand for ivory was greater than it is to-day. Large quantities of it were made into adornments for women, as it was then considered very fashionable to wear a string of ivory beads, as pearls are worn nowadays. A pound weight of ivory, in tusk or block, would fetch from 16s. to 24s., and even more ; and I gathered that the Customs' officers were neither sufficiently wide-awake, nor sufficiently scrupulous, to make the smuggling a particularly difficult job. Don't forget there were no police patrols with motor-launches or steam-pinnaces to come and have a look at your cargo when you were within bounds ; and we were further helped by the fact that the officials of the ports in which we traded our ivory all had one common characteristic—an itching palm !

Well, we discharged our cargo, and I can't truthfully say that I felt very guilty about our wrongdoing. I had conceived a sort of hero-worship for Captain Scratch, and I felt that, if the smuggling game was all right for him, it was all right for me, too.

When we were on our way to Lagos, our next port of call, I was perturbed to see that the Captain stayed in his cabin a great deal of the time, and left the conduct of the ship to Hurricane Joe.

He tottered out one bright, sunny morning to take a walk round the deck, and I was horrified to see how bad he was looking. His beard had completely lost that fine, aggressive jut that I so admired, and his flesh hung in great pouches on his face; as for his eyes, they were sunken and bleared.

"Aren't you well, Captain?" I asked in concern.

"I'm all right," he answered slowly. "Touch of fever, that's all. When do we make Lagos?"

I didn't like that question, for Scratch was one of those men who had only to look over the side to know exactly where he was, but I answered that we were about a week out, and went on to ask him whether he thought we would meet the Captain of the *Louise* when we reached port.

At my question a smile lit up the greyness of his face.

"I don't think so," he answered. "The only place to meet him is at the bottom of the sea. You needn't worry; he's dead sure enough."

As he uttered these words, his knees sagged, and he gave a trembling sigh. Then he pitched forward unconscious on the deck.

My shrieks brought men running quickly to the scene, and gently we carried him to his bunk, where we tended him as best we could. Just on that trip, when we needed him most, we did not carry a doctor, and I was half-crazed with anxiety as I saw how useless was the well-meaning attention of Hurricane Joe.

For the first time, then, I knew what it was to fear the unknown. It was something different from being frightened by lions or apes; it was a pain, poignant and searing. I felt already that the cold hand of Death was near the ship . . . and I was frightened.

Captain Scratch tossed in delirium for three days, and when he regained some sort of consciousness, we all knew that the end was in sight. He knew it, too, and, weak though he was, he insisted on signing documents and giving instructions to the mate.

"When I go," he murmured, in a voice that we could hardly hear, "put me in 'juice,' do your voyage, and take me back with you to Liverpool. Then hand over my coffin, so that they can take me and bury me in Kent—near *her*."

His voice trailed away, and there was silence, broken only by my sobs as I knelt, grief-stricken, at his bedside. The noise that I was making seemed to rouse him, for he opened his eyes, and stretched out his hand weakly to rest it on my bowed head.

"Don't cry, 'Gustus," he said, "we've all got to go,

and I've had all I want of life. See that ' Chips ' makes me an oak coffin, tin-lined—I want to be comfortable ! "

Once again he paused, and when he spoke again the words came in a stream, as if he knew that the shadow of Death was falling upon him.

" In my papers, Joe . . . you'll find instructions . . . where to bury me . . . near *her*."

His eyes were closing, but suddenly they opened wide, and he looked up, over our heads, at something that we could not see. He made a convulsive effort to get up, and he was smiling. He lifted a hand.

" *Mary !* " he called.

When I could see through my tears, Captain Jonathan Scratch, my first friend and the man to whom I owe my manhood, was lying back, dead. His wrinkled face was smoothed out in a smile of pure peace.

MYSTERIES IN THE SOUTH SEA ISLANDS

By
CAPTAIN RAGNAR NYBERG

WHILE Europe and large tracts of Asia and Africa in the year 1914 resounded with the thunder of war, a silence as of the grave descended on the isolated world of the South Seas. No rumble of cannon, no orders for mobilisation, reached the white pioneers on the coral islands of Polynesia and Melanesia. Their sole contact with the outer world had been the visits of buyers—perhaps once or twice a year. But now even these had ceased.

Silence—waiting—suspense—at last despair, and, in some cases, tragedy—this was the echo of the World War in the Pacific. There were not many who knew that there *was* a war on. For those who knew nothing about it, it must have seemed as if the rest of the world had been laid waste by a devastating plague, or had sunk into the ocean, like fabled Atlantis of old.

We sailors on the China coast, on the other hand, lived in the thick of events. Immediately after the outbreak of war, several of the Blue Funnel boats were commandeered for service, either as transport ships or as auxiliary cruisers.

In 1918 I sailed as mate on the *Shangcha*, one of the boats that supplied the British front in Mesopotamia with war material and troops.

We had made several trips between Australia and Basra in Persia, when I was abruptly dismissed the ship in Basra, with orders to report at the company's head office in Hong Kong. The reason for this was that an over-zealous English major at G.H.Q. at Basra had made the terrible discovery that I, a foreigner, occupied a responsible position in a ship carrying " military secrets " ! That these " military secrets " mainly consisted of provisions was not considered of any importance.

Ah well, I for my part was quite glad of a change. The transporting of troops had been far from pleasant work, and Basra was the very opposite of paradise. The only thing that worried me was that perhaps I would be considered unsuitable even for the usual freight work.

But this was far from the case ; for as soon as I showed myself at the office in Hong Kong I was told to sign on as first mate on the 7,000-ton *Chinan*.

On board I was met by the skipper, who turned out to be an old acquaintance. We had spent several months together years before in a sailing vessel, I as ordinary seaman and he as the third mate. His name was Tinson, and he was by now a middle-aged man.

Over the drink of welcome in his cabin I asked what our destination was.

" I haven't the slightest idea," was the astonishing answer. " It seems to be a military secret ! "

" Why, damn it," I said, " then I seem to have come out of the frying-pan into the fire ! " And I told him what had happened in Basra.

" I dare say the company know what they are doing," Tinson replied. " If they have sent you here, you needn't worry. But I'll bet my life there is some mischief brewing ! "

" What do you mean ? " I asked him.

" Well, to start with, look at that ! " growled the skipper, and pointed to some objects sewn into canvas. " Read that, and think it over ! "

I pulled back the canvas—and stared in surprise. For the objects were neither more nor less than a couple of loose nameplates, obviously destined to be placed over the ship's name. *Taikovanui*, they said.

" What's the meaning of this ? " I wondered.

But Tinson merely shook his head.

" Come along with me," he said. " That's not the only thing that's fishy ! "

And it certainly was not ! I was told that we were taking in an extra supply of coal in one of the holds. They had made a hole connecting it with one of the coal-bunkers, so that the coal could be sent through that way. That meant a long voyage !

" And look here ! " Timson went on, showing me another of the holds. It was filled with a mixture of provisions, cheap goods—of the kind that are used in the South Seas when bartering with the natives—and ammunition.

" My orders are to take things as they come," said Tinson. " I have not yet been given a crew. It appears that they will come from Canton."

This proved correct. A week later we had been provided with a complete crew of Canton Chinese. And the day before we received orders to sail sixty harbour coolies came on board, and also a body of twenty Gurkhas (native Indian soldiers, considered the best in the British Empire), led by a sergeant and armed with rifles and bayonets, and also two machine-guns.

Next day we received orders to sail from the head office. The instructions were extremely brief. " Proceed three hundred sea miles east-south-east of Hong Kong ; open the sealed chart and instructions, and inform all on board."

The orders were accompanied by a sealed roll of charts and a fat scroll, likewise sealed, which obviously contained the instructions.

Next day, when we had sailed the three hundred sea miles, our curiosity was satisfied.

We were to visit some fifteen South Sea islands, mostly in the Marshall Group, which had previously been considered German territory, and commandeer everything of value on the plantations without spoiling them. Force was only to be used as a last resource—but we were allowed a " firm hand," as it was called in the instructions. The plantation owners were to be offered as compensation some provisions and other immediate necessities, and also a list, signed by the captain, of all that had been taken, which list would constitute a claim on the British Government after the war.

We were to sail under the British flag, but without the company's flag, and as soon as an island or a ship was sighted, the new name-plates were to be hung out to hide the name *Chinan.*

On the accompanying charts all our routes were marked, but the instructions contained a warning against possible errors in them.

As soon as we had managed to get a full load, we were to return to Hongkong.

. . . . .

When Captain Tinson had read out the instructions, an eloquent silence fell on the officers of the ship assembled in his cabin.

" I've tried a good many things in my day," the skipper said at last, " but I never thought that I would turn pirate in my old age ! "

Still, orders were orders ; and, as we found out later, the British Government had good reason to act as it did. It had, it appears, found out that the Japanese were contemplating the identical move, though they had not yet dared carry it out for fear of the other nations. But for diplomatic reasons the British Government did not wish to take official action ; therefore it was agreed with the Blue Funnel Company that the latter should take charge of the affair. This was why the *Chinan* and nine other Blue Funnel boats were sent out at much the same time to various parts of the Pacific with sealed orders and under false names.

For my part, I did not object to a bit of an adventure, and it was abundantly clear that this trip would bring us something of the kind. You had only to glance at the chart and see the first names on our " visiting list " to gain the impression that we were sailing straight into the realms of adventure.

Subu was the name of the first island. It was not quite in the position the chart ascribed to it, but we had to get used to that sort of thing. In one place, for example, where the chart gave a depth of a hundred and eighty fathoms, we came across three coral islands with a wide belt of dangerous hidden reefs ! We proceeded towards Subu at half speed, sounding continuously.

One afternoon, when the sunset painted sea and horizon with scarlet and gold, we sighted Subu. It was so overgrown with luxuriant vegetation that it looked like an immense, oval emerald resting on the shiny billows. It was a sight that brought us all to the rails, officers and crew, Gurkhas and coolies. By that time every one on board had some idea of the purpose of our expedition, so that their curiosity was easy to understand. But it was a mistake on our part to show how many we were on board.

Slowly we glided nearer and nearer the unknown island. All available telescopes were in use, and all eyes spied eagerly for signs of habitation. But if any living creatures existed in Subu—apart from the sea-birds which circled inquisitively overhead, and flocks of other, gaily hued birds which now and then flew up out of the greenery as if some one had amused himself by throwing up a handful of confetti—they hid themselves carefully. Round the green island ran a belt of glittering white sand, but no outrigger-canoes were drawn up there ; no spirals of smoke rose into the calm air from camp fires ; still less was there any trace of the work of white men ; clearings, plantations, jetties, or sheds for provisions.

Tinson and I stood on the bridge with binoculars glued

to our eyes. Below us murmured and chattered the Gurkhas and coolies along the railing, and our engines beat out a slow rhythm. But—was there not something else that beat ? In a quicker, more excited, measure ?

"*Tom-tom—to-tom-tom—tom-tom——*"

All at once I knew what it was. I shouted to the Chinese to keep quiet, and Tinson and I listened eagerly. Now we could hear it quite plainly ; the monotonous, continuous drumming of *tom-toms*, the natives' signal drums. So there were human beings on Subu, and they had observed our arrival.

But what did the tom-tom signals mean ?

Were there any white men on the island, who also listened to the drum-beats, and perhaps understood them better than we ?

We had now passed along more than two-thirds of the north side of the island without seeing a sign of habitation. Was the plantation on the other shore, or—was there perhaps no longer any plantation ?

Suddenly something caught my eye ; a green-painted roof. Judging by its shape, it was obviously the work of white men. It looked as though we had found what we were seeking.

But it was too late to land that day. We did not want to risk being caught by darkness when on an unfamiliar island full of hostile natives, so we anchored about two sea miles out. The sunset glow quickly died away and night fell —the velvet-black night of the South Seas, with its glittering display of stars. The secretive island melted into the darkness. No fires were seen, but throughout the night the drums murmured, monotonous and threatening. At daybreak I came up on deck and saw the mists rise from the dew-drenched slopes of Subu. The drums were sounding still.

We waited a couple of hours, in case any human being should appear on the beach ; but the white girdle of sand lay there as empty and forsaken as ever. There was only the muttering of the drums.

At last we lowered a steam-launch and a lifeboat. We were two white men—the launch's engineer and myself—a dozen Cantonese sailors, and fourteen Gurkhas. They were armed with rifles and fixed bayonets, and also brought one of the machine-guns with them, and I had my Service revolver.

We made for a little creek just below the green roof. A couple of hundred yards from shore the water suddenly became shallow, and next minute the launch grounded on the sandy bottom. The engineer, two Cantonese, and two Gurkhas stayed behind in it. I changed over into the life-boat. The remaining Cantonese and several of the Gurkhas jumped willingly enough into the water and dragged the lifeboat another hundred yards towards the shore. Here we left it with the rest of the Cantonese and waded ashore. The machine-gun was placed on the beach so that it could sweep the palm forest above us, and three Gurkhas stayed by it. The other nine came with me.

After searching for some time we found an almost over-grown path, which had plainly not been trodden by human feet for a long while, although once upon a time it had been broad and well cleared.

All our senses alert, and our weapons ready for immediate action, we marched in under the shady vault of leaves. Now and then we paused to listen for suspicious sounds. In this respect I trusted more to the Gurkhas than to myself, for these Indians possess a superhuman acuteness of sight and hearing.

Nothing happened for the first two hundred yards or so ; but suddenly one of the Gurkhas stumbled or tripped, and threw himself to one side with a yell of fright. Simultaneously a grey-brown animal rushed like lightning on to the path and twisted itself, grunting and spitting, round the Indian's legs. The man howled with terror, and his comrades shrank back in alarm. With my heart in my mouth I put the muzzle of my revolver to the animal's head and shattered it with a bullet.

It was an ant-eater. It had lain hidden in the under-growth, with its prodigiously long tongue stretched out across the path in the way of an army of red ants that marched along there. The Gurkha had chanced to tread on the ant-eater's tongue, and in its pain and terror the animal had rolled out on the path and fastened on to the leg of its assailant.

The Gurkhas had a good laugh at their comrade's expense, and in a somewhat lighter mood we continued on our way.

The path led to a square clearing, and in the middle of this lay a building with a verandah running round it. A little way from the bungalow was a mud hut. The clearing showed traces of having been cultivated once upon a time, but now it was impossible to distinguish between the weeds and the " corn." For some reason or other, the inhabitants of the house had ceased to take an interest in their garden.

At first sight the bungalow did not differ from hundreds of others that I had seen—except in colour, for it had a curious, leaf-green hue, which even at close quarters seemed to fall in with the surrounding vegetation. The roof had looked darker from at sea because a typhoon had done its best to tear off the covering at one end.

But it was none of these details that made me stop and, as it were, drink in the atmosphere of the place with every sense. It was the *silence*—the deathly silence, which seemed to hang like a pall over everything. I suddenly found that I was shivering, as if I had been wandering about in a raw autumn mist.

"Hallo!" I shouted. A little ripple of breeze rustled through the tops of the palm trees which towered above the damaged gable.

Silence.

I saw that the door of the bungalow was half open. The upper hinge had loosened and the door hung slightly crooked.

I set my teeth, walked briskly over the grass and up on the verandah, and opened the door wide. Then the other hinge broke and the door crashed through the rotten floorboards of the verandah. Next minute the floor creaked ominously under me and I quickly saved myself by crossing the threshold.

At my feet, its head resting against the threshold of the door, lay a skeleton.

Strangely enough, the grim sight reassured me. At any rate a skeleton was a tangible reality—an explanation of the dead silence. I made a hasty examination of it.

It was the skeleton of a man of medium height. A few shreds of clothing, which fell to dust when I touched them, still clung to the bones. As far as I could see, it had been a suit of yellowish flannel—in other words, the clothes of a white man.

Mechanically I began to look for signs of injury; but there was absolutely nothing to suggest that the man had died a violent death.

Well, it might, of course, have been some disease. Plague —for example! I shuddered involuntarily at the thought; but next minute I was ashamed of my childishness. This man had been dead for at least a couple of years—and the germs with him.

The room within was half dark, for the shutters were closed. It was fairly large, and sparsely furnished with things that were mostly home-made. On one wall was a large image of Christ—I am not quite sure now whether it was a picture or a statue—and some embroidered texts in German. On the opposite wall was a piece of furniture, something between a cupboard and a writing-desk. The drawers were pulled out and their contents scattered over the floor, as if some one had carried out an extremely hasty search—or as if he had wanted to leave in a great hurry, only taking the most valuable things with him.

There were not many articles of clothing—actually only a couple of garments partly eaten by insects—but a number of letters, in all probability about a hundred, together with a book which looked like some kind of journal or diary.

I decided to examine it later. First of all I wanted to know what was in the inner room that I could glimpse through the half-open door opposite the entrance. I crawled carefully over the floor, which constantly threatened to give way under my weight. It was practically eaten up from below by ants so that only a thin shell remained.

In the inner room, obviously the bedroom, were two more skeletons. They were in much the same condition as the first. Probably the three people had been struck down by death at the same time.

One was the skeleton of a woman. She lay on the floor near one of the beds. And in this bed lay another, smaller skeleton : that of a child somewhere between five and eight years old.

The woman's skeleton showed no signs of injury, but some one—or something—had crushed the child's head on the left side.

For a moment I stood rooted to the spot. This entirely upset the theory which, half unconsciously, I had formed on the three people's fate ! The child had quite plainly died a violent death. Then what had happened to the two adults ?

Attacked by savages—was my first thought. But the more I looked around me in these two dim, deathly quiet rooms, the more certain I grew that no savage was concerned in whatever had taken place there.

Nothing in disorder—except the cupboard ; nothing shattered ; the few household articles in their proper places ; no—no horde of plundering savages would have passed through so gently !

While I was carrying out my examination, the Gurkhas had little by little followed me as far as the verandah, and one or two of them finally ventured up on it to peep through the door. The floor gave way, and one of them landed with a clatter and a crash on the ground below. This recalled me from my speculations. When all was said and done, I was not there to solve a crime mystery, but to fetch copra and other tangible wares. The dead must be left in peace.

I was already on my way towards the door when my curiosity got the upper hand, and I turned back to the cupboard and collected the letters and the diary. At least I wanted to find out who the dead had been. Perhaps the clue to their fate lay in those papers?

Before I left this home of death I also paid a brief visit to the mud hut. It was fitted with a primitive oven, and had obviously served as kitchen. Nor was there any sign of fighting and plunder here.

When we finally left the bungalow, I noticed a detail, the meaning of which I did not realise at the time. Some one had amused himself by marking off the path running round the house below the verandah with rows of large shells. There had also been placed, one on each side of the verandah stairs, two tortoiseshells with the rounded side up. A third shell lay at one end of the house. I remember thinking that, if they had not been so dirty, I might have taken them with me as souvenirs; but in their present state they were of no value. I glanced at them when I turned round for a last look at the green bungalow. They looked like gigantic grey eyes staring fixedly into space through the swaying tops of the palms.

We made our way back to the beach along the same path and without seeing the faintest shadow of a savage. Without further adventure we embarked and returned to the ship.

One thing I have forgotten to mention. All the while we were ashore the drums kept silence, but as soon as we set foot on deck the dull rumble began again. They had evidently kept an eye on us.

I reported to Captain Tinson. He was interested, but above all disappointed.

"That was a poor start," he muttered. "We must hope it won't go on for ever like that. And now I suppose we'll get under way and try our luck the next place!"

"But oughtn't we to give those people in the bungalow a decent Christian burial?" I asked.

But Tinson thought it would be taking a needless risk to land once more.

That same afternoon we weighed anchor and set our

course for the next island, which according to the chart should lie about twelve hours' journey from Subu. It was called Jaluit. We still proceeded at half speed, for the waters were far more dangerous than the chart would have us believe.

That night I sat in my cabin and read the dead man's letters. Perhaps some of my readers may think that I should not have done this ; but if you consider what I had seen and *guessed* inside that bungalow, I think it is defensible. Personally, I considered it my duty.

His name was Kremle. Unfortunately I have forgotten his Christian name. This Kremle was a German missionary, and had come to Subu some twenty years before and settled there to convert the natives. Whether he was married already at that time and brought his wife with him I do not know ; nor who she was.

From the diary—which was partly a journal over certain experiments in natural science, with which Kremle occupied himself—it became clear that he had been obliged to give up all attempts to convert the savages, and that the last years he had devoted himself solely to studying the island's flora and fauna. He seems to have been particularly interested in vegetable poisons and the native methods of producing them. I am almost certain that this diary would have been a veritable gold mine for a scientist.

Unfortunately I could only decipher a small part of its contents. In the first place, my knowledge of German is limited ; and besides, the entries, like the greater number of the letters, were written in old-fashioned Gothic characters which I found very hard to read.

The discovery that interested *me* most was of *two letters from a Swedish—or perhaps a Swedish-American—missionary in Singapore, called Olov Nilsson, and then two from a certain Mattson in Kumla, Sweden, bearing the Kumla postmark, and the date* 1912 *or* 1913.

These were also written in German, but in ordinary writing, and were therefore easier to read. If the missionary, Olov Nilsson, is still alive, and this account should chance to reach him, I ask him to forgive me for mentioning one detail of his letter which seemed to me extremely important.

For the letter said that the missionary Kremle had a neighbour on the island, a white man, who used his influence over the natives to counteract Kremle's attempts to convert them. But not only that : it also seemed that Kremle had

suffered actual persecution from his neighbour. If I remember
rightly, this was also discussed in the letter from Mattson in
Kumla.

Naturally I was more interested than ever in the fate of
the family Kremle when I had read this. I wondered why
the other white man had not shown himself during our visit
to Subu. Perhaps because his plantation was on the other
side of the island. But even if this were the case, he must
have heard the drum signals, and as he had a certain influence
with the natives they would in all probability have informed
him of our arrival.

Had he any reason for staying away ?

By chance I came across an entry in the diary in which
Kremle referred to some misdeed of the " Englishman's."
Was the " Englishman " the same person as the " neighbour "
mentioned in Nilsson's letter ? Somewhere else Kremle
talked of the " king of Subu." Had his neighbour so much
power over the natives as to justify that title ?

If the " king of Subu " really were an Englishman, he
would surely have no reason to fear a ship sailing under the
English flag ; rather the reverse.

Well, of course, " Subu's king " could have been deposed,
or have died, or fled from the island. The entries in the diary
stopped somewhere in 1915, and evidently after 1914 no
letters had reached Subu. Much could have happened, and
obviously had happened, since then.

So my thoughts ranged to and fro, while I struggled to
decipher the diary.

Suddenly I made still another discovery. In one place
Kremle related how he had found a " phosphor-spring " near
the bungalow. He described his attempts to extract phosphor
from this " spring," and he evidently met with some success,
for a little later he mentioned that he had succeeded in
producing luminous paint.

Next morning I met Captain Tinson on the bridge. He
listened patiently to my account, but the thing that interested
him most was the news that there was in all probability a
plantation on the south side of Subu. We ought to make
a raid there on the return journey, he thought. At the
moment he had other things to think of, for the island of
Jaluit should be sighted at any moment now.

It was ; and, when we rounded a point, we suddenly
caught sight of a little outrigger canoe carrying sail, which
made towards us. In the canoe were three white men. One

of them rose and waved excitedly, and we returned his greeting. Captain Tinson had the engines stopped, and the canoe steered towards the rope-ladder.

This time our Gurkhas and coolies were below deck, and nothing could betray that the ship was on an unusual errand.

One of the men, a dark-haired, thick-set man, came on board and greeted me with a stream of German when I met him at the top of the ladder. His name was Schwarzkopf, he said, and he was delighted to see a ship again at long last. They had been out of touch with the outer world for three years and four months. How long had the war lasted? And were the entire South Seas now German possessions after her victory? It was most thoughtful of the German Government to send such a vessel as the *Taikovanui*! We could have a full load of copra and oil, if only we had some ammunition to spare! They had only forty-eight cartridges left—and Jaluit's 7,000 natives, cannibals until quite recently, had behaved most threateningly towards its seven white inhabitants just lately.

I let the German calm down a little before putting an end, as tactfully as possible, to his misapprehensions. The war was *not* over; Germany had *not* won; and the *Taikovanui* was not a German, but an English boat!

When I had managed to get this into his head, I went on to explain our errand. It suited us very well, I said, that they wanted to get rid of their copra. They could have ammunition and other stores as an advance on the compensation which the British Government promised them after the war.

Schwarzkopf was a sensible man, and accepted the situation without turning a hair. He shouted to his comrades to come on board, and at the same time explained to me that one of them was English.

And so he was—almost—for he was Irish. But most of all he looked like a gorilla, as he came swarming up the rope-ladder. I have never seen such a hulking monster. Even though there was something the matter with his neck, so that his head nestled between the raised shoulder-blades, he must have stood six feet six in his socks. He was chocolate-coloured from sun and wind and possessed a stiff grey beard. His nose was broken. He was about fifty years old and called himself Lande.

When told that he was among his fellow-countrymen, he at once put on an air of authority towards the two Germans.

F.T.S.   2 H

They could thank their lucky stars that he, Lande, happened to be there ! Now they could rely on him to secure as good terms as possible.

While the Irishman was bragging in front of Captain Tinson, I saw my chance to take Schwarzkopf aside and ask him who Lande really was. Schwarzkopf answered that Lande had come sailing in an outrigger canoe about eighteen months earlier, half dead from exposure. Lande had told them that he owned a plantation on some other island, but that he had set off to find out why the trading-ships had stopped calling. When told that there was a war on, he at first seemed very anxious to get back to his island ; but day after day passed without his setting off, and after a while the Germans had begun to consider him as one of them, although they could not quite get used to his bragging manner.

In my heart I agreed with Schwarzkopf. I did not really like this Lande.

Later in the day we landed—escorted by Gurkhas—and inspected the plantation. It was an excellent example of German industry and talent for organisation. A whole row of sheds were stacked full of copra ; there was also coconut, castor, and eucalyptus-oil, and cocos fibre, indigo, and so on. They had quite a number of modern machines, and every square inch of tillable soil was cultivated.

Lately they had lacked the means to pay the natives for their work. Each day they had hoped that the war would come to an end—for, oddly enough, they did know that it had broken out—and that their victorious Kaiser would send a ship to inspect his possessions. But the savages muttered louder and louder, and the flock of willing workers quickly grew smaller, while the concert of drums from the jungle sounded more and more warlike.

At last the seven white men had cared for the plantation unaided, while 7,000 blacks waited, summoning up courage to put an end to them. To scare the savages they had been in the habit of firing a few shots each day. Lately they had restricted themselves to one shot daily, and when we arrived, as I have said, they had exactly forty-eight cartridges left. Forty-eight cartridges—forty-eight days—and then . . .

Ah well, we put an end to their worries for the time being. We relieved them of their stores and in return left as much ammunition and other prime necessities as they wanted. It was no trifle the plantation had yielded during those three years. We got a full load, and under normal conditions its

value would have made every one of the six Germans a rich
man. In war-time it represented a positively staggering sum.
I hope the industrious Germans eventually got a suitable
recompense.

When we were ready to leave Lande asked to be allowed
to come with us. He wanted to be put ashore on his own
island and tempted us with promises of a good consignment
of liquorice roots and indigo.

Tinson declared that he was not interested as he already
had a full load, but if Lande would come with us to Hong
Kong, on the next trip he could pilot us to this island and then
we would see whether we could do business with him.

Lande maintained obstinately that he wanted to go home
to see his wife and two daughters, whom he had not seen for
a year and a half; but finally he bowed to fate.

One day when Lande was lounging about in the chart-
room I asked him to show me just where his island lay.

Without the slightest hesitation he pointed to *Subu* !

There, on the south side, he said, was his plantation. He
had lived there for twenty-one years, and there he had his
wife and his two daughters. His wife was black, a full-blood
Subu savage.

By careful questioning I got him to tell me more about
his life. For many years he had sailed as mate on a little
trading schooner in the South Seas, and knew every nook
and cranny of them. At last he had entered into partnership
with the schooner's two owners, but on the next journey they
had been wrecked and he alone was saved—according to his
own account. It was after this event that he had settled on
Subu.

I asked whether he had been the only white man on the
island.

" Yes . . . no . . . that is to say, there was some sort of
a German missionary, but he—he lived on the north side,
so we never had anything to do with each other. I dare say
he made off when the war broke out."

" But how did he know about that ? " I could not resist
asking. " You hadn't heard of it yourself until you came to
Jaluit, surely ? "

" Oh, well, I expect the German knew it all right," Lande
answered. " The Devil looks after his own, you know ! "

While Lande was talking I conjured up visions of Kremle's
diary and the letters from the missionary Nilsson and from
Mattson in Kumla. Here under my eyes was the man my

imagination had hovered round so persistently—" the Eng-lishman," " the king of Subu," who would have nothing to do with his white brother but set the natives up against him— who had perhaps done more than that. . . .

Here he stood and admitted openly that he knew Kremle ! And I did not dare to ask any more questions for fear of arousing his suspicions.

I told Tinson of my discovery.

" Well, I'll be damned ! " he growled. " Yes, Lande does look born to be hanged ! But I won't have anything to do with the whole business. We'll take him with us to Hong Kong and report the matter to the company, and then they can decide what to do."

And that was that.

In the head office there was immense surprise at seeing us back so soon fully laden. None of the other nine boats had been heard of yet. If they returned with the same amount of cargo the plan would be considered a great success.

Then we reported the Kremle case. The company thought over the matter for a little while ; then they declared that since the expedition was of a secret nature they did not want to get mixed up in any outside matters, such as the possible murder of a German. No, on closer consideration, the company decided that it would be best to do nothing, and to avoid hearing any more about it they made up their minds to burn Kremle's diary and the letters !

And this was accordingly done.

On the other hand, the company was interested in Lande. As an expert on those waters where we were to carry out our raids, he might be extremely useful. Captain Tinson and I were asked whether we had any objection to taking Lande with us as pilot. No, on the contrary, we answered. He had on one or two occasions on the return journey given proof of his skill ; and so far as I was concerned—but I did not tell the company this—I should be glad to visit Subu once more, together with Lande. I had not forgotten the green bungalow, whose dumb inhabitants seemed to me to cry to heaven for vengeance.

I will now tell of one other adventure on our first journey to the South Sea islands in the *Taikovanui*—the voyage on which we discovered Subu, the mysterious island of Lande and the missionary Kremle.

One afternoon we sighted one of the larger islands in

the northern part of the Ellice group. According to our chart it was called Pata.

At half speed, and sounding continuously—for the charts over this part of the Pacific are, to say the least of it, unreliable —we approached the island, and finally towards the close of the afternoon we crept through a relatively narrow inlet into a large lagoon, and let go the anchor. There were still a couple of hours left before dusk, but we would not land that day. The island was in all probability inhabited by hostile savages —at anyrate, hostile towards strangers—and we did not want to risk being overtaken by darkness while landing.

That there were savages on the island, and that we had been observed, we could tell from the dull rumble of the tom-toms which, hour after hour, without a minute's pause, rolled out to us from the impenetrable vegetation on the slopes of the island. But this music did not really worry us very much. We had managed to get used to it in the course of our visits to the other islands. Nor did we take any special precautions. Captain Tinson thought it sufficient to have two sailors on guard on deck. Of course we had our magnificent Gurkha soldiers, but we meant to save them for the landing early next morning.

In the evening the ship's officers assembled for a little celebration in the saloon of the *Taikovanui*. We thought we had earned this, for so far the trip had been successful in every way, far above all our expectations, or the company's. If the island of Pata turned out to be as remunerative as those we had already visited we could set sail for Hong Kong with a clear conscience, carrying one of the richest cargoes that had ever filled the holds of the *Taikovanui*, formerly the *Chinan*.

However, we broke up as early as ten o'clock, so as to be fresh for the morning's work. We really had need of a little sleep, for during our course in these unknown waters, using charts which only occasionally corresponded to reality, the watches had been most strenuous. There were nearly always two of the officers on the bridge. It is said that two pairs of eyes see more than one.

Before turning in I made a tour of the deck to see that everything was in perfect order. It was lively out there, for the Chinese sailors had left their bunks on account of the heat and slept out. I discovered a number of groups that were playing cards or mah-jongg, and I told the players to stop at once and go to sleep. The Chinese are confirmed players and willing to go on all night, or even for days on end when once they have started ; and I knew that, if I said nothing, these gamesters would forget both time and place until they were called in the morning—and then they would be as limp as dead herrings.

I stood for a minute at the railings and looked towards the island. A couple of drums were still in action. They seemed to carry on a continuous, eager argument. At length a third drum entered into the conversation ; it sounded more powerful, more authoritative, than the first two.

The dark mass of the island stretched like a giant wave towards the dark-blue heavens, and almost licked the lowest diamonds in the jewelled ornament called the Southern Cross. Its shadow spread like a black covering over the shining waters of the lagoon. It was so quiet that now and then I could hear nocturnal animals rustling in the bushes along the shore.

I stood there and wondered what the drums' long message could mean ; whether it was a challenge to us, or an order for the dusky warriors to mobilise. Pata is in Melanesia, and its inhabitants were described in our instructions as " particularly unreliable." It was good to know that we were on a large boat, well armed in every way. It was reassuring to peer over the railing and see how far down the water was—more than five yards. We need hardly fear that the natives would try to board us.

As soon as I had given the watch orders to call me and the shore-going party immediately it began to grow light, I went in to my berth. But I did not rest for long. I had probably not slept more than one or, at the most, two hours when I was awakened abruptly by a hard thud against the outer wall of my cabin. It sounded as if a bullet had struck the plate.

I shot out of my bunk like an arrow, threw open the door leading on to the deck and rushed out, bare-footed and in pyjamas. I suppose I was still only half awake, or I would have thought twice about the risk, but at that moment I saw a dark shadow glide towards the railings, climb them swiftly, and throw itself overboard. I could only dimly distinguish the outline of the mysterious figure, but there was something in its movements, lithe and silent as a cat's, which told me that this man did not belong on board the ship—that he was a savage !

I spun round, rushed into my cabin, slamming the door behind me, hunted out both my revolvers, and threw on a black oilskin coat so that my light pyjamas should not afford too easy an aim. Then I opened the door and shouted for all I was worth to the watch. But no one answered !

Instead, something came whistling through the air and landed with a clatter on the deck, hurtled past my feet like lightning, and hit the cabin partition with a crack. I picked it up. It was a long flexible spear. At that minute a revolver began to crackle merrily from the bridge. Simultaneously there was a tumultuous shouting and splashing alongside the ship.

I tore to the railing and poked my head out carefully. What a sight ! Some ten outrigger canoes were being paddled away from the ship for dear life.

I rested my revolver on the railing and began to shoot at the escaping canoes as best I could in the dark. I do not know whether I hit any one. The shooting from the bridge continued. I heard Captain Tinson giving orders up there, swearing and shouting for a light, and asking if any one had managed to capture any of the devils.

Soon the decks were ablaze with lights, but there were no signs of any black men. The decks were almost deserted. The terrified Chinese sailors had fled as fast as their legs could carry them into cabins and saloons ; when I looked down the boiler-room casing I saw a whole cluster of them hanging half-way down the ladder like a bunch of bananas.

But in a dark corner between the deck-houses lay two motionless figures, who neither answered nor seemed to hear our shouts. I went up to them, revolver in hand. But there was no need to shoot.

The first figure I looked at I recognised as one of our look-out men. He lay on his back with outspread arms. In his open mouth he seemed to balance a long, slender stick. When I touched it I felt that it was firmly fixed in the deck. It was a spear, driven with uncanny force in through the poor fellow's open mouth, through the neck and out at the back, so that it nailed him to the deck boards. When I bent down over the unfortunate man I could feel that he was still breathing faintly.

The other figure was one of the stokers, who had obviously used his watch below to play a stolen game of cards with the watchman. Chinese playing-cards were scattered around, sticky with blood. The stoker was dead. One half of his face was cut clean away, presumably either with a sword or a long knife. It was no pleasant sight.

I did not know what to do for the transfixed look-out man.

I did not dare to loosen the spear for fear of hurting him still more. While I was standing there undecided he settled the problem for me by giving a little rattle in the throat and breathing his last.

We examined the ship from bows to stern and found five more spears on deck. Strangely enough, I could not find the one that had first struck my cabin wall and awakened me. Perhaps it had really been some other form of missile that was used, or else—and the thought made the roots of my hair tingle—the figure I saw sneak over the railing a minute later had been back to snatch up his spear.

We made one more discovery. The bo'sun, a big fierce Cantonese, came up and handed me a gun, asking whether I had dropped it. No, I most certainly had not ! I was just about to advise him to ask the rest of the ship's officers when I chanced to look closer at the weapon and discovered that it was a Smith and Wesson of an antiquated model, with a number of strange figures carved into the butt. It obviously did not belong to the ship's arsenal and nobody on board knew anything about it when I made inquiries. It must have been brought on board during the natives' attack !

The discovery that the natives had firearms made us decidedly more uneasy about the forthcoming landing. We had no real desire to risk our lives, nor to start a war with the natives. On the contrary, our instructions said that we were " to set to work with a gentle but firm hand " and only use force as a last resource.

In the morning the ship's officers held a meeting, and after ripe consideration we decided at least to make an attempt to land ; if for no other reason than to be able to enter in our log that we had " visited " the island. Captain Tinson gave me strict orders, if I met with the slightest sign of hostility from the natives, to give up the experiment and return to the ship.

Immediately after sunrise we lowered the two launches. Remembering the events of the past night, the boats were manned exclusively by Gurkhas, with two white mates in each. I was in the first and acted as leader of the whole expedition.

We made for the innermost part of the lagoon, where we saw a couple of little islets which we thought might shelter a harbour or landing-place. Pata reminded me in several ways of Subu ; the island was much the same size and had a range of mountains, probably of volcanic origin.

The whole island was a great sea of luxuriant, creeping, trailing greenery which grew right down to the water's edge and formed an impenetrable wall, behind which the tom-toms once more began to beat. We passed the two islets and continued towards the shore without discovering any sign of habitation. We kept up a good speed in the launches, so that if need arose we could the more easily manœuvre the clumsy boats. Our excitement grew, the nearer we came to the shore, and we were perfectly ready to counter the attack which we felt sure would come.

All at once the other launch, which lay close in our wake, made a sudden yaw to port. The second mate, who was in charge of it, shouted to me and pointed eagerly towards the beach. There were some sheds which appeared as if by magic out of the vegetation. They did not in the least look like native huts, but were unmistakably the work of a white man. A little farther up the creek we then discovered a narrow jetty.

I let the other launch come alongside my own, and side by side we glided gently in towards the jetty. We stopped about a hundred yards out. But no living being appeared. When we had waited five minutes or so I took out an object which Lande had used with great success at other landings. (Lande happened at the moment to be suffering from a number of malignant boils and therefore could not land with us this time.) It was an old, rather ramshackle gramophone, one of those with a large noisy trumpet. This wonder of civilisation acted like a charm on even the shyest of savages, luring them out and making them forget all their hostile intentions.

I set up the gramophone on the engine casing and put on a noisy march from a military band. Already after the introductory flourishes of drums and trumpets I noticed suspicious movements in the bushes nearest the jetty. Soon one black and hideously tattooed face after the other peeped out through the leafage and stared with rolling eyes at the talking machine.

But they were extremely shy and suspicious ! I had to play half a dozen records before a touching Irish folk-song at last drew four of the savages in full war-paint on to the jetty. They came nearer, foot by foot. One of them had stuck his finger in his mouth just like an inquisitive child ; but there the likeness ended, for otherwise he was a big muscular fellow with a treacherous face, armed with spear, bow and arrows, and an impressive long knife. I hurriedly gave an encore of the folk-song. At last they placed themselves at the very end of the jetty and raised their hands as a sign that they wanted to speak to us. I answered with a few arm exercises, and for safety's sake played the folk-song once more before I let the launch proceed a little nearer the shore. When we were a few yards away, however, they seemed to change their minds. I put a fresh record on the gramophone—a jazz tune for a change Then they crept farther out on the jetty again, and at last they were so close that we could begin to negotiate with them.

Meanwhile more and more darkies had begun to peer out of the bushes, and when we moored at the jetty practically all the tribe were assembled in a semi-circle on the shore. Most of the men carried spears and many of them had bows, but I could not see any firearms, which was somewhat reassuring.

I was just about to explain in dumb-show that we wished to land and examine the sheds, when the crowd parted and gave way to a more than usually fantastically rigged savage, whom I took to be the tribe's medicine-man. To my astonishment, he began to talk almost faultless English, explaining that we must go away again at once—or we would be taken prisoners. His voice was, however, fairly friendly, and I therefore hoped to be able to talk a little more with him. I asked him where he had learned his English, and he replied that in his young days he had sailed with an Englishman in a trading schooner.

I asked him whether he liked the English. Yes, he replied, they were good masters. I decided to lie a bit, and said that I was English too, and would be his friend. He thought this over for a while and finally decreed that this could be so—if I would give him the box that blared and teach him to make it give out a noise.

Now it was my turn to think things over. There were several gramophones on board, and I considered the chance to land worth more than an ancient " H.M.V." I told him that he should have the gramophone if I could come ashore. He nodded and gesticulated as a sign that he agreed to the bargain.

So I clambered ashore with the gramophone trumpet under my arm, while two Gurkhas followed with the rest of it and the records. The medicine-man waved to me to follow him and led the way to the open space in front of the sheds. Here he wanted me to set up the gramophone and teach him to work it. I wound it up and put on a record—a "laughter record" sung by Harry Lauder—but this was received with cool indifference. I realised that the temper was about to swing round to my disadvantage. Then I had an idea. I myself began to sing a shanty, and that did the trick ! Soon the whole flock was bursting with laughter.

I seized my opportunity to ask the medicine-man what the sheds were used for, what they contained, and who had built them. But he would not answer these questions ; instead he began to gabble, and gradually worked himself up. He changed to the native tongue, but even so I understood this much : that he wanted us to go away at once. I was in no hurry to do so, but all further efforts to talk to him merely made him gesticulate more frantically than ever and point to a mountain-top far inland.

I specially noted that neither he nor the other natives showed any surprise at our light skins. They were evidently used to white men. I wondered whether these were still alive, or had met their fate—perhaps on that high peak, which was presumably the native place of sacrifice.

However, I realised that it was useless to attempt any further advances that day and, after having tried to rival the medicine-man's elegant gestures, I retired backwards along the jetty and into the launch. The whole time I was ashore the Gurkhas had stood by with their machine-guns and rifles ready for action. I think we all heaved a sigh of relief when at last I was back on board. It was quite exciting when we started up the engines and left the jetty. I was not at all certain that we would not suddenly get a shower of spears over us. But the savages took no notice of us. They were assembled round the medicine-man, who was doing his best to pull out the spring of the gramophone.

When we reached the *Taikovanui*, I gave Captain Tinson an account of our adventures. I said that, in my opinion, there must be something peculiar about that high peak that we could see even from the ship. Perhaps there were actually treasures there which might make a visit worth while.

Who knows ?—I said ; perhaps the mountain was full of minerals and the white adventurers had found precious metals there. Everything is possible in the South Seas. To attempt any further negotiations with the natives seemed useless to me. I suggested instead that we should land on the other side of the island. I believed that it would be easier to make one's way to the top of the mountain from that side.

At last Captain Tinson gave way. I manned one of the launches with a handful of chosen Gurkhas and steered my course along the opposite shore of the island.

The natives had obviously observed our tactics. The drums began to rumble once more and followed us like threatening ghostly voices.

When at last we found a suitable landing-place, however, it was so late in the day that we did not consider it prudent to attempt to land until next morning. I was in some doubt as to whether we should take the risk of spending the night in the launch, or whether we ought to return to the *Taikovanui* ; but I relied on the Gurkhas, who, in contrast to the Chinese, are exceptionally good sentries, to discover the natives in time, should they try to attack us.

But the night passed without incident, and even before sunrise next morning I had landed, followed by three Gurkhas, and started on the climb up the mountain slopes. Nearest the shore was a belt of almost impenetrable bush vegetation, and the Gurkhas had a stiff job to hack a path for us with their bayonets, which had to do duty as hatchets. Before we were half-way up the mountainside the heat became troublesome. The sunshine poured down over the scorched brown hummocks of grass ; you could positively smell the dryness of the earth.

Gradually the vegetation became more sparse. Here and there on the slopes lava-blocks of every size lay strewn about, and I gathered that we were approaching the summit of the extinct volcano.

From behind a block of lava a pair of big birds flew up and began to circle over us. They gave out hoarse, melancholy cries. Suddenly one of the Hindus touched my elbow and pointed up the slope.

Two savages had come out of a cleft in the rock. They were armed with spears. I ordered my soldiers to aim at them, but on no account to shoot until I gave the word. Then I took a few steps alone towards the savages, lifting my hands as a sign that I had peaceful intentions. They remained motionless and simply glared at me. When I took a few more steps forward they retreated, not into the cleft, but farther up towards the summit. I waved to them to come down to me, but they squatted like a pair of apes and laid down their spears beside them. This move reassured me considerably, and I went briskly to the mouth of the cave to see whether there was any one or anything in there.

He glared at me with bloodshot eyes.

It was a strange and unexpected sight that met my eyes. In there stood three great openwork cages, one slightly smaller than the others. The smaller one was empty. It had long staves tied to the sides, which served as handles, and I guessed that it was used for transport. The other two cages were, as I said, larger—yet not so large but that a grown man would have some difficulty in finding room inside.

And there actually was a human being in one of the cages : a stark naked white man, with a long beard and hair that hung down over his face and chest. There he squatted, his knees and palms resting on the floor of the cage. He glared at me with bloodshot eyes.

There was a smell of death in the cave. When I looked towards the third cage I learnt the reason for it. There were the remains of yet another white man in an advanced stage of decomposition.

I signalled to the Gurkhas to come up and ordered them, in a whisper, to catch the two savages alive. They set off at once like a couple of retrievers. Strangely enough, the savages allowed themselves to be caught without offering any resistance, whereupon the Gurkhas proudly hauled them back to me. I gave orders for them to be tied to the smaller cage.

I went up to the living white man and knelt down outside the cage. Slowly and clearly I said in English :

"Don't be frightened. We are friends—Englishmen—who have come to set you free. Who are you, and how long have you been here ? "

To my intense surprise he answered at once, and with remarkable composure, in broken English :

"I am an Austrian ; my name is Schreiber. My friend and I "—he nodded towards the other cage—" have lived on the island four years. In the beginning there were three of us, and we had a boat, but Retzbach, who sailed it, disappeared two years ago with it and has not been heard of since. Of course you must think it odd that we should sit here cooped up, but, as a matter of fact, in a way we do it of our own free will."

"Your free will ! " I exclaimed in amazement.

"Yes," said the Austrian. "We are forced to let the natives do it to keep the peace with them. In their way they think that we are gods, and it seems to be part of their religion that we must, once a year, spend a lunar month shut up in cages here. This is the fourth time we have been here——"

"But your friend is dead!" I cried.

"Yes, I know," Schreiber answered, without showing any signs of emotion. "He was called Hoorn, that lad there. He was never much use. He was always sickly—couldn't stand the heat and the raw food. Last time they came to fetch him he was more dead than alive, and he died on the way up. I asked the medicine-man to have him buried, but he said that—dead or alive—we must stay in the cages till the change of the moon."

I hardly knew what to think. But, of course, it must be true; Schreiber could have no reason to lie to me, and he did not seem to be demented, simply dulled in some way. It was as if all human feeling had died out of him. I could not make out how he could sit there so calmly in his cage while his friend rotted away before his eyes.

I explained in some detail who I was and why we had come to the island. I asked him whether he did not want me to set him free.

"No," he answered, "I think you had better not. The natives can be the very devil. You see, every time I have sat here I have acquired more power than ever over the tribe —become, so to speak, more sacred every time—and if only I can keep it up a few more years, perhaps I can rule the entire island—at anyrate when the medicine-man is dead. It isn't so difficult to sit here, once you are used to it. The food's the worst of it—nothing but raw fish and birds the whole time. But you can get used to that too."

I could see that he spoke the truth. The ground around his cage was strewn with feathers, bones of birds, and rotting remains of fish.

"You've been here for ten days now, I take it?" I said, and he nodded. "Isn't there anything you want?"

"No—well, yes, as a matter of fact . . . if you happen to have some brandy on you. I haven't tasted any for three years."

I had, as luck would have it, a hip flask full of brandy, and this I handed him. He emptied it greedily at one draught.

"Now I think you had better go away," he said, "before there is trouble with the natives. Set those two sentries free or I may get the blame."

"Are you really sure that you don't want me to let you out? Won't you come on board and return to civilisation with us? We are on our way to Hong Kong."

" No—what should I do there ? " he replied. " If there's a war on, as you say, I suppose I should be interned as a prisoner of war, coming on board an English ship."

I stayed there a little longer and asked him what they had grown on their plantation, and whether they had any stores that were worth taking over. He said something about there being a good deal of mangosteen oil in the sheds, and that if we could negotiate with the natives they probably had quite a large stock of raffia and woven goods. I then took my leave of the queer hermit on the mountain-top, set free the two savages—to the obvious resentment of the Gurkhas—and returned to the launch. At dusk we reached the *Taikovanui*, where they had been growing steadily more and more anxious for our safety during the last few hours.

Captain Tinson was dissatisfied with me for leaving the Austrian in his cage. But it soon turned out that the move had been wise. When we landed again next morning at the jetty below the sheds, the entire tribe met us with obvious signs of friendliness, and the English-speaking medicine-man was so eager to exchange greetings with me that he fell into the water off the jetty. It was only by the skin of his teeth that he escaped drowning, for he was so tricked out with metal ornaments that he could not swim. He had a heavy chain draped round his neck and around his body under the arms, and also huge rings of iron and copper-wire around his wrists and ankles.

When at last we had hauled him up on dry land again and had emptied the water out of him, he explained the reason for his hurry. Something had gone wrong with the gramophone—it would not talk any more.

I was afraid that the worthy medicine-man had succeeded in pulling out the spring, but after a hurried examination I discovered that the only thing wrong was that the works needed winding. I looked in vain for the handle. I explained to him that this was an essential part of the outfit, and advised him to find out what had become of it.

After a while a couple of warriors turned up leading a man who wore the gramophone handle as an ornament in a newly pierced hole in one ear. The medicine-man promptly tugged it out, so roughly that a portion of the ear came with it.

When the sweet strains of the Irish song once more quavered out of the horn, there was general rejoicing. I left the second engineer to mind the gramophone and persuaded the medicine-man to come with me for a little walk up into the village itself. Nearby I discovered the bungalow of the Austrians. The medicine-man happened to have some errand in one of the huts, and meanwhile I seized my chance to go a little closer. Outside it I found something which aroused my curiosity. There stood a couple of large lava blocks, hollowed out on top, and with a number of symbolic figures carved on the sides. A thin column of smoke rose from these cauldrons, and I guessed that they were some kind of sacrificial altar, or incense-burners belonging to the medicine-man's equipment. While I stood there looking at the curious stones and trying to make out the meaning of the hieroglyphics, I heard angry shouts behind me and saw the medicine-man come rushing towards me, gesticulating and yelling for all he was worth. He was evidently extremely annoyed with me for having profaned his sacred objects with my curious eyes.

It was then that I took a hasty and perhaps a very daring decision. I suspected that it was the medicine-man who had thought of making " gods " of Schreiber and his unfortunate friend. But now I would teach him a lesson ! I would show him that he could not with impunity cage white men as if they were monkeys ! And if my action had the intended effect, then in future it would be Schreiber who decided who was to be shut up on this island !

Quick as thought I employed a jujitsu catch on the medicine-man, swung him round a few times so that he got dizzy, and then pressed him firmly in a sitting posture into the hollow on one of the stones. I do not know whether his posterior came into direct contact with the fire that smouldered there ; but in any case it must have been sufficiently hot to give him an advance taste of purgatory.

He was so startled that he did not even manage to let out a sound. I gave him a crack on the head with a baton that I always carried. His chin sank down on his chest and I knew it would take several minutes before he came round again— even though he was sitting on glowing coal.

Then I hurried back to the beach and shouted to my men to gather round me and to have their weapons ready in case the savages attacked us. In close formation we marched up to the bungalow.

The natives showed no signs of interfering with us ; they crept irresolutely at our heels and stared like a flock of sheep at the medicine-man.

With the help of the second engineer I lifted him out and

after a few minutes succeeded in bringing my victim round. The first thing he did was to rub his hands over his backside and let out a wild yell ; but when he caught sight of his tribesmen he stopped screaming, probably realising that it might impair his dignity.

I then placed myself in front of him and read him a long lecture. I asked him whether he knew what had happened— whether he had felt a pair of gigantic hands stretch down from the top of the mountain, seize him and push him into the incense-burner ! He blinked uncertainly, evidently ready to believe absolutely anything. Well, this was the vengeance of the gods, I continued, and it would grow worse still if he did not immediately obey their commands and free the white man from his cage.

When I had finished speaking I ordered two Gurkhas to help him to his feet. I have seldom seen a more miserable sight. He turned to his tribesmen and spoke a few words in dialect, which, of course, I did not understand.

The result was instantaneous. The whole tribe set off towards their huts, the drums began to sound, and I wondered whether there was going to be trouble.

But the savages took no notice of us. They trooped off in a body along a path which seemed to lead to the mountain where Schreiber was imprisoned. Next minute there was not a native in sight, except the medicine-man, who had sunk down on his knees, whimpering plaintively, to examine his injuries.

I determined to profit by the occasion ; I let a couple of Gurkhas carry him down to the launch and ordered every one else to get in as well. We returned to the ship, and when I had reported to Captain Tinson he decided that we ought to take our chance while the natives were absent, and try to get hold of whatever the sheds contained. I had made a hasty inspection and discovered a number of barrels of mangosteen oil and a good many bales of raffia.

I launched our lighter and manned it with coolies who were to attend to the loading. Then we returned to the shore and set to work.

For several hours we worked undisturbed, without seeing as much as a trace of a savage ; but in the afternoon we heard the drums approaching and prepared for a possible attack.

But when the flock of savages broke through the shrubbery we caught sight of Schreiber at their head. He stretched up his arms as a sign of friendliness. I answered in the same way and went towards him.

I hurriedly explained that, in accordance with our instructions, we were seizing the goods in the sheds, and that as soon as their value had been reckoned he would get a chit for it which would entitle him to suitable compensation from the British Government when the war was over.

"Yes, that is probably all right," he said, "but what on earth have you done to the savages to make them come up like that and let me out of the cage in spite of the fact that there is still a fortnight left of the month? And where is the medicine-man?"

I explained briefly how it had occurred to me to put the medicine-man in his place, for Schreiber's benefit. I said that I was delighted to find that my idea had been so effective. And then I advised him to strike while the iron was hot and to let the medicine-man take his place in the cage for the rest of the month!

Schreiber found this idea very attractive, and we handed over the medicine-man to him.

Schreiber had already put on all the airs of a chief, and he gave a brisk command to some of the warriors. I could make out that it concerned the medicine-man.

I stayed ashore all the afternoon talking to him. I told him of the night attack, and of the rifle we had found.

"But that's mine!" he exclaimed. "It must be the medicine-man who has stolen it! It disappeared almost a year ago. But I don't think it was much good to him, for it wasn't loaded!" (And sure enough: I examined the gun when I got back on board, and it was unloaded. Besides, the barrel was quite choked with rust.)

Getting the barrels of oil and the raffia bales on board took us two days. We tried several times to make Schreiber come on board too, but he would not.

"I don't think it would improve my reputation as a chief," he said, "and besides, I am not sure that you aren't planning to shut me up and take me with you to Hong Kong. And I'm not having any of *that*!"

On the morning of the third day we weighed anchor after paying a last visit ashore to take leave of Karl Schreiber, that queer white recluse, the new chief of Pata. When our launches finally left the jetty, we watched him for a long time as he stood there on the beach, naked, sunburnt and lean, with hair and beard billowing round his face and chest, leaning on his old rusty Smith and Wesson rifle.

THE DEN OF DEATH

By

"TIGER" O'REILLY

*The date of this story is about 1897, when the author was fourteen.
He was attached to a travelling circus as a bareback rider, while his
father had been engaged as the circus farrier.*

WE remained with that circus, my Da and I, for quite
a long time.

For three years I did my bareback riding act, and
in the end the public began to get a bit bored with it. The
fact was that though a good enough rider, and fond of horses,
doing acrobatics on the ambling old pad-horse wasn't
exciting enough for me ! I wanted to do something hair-
raising—a high-trapeze act, or something of that sort. But,
above all, I wanted the guv'nor to put on some sort of a
boxing act, with me in the star part, but I could never get
him to see it.

I had lost all interest in the bareback act, and, as a result,
the public did the same. The guv'nor spoke to me about
it, and I opened my heart to him. Anyway, he said :

" You'd better come off it, then ! Anyway, you're getting
too big for a boy-equestrian act. I'll find something else for
you—and I'll try to make it hair-raising ! "

And he did ! We had recently acquired (*vide* bills) a
" ferocious, forest-bred lion " named Menelik. Now, Menelik
might have been forest-born, but his breeding, I should
think, had been nipped in the bud by the nets of the catcher.
He had grown old in the show-business, and he knew his
oats down to the very last ear. He knew as much about
showmanship and handling an audience as did the oldest
human-hand in the circus. And, for all his age, he could
look both imposing and ferocious when he liked, as he always
did when performing.

Now the boss read in a paper somewhere, about a boy
who had gone into the lion's cage in a circus for a reward
of five pounds.

So he decided on a fine new gag—which amounted to no

less than that I should go into the lion's cage and earn five pounds—which would, of course, be returned to the management afterwards !

The way the " gag " was worked was this. We were billed to visit East Grinstead, on the Sussex borders. Two days before the circus arrived there, Mr. Smith and his little boy came into the town, and took a room in one of the more modest inns.

Mr. Smith, I may say, was an agent of the circus—and I was his little boy !

Then came the circus, and to the first performance went Mr. Smith—and his little boy. Menelik did his stuff—tearing and snarling at the bars of his cage, and roaring fit to wake the dead (and he certainly had a wonderful roar, had that lion—his trainer, old Sam Noakes, billed as " Signor Leonardo," admitted that it even put the fear of God into *him*, sometimes !). He ate a lump of horse-flesh, growling over it, and rending it with his teeth, in a way that made the flesh of the audience creep well and truly !

Then spoke the Ringmaster, with a crack of his whip (at which the lion snarled fearsomely) to compel attention :

" Lad-ees and gent-el-men ! We are now going to present to you an act of daring unsurpassed and unparalleled in all the history of circus showmanship ! You have all witnessed the ferocity of this untamed, forest-bred lion ! And when I say untamed, I can add also that Menelik is untamable ! Signor Leonardo, the greatest tamer of wild beasts in the world, has tried for months to break even a little of the spirit of this terrible animal—and has failed ! Before a man can tame a lion, that lion must fear him—and this magnificent creature fears *nothing* ! Signor Leonardo has failed, and, like a sportsman, he admits it. But, although he has failed to tame the king of the jungle, he will not admit that he has, in any other way, been beaten by him ! And to prove this, ladies and gentlemen, you are to-night going to have the privilege of seeing this undaunted and undauntable man enter, alone and practically unarmed, the cage in which this ravening monster is confined ! Lad-ees and gent-el-men—*Signor Leonardo* ! "

A blaring " chord-on," and old Sam Noakes, resplendent in dark wig, false moustache, and a wonderful uniform of blue and silver, with shining top-boots of patent leather, complete with golden tassels and huge brass spurs, came striding on, whip in hand, and bowed curtly and clumsily to the thrilled, applauding audience. He was the Big, Strong Man, this Leonardo—he did not fawn or cringe to his public, and his bow was curtness itself.

He (for some unknown reason) tried the strength of the bars of the cage, by shaking at them with his hands, what time Menelik snarled and struck at them (but always missed) with his great paws. Then Leonardo issued some brief instructions. Two big niggers brought on a brazier, in which glowed red-hot irons. Two other men, dressed to resemble big-game hunters, strolled, with obtrusive casualness, into the ring, each bearing a huge rifle. They took their stand at either end of the cage, a short distance away from it, and with their faces towards the snarling animal.

The audience held their breath !

There were two doors to the cage—both in the front, and one at either end.

Now Leonardo sprang on to the narrow platform which ran round the outside of the cage. He caught hold of one of the doors, and made as though to open it. Instantly Menelik emitted a most terrific roar, and hurled himself at the bars, crashing against them just as the trainer sprang back. Several women in the audience screamed.

Leonardo ran to the other door, but Menelik, his teeth showing and his mane bristling in the most awesome fashion, was there before him. Leonardo sprang back to the other door, but again Menelik got there first !

For some five minutes this went on, and then the trainer paused, and wiped the sweat from his forehead. The Ringmaster came forward again :

"Lad-ees and gent-el-men ! " he cried. "I am sorry ! I must apologise ! But you can see for yourselves that, in the lion's present temper, it is impossible to enter his cage. It would be madness—suicide ! I am sorry, ladies and gentlemen ! "

Instantly Leonardo turned on him and spoke, for the first and only time. Plainly he was very angry :

"Not zo ! " he shouted in the most marvellous broken English. "Leonardo never deesapoint hees audience ! I enter ! "

Wild cheers and shouts from the audience. Leonardo gave more instructions. The two niggers went off, and returned with a sort of wooden shutter. The two other men laid down their guns, and, picking up iron-tipped poles, drove the snarling lion into one corner of his cage. Then the slide was pushed through the bars, thus converting the cage into two compartments, each with its separate door.

Immediately Leonardo, drawing a small, silver-plated revolver from his hip pocket, and grasping his whip firmly in his right hand, entered the empty compartment, and carefully closed the door behind him. Thus they stood side by side—the lion in one compartment; the trainer in the other—and the shutter between them.

Then Leonardo slowly lifted his hand, while the audience gazed, breathless. Leonardo dropped his hand. Instantly the niggers pulled out the slide, and, with a terrible roar, the lion sprang straight at the trainer!

There followed a moment or two of apparent confusion. The lion missed Leonardo, who sprang aside, cracking his whip and firing his revolver. The attendants shouted. The effect of all this was a fine confusion of sound—the roaring of the lion, the reports of the revolver, the cracking of the whip, the shouts of the attendants, and the rattling of the cage as the lion and Leonardo sprang about, all mingled together and served to help work up the excitement of the audience.

From side to side of his cage the tawny beast leapt, apparently striving its utmost to spring upon Leonardo, but always just missing him. It only lasted a few seconds in all, but it must have appeared a long time to those watching.

Then Leonardo suddenly cracked his whip and fired the last chamber of his revolver right in Menelik's face, and, as the beast recoiled, opened the door and sprang out of the cage. The lion himself closed the door (which, of course, opened inwards), as he sprang against it in his pursuit of the trainer.

And how the audience ate it up! How they roared and yelled and cheered as Leonardo, seeming to be exhausted, leaned against the side of the cage and wiped the sweat from his brow! Menelik stood close to the bars, his great tail lashing and his enormous white teeth flashing in the lights as he snarled angrily. He was a great actor, that lion!

As the applause died away a man on the farther side of the ring shouted something. The Ringmaster swung round angrily :

"What's that you say, sir? Oh, indeed . . .?" He jumped up on a rostrum, and cracked his whip for the attention of the audience : " Ladies and gentlemen ! After you have witnessed this stirring spectacle—after you have seen the gallant Signor Leonardo recklessly risk his life—

and shown your appreciation of it—here is a gentleman who is not satisfied ! He says that it is all a fake—that the lion is trained to do this, and is really quite harmless ! Is that right, sir ? "

" Yes, that's right ! " shouted the man.

" What do you say to that, Signor ? "

Leonardo appeared to be very angry. He spoke rapidly to the Ringmaster in what seemed to be a foreign tongue, with many gesticulations. The Ringmaster cracked his whip again, and then turned to the barracker :

" So you say that scene is all a fake, sir, do you ? "

" Yes, I do ! " shouted the man.

" Are you sure of that ? "

" I'm dead certain ! "

" Good ! " cried the Ringmaster. " Then, sir, I take it you have the courage of your convictions ! And, therefore, you will be glad to accept Signor Leonardo's offer—that you shall go into the cage with him for a couple of minutes ! He will guarantee that, at any rate, he will be killed before you will ! "

Then came a shout of delight from the audience at this. In the meantime Leonardo was giving directions, and the shutter was brought forward again, while the niggers were busy heating up their irons and the riflemen looking to their weapons.

" Now, sir ? " shouted the Ringmaster. " What about it ? "

The man was stammering and stuttering, and plainly considerably nonplussed.

" Why, sir," shouted the Ringmaster, " you're not afraid of a lion, surely, are you ? You're an Englishman, aren't you ? Remember that the lion is the heraldic animal of your country ! And, besides, this one is quite tame—it's all a fake, you know ! You're not afraid of a fake, are you ? "

Stirred up furtively by one of the attendants, Menelik at this moment let out a terrible roar, and this appeared to be too much for the barracker, who turned suddenly and literally ran out of the tent, to the accompaniment of a storm of jeers and catcalls from the audience. (He went straight round to the back, changed his clothes, and got busy helping to prepare the men's supper. His job with the circus was that of cook's mate !)

A uniformed attendant ran into the ring, and seemed to convey a message to the Ringmaster. When the laughter and jeering had subsided, the Ringmaster cracked his whip again, and addressed the audience once more :

"Well, ladies and gentlemen, you see how much faith that gentleman had in his own grounds for complaint ! But, in case any of you might still think that the act is faked, and that Menelik is a tamed and trained lion, I have just received instructions from the proprietor of the circus to make an offer of five pounds—five beautiful golden sovereigns—to any person who will go into that cage with Signor Leonardo, and who will remain there for a space of not less than one minute ! Now—any takers ! "

There was more laughter at this, and the young men looked sheepishly at each other, and nudged one another on. But no one accepted the offer !

"Oh, come along, ladies and gentlemen ! You're already heard that the lion is quite harmless ! Isn't there one of you who, for the honour and glory of Old England, will enter that cage, and earn five pounds ? We don't care who it is—man, woman, or child ! "

That was my prearranged cue, the word " child ! "

I immediately jumped over the barrier, and ran a step or two into the ring, shouting : " I will ! I'm not afraid of any old lion."

Another roar from the audience, when they realised what it all meant. Then the Ringmaster called out :

"Why, this is only a baby ! We'll have to ask your father about this, my little man ! Where is he ? "

"There he is ! " I answered, pointing to my " father " of the moment.

"Hey, you, sir ! Are you willing your little boy should go into the cage with Menelik, the forest-bred lion ? "

My " father " rose. He was an old actor, and had a fine, deep voice :

"You mentioned the honour of Old England just now, sir ! " was his reply. " For that cause—so that the honour of our great flag shall remain unsullied—I am willing to risk the life of my only son ! "

Good Lord, how that fetched 'em ! The audience got up in their seats, shouting and roaring and stamping and cheering in their patriotic fervour. The band, previously coached, of course, rose to their feet and played " Rule, Britannia " lustily.

When silence was restored once more the Ringmaster said :

"Very well, sir, your patriotic offer will be accepted by the Management ! " Then, to the audience : " Ladies and gentlemen ! It is too late to attempt this sensational and spectacular feat to-night—and, besides, Signor Leonardo is already exhausted by his previous performance with the lion. But to-morrow night, at nine o'clock precisely, this young man will accompany Signor Leonardo into the cage of this ferocious animal ! Unless, of course, the young man thinks better of it before then ! "

Whereupon I, still playing my part faithfully, shouted :

" Don't you worry—I shan't funk ! I want to buy a bicycle ! "

Which elicited another shout of laughter from the audience.

The next day was rather fun. For the first time in my life I was a celebrity ! In a town like that, where everybody knew everybody else's business, and anything sensational very seldom happened, I was, of course, the cynosure of all eyes. Wherever I went people paused to gape at me, and a little crowd of admiring small boys followed me all the time. I fancy some of them must have " hopped the twig " from school for the delight of following me around. I was talked to, patted on the back, and stood more sweets and ice-creams than any normal boy could possibly consume, so that my volunteer escort did not follow me around for nothing, by any means !

I was also interviewed by local reporters, and a pencil sketch was made of me by an artist. I heard him say to one of the reporters :

" This will be worth no end of money—if that darned lion eats him ! "

This was a new point of view for me, and gave me something of a shock ! It had never occurred to me that I was running any real risk at all up to then but, at that fellow's words, I commenced to see visions of Menelik seizing me in his great jaws—playing with me as a cat plays with a mouse ! . . . The words : " If anything *should* go wrong ! " kept trickling through my mind, and my sense of enjoyment commenced to wane a little !

Then I discovered that a lot of people—particularly young girls and old ladies—were looking at me with a sort of compassionate curiosity, and I could fancy them saying to each other : " Oh, dear, to think that that poor little boy may be a mangled corpse in a few hours' time ! "

I couldn't get much comfort out of my " father," either. In response to my slightly tremulous efforts to get a little reassurance out of him, he only said : " Oh, I *expect* it will be all right ! '' and then went on to relate some grisly re-miniscences of lion-tamers who, in the past, had been chewed up by their animals !

So it was that, as the evening began to draw near, I grew more than a little scared. The town was plastered with posters :

> " TO-NIGHT—SENSATIONAL SPECTACLE—LOCAL BOY WILL RISK HIS LIFE IN THE LION'S DEN !—THE THRILL OF THE CENTURY ! ! !—COME IN YOUR THOUSANDS—SEATS ARE LIMITED, BUT PRICES THE SAME ! TO-NIGHT ! ''

In the procession that day Menelik was the star-turn, dragged around in a great gilded cage, and roaring like a whole forest full of lions ! I didn't like that phrase " will risk his life "—and I hated the very sight of Menelik !

As for my " father," he had the very devil of a good time ! In the course of the morning he had so many drinks stood him, and got so completely " oiled " that I was frightened he would give the game away. So I got word down to the circus, and the guv'nor sent out and collected him on the excuse of a " business interview ! ''

The evening came at last. Outside the entrance to the circus they put Menelik in his golden cage, and they made me stand beside him ! Menelik kept snarling, and jumping at the bars of his cage—and every time he did that I had the devil's own job not to jump too !

My " father " and I were almost the last to enter the tent that night. The " house " was packed, but a special seat was reserved for us, draped with the Union Jack. The band played " See the Conquering Hero Comes " when we came in, and the audience cheered like the devil—but I reckon no one ever felt much less like a Conquering Hero than I did, just then ! My breeches were sticking to me with the nervous sweat I was in !

The great moment came at last. The snarling, roaring Menelik was wheeled into the arena in his cage. The Ring-master made a wonderful speech. He spoke of the courage and the bulldog tenacity of the British race. He introduced " Casabianca," and drew such a picture of the small boy on that burning deck that quite a lot of the ladies burst into tears (and so, at the obvious comparison, did I—but not for the same reason !). He spoke of me, personally, too—and in the tone one uses in speaking of those foredoomed to a sticky end ! His peroration nearly finished me altogether :

"Ladies and gentlemen ! I am not going to conceal from you the terrible risk this small boy is taking in entering the den of this terrible animal which, I may tell you, has already slain several fully grown men ! " (I suppressed a start and a shudder, with an effort !) " If, as it may do, the worst should happen, I can only beg of you to close your eyes, or turn your heads away. Put your hands over your ears, that you may not be tortured by the sounds of his dying shrieks ! But this I would impress upon you—whatever happens, let there be no panic ! Every precaution has been taken for your safety, as you will see in a moment, and there is no need whatever for you to be nervous—whatever happens, *you* are safe ! "

By this time my imagination was getting full play, and I was shivering like a jelly. There was a buzzing inside my head, too, and things were getting a bit jumbled in front of my eyes.

As from a great distance, I heard the Ringmaster's voice :

" Perhaps our young hero—this gallant defender of the honour of the Great British Empire " (loud applause) " will step into the ring ! "

Aided by my " father," I climbed mighty shakily over the barrier. I realised that I was shivering so much that it was impossible for me to walk steadily across the space between myself and what I was commencing to regard as the scene of my sacrifice, so I ran ! The band was thumping and blaring out " Rule Britannia " and then " For He's a Jolly Good Fellow ! " and the audience were clapping and cheering for all they were worth. But none of this comforted me much !

I got to the side of the cage, somehow, and leaned against it. I gather that I appeared to have adopted a nonchalant attitude—actually I was hanging on to the wheel of the cage-wagon to keep myself from collapsing ! I was soaked with perspiration, and my heart was thumping like a steam-hammer.

In fact, for the first time since boxing with my father in the old kitchen at Battersea, I was scared stiff !

And now there streamed into the ring a procession which, had it been possible, might have made me feel worse ! Nearly all the circus hands not actually in the ring must have been enrolled. There were several braziers, with hot irons complete, about a dozen men with rifles, and a lot of others with spears and pitch-forks. And last of all (and the crowning touch of all) two solemn-looking gentlemen who walked in carrying a rolled up stretcher!

All these preparations were, of course, done to impress and thrill the audience—but I'm betting that there wasn't one person in that mob who was half so impressed and thrilled as I was!

The myrmidons took up their position in a semi-circle round the front of the cage. The men with the rifles made a great show of loading them. I stared around like a cornered rat, and wondered what would happen if I made a sudden bolt and dived out through one of the tent flaps! . . . Then I decided that I was too frightened to even run!

There came a terrific burst of applause as Leonardo, resplendent in his uniform, came into the ring. He strode up to the cage, bowed in his curt, clumsy manner to the audience, and then regarded me. After which he folded his arms, and said, in a deep voice:

"Eet is goot! 'Ere ees a leetle 'ero!"

Under his breath he whispered:

"Blimey, young 'un, you ought to be on the stage! You don't 'arf look scared—actin' to the life, you are!"

At which, despite my scared condition, I nearly laughed!

I wanted to get the thing over, for now I think I was more scared that I should break down than I was of the lion itself! But the Ringmaster was making the most of the show, and the preparations were as slow as they were thorough —and through it all old Menelik was roaring and snarling in a way that sent continual cold shivers down my spine!

Leonardo "tested out" the lion by attempting to enter the cage as he had done the previous night, and with the same result, of course. Then the shutter was inserted, and he was penned up in the one side of the cage.

"Come on, boy—up you come!" said Leonardo to me, and he put out his hand to help me up the steps to the narrow platform. It was as well he did, for I don't think I could ever have climbed them alone! As it was Menelik suddenly let out a terrific roar just as my head appeared above the edge of the platform. I appeared to stumble—actually I had nearly jumped out of my skin!

But I got up somehow, and, somehow, I managed to keep on my feet. And then, just when I was all keyed up to it, that infernal Ringmaster thought of another bit of showmanship !

He cracked his whip for silence, and then said—in the deep, reverent tones of one attending a funeral :

"You, sir ! In case—in case anything untoward occurs, would you not like to say farewell to your brave young son before he enters the cage ? "

My "father," being an old actor, took the cue instantly. He rose from his seat, and, with a bow and a sonorous : "I thank you, sir ! " he stepped over the barrier and strode across the ring. At the foot of the platform he suddenly extended his arms, and cried out :

"Adieu, my brave boy, adieu ! If you die, you die for the honour of our glorious country ! "

And then he kissed me !

The audience went mad. Women wept, and even strong men blew their noses between their cheers and plaudits. My father seemed to be overcome with grief. I was almost completely overcome with other emotions—but luckily my "father's " breath stank so vilely of stale beer that I think sheer disgust revived me a little !

"Now ! " thundered the Ringmaster. And then : "Silence, every one, please ! "

The band drummer gave a great roll on his drum. Old Sam Noakes, otherwise "Leonardo," whispered in my ear : "Keep tight 'old on my belt, kid, an' keep close to me ! Then you'll be orlright ! "

And then we stepped into the cage !

I was too dazed now to be frightened. I saw the shutter slide away, and then the huge, tawny body of the lion seemed to be all round us. I noticed with what deliberate skill the brute avoided actually touching us. The revolver banged and the whip cracked and the attendants shouted. I stepped mechanically backwards and forwards with Leonardo, keeping a tight hold on his belt, until he whispered : "Let go ! "

I obeyed, and he then appeared to drive the lion back into the corner of the cage, calling as he did so :

"Ze shuttaire—queeckly ! "

The shutter was slid half-way home. He slipped back through the space left, and the shutter was slammed home as the snarling, scratching Menelik hurled his great body against it. Then Leonardo caught hold of me and dragged me through the door.

Leonardo wiped the sweat from his brow. I swayed on my heels, and had to be helped down the steps, and I heard Leonardo mutter :

" Blimey, the kid's good ! 'E does it to the life—any one 'ud think 'e was scared stiff ! "

Yes, I suppose any one *would* ! For my part, I was dead certain of it !

The audience went mad, and, after I had been solemnly presented with five pounds by the Ringmaster, they started chucking money into the ring. The clowns got a lot of it, but I managed to collect about twenty-five shillings. Of course, I had to hand the five pounds back to the guv'nor later, but when he suggested I should hand over the other as well I kicked.

" I'm sorry, sir," said I. " But, if you don't mind, I reckon I've earned that ! "

" Earned it ? " said he, surprised. " How d'ye make that out ? You've been lounging about, having a darned good time for three days, and not a stroke of work except go into that cat's cage for a couple of minutes. Where you get the ' earn ' from, I don't see ! "

" No, sir ? " I retorted. " Well, I can tell you this—if I had had five pounds in my pocket I'd have willingly given it to get out of going into that cage ! "

He stared at me.

" D'you mean you were scared ? "

" Scareder than I've ever been before in my life, sir ! "

He contemplated me for a moment—then he said :

" Well, by the saying it takes a coward to be a brave man, you must be a good plucked 'un ! " said he, at last.

He didn't say any more about the twenty-five bob, so I stuck to that all right.

THE
"GREASER" MEETS HIS MATCH

By
JO HALLAM

After years of varied occupations the writer arrives in New York in 1889 to find first a lodging and then a job.

I STOPPED a man in the street and asked him if he knew of a good lodging-house. He directed me to a place in the notorious *Bowery Camp* neighbourhood. It was rather a dirty, drab-looking place, I thought, but I went in and asked if they could give me a room. A little woman with sharp angular features and small beady eyes peered out at me from the gloom.

"An' how much are you paying?" she asked.

"What have you got?" I enquired.

Then she reeled off a long list of terms. Every price she mentioned had a picturesque name of its own. For instance, for 1 dollar 25 cents you could get a "Modest," and this was the one I chose.

There was a bar on the ground floor which any one could go into and one of the first things I did was to go in and have a drink. There I saw a pretty rough crowd—a mixture of hoodlums, bums, and highjackers. There was a man in there who was very drunk, but I didn't take much notice of him until he came up to me and started making a nuisance of himself. He was chewing some filthy tobacco, and when I turned away in disgust he caught hold of my shoulder, swung me round, and deliberately spat in my eye.

My fist shot out and a second later he was sprawling on the floor. He let out a foul oath and leapt to his feet again. He was a huge, lithe, active fellow, and I could see at once I had been foolish to attack him. He sprang at me and his heavy boots crushed down on my feet, making me yell with pain. Then he caught hold of my forehead with both his hands and pressed my eyes with his thumbs. I was pinned against the bar and helpless. Not a man moved to my aid though there were plenty hanging around. The people behind the bar went on serving as if nothing were happening. I suppose they were used to it.

I felt as if my eyes were being gouged out.

"Do you know who I am?" he leered. "I'm the Greaser. And you b—— well can't do things like that to the Greaser!"

I felt his foul breath against my face and a strong feeling of repulsion swept over me. My head was throbbing.

"You won't forget the Greaser in a hurry!" he snarled.

He relaxed his grip for a moment and I tried to get free, but he picked me up as if I were a child. There was a sudden silence in the room as every one turned to look. I didn't hear the crash as he flung me through the window for the world suddenly went black. . . .

I suppose it was some hours later that I woke up in hospital. My head felt as if it was split in two and I found it was covered with bandages. Painfully I turned round in my bed to survey the other occupants of the ward. There was an enormous hump in the next bed to mine but no sign of a human form. I looked a little farther afield and saw a number of inanimate objects sprawling in various strange postures in bed. Most of them were asleep and there was not a sound in the whole place except an occasional groan from some unfortunate fellow at the far end. It was very depressing.

Suddenly a deep musical voice sounded close to my ear.

"And what Chinaman's been making Chop Suey of you?"

I stared at the hump in the bed beside me. There was a thin wisp of greyish hair appearing slowly from under the bedclothes.

"Some one slung me through a window that wasn't open," I told the wisp of hair.

There was an upheaval of the bedclothes and a cheery bearded face appeared.

"I've been having a wee snooze," said the owner of the face, "for I didna ken there'd be company so soon after the tragedy."

"What tragedy?" I enquired.

"Och, mon! Did you ever hear the like?" He threw his hands in the air in mock astonishment. "Why, there's a fellow been and died in that self-same bed not three hours gone!"

He threw his head back and howled with laughter, but I did not feel inclined to share it. The prospect of sleeping in a death-bed did not please me and I thought his humour a little misplaced.

"Come, mannie now, cheer up!" he roared. "What do they call you?"

"My name's Hallam," I said, "Jo Hallam." (I had decided to adopt my mother's name some years before.)

"And my name is Andy McNabb. You can call me Andy," he told me.

At that moment a nurse came on the scene and seemed a little surprised to find me alive and kicking. She told me to lie down and take things quietly. Then she turned to Andy McNabb.

"You ought to be ashamed of yourself, making all this noise," she stormed. "The whole ward will be dying if you stay here much longer."

"Sorry, sister," Andy replied meekly, at the same time giving me an enormous wink. When the nurse had gone he turned to me.

"Regular tyrant, that woman," he said, "but a bonnie wee waist she has, and no mistake!"

Well, the days went by and I got to know Andy pretty well. He asked me on one occasion who it was had thrown me through the window.

"You look a fairly tough laddie," he said. "Who was the strong man who did the dirty deed?"

"He said he was the Greaser."

"Ah, and do you know what that means?"

I shook my head.

"A greaser is a wrestler," he told me. "You'll find a good many of them round these parts, and a nasty crew most of them are too."

I said that if any of them were half as bad as the one I encountered they must indeed be a nasty crew.

"But," I added, "I'll have my revenge on that fellow yet."

"I shouldn't do that," Andy advised. "You'll be back here in no time if you do."

But I swore that I would.

Andy had a wooden leg and he had to come to the hospital from time to time for a small operation after which it always had to be lengthened. Originally, he told me, his leg had been amputated about an inch above the ankle but every now and again it festered or " went bad " as he put it cheerfully, and he had to lie up for a time while more of it was taken off. It seemed to me an extraordinary story but he assured me it was true. It seemed to me it would have been much better to have had the whole leg off from the first, instead of having to undergo an operation every now and again to get some more of it cut away. However, Andy was very cheery about it all. He seemed to have no cares in the world.

He was the skipper, he said, of a four-masted schooner which plied usually between New York and Sydney, or sometimes Fremantle, in Australia. At present they were going a trip without him and were due back in a few days' time. They'd been away about nine months and Andy said he'd be mighty pleased when he could get aboard her again.

I told him all about my upbringing on the *Kanyan Candy* and of my adventures since. He was very interested, and when I told him I had about twelve thousand dollars and was looking around for something to do, he was more interested still.

" How would you like to join me, eh, laddie ? "

" I'd like to take to the sea again," I said. " I'd give my stars for a three months' voyage."

A few days later news came to Andy that the *Angus McVite*, which was the name of the schooner, had just arrived. Andy was in a great state of excitement and that afternoon his officers came into the hospital to see him. He introduced me to them and I thought they were a decent lot of fellows. They all seemed very glad to see Andy and he seemed on the best of terms with them. I felt more sure than ever that I would do well to accept his offer.

By this time I was nearly better again. The doctor had spent most of his time, as far as I could make out, in extracting bits of glass from various parts of my anatomy. As it happened Andy was allowed to leave on the same day and he asked me to come straight down to the schooner with him.

" No," I said, " I'm going to settle accounts with the Greaser first."

However, I drove with him as far as the dockside, and then I told the cabby to drive me to the Bowery Camp. I got out when we arrived at my former lodgings and told the man to wait. The little beady-eyed woman was standing in the doorway and she looked very surprised when she saw me.

" I never thought you'd come back here again," she exclaimed.

" Is the Greaser anywhere about," I asked her curtly.

She jerked her head towards the bar.

" Drinking as usual," she said.

I went back to the cabby.

" Can this horse gallop ? " I asked him.

" Yeah, I should say so."

" And you'll be ready to move off the instant I come out ? "

" Here, what's the game ? Highjacking ? "

" No, only a little joke," I reassured him. " But you'll be ready for a gallop, won't you ? "

" Why, sure, gov."

I went back to the woman.

" I want to see the Greaser," I said. " I've come to thank him for what he's done to me."

" Eh ? "

" Go and fetch him ! " I said sharply.

She moved off shrugging her shoulders in the direction of the bar.

A second later Greaser appeared. He stood in the entrance of the doorway and glowered at me.

" Hallo, you glue-pot, asking for some more trouble ? " he greeted me.

" No, I've come to say thank-you," I replied, and thereupon gave him the biggest blow on the jaw I've ever given to any man in all my life. He staggered back cursing and spitting out teeth.

I bolted back to the cab.

" Where to ? " asked the cabby.

" I don't know," I said, " but keep going ! "

I glanced back as we galloped off and saw that there was a great hullabaloo going on in front of the lodgings. I heard them shouting for us to stop but I urged the cabby on. He well deserved the double fare I gave him when I stopped him finally at the other end of the city.

SAVING A WORTHLESS LIFE

By
BOB DYKER

The author is a North-West Mounted policeman and he is stationed at Indian Head in Saskatchewan, Canada.

I WAS out on patrol some distance from Indian Head when I heard of trouble a little way ahead. It's surprising the way news travels in those parts ; more surprising still in the lonely frozen North where it seems to travel just as quickly as in the more civilised districts. The man who gave me the information was a miner, a bleary-eyed unprepossessing individual. He stopped me as I was riding through a little mining village, a village that consisted solely of a few tumble-down, squalid dwellings in which the miners lived.

When I stopped he came up to me with a wink and cocked a dirty thumb over his shoulder.

" Lookin' for trouble ? "

" What's the matter ? " I asked him quietly.

" Notice anything queer about the village ? "

" No, I can't say I've noticed anything."

He guffawed loudly and spat on the ground with relish.

" Waal," he drawled, " I reckon you p'licemen are a poor lot."

I was getting impatient.

" If you've got anything to tell me," I said shortly, " spout it out. If you haven't you'd better clear off and mighty quick too."

He looked at me nastily.

" Yeah ? "

" Yeah."

Then he grinned.

" All right, Mr. P'liceman," he said. " I'll tell you. It's no good us quarrelling. I guess you and I are the only men left in this little hole."

Involuntarily I glanced around at the cluster of hut-like houses. There were a couple of women scraping pots outside their dwellings. Otherwise no sign of life. The man seemed to be right ; we were, as far as I could see, the only men there.

He continued : " There's been a quack doctor here. Doc Morton he's called. He's been selling patent medicine, and giving watches away with it. They're all dud ; so's the dope. I knew it from the start, but when I told the boys they got nasty, so I left them to it. He made a nice packet out of 'em, that Doc did. Then he cleared in the night. In the morning the boys realised they'd been had. The watches wouldn't go properly, an' they found they all had the same dope though they all had different complaints ! It makes me laugh ! "

The miner spat again emphatically.

" Where've they all gone ? " I asked. " After the doctor ? "

He nodded.

" Yeah, that's it. An' I reckon there'll be trouble. Thought I'd just tell you."

His voice was casual, but I could see he hoped there would be trouble. I'd already summed him up. He obviously wasn't popular with the rest of the miners (he was certainly a nasty specimen), and, as he appeared to be the only man not to be taken in by the " doctor," he was probably still less popular on that account. Here was his chance of getting his own back on the miners who had no doubt given him a bad time.

He glanced round furtively and then shielding his mouth with his hand, whispered something to me. This confirmed what I thought. He had told me that the miners were all drunk. This was not unlikely ; they had probably been attempting to drown their sorrow ! But it made me quite certain that my informer was only too anxious for me to make a few arrests. Mentally I decided to avoid doing so if I possibly could.

The " doctor," the miner thought, belonged to a travelling fair and circus and had come over from a larger village about eight miles away. No doubt he had gone back there. Anyway, that was the spot the boys were making for.

With a curt nod I thanked him for his information and kicked Paddy into a smart trot. The man seemed irritated by my abrupt departure, but when I turned round in the saddle a second or two later I saw that he was rubbing his hands together in pleased anticipation of the fate he thought was about to descend on the heads of his comrades.

Things were looking very bad for the " doctor " when I

arrived. The fair was not a large one and the centre of attraction was the doctor's patent-medicine stall. There was a large crowd round it ; most of them appeared to be carrying sticks or weapons of some sort. They were shouting abusive language at the doctor but he stood quite still with folded arms on his little platform. He was smiling. I was astonished at the audacity of the man. I could see at a glance that he only infuriated the miners all the more by appearing un-concerned. It looked to me as if they meant business, though for the present they seemed content to abuse and threaten him. Most of the miners appeared to be drunk, though the rest of the mob was made up of harmless folk who had come along to see the fun.

They scattered a bit when I cantered up on my horse.

" What's all this about ? " I demanded.

For a second there was silence, but only for a second. Then the hullabaloo broke out again more fiercely than before. The miners were drunk—there was no doubt about that—and in that condition none of them had any respect for the Law. The miners were mostly a tough lot round that district but they were a law-abiding, good-hearted crowd as a rule ; it was only because they were drunk that they were uncontrollable.

The noise was deafening. At any moment I expected the enraged men to break down the " doctor's " stall and attack him.

" Give us back our money ! " they were shouting.

" Dirty thief ! "

" Son of a gun ! Let me get at 'im ! "

" Burn up his palace ! Haw ! Haw ! "

And a number of unrepeatable but colourful phrases besides.

Their menacing attitude increased. Somehow I must save that man from their folly. If I could only get him away somehow. . . . But I would never be able to persuade him to leave his belongings behind. And how get him away, if I could persuade him ?

The circus was pitched a little way outside the village, so that, if only I could get hold of a horse for him he could make for open country and be well away before the miners had realised he had escaped. Then I had an idea.

I dismounted, tethered Paddy, and went behind the scenes of the Doc's stall. Then I made my way through to the front and mounted the platform beside him.

He turned to me and shrugged his shoulders.

The shouting and roaring increased in volume, but they did not dare to throw things while I was beside him.

" Beat it ! " I said to him curtly. " It's madness to stay here."

" They'll wreck my stall if I go, and it's my only means of livelihood."

This was unanswerable.

" Well, if you won't do what I say, I can't help you," I said and turning my back on 'him, began to make my way out again.

As soon as the mob saw me going they started throwing dirt and stones and other missiles at the unfortunate " doctor." I heard him cry out as a heavy object hit him in the face. Then he ran after me.

" I must get away ! You're plumb right ! They'll murder me, the hounds ! " He shook his fist at them.

" Now, look here," I said to him roughly, " you understand, I'm helping you to get away because I think they might kill you if I didn't. But I still think you're a dirty trickster ! "

He did not reply.

" If you give them back their money it might be all right even now," I went on, " but I doubt it. They want your blood."

" I won't part with a dime," he said obstinately.

We heard the sound of splitting woodwork as they started breaking through in front. At the sound the Doc's nerve broke.

" Get me away somehow ! " he wailed. " Get me away from the devils ! "

Paddy was tethered at the back of the stall, out of sight of the mob. I untethered him and almost pushed the doctor into the saddle.

" I'm trusting you," I said quietly, " to ride this horse no more than a couple of miles. Then leave him. He'll come back again, and you'll be a safe distance away. Can I trust you ? "

" Sure."

He was off in a flash. I hurried back to the front of the stall. Some of the men were about to climb up on the platform. The platform was thick with dirt and stones. When they saw me they fell back.

I tried to reason with them. I told them that the Doc had gone behind to get his money and would no doubt be back again in a moment to repay them. But repayment didn't seem to interest them.

" We want the Doc ! " they yelled.

But they dared not do much while I was standing there. Even in their drunkenness they recognised the red tunic and respected it.

The rest of the crowd had dwindled when they thought there was going to be trouble, and only the miners remained. So now I only had the drunken men to deal with. If they had been sober I could not have got away with my little trick. They would at once have suspected a ruse when the Doc and I disappeared behind the scenes. But apparently it did not occur to them that he could have escaped. They knew he had no horse near the stall and the notion that I might part with my horse was too incredible to enter their minds. Mind you, I could not have done it with any other horse ; but I was convinced that Paddy would return to me, as he always did.

I could see that I was rapidly losing control over the miners, and I was thankful when I heard a familiar whinny from behind me. I dashed out of the stall and mounted my horse who seemed none the worse for his hard ride.

Then I cantered round to the front of the stall to see what was happening.

The miners had already broken in. They were smashing everything they could lay their hands on. Watches, bottles, everything that belonged to the " doctor's " precious medicine-chest were flung to the ground and trampled on. I made no attempt to stop them. I knew that it would be useless.

Then the cry went up : " Where's the Doc ? "

They searched the little room at the back of the stall, they hunted around everywhere. Then they came back and stared suspiciously at me.

I just sat silently and grimly on my horse, staring back at them. They muttered sullenly, knowing that somehow I had managed to get the doctor away. Then they turned back with added zest to their destruction. My faith in the power of my red tunic was justified. They dared not attack a Mounted Policeman. Besides they knew my gun contained bullets that would kill !

Having smashed up everything they could lay their hands on, they set the place ablaze. Crowds gathered round again when the flames shot skywards, and then I thought it was time I took my departure. It was useless to take any action against these miners. At best I could only arrest one or two. Besides I was not over-anxious to arrest any of them. The " doctor " had got what he deserved, and anyway I wasn't keen on gratifying the desire of my unpleasant informer of some hours ago.

It seemed to me that I'd done all that I could have been expected to do. The " doctor " was the one who had come off worst, and that was as it should be, for his was the crime in the first place. At the same time, I had saved him from a severe lynching in which he might well have been killed, for that bunch of drunken enraged toughs were capable of anything.

I returned to barracks that night with the satisfactory feeling of a day's work well done.

LOG OF A HELL SHIP

By
PETULENGRO

Although a musician by profession, in order to get from Australia to England the author decides to work his passage over in a German vessel as a deck hand. His salary has been fixed at 1s. per month.

I THINK my official position aboard was that of " general servant." My duties included holystoning the deck, painting the hull in calm weather slung over the side in a bo'sun's cradle, and keeping a watch.

The usual duration of a watch is, of course, four hours, with the two dog-watches of two hours each to allow rotation of the members of the crew on the various watches. My watch aboard that vessel began at eleven o'clock at night and did not finish until five in the morning.

My sleeping quarters were supposed to be in a cramped apartment, full of awkward corners, called, if I remember, " the lower forecastle " ; but the place was so airless, so dark and damp, so vermin-ridden and thick with the stench of filthy humanity, that I did not sleep a wink there throughout the voyage. I shared it with ten other down-and-outs, the veriest scum of humanity, who had been shipped aboard because eleven good seamen had jumped the ship at Sydney. The lordly A.B.'s slept in some other infinitely luxurious fo'c'stle.

In the bunk below mine was a Finn suffering from a loathsome infectious disease. After we had been at sea for a couple of weeks, he went down under it and could not leave his bunk, where he lay sweating and continually moaning, occasionally breaking out into wild raving in his native tongue.

Almost from the start of the voyage, I did not attempt to face the vile squalor of that fo'c'stle. In the daylight hours when I should have been sleeping, I wandered about, seeking for a corner where I might be alone and rest. To find such a spot in the restricted area where the crew might put their feet was impossible. And I was " general servant." They called me " Spider."

I would be straying about the deck, half-dead from sleeplessness after my watch, when some one in authority would catch sight of me. Then it would be :

"Here, Spider ! Havin' a holiday ? Let's see you holystone this bit of deck."

I was the lowest thing aboard. I got all the dirtiest, most stomach-turning jobs to do. Because I was under no one man in particular, I was anybody's slave.

For the use of our fo'c'stle, there was one lavatory. It was doorless, and my peculiar training had inhibited me against performing my bodily functions in public. I made and carried out elaborate plans for using the other lavatories on board, without being caught. Only because it was one of my more unpleasant duties to clean them out was this made possible. As for the sty designed for the use of the fo'c'stle, I was never asked to clean it ; so it is certain that it was not cleaned throughout the voyage, for who was there lower than myself to perform this degrading task ?

I was ignorant, wild, and rather queer. To me it seemed degrading to line up with one's plate for the disgusting food we got. It savoured to me of begging. I preferred to steal food from the pantry.

The first hour of my watch, from eleven to midnight, I would play cards. The officer of the watch did not appear. I had orders to waken him at the times of inspection. Being a high personage aboard, he was entitled to the incredible privilege of sleep.

At twelve I was joined by one who seemed to me the only human being aboard. He was an A.B., a Scotsman, and the sole friend I had. After reporting on the bridge, I could indulge in the supreme luxury of sleeping for an hour, while Jock watched. I did so on the settee of the saloon.

At one Jock woke me, and I kept awake while he slept. For the next hour I had to keep awake, and I did so by catching rats in the pantry where I went to make cocoa for the officer on the bridge. In the intervals of catching the rats, I made my best meal of the day.

At two, I woke Jock, for it was a dangerous time from now on to attempt to sleep. We would play cards for matches, and talk, and sometimes I would play Scots airs for him on the fiddle—very softly. I am sure Jock never realised what his companionship meant to me during that nightmare voyage. Perhaps it saved my sanity. I wonder if he was a very low type of man to have had any truck with such as I ?

Naturally this system of having but one hour's sleep out of twenty-four could not go on for long. There came a time when I was forced to capitulate and brave the filth and the odour of the lower fo'c'stle. My desire for privacy was understandable as regards the lavatory, but it went further than that. Something in my nature made me revolt against undressing—that is to say, partly undressing—along with the other derelicts in the fo'c'stle. So I hung rags and strips of old blanket in front of my bunk and crawled in behind the barrier like an animal into its hole. The foul air could not keep me awake. The snoring of the men about me could not. Not even the painful breathing and low mumbling of the sick man in the bunk below me could retard my exhausted mind and body from slipping deep into sleep.

I awakened in a dead silence. Peering about me through my curtain of rags, I could see that all the other bunks were empty. It was matter for relief, yet I felt uneasy. The silence which should have soothed me, disquieted me.

Abruptly I realised the cause. The Finn in the bunk below me had ceased his raving. I climbed out of my bunk, and, as I dropped to the ground, I saw the Finn. He was dead, with his eyes staring and jaw dropped.

They buried him the same day. The other men would not go back into the fo'c'stle for fear of infection, although why they should fear it more after the Finn's death than before, I could not fathom.

My sleep had not nearly made up for all the rest I had missed since coming aboard. Like the others, I was afraid of infection, but the longing for sleep was stronger than my fear ; and there was the fo'c'stle empty of the filthy bodies of my fellows. I went below and slunk behind my screen of rags. I slept.

Choking and coughing, I awoke. The apartment was full of acrid yellow smoke. My lungs were full of the fumes of burning sulphur. I leaped out of my bunk and blundered towards the door. It was locked. Coughing till I vomited, I wrestled with the unmoving door, and banged on it with my fists and tried to shout.

In the middle of the floor, I saw the glow of the burning sulphur. It was on a shovel. The smoulder of it through the heavy yellow fog was inexpressibly weird.

I kicked the shovel over and stamped on the burning sulphur, but it was extraordinarily difficult to put it out.

I flung myself at the door again. I coughed and coughed, and it seemed as though my lungs were being bitten out by those ghastly fumes and that I must vomit them up at any moment. I was very light-headed. The dark fo'c'stle, wreathed in great flying swathes of yellow smoke swirled round my head, rotating faster and faster.

I beat at the door till my hands were broken and bloody. It seemed impossible that nobody could hear me : impossible but true. No easy death, this. No gentle sinking into nothingness on the wings of weakness. The weaker I felt, the nearer I came towards unconsciousness, the greater choking torture I suffered.

Then, away at the other end of the world, through an infinite corridor of half-consciousness, I heard a voice. It came from the other side of the door. I beat at the door again with the crazy energy of a final frenzy. There was a small click. A sniff of fetid life-giving air came to me as the door opened inwards, knocking me down. I coughed, and then I fainted.

I took very little hurt from my experience, although I heard from the ship's doctor that I had had a very narrow escape from being suffocated. Very wisely, it had been decided to fumigate the fo'c'stle after the Finn's death, and I, sleeping behind my screen of rags, had remained unnoticed when they were busy lighting the sulphur and hermetically sealing-up the apartment. I very nearly paid with my life for my stolen sleep.

From then on, I kept out of the fo'c'stle altogether. At odd times I slept unashamedly and unrepentantly on the tops of hatches above decks. It meant being kicked into wakefulness dozens of times and sent to do some job or other, and it was little sleep I stole for the rest of the voyage, but I had good reason to prefer that to the sepulchre below.

Presently I fell foul of the pantryman. I had been helping myself to food from the pantry since the beginning of the trip, and he must have noticed the thefts. There came a watch when, during the preparation of cocoa for the officer on the bridge, I was eating beans from a tin with a spoon. Without warning, the door of the pantry was flung open, and the fat German pantryman charged in on me.

He flung a mouthful of furious German at me, spat in my face and, lifting a heavy pot, made a murderous swipe at my head. I ducked and backed into a corner. My position was a serious one. He was much heavier than I, and in that confined space could have almost smothered me by sheer force of weight. I flung the tin of beans at him.

It struck him just above one eye and the mess of beans spewed itself down one cheek. It checked him just long enough for my purpose. I smashed my right to his jaw and my left to his stomach. As he half doubled up, I hit him on the jaw again. He went down, and the pot he held slid across the floor. I dodged round him and got my back to the door.

Blowing, he got to his feet and came for me again with his fists. But in that sort of scrapping, the fair-grounds had taught me more than the sea had taught him. I kept him at a distance with my left and punished him with my right until his fine rage had cooled down completely. He was the type just built for being hit about the body, and I did not spare it. After about ten minutes, I finished him off with a swing to the solar plexus that left him squirming on the floor, able to get up but not wanting any more.

My watch finished, I sought out a hatch and slept. My awakening was a rude one. I was hauled bodily off the hatch, and, as my body thumped on the deck, a heavy boot kicked me in the back.

It was the Master-at-Arms, one of that blond, beefy type of German which wrestles and does feats of strength at music-halls ; a giant of a man, and no friend of mine.

" So ! " he growled. " You're de great fighting man, eh ? Get up, an' show what you can do."

I got up. As I was doing so, he swung his boot at my face. But I had seen that trick before. I dodged and jumped back on my toes. He flung himself at me, and he did not come at me with his fists. His hands were open, claw-like, a typical wrestler's attitude.

I did not mean to get between these arms if I could help it. I brought my right across and down like a hammer, striking his left inwards with the bone of my forearm. As he slewed round, I hit him over his shoulder on the side of his jaw.

He came at me again. Again I knocked his arm inwards and landed on his face ; this time flush on his left eye. So it went on, each of us performing the same manœuvres—but not for long. He was so much bigger and stronger than I that it was merely a matter of time before he got to close quarters and could ram home his advantage. By this time, his injured eye had swollen badly, and he was mad with pain and rage.

He grabbed me by one arm and pulled me to him. With

his other hand he gripped me by both lapels of the ragged jacket I was wearing.

"Now!" he said, and jammed me against the bulwark with such force that it seemed to me as if every bone in my body had been shaken out of its proper place.

Then he proceeded literally to wipe the floor with me. He was familiar with a wide variety of ferocious wrestling holds, and he demonstrated the lot on my carcase. He flung me over his shoulder on to the deck, jumped on me, picked me up, and flung me into the scuppers, picked me up again and tied me into a knot, untied me agonisingly, and flung me down again. As a finale, he got me arched over the same hatch on which I had been sleeping, and, holding me down helplessly with one hand, pounded my face with the other.

I was numb and only semi-conscious, past feeling pain, when I heard a sharp voice speaking, and at the same moment I was released. I could not move, but lay where I was on the hatch, with my back bent over it like a bow.

There was another order, and many hands lifted me up.

I do not know what happened to me immediately after that ; but, when I awoke, I was lying—not in my filthy bunk in the fo'c'stle, but between starched white sheets in the passenger's sick-bay.

From that moment onwards, my troubles were over. Apparently what had happened was that one of the passengers had seen the fight, and immediately gone to the Captain and told him that a youth among the crew—I was only seventeen at the time—was being unmercifully beaten up by the Master-at-Arms. The second officer had been sent instantly to stop the massacre, and I, thanks to the indignant demands of the passenger who had witnessed the business, was installed in the clean white splendour of the sick-bay.

I was a nasty mess when they brought me in, and it was feared that I was seriously injured ; but it turned out that apart from a couple of broken ribs my hurts looked and felt worse than they were.

When I was ready to be up and about again, I discovered myself to be an object of intense interest and sympathy among the passengers. The rags I had been wearing on coming aboard had been finally torn to small pieces by the hands of the Master-at-Arms. I took one look at them, and flung them overboard. Upon which the passengers held a drive among themselves which provided me with a strange collection of garments. I had the jacket of a man half my size, and the trousers of a man twice my size, and shoes and shirts equally assorted ; but they were clean and whole, and I was glad of them.

I did not go forrard again. An empty cabin was found for me in the passengers' quarters, and, during the remainder of the voyage, I paid with my fiddling for my bunk and board and the clothes I had been given.

What orgies of sleep I had ! What banquets—not of beans, but of exactly similar food to that which the Captain himself was eating ! During the day I loafed consistently. In the evenings I played solos. It was a good life.

My fractured ribs mended quickly. By the time we docked at Tilbury I was as good as new again. As for the Master-at-Arms, my benefactors among the passengers were for making him suffer a host of dreadful penalties for the damage he had done to my person ; but whether he got into serious trouble over the affair or not, I never found out.

I am not sentimental. I have been out of England often enough to be glad to return to her. But I do not get a lump in my throat and a stinging moistness in my eyes when I see her white bulwarks defying the sea. When I caught my first glimpse of her cliffs near the end of that voyage, however, jutting up through the gloom and driving rain of a typical Channel evening, I had a number of unwonted symptoms which might, if allowed, have developed into the authentic sob and tear of the returned wanderer. In other words, it was good to be back.

ON THE SPOT

By

J. MILLIGAN

The author has just returned from serving in the Great War.

I ARRIVED back in America a hero—and practically penniless. It was the first time I'd ever been in New York, and I didn't know my way around, but folks were full of sentiment about us " conquering heroes " and I landed a job easily enough—in a big department-store on Forty-Fourth Street.

For over a year and a half I held down that job, sleeping in Brooklyn and crossing the river twice a day to my work. Without any conscious intention of doing so, I found myself going straight, and living the dreary life of a typical city shop-assistant. Maybe it was creditable, but it was dull.

For all that, I'd got firmly set in my rut, and, if things had been left to my own volition, I might have stayed in that rut till I died of old age. But things weren't left to my own choice.

I left the store late one night, and it so happened that I met a fellow who'd been in France with me. It was naturally an occasion for a drink, and he took me down to a speakeasy in the Bowery that he said he frequented.

We had several drinks there ; then went to another speakeasy for some more.

Having done most of my hard drinking before Prohibition had hit the country, the bootleg hooch got me down, and it was the same with my friend. Late at night I seemed to rise out of a thick mist of semi-consciousness, and found myself sitting at a bar in a place I'd no recollection of entering. Of my war-time pal there was no sign. Somehow or other we'd got separated.

In the moments of returning clarity, I ate a few pretzels and drank some " Canadian " beer, and began to sober up a bit. I began to notice things, and I noticed particularly that a big gorilla of a fellow standing near me at the bar was watching me with a look that was half-puzzled, half-thoughtful.

I was stiff enough with moonshine not to give a damn for his size and tough looks.   I resented the way he was staring at me.

" You'll know me next time, brother ! " I told him.

He didn't show by either look or speech that he'd heard me. He just went on staring. I got off my stool, and staggered up to him. I caught hold of the lapel of his coat and gave it a jerk, though I was only half his size and I ought to have been glad he wasn't showing any signs of starting any rough stuff with me.

" See here," I declared, waving my free arm drunkenly. " There's the whole of li'l old New York for you to glare at— so take your lamps off me. I don't like being stared at, see ? "

" Take it easy, pal," said the big guy slowly and soothingly. " You don't wanna get sore at me. You just reminded me of a guy I know—my brother way back home—an' a whiter man never was whelped. Say now, what about having a little drink with me, an' bein' friendly ? "

I was on my tipsy dignity and wouldn't say yes right away. I waited a second or two, then I said ungraciously :

" Okay, then. Forget it. I don't mind having a little drink with you—I'll have a shot of bourbon."

I had a shot, and a couple more after that. And, by the time I'd finished the third, I was half-weeping over his yarns of his " brother way back home," and was trying to get in a word edgeways about my " dear old mother."

" Say, this is a punk joint, ain't it, pal ? " said my new friend ingratiatingly. " 'Tain't our class. C'mon, let's go places. I know a little place just down the way where there's some life. How's about it—do we hit the bricks ? "

" Sure we do ! " I answered recklessly. " Bit of life— that's what we want. Let's go."

" My roadster's outside," said the other man. " We'll ride in comfort."

We went outside and I found myself in a dark alley. We walked down the alley and came out into a mean, badly-lit street. Sure enough, parked by the sidewalk was an expensive-looking roadster. After the thick atmosphere of the speakeasy, the night air hit me like a sledgehammer, and I staggered wildly.

My companion opened the door of the back seat for me.

" Get in behind, buddy. It's more comfortable," he invited.

I bent my head to climb in ; and, at that instant, I felt

a terrific blow behind one ear and blinding pain go singing through my head. The split second before I lost consciousness, I saw the dark interior of the roadster leaping up to engulf me as I fell. . . .

. . . .

I came to in a room that was so packed with brand-new furniture that it looked like the show-window of a house-furnisher. The heavy yellow velvet curtains were drawn and all over the room were masses of flowers, which gave out an overpowering stench of sweetness in the hot thick air.

I looked round me blearily, and, standing with his back to a mantelpiece that looked like a marriage-cake in marble, was a slim, smallish man with sleek dark hair. He wore spats and clothes that were too tight for him, and he was smoking a cigar a foot long.

" Who the hell are you ? " I demanded.

He had been grinning, but at my question the grin was wiped off his face.

" Who am I ! How d'you get that way ! Mean to say you don't know me ? "

" Not from Adam."

" Why, you——! " He clenched his right fist and took a step forward as if he was coming over to the couch on which I was lying to sock me on the jaw.

He restrained himself.

" My name's Eddie Tasso. Maybe you know me now ? "

I whistled. Eddie Tasso was one of the celebrities of the New America. Blackmail, murder and gunfights were the mode, and Eddie was one of the leaders of fashion. You could hardly pick up a tabloid-newspaper without seeing his name in it.

" Tasso. . . . The big gang-leader, eh . . . ? And what do you want with me ? "

" Plenty. Get up and come across here."

I got up ; and promptly put my hand to my aching head.

" I could do a drink. . . ."

" On the table behind you."

I tottered across to the table indicated and helped myself to a four-finger shot of Scotch—real Scotch it was, too. Then Tasso jerked his head to motion me across, and I walked towards the mantelpiece.

" Look in there," he ordered, nodding towards the huge gilt mirror overlooking the hearth.

I looked. I saw myself and Tasso standing side by side, and I noticed immediately that we might have been brothers, we were so much alike. The resemblance wasn't enough to make you gasp, but it was close enough to be remarkable.

" Catch on ? " Tasso inquired. " Slick down your hair with oil and part it nearer the middle, and you'll look like enough me at a distance to pass."

" What's it signify ? " I asked.

" This. The Casey gang's lookin' for me to eat at the ' Green Gridiron ' back of Times Square to-morrow night, and they'll be out in force. So while they're elsewhere, I'm goin' to stage a little raid on their territory to pick up Frankie McBann that bumped off two of my boys in that gunfight last week. It's a job I wanna do myself, but I want an alibi —and you're it."

He pulled a cigar-case out of his pocket and held it out to me.

" Smoke a real cigar ? No. . . ? You see, the idea was Packy Brannigan's—one of my gorillas. He spots you in some joint, sees you ain't unlike me, thinks it over, and gets the idea about sendin' you to the ' Gridiron ' in my place. So he picks you up and brings you along here. I just can't get over a bonehead like Packy thinkin' up a gag like that—swell, ain't it ? "

" Swell," I agreed without much enthusiasm.

" Well, that's the lay-out. Beat it now an' get some sleep —through that door there on the couch. You're hittin' the hay right in my room to-night, brother : I ain't lettin' you out of my sight. Have another Scotch, an' look happier— the pay-off to you for this job is a thousand bucks."

I went and had my drink, and tried to sleep in the stifling splendour of the great man's bedroom. I didn't sleep much.

. . . . .

With Packy Brannigan slouching at my side, looking more like a gorilla than ever in his tuxedo, I followed the waiter to my reserved table in the " Green Gridiron." My hair was slicked down with about half a pint of oil, and I was wearing a tuxedo of Tasso's that fitted me like corsets : truly I reckon one would have had to be pretty close to me to find out that I wasn't the gang-leader. On coming in, the manager of the joint had addressed me as " Mr. Tasso."

We sat down and, in obedience to orders, I asked the waiter to bring me a succession of Italian dishes. I sat there looking about me glumly, sipping a cocktail that tasted like turpentine.

" See across there in the far corner ? " Packy whispered. " Them's some of the Casey boys."

I saw. Round a table in that corner five men sat with their chairs arranged so that they were all facing me. Their faces were hard and blank as bricks, and their eyes were fixed unwinkingly on my face.

I had felt nervous before. Now I was sick with fright. I knew that, as long as I served his purpose, Tasso wouldn't give a straw whether I was killed in the process or not. I also knew that he would have killed me himself without the least hesitation if I'd made any fuss about the impersonation—that was why I had come here so quietly.

" Casey ain't along himself," Packy was going on. " Reckon he won't show up at all. He's a wise guy—lets his hoodlums do all his killing for him."

" What happens now ? "

" Nothin' We just sits here an' waits. These guys won't spring anything in here. They'll wait till we go out—an' by then Tasso'll have a bodyguard waitin' to see we don't hit no trouble. Take it easy, buddy. You won't get hurt."

There was a small smile on his mouth as he spoke I didn't like his expression at all.

We ate spaghetti and risotto and God knows what—that is, I tried to eat ; and all the time the unwavering eyes of the five men in the corner were fixed on me. Not only their eyes, either. Most of the other diners kept watching me covertly from time to time. They knew Tasso's face from the newspaper photographs, and thought they were seeing the great man in the flesh.

Just as the last course arrived, Packy got to his feet.

" I gotta phone Tasso," he announced. " Gotta tip him off to have that bodyguard on time, so's we'll get outa here with our skins whole."

He had gone before I could say a word. I saw the eyes of Casey's men follow him as he strode out. One of them got up and went after him. In less than a minute this man came back and joined his friends. He seemed to be telling them something. They turned to look at me again, and one of them was smiling.

I was debating with myself whether I'd stand a chance of beating it. If I was to try, it must be now while Packy was out of the way. . . .

But I was given no chance of even trying. I saw one of the men in the corner say a couple of words to the rest, and they rose in a body and came leisurely across to my table.

They stood in a circle about it, looking down at me with their unwinking eyes. I looked up from my dessert and round the arc of their faces.

" Howdy, Tasso, we just came to invite you to a party," said the one who appeared to be the leader—a slim fair youth with hard eyes and a baby mouth.

" Why do you call me Tasso? That ain't my name." There was a tight feeling in my throat, and I could hardly speak the words.

The fair youth smiled.

" What does it matter? To us you're Tasso, an' we figure to take you along to our party—Tasso. . . . Take it easy, though. There ain't no hurry. We'll wait till you finish your eats. Sit down, boys."

There were three vacant chairs at the table. Three of the men sat down ; the others remained standing.

I pushed my plate away.

" Listen here and get it straight : I'm not Tasso," I said desperately. " My name's Milligan. Packy Brannigan spotted my likeness to Tasso and brought me along here to-night in his place. On the level, you're making a mistake——! "

" I guess not," the fair youth retorted. " Casey tipped us off Tasso was comin' here to-night—an' Casey don't make no mistakes. Don't make me laugh with your comic cracks about bein' somebody else. Sure Packy Brannigan came along with you to-night—we saw him didn't we ?—but he came as your bodyguard. Guess he wasn't so sure about playin' bodyguard when he saw how many of us boys were here—he's beat it."

" He went to phone ! "

" He walked straight out of the joint and beat it for his life—scared stiff."

" Please give me a hearing ! " I begged. " I've been double-crossed, and so have you. Tasso's raiding into your territory right at this minute. He sent me here as a set-up——! "

The fair youth yawned.

" You're making me tired," he said. " Guess we won't wait till you finish your eats after all—or Brannigan might be back with some more of your boys. Come on, Tasso ;

snap out of it. You're comin' with us now—for a nice little ride in the country. . . ."

"You can't take me!" I shouted. "I tell you I ain't Tasso—— !"

The youth gave a tiny nod, and I was grabbed from both sides. I began to struggle madly. I heard men shouting and women screaming. I fought like hell, but it was useless. They dragged me across the floor and out through the swing-doors of the place.

Just outside a big Packard limousine was standing. I was flung inside, with two men on top of me. Within a second or two, the car was started, and went swinging off round the first corner, doubling among the side-streets.

I was dragged into a sitting position, and hands were run over me to search for weapons. I was propped up in the middle of the back-seat, with a hoodlum on either side of me. Two guns prodded the back of my ribs.

I was helpless. All I could think of to get myself out of this ghastly mess was to smash one of the windows of the car and scream for help. But I knew I'd never have a ghost of a chance of getting away with it. At my first movement, both these guns sticking into my back would pump lead into my body. I think it was just then that I realised for the first time, the true significance of the words, "tight-corner." I was jammed in my corner tighter than a sardine in a can—and I could see no way out.

I felt that nothing less than a miracle could save me, and when my rescue did come, I couldn't look on it as anything else. Looking back, I still see it as something miraculous.

The limousine roared through the New York streets, heading west. At first they were unfamiliar streets; then I saw Central Park out of the left-hand window, and realised we were on Fifth Avenue.

None of my captors spoke a word, and I didn't speak either. Protesting was useless. I'd done all that already, and I could see they'd never believe my story. I was being driven to an appointment with death through these busy streets, and I couldn't raise a finger to help myself. . . . A queer way to die—in another man's place. In the past men had hunted me for things I had done, and I had escaped. And now I was to die for another man's deeds, a man I'd known for only an hour or two. . . .

Suddenly one of the men by my side leaned forward and shouted urgently to the driver :

"Slow down, Sam! That's a police-car just in front!"

Fifth Avenue was fairly quiet at that hour, and we had been going fairly fast. We slackened speed. Through the windscreen, I saw the police-car. It was about twenty yards in front and near the middle of the road. Even as I watched, it swung abruptly across our path, so that our nose was turned towards the kerb. The driver of the police-car pulled up, and so did ours; he couldn't help himself.

A big copper jumped out of the police-car and came across to ours, dragging open the door.

"We been chasin' car-bandits, an' we lost them," he announced. "Youse guys seen anything of a blue coupé passin' this way?"

"Not a thing," said the man on my right surlily. The pressure of the guns against my ribs was noticeably stronger.

My mind was working at lightning speed. My first impulse was to yell at the top of my voice to the cop: "These men are gangsters taking me for a ride!" But I thought better of it. Once I unmasked them, they would be utterly reckless of what happened. Expecting a shoot up with the cops in any case, they would certainly make sure of me first by pulling the triggers of these guns whose muzzles were digging into my hide, then try and shoot their way past the cops to safety.

If only I could think of some way of using this heaven-sent advent of the police-car without actually letting on that my companions in the car were killers intent on bumping me off. . . . I tried to catch the copper's eye and convey something to him by grimaces. But he didn't look at me once. Already he was in the act of swinging the door shut again.

"Hey, officer!" I called out. The guns poked deeper into me—but they weren't discharged. The cop hesitated, and pulled the door wide again.

"Yes?"

When I called out, I hadn't had an idea of what excuse I could give for detaining him; but in that moment it came to me. I had hailed the copper, and I hadn't been plugged. That seemed to signify that I wouldn't be plugged if I could get the coppers to take me right out of the jam—so long as I didn't give my captors away.

"A blue coupé you said? I've just remembered. I saw it just back a little ways. . . ."

"Make up your mind," said the cop sharply. "We're in a hurry."

The pressure of the gun was noticeably stronger.

" I'm certain about it—a blue coupé. It turned up a kind of an alley in a side-street just back there off the Avenue."

" What street ? "

" I don't know the name—I'm a stranger to New York. But I know the street. I'll show you if you like. . . ."

I was lying like mad, but it seemed to be coming off.

" Quick then," said the cop. " Get outa that an' into our car."

" Bet your life I will ! " I answered fervently.

I was out of that limousine like a streak of lightning. The guys inside were looking at me with murder in their eyes—but they hadn't used their guns yet, and I was certain now that they wouldn't call my bluff.

The copper almost flung me into the police-car. It swung round and went tearing back in the direction from which we'd come.

" Stop ! " I shouted. " Stop the car ! I never saw that blue coupé—but I'll put you on to something bigger than car-bandits. . . . These guys in that car belong to the Casey gang. They were taking me for a ride ! I just pulled that yarn about seeing the coupé to get away from them——! "

The cops in the police-car stared at me incredulously.

" On the level ? "

" I ought to know ! I've had two gats sticking in my ribs for the last ten minutes. They mistook me for Eddie Tasso."

The copper who had dragged me out of the limousine looked hard into my face.

" Hell's Bells ! you do look somethin' like Tasso ! " he exclaimed. Then, to the driver : " Hey, Mike ! Turn her round again an' get after that limousine we just stopped. . . . Hell ! We've been askin' the way of a bunch of killers ! "

WHITE MAN'S GROUND

By
"SELIM"

IT is now nearly thirty years since I was in charge of the
district of Akele, in what is now, I believe, the Western
Province of Southern Nigeria. My headquarters were
on the banks of a tributary of the Cross River, swift and
deep, but not very wide. It was the first district of which
I had had sole charge, and I was very proud of it. With
the help of a European carpenter and half a dozen natives
I designed and built the wooden mess-house, and a very
pretty little place it was, infinitely more sightly than the
" tin " monstrosities which did duty for mess-houses at old
Calabar and Bonny. We also constructed a small wharf, and
I laid out and planted a short avenue of palms between the
mess-house and the wharf. Very proud of it I was, and very
pleased with myself when it was finished. I suppose there is
no trace of it left now, for it was abandoned for a healthier
site in the first or second year of this century, though it was
still in use as a " Rest House " and in fair condition when
I last saw it in 1908.

I had another reason for being proud : I had had no
trouble with the natives. I got on very well with them indeed,
and they seemed to like me. My last tour of service had been
in the country of those horrible Eku Mekus (the Silent Ones)
on the north bank of the Niger in behind Asaba, and I greatly
appreciated the change from those grim and murderous
warriors to the quiet people of Akele.

The chief—he called himself " king "—of that part of
my district in which my headquarters stood had a name
that sounded like " Jacky," and that is what we called
him, and he answered to it cheerfully. He was a fine figure
of a man, somewhere about forty I should say, though it is
hard sometimes to judge a negro's age. He had a sort of
herald who always accompanied him on his visits, and who
carried messages to and from him. We called him " Old
Tom," and he well deserved the name, for the amount of
" squareface " (gin) he could drink without turning a hair
was amazing.

He, too, was a fine man, in spite of his age. He stood about six feet two, was as straight as a dart, though he must have been over seventy, and his hair was snow-white. He always carried a sort of wand of office, a long straight staff bound round all up its length with copper wire. We called him " Copper stick in waiting." He spoke English of a sort, and his mouth seemed set in a perpetual grin.

The trouble came towards the end of my first year there, when I was beginning to think about leave. We got leave every year then, and we needed it. I was alone at the time, for the doctor had died three weeks before of blackwater. He was the fifth white man to die at Akele that year, the carpenter and three " travelling officers " being the others. The climate was pretty deadly then, or perhaps we did not understand it.

Jacky and Old Tom had got into a habit of coming to see me two or three times a week. They used to come in the mornings and drink " squareface " till I wondered how they could stand or see. It did not affect them in the least ; it would have killed me.

These visits suddenly ceased, and for nearly a fortnight neither Jacky nor Old Tom came near me. I did not understand it at all, for we had had no quarrel or the least semblance of one, and I did not like it. My interpreter, a man of the same race but a different tribe, was plainly growing very uneasy. He said that the Ju-Ju men, the priests, were stirring up trouble, and he was most probably right. They were at the bottom of all the trouble all over the country at that time ; there was never a month in all my years of service when there was not a little war—we called them " shows " —going on somewhere or other out there, and in every case the trouble could be traced to the priests.

At last—it was a Sunday evening—the interpreter rushed into my room in a state of absolute panic. He said that he had just been down to the neighbouring village, and found that all the women and children had left it, and that all the live stock had been driven off. There could be no misreading such signs as these, and I saw that if I would save my life I must be prepared to get away at once. Resistance was out of the question : my total force consisted of three native policemen, and though they were armed with Martini carbines, I knew that they could be safely trusted to run away at the first shot.

Steam launches were not so plentiful then as I hear they

are now, and my district was not provided with one ; but I had a good whaleboat and six stout Kroo boys to man it, and there are no better boatmen in the world than Kroo boys. They are plucky enough too, but I had no arms for them, and they are not much good on land.

There was about £100 in silver in the office, and this, with some of the most important papers and some tinned provisions, I had carried down to the boat. The Kroo boys, the policemen, my two house boys and the interpreter scrambled in as fast as they could, and begged me to be off at once.

But I felt that I could not present myself at headquarters without something definite to report. Suppose it was a false alarm ! What a fool I should look ! After all, I had only the word of a panic-stricken native, and the fact that Jacky had not been to see me for a fortnight, to go on ; I did not even know for certain that the village was deserted. So, although I was beginning to quake, I told the boatmen to wait for me at the wharf while I reconnoitred a bit. I ordered the policemen to come with me, but they flatly refused, and urged me to get away at once.

Fortunately the night was dark, but not too dark for me to see my way. I stole gently past the mess-house and— I was in a blue funk by then—through the deserted village. I remember I called it that in my mind, and, idiotic as it may seem, I thought of Goldsmith.

Once past the village I was in the bush, and the futility of going on struck me at once ; I could not see three yards in front of my face. I stopped and listened, but could not hear a sound. It was like being back in the Eku Mekus' country again, and, indeed, the natives of Akele turned out to be very much like them in their methods of warfare. They never make a sound till they attack ; they get through the bush as silently as snakes and strike before you know they are anywhere near.

I listened intently for about five minutes, and those five minutes were very nearly my undoing ; the silence was profound, till suddenly and quite close to me a horn or conch was blown.

I turned at once and started to run for the boat, but I was very nearly too late. As I emerged into the open three men sprang at me. I shot two with my revolver, the third stumbled or flinched, I do not know which, and I got through. I dashed at full speed through the empty village, several shots being fired at me as I ran. Fortunately bundooks (long flint-lock guns) do not shoot very straight. It was pretty dark, and I was sprinting for all I was worth, so I got away untouched.

But I was in most deadly fear. There flashed across my mind, " Suppose the shots have frightened the men and the boat has started." I knew that all in the boat, even the Kroo boys, were in a state of panic ; they knew, and I knew, the horrible fate of those who fell into the hands of these cannibals, for cannibals they were, as were practically all natives then in the Niger Delta and right down to the Cameroons and beyond ; they knew, and I knew, the horrible obscene tortures they inflicted on their victims, the dreadful lingering death.

I got through the village, dashed past the mess-house and down the avenue to the wharf, only to find that my worst fears were realised and the boat was gone.

I have gone through many "scraps" in my time and been in many tight corners, and I hope I have behaved as well as most, though I have known what fear is many times ; but never before or since have I known such fear as then. All that I had heard of native cruelty—and seen too—crowded back in my mind with paralysing force. The stream before me, then as now, was infested with crocodiles, but Jacky's men were close behind me, and any fate was better than falling into their hands—I dived into the deep water off the wharf.

Only just in time ! The fiends reached the wharf just as my head emerged from the water. But now the darkness stood me in good stead. They could not see me, and after peering this way and that for some seconds, they blazed off in a direction well away from me. I verily believe they fired at sounds the ripples made by a crocodile disturbed by my dive. It sounds fantastic, but I have always believed that.

Paddling quietly with the swift current I soon had no immediate fear of my pursuers ; but as my fear of the savages died down, fear of the crocodiles took its place, and it seemed to me that I had only escaped a horrible fate on land to meet a fate almost as horrible in the water. Fortunately—and I do not think I could have endured much more— my Kroo boys had plucked up courage again. Once on their native element, and with a stout boat beneath them, they had regained confidence, and had come back to search for me as soon as they heard the splash and the yell I gave when I dived—I was not conscious of having uttered a sound. They found me, and picked me up pretty well exhausted.

I shall never forget the intense feeling of relief I experienced as I sank down in the boat. Pursuit was possible, but not likely. Small canoes we could easily keep at a distance with the three Martinis and my double express, and the only two large canoes were, I knew, drawn up high and dry on the bank. It would take a long time to launch them and get the crews together (about eighty or ninety to each canoe), and long before they could overtake us we should be out of Jacky's country. He dare not pursue us beyond his own borders for fear of the neighbouring tribe, as the local chiefs then were very jealous of their " water rights," and each was kept very strictly to his own stretch of water, except when on purely trading journeys.

After an uncomfortable journey of seven or eight days I landed, very stiff and half-starved, at Old Calabar. I made my report, and it was decided that an expedition should start for my district at once. Little " shows " were common then, and the troops were always ready. Jacky was only a small " king," and fifty men with a maxim were thought sufficient.

The troops were Hausas—I do not think we had begun to call them " Waffs "[1] then. I would rather have 100 Hausas than 200 of any other native troops in the world, not even excepting Sikhs or Gurkhas, and I have known all three ; they had just been armed with Lee-Metfords too.

Stanley, a young subaltern—local captain—was in command. There was an English sergeant—a real good man—a doctor, and, of course, myself as Political Officer, though we did not call ourselves that as they do in India. Two large steel canoes lashed on each side of a powerful steam launch constituted our flotilla, and off we started.

When we arrived at Akele I was very glad to find the mess-house standing, though, of course, everything in it had been looted. Jacky told me afterwards that he had intended to use it as a sort of " riverside residence," and that was why he had not burnt it. However, I was more than glad to find it intact, and we made it our headquarters.

And then our troubles began. Only those who have been through one of these old-time " shows " can realise what it was like, and do what we could we could not find the enemy. There were no roads, just brown paths, only wide enough

[1] West African Frontier Force.

for one man to pass along at a time, so that if he stuck out his arms on either side they would touch the thick almost impenetrable bush, while the trees meeting overhead made a kind of twilight. It was like going through a badly lit tunnel.

The brown path goes on fairly straight for seventy or eighty yards and then turns a corner. When you come to the corner you see another seventy or eighty yards of brown path, and so on hour after hour. Every now and then as you turn a corner, you see a puff of smoke come from the bush near the next corner, and a shower of slugs comes swishing amongst you. The said " slugs " consist mostly of rusty nails and pieces of old broken cooking-pots, and they make ugly wounds. You can only fire at the puff of smoke, and it is a thousand to one against your hitting any one.

After the first few hours Stanley had the Maxim pushed on in front of everybody. It had a light steel shield fixed to it, which partly protected the gunners. After that, when a puff of smoke was seen, the Maxim was loosed off at it for twenty seconds or so, and that way we sometimes got one of the marksmen, but not always even then. As for fighting, there was not a semblance of it, but it was a most nerve-racking business all the same.

Then the flanking parties ! It was necessary to have a small party out on each flank. These men had to carve out " tunnels " for themselves. They first started at right angles to the main column, then turned at right angles again and went on parallel to it, cutting " tunnels " all the way ; and the main column had to regulate its pace by the flanking parties. We sometimes hardly made five miles in a day. And then the heat ! The flies ! The mosquitoes ! The difficulty in getting water ! It was wellnigh intolerable. Moreover, our 400 carriers, recruited from a neighbouring tribe, were even more exasperating than carriers usually are.

Every now and then we came upon a native village, which we solemnly burnt. This pleased us, but did not hurt the natives much. Everything movable had been carried off, and we had neither the time nor the means to destroy the tough mud walls. It would not take more than five or six days to reroof any of their villages.

After about three weeks of this we returned to Akele. We had traversed the country in all directions—Jacky's country was only about twenty miles square—and had utterly failed to bring the enemy to action. We had killed

five of the enemy for certain, and killed or wounded perhaps
about a dozen more. We had one Hausa killed and eight
wounded ; we had used up a lot of Maxim ammunition, and
nearly all our stores. We all had fever more or less, and we
were, all of us, heartily sick and tired of the whole business.

Poor Stanley ! He had been so tremendously keen ;
he was not one of those subs who came out there for financial
reasons, as many of them did at that time, attracted by
the very high rate of pay. He had money of his own, and his
only reason for coming out had been to see active service and
advance himself in his chosen profession. He had been so
overjoyed at receiving an independent command, and had
set out with such high hopes. Moreover, I will say this, he
had shown himself to be a skilful as well as a careful leader,
plucky, untiring and outwardly cheerful through it all. Our
utter failure so far was a bitter disappointment to him.

We held a council after our evening meal, and we called
in the sergeant to assist in our deliberations.

" Tell me, you men," said Stanley, " is there anything
I have done which I should not have done ? Is there anything
I have not done which I should have done ? "

" Not that I can see," said the doctor.

" Nor I, sir," said the sergeant.

" What do you say ? " said Stanley to me.

" Well," said I, " I have been through three shows
before, as you know, and I can only say that I haven't
seen one better handled or better led than this."

" Thanks, old chap, that's some consolation, at anyrate ;
but what the blazes am I to do now ? Send for reinforcements ? If I do I shall never hear the end of it ; I shall be a
laughing-stock from one end of the country to the other.
Fifty men were considered sufficient to smash this tinpot
" king," and so they would be if I could only find him. The
chief would be coming up here himself in a rage, and I should
get a large piece of his mind."

" Don't be afraid of that, old man," I said. " The
chief has been on too many shows himself to blame you ;
he has been in the same fix himself before now, as I very
well know. I should send for reinforcements at once if I
were you. Your force is too small to divide, but if two or
three columns were operating in different directions, one or
the other of them would be sure to corner old Jacky."

" That's all very well," said Stanley. " But in that
case it would no longer be my show ; a senior officer would

be sent up in command, and he would eventually get all the credit, even if it was my column which brought Jacky to book, and after the cursed luck I have had so far, I'm dam' sure it would be some other fellow's column."

Just then my native boy came in.

" Old Tom want you, sah."

" What ! " said I. " Bring him in at once."

In came Old Tom in his voluminous white robe that looked so like a Roman toga, and carrying his " copper stick " as usual.

" The king greet you, sah," said he to me.

" Greet the king for me," I said, " and ask him why the devil he tried to cut my throat six weeks ago."

Old Tom grinned, but he took no other notice of my question.

" The king greet you, sah," he said again, " and he say he want for fight you."

" Good Lord ! " said Stanley, jumping up ; " then why the blazes doesn't he fight us ? We've been wanting to fight him, and trying our damnedest to fight him for the last three weeks."

" The king say, sah," said Old Tom, turning to Stanley, " you hab gun dat shoot all day (the Maxim), no be fair. Suppose you no use dem gun, the king fight you."

We were all so taken aback by this novel proposition that no one spoke for at least a minute. Old Tom went on grinning, the sergeant grinned, and I believe I did too. Stanley was staring straight before him into the night.

" I'll do it, damned if I don't," said he at last. " Look here, Old Tom, if our gun no fair, it no be fair for your king to fight in bush when we no see him. You savvy dem ' white man's ground ' ? "

" Savvy," said Old Tom.

" Tell your king suppose he fight me on white man's ground, I no use dem gun."

" I go, sah," said Old Tom. " To-morrow I come back."

I told my boy to give him a good shot of " squareface," and he departed grinning more than ever.

" White man's ground " was the name the natives had given to an open space four miles to the north of us. Some idiot had tried to grow cotton there a couple of years before. He had got the concession from Jacky, and had had the ground cleared and planted. It came to nothing ; the soil was quite unsuitable. I had often passed over the spot and seen the remains of the crop : it all turned black. The space was roughly a circle about a thousand yards in diameter.

As you may suppose, we had a lot of talk about the matter both that night and the next day. I did not like it at all, and said so. The more I thought of it the less I liked it. I had had too much experience of native treachery —of Jacky's in particular—and I did not expect for one moment that he would give us a " square deal." However, I was wrong, as you shall hear.

Old Tom duly returned the next night, and said that Jacky was quite agreeable to fight on the ground selected, and he actually asked Stanley—it sounds unbelievable, but it is absolutely true—if next Thursday would suit him, for all the world as if he were asking him to dinner.

Stanley told him gravely that Thursday would suit him very well. Old Tom departed with more " squareface " inside him (and still grinning), and so we stood committed.

On Thursday we started very early, and Stanley neglected none of his former precautions, as I had half-feared he would. We made our way to the field of battle with the Maxim in front as usual, and with parties out on each flank, so that it was nearly two in the afternoon before we reached our destination.

When we got out of the bush Stanley deployed his men and sent the Maxim to the rear. He put it in my charge, with strict orders that it was not to be used in the open. It was blazing hot, and we felt it the more after the shade in the bush. The ground was covered with coarse grass and weeds, and here and there with the remains of the cotton.

Stanley advanced slowly and cautiously, with his flanks slightly thrown back, uncertain from which point of the compass the enemy would make their attack—that is, if they did attack—for, of course, the whole thing might have been just a ruse to get us away from the river or to lead us into some trap. This is what I had feared all along, and Stanley, in his eagerness to finish the business himself, had risked it. However, Jacky turned out to be a sportsman, and a very brave sportsman at that. He made a direct frontal attack.

When we had advanced very slowly and cautiously about 300 yards, Jacky and his men burst out of the bush right opposite us with ear-splitting yells, and the great battle began.

They came on first in a dense mass—Jacky well in front— about 800 of them, I should say, but, of course, in that formation they had no chance. The Hausas are not crack shots, but they are fairly useful, and up to 500 yards pretty deadly, and they could hardly miss that mass of humanity at that range ; they were very steady, too. The " bundooks," with which Jacky's men were armed, will not carry more than 150 yards.

The enemy did not get to within 300 yards of us, and after losing very heavily, they fell back to the bush again. In about an hour they came on again scattered over a wide front. They got on much better then, and many of them got near enough to loose off their bundooks. We began to get a taste of the slugs, and the doctor became busy. They also enveloped our flanks and began to work round towards our rear, and for a little while matters looked a bit ugly. I know I had to keep a tight hold on the crew of the Maxim to prevent them bringing it into action. However, the Hausas were very steady, Stanley and the sergeant setting a splendid example, and the enemy, brave as they were, could not stand up very long to that deadly fire. They stood it for nearly an hour, and then retired to the bush again. Jacky had been in the forefront of both attacks, but came through without a scratch. I believe that the Hausas, who greatly admire bravery, deliberately spared him.

As soon as the enemy had disappeared into the bush, to our astonishment, Jacky and Old Tom, accompanied only by two lads, reappeared and came straight towards us ; Stanley gave orders not to fire at them, and Jacky came straight up to me. As if nothing had happened, he coolly asked me for some gin.

I told him that I had none with me, but that if he would come back with me to the mess-house I would give him some with pleasure. He came without the slightest hesitation, and then and there on the verandah of the mess-house we made peace. He agreed to return all loot, to pay 500 goats, and I forget how much oil, and to give up his three eldest sons as hostages. Finally, for the first and last time to my knowledge, he got gloriously drunk, and fell asleep on the floor.

We never had any more trouble in the district. We sent Jacky's sons down to Bonny to be educated (the school was at Ogugumanga then). They turned out eventually as good specimens of natives as you would wish to see. It is a great mistake, and very cruel, to send natives to be educated in England. I never found out for certain why Jacky had so suddenly turned on me, though I have no doubt that my interpreter was right in his surmise.

THE PRINCE OF ESCAPERS

By
P. L. RICHARD

ON the 3rd September 1916 I took off in a plane piloted by Sergeant Rousseau, with orders to direct the barrage fire between Combles and the Somme. In spite of very poor visibility we were determined to carry out our mission and do what we could to help our infantry. On the return flight we were attacked by five enemy monoplanes, and at the very beginning of the scrap my left arm was shot through by a machine-gun bullet. I bled profusely from the wound, which was nearly six inches long, and had only time before I fainted to call to Rousseau to dive down through the fog.

When I came to myself again we were at an altitude of some two hundred yards, over enemy territory. We were close to the English lines, and Rousseau did his best to reach them, the enemy machine-guns spraying us liberally from the ground in the meantime. Two black-cross 'planes followed us at a distance of twenty-five yards, machine-gunning us continuously. In spite of the pain of my wound, I was able to manage my machine-gun with my right hand, and answer them appropriately. Finally they abandoned the chase.

We were barely two miles from the English lines now, and that was none too close. Our 'plane was literally riddled, my seat being almost cut in two by the bullets ; it was a miracle that the machine still managed to keep the air. Would it be possible to land without crashing ?

Suddenly the motor stopped, and with safety only a few hundred yards distant, we had to make a forced landing. We turned turtle, and I got my chin bashed in in the process.

I lay half-stunned beside the capsized machine. Rousseau was unhurt, though his coat had been pierced by bullets in several places.

I shouted to him, " Fire ! Set fire to the machine ! "

He set a match to a leak in one of the petrol-tanks, which had been crushed in by the fall ; and when the Germans came up the 'plane was one huge bonfire. The heat was so intense that I had to roll over on my wounded arm to escape being burned, as I was unable to get to my feet.

The cartridge-belts left in the machine were exploding on every side, so the enemy retired to a prudent distance, and formed up in a circle about their capture, having first arrested us both. An officer shook his sabre at me, and asked me reproachfully, "Why did you burn your machine, monsieur?" J contented myself with giving my name and rank, and then tried to calm Rousseau, who was surrounded by a group of soldiers and was beginning to lose his temper.

The excitement died down at last and we were taken to the post of the commanding officer, a general. I was carried to the liaison officer's dug-out, and a first field-dressing was put on my wound. From there I was taken in a motor ambulance to the dressing-station of Bapaume, where my wound was dressed again and where, to my great regret, I was separated from my companion.

I was put to bed, and five German aviators—those who had brought us down—came and asked for details of the fight as it had appeared from my side. Their behaviour and manners were perfectly correct, but I had no desire to shake hands with them at that moment.

A few days later I was taken by motor ambulance to Barastre, and deposited in the church, which had been transformed into a hospital. The next evening I was moved again, to the evacuation hospital of Velu, installed in the château, near the station; finally, on the following day, I was transferred by hospital train to Caudry.

. . . . . .

I was still in French territory, though occupied by the Germans, and I realised that my best chance was to escape at once while the people were my own people, though under the heel of the enemy.

By chance I got into touch in the hospital with a young Frenchman of eighteen, called Bonvoisin, who had been requisitioned by the Germans for work behind the lines. We arranged that I should escape from the hospital of Caudry and get to his home where the Bonvoisin family would hide me until my wound was sufficiently healed, and then help me to reach the Dutch or the Belgian frontier. Unfortunately, very soon after I got to Caudry I was separated from my good friend Bonvoisin. During the ten days I spent there I did my utmost to realise the plan of escape I had sketched out, but I received word from his family, without explanation,

that "there was nothing doing," and so my first plan fell
through.

From Caudry I was sent into Germany, on a hospital train
that was a veritable palace, though not very well supplied
with food. After travelling for two days, I arrived at Grafen-
wohr, near Bayreuth, in Bavaria, about twelve miles from
the Austrian frontier. The prisoners' quarters were installed
in an artillery barracks, surrounded by a barbed-wire fence
and guarded by numerous sentries.

Corporal Jourdain, of the 111th Infantry Regiment, who
was entrusted with the internal administration of the camp,
struck up a friendship with me at once, and one day he said
to me, point-blank, " *Mon lieutenant*, you are going to try to
escape ! "

" Why do you think that ? " I asked.

" Because you don't look like a quitter, *mon lieutenant*."

I admitted that his intuition had not deceived him, and
that such was my intention. But how to set about it ? It
would be out of the question to set off on foot ; nearly three
hundred miles lay between the hospital and the Swiss frontier,
autumn was coming on, and my physical condition was far
from satisfactory. My wound would not be entirely healed
for some weeks to come. Jourdain said that he thought he
could get a couple of bicycles in the neighbouring village.
One prisoner had already escaped by that means, a certain
Debroe, who later joined the Air Force. He had made the
trip without being in any way molested.

Close by the hospital was a soldier-prisoners' camp and
they were allowed far more liberty than the officers. In this
camp was a sergeant who was often allowed to go into the
town to buy supplies, though always escorted by a guard.
We arranged with him to get the bicycles. He was a quick-
witted fellow, and would probably find a way to manage the
affair. He was to buy civilian clothes, too, and maps, compasses and Tirolean knapsacks.

This sergeant told the old woman who kept the bicycle
shop that, wishing to make a handsome present to the
Feldwebel of the camp, he wanted to buy two machines, a
man's and a woman's. A French soldier, disguised as a
German, was to call for the machines, passing himself off as
the *Feldwebel's* orderly, and then hide them in the country,
at a place we had agreed upon. The price of the bicycles, two
hundred marks, was paid in advance by the sergeant. All
seemed to be going well. The disguised soldier duly went to

fetch the bicycles, but the old woman, being suspicious, had asked her brother-in-law to be present when he came. He in his turn had warned the police ; and when the soldier presented himself he was inundated by a flood of questions, and in the midst of it a policeman turned up. The disguised Frenchman took to his heels at that, and managed, thanks to the twilight, to out-distance his pursuers.

The scheme had failed—and, worse still, the money was probably lost. But the sergeant had the infernal cheek to go the next day and demand its return, terrifying the old woman by telling her that if she didn't give it up, he would denounce her as an accomplice ! And she ended by refunding the two hundred marks.

As I couldn't get what I needed with French help I decided to try the Germans, and approached a male nurse who had already supplied me with various forbidden articles. At that time I knew no German, and the man himself spoke only a dozen or so words of French, so the negotiations were somewhat complicated. But that affair too was a failure, and got me no more than a few unwanted emotions.

Furthermore, I developed blood-poisoning in my wrist, the result of my wound, so I was scarcely in a fit state to undergo the fatigues of an escape.

Then I wrote to my sister. We had, before I left for the war, made a code between us in case anything of this sort happened. In all my future attempts at escape my sister was my guardian angel. This time in a code letter, I asked her to send me the parts of two bicycles dismantled and secreted in various packages that I expected, thanks to the aid of French accomplices, to be able to smuggle through the German control. But the plan was condemned in France as being impracticable. A second was proposed in its place. At a given spot a man, German or speaking perfect German, was to meet me, to travel with me, and leave me at a certain distance from the frontier.

On about the 10th June 1916 the long-awaited message came : " The man, a German democrat, will be at the place indicated, at midnight, on the night of 29th to 30th November. You can bring a friend with you." Corporal Jourdain and I at once imagined that we were already back in France !

On the following day Jourdain came to tell me that he had been deprived of his post at the hospital and was being sent back to the neighbouring soldiers'-prison camp. We agreed to meet on the night of the 28th to 29th November, as we preferred to try to get out of the prison and hospital twenty-four hours in advance of the great day.

Everything went well. I found little difficulty in getting out of the hospital, and we met at the exact time we had arranged. After spending the day in a wood, we went to wait for the promised messenger from Switzerland. Nobody. We waited for two hours, still hoping, but in vain.

Should we try to do the three hundred miles on foot? Impossible. I was still weak from my wound and my two operations, shivering with fever, and even at times a little delirious. The cold brought on a sort of cerebral congestion, and everything that the faithful Jourdain could do to relieve me was without effect.

Three courses were open to us : to wait by the roadside to be arrested and taken to prison ; to risk, ill as I was, dying in the open ; or to make our way back. We decided on this last course, as Jourdain refused to go on alone. A few hours later I returned—how I do not know, for I was wildly delirious —to the camp I had just left with so much enthusiasm. The doctor visited me three times a day—an unaccountable relapse !—and seemed to be doubtful of my recovery. But fortunately I was naturally very robust, and shortly I began to mend. Twelve days after my attempted escape I was declared to be fit and sent to a fortress as a punishment. As for Jourdain, he had managed to get back into the camp unnoticed, thanks to the German uniform he had with him.

Over a month later, at Ingolstadt, I was punished with six days' confinement—the price of my first escape, which, after all, was not too dear.

I might perhaps have escaped from the train while I was being taken to Ingolstadt, but I was still too weak to make the attempt. Furthermore, I no longer had a uniform, a map or a compass. There was nothing for it but to wait for a more favourable opportunity, spend the winter in getting back my strength and have another try in the spring.

. . . . .

Prince Karl Fortress of Ingolstadt was one of the best guarded in the whole of Germany, especially since the escape of two officers from there the year before. The fortress, surrounded by a moat six yards deep, was watched in the daytime by sentries placed high up on the parapet, so that nothing escaped their notice. At night they were reinforced, sentries being placed in the moat itself; there were no less than eighteen guardians.

I began to collect kit. I got it in innumerable ways. Some came in parcels from home, concealed in tins and false bottoms of boxes. Some was brought by orderlies who did our shopping, or from the German sentries, as some of these were ready to sell anything for a little ready cash.

There was a Lieutenant Sombsthay in the fortress, and we soon combined on the same lines. Together we watched the details of the fortifications and the barbed wire and the routine of the garrison and sentries. We studied and worked at German until I began to get some knowledge of the language, as there were several prisoners in the fortress who knew it well. It was all a weary, slow business which took months of patient work and the constant danger of being suspected and found out.

Luck came to our aid. During the last days of March a part of the outside retaining wall of the moat collapsed through heavy rain. That gave a good enough excuse for wandering about in the moat, provided one was able to take on the aspect of a labourer—though the orders were to fire on any prisoner found there, without even challenging. The Germans themselves were not allowed access to it, unless they were accompanied by one of the soldiers on permanent duty at the fortress.

We worked out a plan and this was what we proposed to do. Lieutenant Sombsthay and myself would disguise ourselves as masons, putting on voluminous overalls, under which we could hide our provisions. A Russian lieutenant, de Medem, who spoke perfect German, was to go with us, playing the part of escort. We had stolen out of a floor a number of planks and with the sweat of hours made them into some sort of a ladder. We had also constructed what looked like a carpenter's rule and plumb-line.

Our scheme was that we should, escorted by de Medem, pretend to be busy taking measurements for repairs to the moat, and bit by bit we would edge along until we could put up our ladder and continue to work on the outer wall. De Medem, the fake Landsturm, was to follow us closely, and inspect our efforts with a critical eye. Then, strolling carelessly, we would come to where there was a blind angle of the wall, and from there we would be able to reach the open country. All that troubled us was the danger in leaving the barracks to go to the moat, of meeting one of the Germans of the permanent garrison, all of whom knew the prisoners by sight.

Three days after having thought out our plan we put it to the proof. At four o'clock in the afternoon we were ready, and went out into the corridor with our ladder and our tools, when a French orderly, who was in our confidence, came and warned us that the German quartermaster was going to distribute wood in the court in about two minutes. We had to rush back again and resign ourselves to waiting. At half-past four the way seemed clear, and Lieutenant Sombsthay went out first, carrying his half of the ladder. I followed him with the other half ; but all of a sudden we heard a great to-do in the corridor, and " Halt ! Halt ! " was roared after us. We were taken.

This is what had happened. Next to our room was the French orderlies' dormitory, and a German non-com., need-ing a man for fatigue duty, had turned up there unexpectedly, too suddenly for us to be warned in time. He had seen Sombsthay with his ladder, and had at once tumbled to the situation, and through the half-open door he had seen de Medem and myself in our disguises.

Sombsthay came flying back, followed by the guard, who ran to the window, calling for help as though he were being murdered. We, in the meantime, undressed in frantic haste, trying to save our " props," and above all to get rid of de Medem's German uniform, which might cause some un-pleasantness for us if found.

As the guard did not at once come to his cries, the non-com. left the room in search of support and assistance.

We immediately took advantage of his absence to throw the German uniform—made with what loving care and trouble !—into the stove.

Presently a captain came, with the guard. We were all three searched, but we managed to save a good deal of our material, and nothing was ever said about de Medem's uniform.

The retail price of that escapade was as follows : forty-two days' confinement for myself, thirty for Sombsthay, and ten for de Medem. Why these three different systems of weights and measures I never discovered.

When I had done my term I was sent back to the Prince Karl ; that was on the 26th September, but my days locked away alone had given me time to think out a new plan, and I began to prepare.

Every day a fatigue-party of two French soldiers went from the fortress to the neighbouring village for milk. In summer this fact could not be of much use to me ; but autumn was approaching, and perhaps with the early night-fall I might be able to turn it to my own ends. It was a question of coming to an understanding with one of the two soldiers that I should go to the village in his place, and once outside the camp, take advantage of the early darkness to make full steam ahead for the open sea. But, alas ! I had barely returned to the fortress when another officer made use of that very plan, and succeeded in reaching Switzerland after crossing Lake Constance in a rowing-boat. His success did something to assuage my disappointment, but, neverthe-less, I had to start plotting all over again. Why not organise a fake fatigue-party, composed of two French officers dis-guised as the orderlies and a third disguised as a German? For since Henrion's escape a German soldier always accom-panied the party.

The three of us would, at the regulation hour, take to ourselves the milk-cans set out before the kitchen door, and thus armed simply walk out of the gate of the fortress. The two genuine orderlies of the fatigue-party would, in con-nivance with us, arrive for duty a few minutes late. The trick would be turned by that time, and we would be outside before the alarm was given.

We constructed all the " props " with laborious care—the orderlies' uniforms, the uniform of the German guard on escort, a wooden rifle—when, just as all was ready on the 4th November, I was told by the commanding officer of the fortress that I was to be sent on the next day to Fort IX, a special home for habitual runaways—in consideration of my attempt of the 31st March. That made it look as if this little escapade was to be a failure too ! So, with my friends Lieutenants Bonzon and Schuler, I decided to have a try for it that very night. I went to warn the orderlies, but dis-covered to my intense sorrow that, since the evening before, the fatigue-party was composed only of German soldiers. Our little stratagem deserved a better fate !

. . . . . .

The next day I was sent off under armed escort to Fort IX. It resembled the Prince Karl, but with the aggravating circumstance that the moat was full of water. This moat was no more than twelve yards wide in front of the bastion of the fort, but a net of barbed wire was submerged in the water, and surmounted by little bells that rang at the slightest contact, making escape by swimming impossible from that side of the fort, while on the other sides the stretch of water was from forty to fifty metres wide.

I was soon able to discover that the fort was not guarded so severely as the Prince Karl had been. If I could obtain the silence of one of the chain of sentries that surrounded it, the attempt, though still dangerous, might have some chance of success. I worked on the idea for weeks, patiently, for the least indiscretion might lead to betrayal and court-martial. At last I managed to bribe a sentry.

Early in December the weather became very cold and it began to freeze. The ice on the moat became a solid floor which it would be possible to creep across, starting from the post of the bribed sentry and draped in white sheets. But the sentry must be at the favourable point. This had been chosen by myself and Lieutenant Leireau, of the 10th Chasseurs, who had agreed to accompany me.

On the 23rd December our sentry was at the correct place. At eleven o'clock at night some Russian accomplices of ours started to saw through the bars of the wash-room window that gave on to the ice. Opposite it the sentry was as deaf as a post ; but unfortunately his two companions were not so afflicted. They heard and called on their comrade to investigate. He refused. At that moment we were squeezing and squirming our way through the sawn bars. The other two sentries rushed up with fixed bayonets. I was already half out of the window, with my shoulders through and my legs inside. Luckily the night was pitch dark, and though they were within a few feet of me and just below me the sentries could not see me. I could hear them fumbling the bolts ready to fire, but I was able, inch by inch, to draw back and drop back into the room without being identified and with our material intact. Our friendly sentry obtained the silence of his colleagues by threats of some sort, and promised to help us again at the first opportune moment. But unfortunately the guard of the fort was relieved a few days later, and our assistant went with them.

Then the idea came to me of simply walking out of the door, an idea that may sound grotesque, but that, in reality, had some chances of success. There were three successive doors, each guarded by a sentry. Theoretically the password should be given to each of them by anybody going out, but

I had noticed that in practice the permanent staff of the fort when they went out at about seven o'clock in the evening, at dusk, scarcely ever bothered to give the word to the first sentry. As for the third, he was posted in the exterior courtyard of the fort, on the other side of the moat, and could be avoided by scaling the outside wall instead of passing through the door.

I made myself a German private's uniform—the third—for during the last search of the fort two complete outfits of mine had been found and destroyed. I made a round cap without a visor, out of grey canvas cut from a Tirolean knapsack and a piece of red French uniform cloth. The cockades I cut out of pieces of an empty tin and painted them with oil-colours. As for the overcoat, I managed to get hold of an old discarded one that had been given to an orderly. A pair of navy-blue trousers completed the outfit.

At seven o'clock on the 2nd February 1918 I made the venture. I presented myself before the first door, while a group of French officers in the corridor behind me quarrelled loudly to distract the sentry's attention. The precaution was an unfortunate one, for after I had passed the sentry the man, realising that he had not seen who I was, reopened the door and called after me. I turned round and answered in a surprised voice, " *Was*? *Was*? "

The trick worked and the man shut the door again ; but the next sentry, hearing the first one challenge, had already taken up his rifle and came forward with his bayonet ready for business. It was a critical moment, but risking everything, I called out, " The man is a fool, a complete fool ! " and went calmly on my way. Miracle ! My words seemed completely to reassure the man, and he slung his rifle over his shoulder again. So as to allow him no time for meditation I opened the gate myself ; but the man, smitten with a sudden sense of duty, demanded the password. I muttered something or other between my teeth, and he let me pass. There was still the wall to be climbed. I walked hurriedly in the direction of the guard-house as though I had some order to give, then of a sudden I flung myself at the wall, moving so rapidly that the third sentry had no time to open fire.

The sentries on the far side of the moat, and whose beats were close under the wall and to the left, did not see me. I was over the wall in double quick time and racing for the open country. Behind me I heard the alarm given, the clanging of bells, whistles, shouts, the sound of the guard turning out and men running. The patrols were out after me, but in the darkness I got away from them.

I guessed that my escape from Fort IX would be immediately notified by telephone to every railway and police station within a very wide area. I had therefore decided to take the train at Augsburg, which meant that I would have to cover about thirty miles on foot.

I walked all night, hiding in a little wood at dawn. I still had on my German uniform. At about four o'clock in the afternoon a band of children began playing near the copse where I was hidden, so I threw away my military overcoat and left the wood on the far side from them, reappearing as an honest civilian. I decided then to take the bull by the horns and make for Augsburg in full daylight by the main road.

Passing through a village, I came across a band of youngsters playing at soldiers with wooden rifles and swords. Horror on my part, children often being far more suspicious than their elders. I thought it might be more imprudent to turn back than to go boldly on ; and as I passed the little group the youngster who was taking the part of commanding officer lined up his troop and ordered them to pay me military honours as I went by. Had they only known that their solemn salute was addressed to an escaped French prisoner ! I gave them a bright and cheerful " Good-day " and went on my way rejoicing.

I reached Augsburg at nine o'clock in the evening, and found that there was no train for Ulm until the next morning. I wandered about the streets, resting in dark corners or empty fields. It was freezing. I was exhausted after my miles of forced marching, and had had nothing but a few biscuits and a piece of chocolate to eat. The hours seemed centuries long.

At last the train arrived and I took it as far as Memmingen, where I arrived at ten o'clock in the morning. There I had to wait until two in the afternoon for another to take me to Ulm. I got to my destination at five, and walked about until twenty to eight, when I took a train for Sigmaringen, situated at about thirty-five miles from the Swiss frontier. I arrived at midnight and set out at once on foot.

I no longer felt tired and walked quickly—perhaps too quickly—through the fog. The evening before, in my haste to get out of the copse where the children had disturbed me, I had thrown away my military overcoat, completely forgetting that my electric torch was in the pocket of it, so I could neither consult my map nor the signposts along the way. Trusting to my memory I pushed on, and came to the outskirts of a village where was a bridge that I knew to be guarded. But I was under the impression that a good distance separated the bridge-head from the last houses of the village, whereas, in fact, it gave directly on the orchards surrounding the place, and the road leading to it was bordered on either side with enclosed gardens, making it extremely dangerous. It was in fact a veritable rat-trap I had walked into.

Suddenly the figure of a man loomed up in front of me out of the fog. I thought at first it was only somebody out for a stroll, but the point of a bayonet presented at my stomach enlightened me. The soldier at once gave the alarm, while a second sentry barred the way behind me. There was nothing to be done about it.

I was questioned at the guard-house of the frontier, and stated that I was a Swiss civilian working in Germany, and that I had lost my passport and had nothing but Swiss papers on me. These I exhibited. They were false papers that my sister had procured for me in the name of Antoine Lang, professor of drawing at Fribourg. The officer of the guard was uncertain and almost convinced, but at last he decided to wait for morning before he came to a decision.

At eight o'clock he sent me, escorted by the sentry who had caught me, to the company commander of Möhringen, where we arrived at noon. After another interrogation it was decided to take me before the officer in command of the frontier at Constance.

When we changed train at Singen, within four miles of the Swiss frontier, I tried to escape by pretending a visit to the lavatories ; but one of my guardians, not having complete faith in me, put his foot in the door to prevent my closing it. Hopeless ! We arrived at Constance at about nine o'clock, and I passed the night in the guard-house of the lake patrol.

In the morning I was questioned by three guards simultaneously, who left nothing to chance. They stripped me, and searched me thoroughly, and in so doing they discovered a thing which had so far passed unnoticed. My hat was made over a straw foundation, covered with a piece of grey woollen blanket. They tore off the covering and disclosed underneath it its foundation of the only too well-known coarse straw of a hat such as was supplied to prisoners. They also discovered the narrow red stripes down the seams of my regimental trousers. I was completely unmasked. It was useless to protest further, so I told a part at least of the truth. I admitted being French, but declared that I was a non-commissioned officer, the Adjutant-Pilot Reservat, whom I knew to have escaped some weeks earlier. I refused to say to what camp I belonged, so as to avoid an interview with the commandant. I knew very well that my lie would not serve me very long, but I tried at all costs to gain time, and the essential was to avoid being sent back to Fort IX, and in the meantime I might yet manage to get away again.

My efforts met with little success. Sent to the civilian prison of Constance under the name of Reservat, I was forced on the next day to admit my true identity, as the guards of the frontier had in the meantime received all particulars about me from Ingolstadt. And at the end of four days, under the escort of a *Feldwebel* and a soldier, I took my melancholy way back to Fort IX. There I managed to get sent to hospital, but found that while I could get in I could not for all my efforts get out. A little later I was sent to Strassburg—not in Alsace, but in Eastern Prussia—on the frontier of Poland. I arrived there, after three days of travel, on the 28th April.

On the 2nd May I had another little holiday—eighteen days' confinement in cells for my little escapade on the Swiss frontier. But during the preceding two days I had had time to get into touch with the officers of the camp who were interested in the sport of escaping, particularly with Lieutenant-Observer Blehaut.

. . . . .

On leaving my cell, Captain Atgers informed me that he and several other prisoners were at work on a tunnel ; and in view of my own modest record as a runaway he invited me to join the group and collaborate in its labours in the capacity of outpost, the working-parties being already fully organised.

The tunnel started in a room used for Protestant services. The trap-door had been cut with such skill that, once in place, it was impossible to detect it ; and for greater security it had been covered over with a carpet. Work was carried on with the trap-door closed, and above it was placed a table at which sat an officer piously reading the Bible, but holding himself in readiness to signal by tapping with his foot on the floor in case of danger. It is easy to imagine how unpleasant life in the tunnel was. Every ten or twelve minutes the air in it had to be renewed by means of a little ventilator, made by the prisoners out of pieces of wood.

It is easy to imagine how unpleasant the tunnel was.

In the afternoon of the 5th June 1918 it became evident that we would be able to " uncork " our tunnel that very night. We were in a state of nervous strain—especially as in spite of all our efforts to keep the thing secret an ever-increasing number of prisoners got wind of it. One slip, one imprudence would be enough. The number of participants was also pretty high, Captain Atgers having authorised twenty-two officers to try their luck with him.

We could do nothing before eleven o'clock at night, and we were afraid that not all of us would be able to make the trip undetected across the deserted courtyard to the room where our tunnel began. On the other hand, we could not leave our room too early because of the frequent roll-calls —and twenty-two empty beds could not fail to arouse comment ! There was another danger too ; because of the risk of denunciation we had had to hasten our work and make the exit of our tunnel immediately outside the wall of the camp, in a brightly lighted spot in plain view of a sentry. My chosen companion of the road, Lieutenant Blehaut, and I received the numbers 11 and 12.

By half-past midnight the first ten had passed safely and five minutes later Blehaut and I were outside in our turn.

Blehaut had managed, through the intermediary of a German, to get into touch with a fisherman of Danzig, who was also a smuggler, and who had consented to take us in his boat to Sweden. This was an unusual route, but the great distance to the Dutch frontier made escape by that way more than doubtful.

Realising that such a wholesale escape would put the Germans on their mettle, and that they would move heaven and earth to catch us, we had decided to make the first part of our journey on foot, until we were outside the danger zone, travelling by night, and through the less populous regions. It was June, the nights were short, only four hours being dark enough for safety ; the other twenty, when we had to lie hidden, seemed interminable. Although we walked rapidly, we could scarcely do more than twelve or thirteen miles a night.

On the third night we ran into the village of Saint Pietrowicz, a mile and a half to the north of Bischofwerder. The place was surrounded by marshes, making it impossible to skirt round it, and day was coming. So we let all our good resolutions of prudence go to the winds, and with a common accord we started boldly down the main street. Surely, for once, we might hope to have a little luck ! We crossed the whole village without trouble ; but, alas ! from the very last house on our left the cry of " Halt ! " rang out.

We were pinched.

Blehaut had always declared that if such a contingency as the present one should arise he would parley with our agressors, or try to occupy their attention in some manner or other, in order to gain a few seconds of time so that I myself might make good my escape. He argued that, as I had been longer in prison than he, I should have the first chance of escaping ; and now he proceeded to make good his extraordinarily generous offer.

At the order of " Halt ! " he turned to the left and walked towards the two soldiers, whom we could dimly see in the darkness. As for myself I took to my heels. Almost immediately a dog was snapping at my heels, but I kept on going. Again came the cry, " Halt ! Halt, or I fire ! " A shot rang out and then another.

I left the road and ran into what I thought was a field of barley, but my eyes had deceived me in the darkness, and I found myself on a naked plain that offered not the slightest cover. The dog had its teeth well fixed in the calf of my leg. I struck at it and it let go, but immediately returned to the attack. I shook it off a second and a third time ; but in the meantime I was unable to run. The soldier, the dog's master, was within three yards of me now, and he levelled his rifle at me. In another minute he would fire. I tried to argue with him, so that I could profit by a moment's inattention to make off again. But the man knew his business and refused to lower his rifle, while I still refused to surrender. He was obviously as afraid of me as I was of him ; he kept shouting to me to keep my distance, and was visibly itching to open fire. The scene had its humorous side. He quieted down at last and, threatening me with his bayonet, made me walk back down the road where Lieutenant Blehaut and the other sentry were waiting for us.

We told them we were French officers, whereupon they proceeded to march us off to Bischofwerder, jabbing us from time to time with their bayonets in order to discourage any idea of flight on the way. We arrived at Bischofwerder escorted by our two sentries and the dog, where we were far more pleasantly received by the *Feldwebel* in charge of the prison. Then, having been told all the gruesome details of our probable fate, we were thrust into the lock-up to await the next day. At noon we were taken out, under the escort of the two soldiers of the night before, and one of them found it good to make Blehaut carry for him a huge bundle of smuggled foodstuffs that he had obtained by illicit means for his own personal and private consumption !

Towards the evening we reached the camp of Preussich Holland, between Elbing and Königsberg. On the way we were able to ascertain the formidable impression that had been produced on the neighbourhood by the excessive number of prisoners who had escaped by the tunnel. All the police stations, all the military posts, all the guards of the region had been called up, troops of cavalry and bicycle units patrolled unceasingly, while aeroplanes flew low down over the fields of growing crops. One of these had flown directly over us without seeing us.

．　　　．　　　．　　　．　　　．

The camp of Preussich Holland was composed of wooden barracks built about two courtyards, of which one was for Russian and French soldiers, the other housing some fifteen hundred Russian officers, taken, for the most part, after the Treaty of Brest-Litovsk, when they were already demobilised.

As soon as we arrived we set about looking for a way to get out. On the next day we decided to try our luck, with the help of some Russian officers. At about midday I called to the guard on duty and asked him to take me to the lavatories, the windows of which were not barred. I easily slid out, and let myself drop to the ground three yards below. Then, slipping through the wire fence that divided the camp, I made for the block of barracks that the Russian officers had pointed out to me. There I rapidly exchanged my civilian clothes for a Russian officer's uniform, and was then taken to another barracks, where my costume was again changed. I went from barracks to barracks, so as to spoil the scent as well as possible. Finally, I was put into a sort of box hollowed out under the planks of the flooring. My protectors gave me an overcoat to protect me against the damp, a little food, and then shut down the lid on me, telling me not to move on any pretext.

Very soon I heard a noise in the distance, orders shouted in German, the sound of running footsteps ; the alarm was given and the search begun. Then I heard dogs running back and forth over the very place where I was hidden. I was not reassured ! But nothing was discovered, and soon quiet reigned once more.

A Russian officer lifted the lid of my box. " All is well ! " he said, and shut me into the darkness again.

I stayed there thirty hours ; then I was taken out and put for greater safety into another hiding-place.

What my jailers had not been able to find by searching they tried to discover by strategy. The Russians were in desperate want of food. Because of the internal condition of their country they received no packages from home, and their rations in the camp consisted of black bread and a little barley soup. Two weeks' double rations and three big loaves of bread were promised to any Russian giving information leading to my arrest. Fearing that one of their starving soldiers might fall to so great a temptation and give me up, the Russian officers redoubled their precautions, choosing the most unusual and astonishing hiding-places for me.

But how was I to get out of the camp? The exterior guards had been doubled since my disappearance, and I would have to wait until the memory of it had somewhat dimmed. The date at which I was to join the boat at Danzig was still some way off, and I could afford to wait a little. So I stayed in hiding, guarded with the most admirable faithfulness by my Russian friends. The game was carried on for eleven days. Sometimes, to go from one hiding-place to another, I crossed the whole camp, but always disguised. One day I met the German commandant himself, and saluted him politely, without being recognised.

On the eleventh day I was ready to try to cross the barbed wire, accompanied by a Cossack captain and another officer ; but the guard was too wideawake that night, and we had to put off our attempt until the next night. I slept in the Cossack's room. In the morning two orderlies saw me there, and one of them, doubtless tempted beyond his strength by the thought of the double rations, denounced me. I was sitting at noon in the same barrack-room, sharing the more than modest pittance of my friends, when a German officer came in, with an interpreter. After a few minutes of seeming indifference, he asked several of the Russian officers their names ; then turning to me, he said, " And what is your name ? "

" Skoloff," I said.

" Skoloff ? Curious ! I don't know of any Skoloff here."

Then he made the interpreter question my unhappy self in Russian, and I did my best to answer in the same language, saying " I don't understand."

Then I turned to the German officer and said, " I don't know where your interpreter learned his Russian, but he speaks it extraordinarily badly ; he is quite unintelligible. Tell him to speak to me in German, will you ? "

My ruse did not succeed very brilliantly. The officer had not the slightest doubt as to who I was, and took me to the prison of the camp, where I was thoroughly searched—happily without result !

As I still insisted that I was called Skoloff, my accuser sent for another officer, the one who had received me when I entered the camp, and who recognised me at once.

Further denial seemed to be useless. So that I should not escape them again, the Germans took me out of the camp and shut me up in an exterior barracks, in which was quartered a guard of eighty men. On the next day I was taken back to the camp of Strassburg-Ostpreussen.

I left at four o'clock, wearing only a thin sweater and a pair of pants, my Russian outfit having been confiscated, and I arrived at seven in the evening, worn out and shivering with cold, although the month was June. I was questioned again, and told that as the cells were all occupied I was to spend the night in the guard-house. There was good reasons for the cells being overcrowded, since of the twenty-two officers who had escaped on the 5th June all had been retaken, with the exception of Captain Atgers and a Belgian lieutenant, Damery, who had succeeded in reaching the frontier.

After spending twenty-one hours in the guard-house I was put in a cell. I only remained there a week, for on the 30th June all the twenty of us who had been retaken were sent together to the camp of Strohen (Hanover). Having no civilian clothing, maps or German money, I could not try to escape on the way.

As soon as I reached Strohen, on the 2nd July, I set about laying in a new civilian wardrobe. Lieutenant Bruno cut out a jacket for me from a blue overcoat, and for several weeks I became a dressmaker, plying my needle industriously. Then came twenty-three days of cells, that I still owed for my previous misbehaviour.

During this time my crowd from Strassburg, reinforced by a few other friends, had started to dig two tunnels. Captain Duval, who had escaped from Maubeuge in 1914, and who, since his recapture, had added four more attempts to his list, was in charge of one of the tunnels. He kept a place open for me in his working-party until I should come out of prison on the 2nd August.

But the suspicions of the Germans had been aroused ; and on the very morning of my release they began digging a deep trench around the whole camp, on the outside of the barbed wire—the classical method for detecting tunnels. By eleven o'clock both the tunnels had been unearthed. In the afternoon Captain Duval and Lieutenant Gueringer crawled along one of the tunnels, and, taking advantage of a moment's inattention on the part of the sentry, bolted like rabbits under his very nose, through the hole the Germans themselves had made in breaking through. Both made a good getaway, but unfortunately Captain Duval was retaken.

On the 19th August almost all the officers of the camp of Strohen were taken by rail to the camp of Burg. I did my best to escape on the way, but we were too closely watched. But on arriving at Burg I managed to smuggle all my escaper's outfit in with me.

The camp at Burg had a double enclosure, two barbed-wire fences with a ditch between them. At night the place was a blaze of electric light. Around the camp on the outside were posted twenty-four sentries, and on the inside a patrol with dogs watched all night. It was a saying throughout all the prison camps of Germany, " Nobody ever escapes from Burg " ; and experience had justified the saying.

I would have to do some careful planning. Fortunately chance showed me a way almost at once. Bringing all my hard-won personal experience into play, I inspected the organisation of the place minutely, and in so doing I discovered that the rubbish of the place was taken out in a two-horse cart, escorted by the driver and two men with shovels, and watched by an armed guard from the moment of its arrival until its departure. For several days I followed the cart back and forth about the camp. One day I happened to look closely at one of the civilian workmen who came with it, and he gave me a quick smile. I replied to him and signed to him to try to come and speak to me. A little later he complained of a violent stomach-ache to the sentry, who was foolish enough to let him go. I at once joined him and spoke to him in German. I learned in a few hasty sentences that he was an old Polish soldier who had been wounded in the knee, evacuated, and was now a civilian prisoner. Risking everything, I proposed to him to hide me in the garbage-cart, which was emptied, unguarded, in a field at some distance from the camp. I gave my Pole a few biscuits, and promised him a hundred marks if I were successful.

But the thing was not so easy as all that. The cart entered the camp, emptied a first dust-bin placed in a court that was infested with Germans, and then a second placed near a sentry-box—with a sentry in it. After that it left the camp.

My first care was to make myself a kind of dust-cover, to protect my precious civilian clothes from the dirt, and to prepare a week-end bag small enough to allow me to jump easily into the cart with it, should we be able to distract the sentry's attention. I had to find a hiding-place at both the places where the cart stopped to load, so that I could change my clothes at a moment's notice. I chose the entry of the corridor leading to the prisoners' theatre, which was within ten yards of the first stopping-place, and for the second the room of a barracks that was very close by.

The cart came at very irregular intervals, so that I had to be incessantly on the watch, and keep all my materials always under my clothing. The constant strain did my nerves no good.

At last, at ten o'clock in the morning on the 3rd September, my chance came. The cart was loading up at its first port of call, and the sentry left it for a few minutes. I leaped out of my uniform and got ready ; and although there were several Germans in the neighbourhood nobody saw me.

I found a lot of cut grass in the cart, and wrapped it about my head and shoulders as well as I could, so as to protect myself from the garbage. The two Poles who were loading the cart covered me up conscientiously, and little by little the pile of cinders, stones, broken china and other rubbish rose above me in a reassuring but nauseating fashion. I managed to keep an air-hole open, so that while my legs were crushed under an ever-increasing weight, my head was fairly free and I could breathe a bit. At last the work was finished, the cart loaded, and ready to drive away as soon as the horses were brought back and harnessed to.

Alas for the best laid plan of this man ! For the very first time the horses were not immediately forthcoming. The Poles and the sentry went away. Then I heard nothing, except the footsteps of some of my fellow-prisoners strolling about the court, all unaware of my presence. The horses must be in use elsewhere, but for how long ? I must hang on as long as possible, but the position was not an agreeable one.

An hour passed, bearable but unpleasant. But little by little the crushing weight on my legs became unbearable. Lieutenant Blehaut, who had been with me since Strassburg, and was the only man I had taken into my confidence, strolled by from time to time to ask me if I was still all right. Towards noon, I had to tell him to fetch an orderly we could trust, and ask him to climb up on the cart as though he were working there and try to ease my position for me. A soldier, David, agreed to do this, although he risked a long term of imprisonment if he should be caught trying to help me. But he saw immediately that he could not do anything for me without at least partially emptying the cart. He nevertheless tried his best to shift the weight off me a little, but the result was not what I had hoped, for when the released blood began to circulate again through my crushed legs the pain was so great that I was afraid I should faint if I had to stay there. I told David to fetch two or three friends and openly unload the cart, without trying to conceal their activities. If any German questioned them they were to say that they had lost some money in the garbage and were looking for it.

I only took this decision when it became quite obvious that I could not stay in the cart much longer without being suffocated, and that all that was left to do was to try to get out of it without being seen. I was anxious to do this not to avoid a few days in the cells—I was well hardened to that, having already passed one hundred and four days there—but in order to save my civilian clothing, my maps and money, and so be in a position to have another try for it at the first opportunity. But it seemed nearly impossible that such a delicate operation could be carried out unnoticed in the middle of a crowded courtyard. And indeed it was not possible, for no sooner had the three orderlies set to work to unbury me than a German came up and asked them what they were doing. David answered as I had told him, and the man accepted his explanation and went away.

As for myself, it was high time that I was disinterred, for the pain had become so intense that I was afraid of betraying myself by crying out. My rescuers worked as fast as they could, but there was a thickness of over a yard of debris over me and it took time to move it all.

A second German soldier came and demanded explanations. He was not so easily satisfied as the first, but in the end he went away. Then the camp gatekeeper himself came up, and reprimanded the orderlies sharply, but they kept their heads and repeated their little story for the third time. But this time the tailboard of the cart had been taken out, and the German came to have a look inside. The whole upper part of my body and my head had already been dug out, and were in consequence perfectly visible. I kept rigidly still, waiting to see what would happen, and sure that I was discovered. I could see the German, and he could see me perfectly well, but I was so thoroughly camouflaged with garbage that he did not identify me as being a human being. He went away as he had come, instructing the orderlies to leave everything tidy when they had finished.

And now came the most difficult part of all : to slip out of the cart and get unseen into the barracks opposite. It was only ten yards distant, but ten yards is a long way to go without attracting attention when one is a walking garbage-heap. I slid to the end of the cart, waiting for the signal to go. When it came I found that my legs were so paralysed that I had great difficulty in getting on to my feet, but nevertheless I succeeded in reaching my destination, where my friends took care of me and helped me to undress. It took a thorough scraping to make me look like a human being again.

As I had not been caught red-handed there was no reason why I should not try the same trick again, provided the suspicions of the Germans had not been aroused. But in any case I would have to wait a bit, and in the meantime I tried to get into the good graces of a sentry, and continued to observe the comings and goings of the garbage-cart. After my last attempt the cart had not left the camp all night ; so I would have to lay my plans more carefully in the future. During the whole of September and October I waited for my opportunity.

I decided, in agreement with my two Poles, that, instead of getting into the cart while it was being filled, they should arrange the load in such a fashion as to leave an empty space at the end of it for me, and as soon as I was in they would throw a pile of old newspapers over me, so that I would be hidden without being crushed. But unforeseen circumstances put a stop to this plan.

But, nevertheless, I clung to my determination to escape in some way or other ; the idea was never for an instant out of my head. But yet, after two years of constant efforts, I felt that my nerves would not stand much more, and my physical strength was giving out too. I had no idea that the war was nearly over, and I began to ask myself if I could carry on much longer. I felt that I must succeed at once or not at all.

The idea became such an obsession with me that I am sure my friends began to think that I had lost my mind. I realised then, and I realise now, that I behaved as though I had.

At last, at three in the afternoon of the 27th October, the propitious moment seemed to have arrived. The cart was picking up its second load before the barracks ; the sentry, in his box, seemed to be a bit absent-minded, and I saw the two horses being brought back to be harnessed to their load. I came down from my observation-post, and took off my uniform that I was wearing over my " escaping-clothes." I jumped into the cart and crouched down, my heart beating a tattoo against my ribs. Ten minutes passed and then one of my friends whispered to me, " No luck ! The horses have just been harnessed to another cart and are being taken away."

I swore savagely but silently. Curse the luck ! But perhaps the horses would come back. Hadn't I better hold on a bit ? I waited, while dust-bin after dust-bin was emptied over me. Night came and the horses had not been brought back. So, with the help of Lieutenant Blehaut, I reluctantly left my chariot. I was again lucky enough to escape being seen ; but I had failed once more, and even my good fortune in not being caught could not deaden my disappointment.

. . . . .

I then turned all my attentions towards another plan that I had been meditating for the past month. It was a fairly risky one, entailing the climbing of the enclosure, and since the beginning of the war, out of the constant population of seven hundred officers and three hundred men that were confined at Burg, only three, a Belgian, and two Russians, had succeeded in climbing the enclosure, and of these one Russian was killed while making the attempt, the other wounded, and the Belgian taken by the sentry.

There were two enclosures around the camp, separated by a ditch. During the first days I had noticed that this ditch, intended to be an obstacle to flight, might be turned into an aid. It was divided at regular intervals by walls of earth, perpendicular to the ditch itself, and reaching to the same height as its banks. These walls had been obtained by leaving pieces of ground a yard broad untouched while digging the ditch, which in consequence presented the appearance of a series of basins about a yard and a half deep six long and three wide, so that a man lying on his stomach in one of them would be invisible to the sentry on the far side of the second enclosure, which, like the first, was composed of a meshwork of barbed wire. Each mesh formed a rectangle six and a half inches by seventeen and a half, barely enough to allow the passage of a human body. But I had the idea of enlarging the meshes by straining apart the strands of wire and fixing them by means of iron hooks to the strands immediately above and below. These I could remove after I had passed through the first enclosure and use again on the second. A friend of mine—a clever worker in iron—made them for me. But there was still another important detail to be overcome : the lower strand of wire would have to support the whole weight of my body while I was crawling through, and in consequence its spikes would dig into me and tear my precious civilian clothes to ribbons. The remedy for this was not far to seek : a blanket, folded in eight, would make a cushion thick enough to protect me from more than superficial scratches.

Then there still remained the question of my costume. On the one hand, the brilliant electric lighting demanded neutral-coloured garments, as much the same tone as the ground as possible ; and on the other, if I wore my " escaping-clothes," I would risk tearing them so badly, in spite of my blanket, as to make them unwearable. So out of an old pair of Russian soldier's trousers and a sweater, I made a sort of dirt-coloured overall, and wrapped my civilian clothes in a package of the same colour, small enough to pass easily between the meshes of barbed wire.

I was ready. The only thing that remained was to try to obtain the neutrality of a sentry. This caused me long and difficult negotiations, on the details of which I need not linger here. In my case, by the 27th October, the day of my escape, I was fairly certain that out of the three sentries who guarded the side of the camp, about one hundred and fifty yards long, from which I intended to leave, one at least would be less dangerous to me than the rest. But there still remained the other two. My task then was to crawl through two barbed-wire fences in a full blaze of light, and within seventy-five yards of a sentry. Actually I passed much closer.

I asked two trustworthy friends of mine, Lieutenants Levavasseur and Blehaut—always he !—to help me through the first fence, pushing me by the legs, while two others removed the iron hooks behind me. A Belgian, Lieutenant Houdemont, agreed to keep watch.

At six o'clock in the evening I started watching the sentries, waiting for the opportune moment. The time passed slowly. A German officer came by, and I had to snatch away my blanket, already laid across the barbed wire. An hour went by. Then at last the time came. My two friends pushed me through the first barbed-wire fence. At that moment I felt such fear as I had never experienced during my two years at the front, and had I hesitated even for an instant I would never have gone forward. Anybody who has gone through the experience knows what a tremendous effort of the will is required to surmount the terror of that one first critical moment.

Before me the ditch was inundated with light. To the right and left were sentries, so close that I could see the colour of their moustaches. Only the neutral tint of my clothing and my absolute immobility saved me from being spotted at once. As soon as the two guards turned their backs I let myself slide to the bottom of one of the basins of the ditch. Outside nothing stirred. I crawled carefully up the farther side of the basin and looked cautiously out. Everything was all right. I crouched against the second barbed-wire fence, making myself as small as possible, while I put my iron hooks into place. Then I laid my blanket over the lower strand of barbed wire and crawled through, but not without tearing myself badly, as the meshes of the second fence were smaller than those of the first. It was fortunate that I had my " escaping-costume " in a bag instead of on my back !

I was through ! Before me was the sentries' beat, and beyond that nothing but fields and the welcome darkness. Crouched against the fence, but on the outside this time, I watched the movements of the sentries. Then, when the moment came, I leaped to my feet and dashed across the path of their beat. I was away and unseen, and I had some reason to congratulate myself, for the escape had succeeded beyond my wildest hopes—the first of its kind to be made from the camp of Burg.

Knowing that the alarm might be given immediately— although in fact it was not—I started off at once on foot for the station of Magdeburg, twenty miles distant.

After going a few miles I stopped in a little wood near the railway line and changed my torn clothes for my

real " escaping-costume," a navy blue suit and a green
hat.

I walked across the fields for about an hour, managing
in the meantime to stumble into a muddy stream that I had
not seen in the darkness. That accident worried me all
night, and it was only at daybreak that I was able to assure
myself that my trousers had not suffered too greatly from
their bath. Had they been too badly soiled it would have
been impossible to take the train.

I arrived at Magdeburg at about midnight and made
straight for the station. I had no map of the town and asked
my way of two women. When I reached it, it was to find
that there was no train in the direction I wanted before five
in the morning, so all the rest of the night I wandered about
the streets of the town.

At five o'clock I took a fourth-class ticket for Brunswick.
I had no trouble, and reached my destination at eight. There
I went into the lavatories for a clean-up, under the watchful
gaze of the good lady in charge of the place. I hurried as
much as I could, and then took refuge in a huge public
garden, fortunately nearly deserted, where I was able to sew
in a sleeve of my coat that was nearly torn out. At noon
I took another train for Hanover, where I arrived at four
o'clock, and a quarter of an hour later I left for Dusseldorf.

So far everything had gone smoothly, but from now on
life was to be a little more exciting. At about six o'clock
a young man got into my carriage and asked me a question
that I didn't understand. I answered as unpleasantly as I
could, " I don't know." The man looked at me in astonishment and repeated his question. I gave him the same
answer, as rudely as I knew how. He did not insist and
addressed himself to another traveller. I waited a few
minutes, and then, taking advantage of a stop at a station,
I got out and found a carriage at the other end of the train,
in which the lights were out of order.

But I soon heard a fellow-passenger move in the darkness,
and he too spoke to me. But fortunately this time I understood what was said to me. He asked for a match, which
I gave him. But that did not stop the flow of his conversation,
and in a short time he had told me his whole family history.
He was a railway mechanic. I told him I was a draughtsman
in a war-factory, and when he learned that I too was going
to Dusseldorf he was delighted. He was bent on my going
to his hotel with him, and said, " You'll see, we'll be able

to get a good dinner there when we arrive. They know me well, and they'll give us anything we like without bothering about food-cards."

It seemed to be impossible to shake this fellow off. I told him that my family was meeting me at the station, but in vain. When we arrived I rushed headlong into the crowd, calling out to my companion that I could see my relatives, waving wildly in their supposed direction, and at last I managed to lose him.

From half-past eleven at night until four in the morning I wandered about Dusseldorf, waiting for my train for Cologne. I arrived there at six, remained only half an hour, and, at dawn, was on my way to Aix-la-Chapelle, the last stage of my journey, which I reached at nine in the morning.

I walked about the town all the morning, visiting church after church to avoid too curious eyes. Towards noon I took the Promenade of Bellevue in the northern part of Aix. This promenade runs through a fairly large wood, from whence it is possible to see as far as the frontier, about four and a half miles away. There I made out my route for the night. I also ate a few biscuits and some chocolate, the only food I had taken since my escape. Then, going to a view-point on a little hill, I took advantage of my solitude to get out my map and compare it with the country that lay before me. I became much too absorbed in my work, for when I lifted my head I saw a German officer standing within thirty paces of me and watching me with much curiosity.

A critical moment ! Keeping as calm as I could, I looked at him indifferently, and went back to the study of my map ; then, folding it up carelessly and putting it away, I took a German newspaper out of my pocket and began to read it diligently. Presently I got up and began to stroll slowly in the opposite direction to the officer. He followed me. I towed him thus in my wake up and down lonely paths for a quarter of an hour, making numerous twists and turns so as to be able to see if he were still after me without having to look over my shoulder. Alas, he was, and he was becoming really dangerous.

What should I do ? Seeing a clump of bushes I went towards them and managed to hide behind them for a moment, then I grasped the opportunity to make off at top speed through the woods. I had at last managed to lose

my officer, but he might well give the alarm at Aix. Would
it be prudent for me to go back to the town?

I decided to go towards the frontier. Dressed as I was,
and in the daytime, I could move about with but little
danger to within a mile of my dreamed-of goal, while at
night the roads would be well guarded and dangerous.

I followed the road to Richterich for a couple of miles
without mishap. Then I passed a detachment of some thirty
soldiers in field-uniform who had just been relieved from
duty on the frontier. Behind them marched a non-commissioned officer who scrutinised me closely, and I could feel
that he turned to look after me, but I kept on my way.
A little farther along I saw another similar group, standing
at the foot of a viaduct, so, thinking that prudence was the
better part of valour, I turned back in the direction of Aix.
A few minutes later, at a tram halt, I saw the same non-
com. who had previously looked after me with so much
curiosity. I saw that he too recognised me, so I went up
to him boldly and asked him if the tram had already passed.
"About five minutes ago," he answered. "Well," I said,
"it can't be helped. I shall have to go back to Aix on
foot." The man seemed to be quite reassured and let me
go on my way unhindered. I went back as far as the
Western Station then took a road leading to the village of
Seffen.

What with the fine weather the fields were full of peasants
and farmers, who looked with some astonishment at the
well-dressed civilian walking along their little road within
three or four miles of the frontier. Many of them stopped
in their work to stare after me.

The situation was dangerous. In order to quiet their
suspicions, I walked slowly, reading my newspaper and
admiring the countryside, and from time to time sitting
down on a bank or a milestone. Little by little I drew near
to a little wood situated on the hill of Laurensberg, only
a little over half a mile from the frontier. There I hoped
to be able to hide until nightfall.

I was within five hundred yards of it, sitting by the roadside deep in my newspaper, when I heard the galloping of
a horse. The rider was coming towards me at top speed.
Was I taken? The horseman pulled up his mount before
me, and I called to him in my best German, "Good-evening!
Where are you off to in such a hurry?"

He was rather taken aback and looked at me in silence

for a moment, then answered, " I am going to inspect the Russian prisoners working over there."

Obviously he was lying. Without giving him time for reflection I asked, " Are you a farmer of Laurensberg ? "

" Yes."

" For myself, I am taking advantage of the fine weather for a stroll. I live at Aix-la-Chapelle."

Little by little his suspicions fell. We discussed the labour question, and then the German went off, perhaps only half reassured, for he must have found my presence suspicious, but not certain enough to dare to ask to see my papers. I gave a sigh of relief. But were my troubles over ?

I must in some way manage to get into the little wood and hide there. But how ? There were groups of peasants dotted all over the neighbouring fields, and they would be there for some time to come, for it was only four o'clock.

Presently a nun and a little girl came walking from the direction of the village, and when they had come up to me I raised my hat to the nun and remarked on the state of the weather. Then, " Where are you going ? " I asked.

" We are taking some food to a labourer who is working near the woods," she said. What a windfall ! I got up and walked with her to the top of the hill where the peasant was working. Then I told her the same tale I had told the horse-man, adding that I thought I would walk on a little farther. I went and sat for a bit on the outskirts of the wood, and presently went a little way into it to see if the Germans in the neighbourhood would make any objections. I came out after a few minutes, but nobody seemed to bother about me. I sat down again for a little and then went boldly into the wood, where I searched out the densest thicket I could find and, trying to ignore the thorns, lay down inside it. I had only to wait for darkness now. At eight o'clock I put on the neutral-coloured garment that I had worn for my escape from the camp.

.   .   .   .   .

Between myself and the Dutch frontier there was little over half a mile of meadowland, sloping gently towards the north-west. In that zone there was a continuous movement of reliefs and patrols. A cordon of sentries, spaced at intervals of one hundred or one hundred and fifty yards, was placed along a little path a few yards on this side of the frontier. The meadows were bounded on the north by a railway line running east and west, and on the south by a road parallel with the line. There could then be no possibility of error. Furthermore, I had a regulation French luminous compass and a map of 50,000^{ème}, which in any case I knew by heart.

The edge of the wood on the frontier side was lined with a barrier of barbed wire, arranged in such a fashion as to give the alarm if it were touched, even lightly. I tried to circle round it, but found that it would take too much time. The night was not dark, and I had to go forward crawling on my stomach. Finally, when I had at last managed to get into the meadow by climbing over the hedge, I fell into a herd of calves that were lying down below the hedge. Frightened by my sudden advent in their midst they dashed away. I kept perfectly still for a moment, thinking that their precipitate flight would betray my presence. Then I realised that they were running in the direction that I wanted to take, towards the frontier. An idea came to me : Why should I not be a calf myself? Immediately I dropped on all-fours and with great energy, but very little grace, lumbered off in the midst of them. In this fashion I gained three or four hundred yards in a very few minutes, a distance that it might have taken me an hour to crawl on my stomach. Then I climbed over the hedge on the far side of the meadow, and found myself in a ploughed field.

I heard footsteps approaching, and presently nine soldiers came towards me, following the little path. I froze into absolute immobility, and the patrol passed within twenty yards without seeing me, and after waiting a little I started crawling forward again. I heard some one talking German on my right, and turned to the left. Was it one of the cordon of sentries or an advanced guard ? I had been crawling on my stomach for an hour and a half now—surely I must have crossed the dreamed-of line by this time ? So far I had been moving north-east-by-east, but now I decided to strike due north in order to try to find the railway line. I came upon it in a few minutes, and noticed that it ran towards the north-west and that it was raised on an embankment, while along the whole of its course through Germany it ran through cuttings and due west. I must be in Holland ! There were two houses close by, both of them lighted. I went towards the first one, and when I was within a yard of it a man, hidden on the porch, suddenly called out to me—in German ! Consternation !

" Have you got the word ? " he asked me.

My heart went down into my boots.

" The word ? " I said. " Well, no, I haven't."

" What ? What ? What do you mean ? " he literally shrieked at me.

I didn't wait to argue the matter, but ran like a rabbit into the darkness. The man did not pursue me. He must have been a smuggler waiting for his German accomplices to come and get his packages, and who, on finding that I had not the password of his band, shouted at the top of his voice in order to warn the people inside the house to hide their illegal goods. He had doubtless taken me for a Dutch customs officer.

I then went towards the second house, and listened for a long time at the door. Two men and a woman were talking in a language I couldn't understand. I knocked, ready to fly at a minute's notice, and asked in German, keeping my foot prudently on the doorstep the while, " Am I in Germany or in Holland ? "

The answer that I got was the most charming music that has ever fallen upon my ears ; I listened to it voluptuously. It was a young woman with a baby in her arms who spoke. " You are in Holland, of course," she said ; " in the village of Bocholz."

.   .   .   .   .

Thus at ten o'clock on the night of the 29th October, 1918, after twenty-five months of efforts and eight unsuccessful attempts at escape, the ninth was crowned with success.

RETALIATION

By
"POUSSE CAILLOUX"

There is a small feeding-place, buried in Soho, where, on occasion you may find gathered together those who have retired from the outer fringes of the Empire and have unbuckled the harness : just such gatherings of spasmodically reminiscent cronies as those who swopped yarns with the immortal Brigadier Gerard in that snug little pub in Toulouse, Here, one evening last winter, Gillespie, late Colonel of Gurkhas, told the tale that follows.

Omitting inverted commas, hear him tell it, inadequately though this scribe may have memorised it and haltingly written it.

WALI MAHOMED KHAN, Pathan, of the Achakzai clan which lies astride our Afghan Border area, was one of the finest specimens of natural manhood whom it has been my good fortune to know. We called him " Wallu " for short, and I don't think half a dozen of us even knew what his full patronymic was.

Born and brought up, in the wild Pathan fashion, in the mountain country which lies between one of our large frontier headquarters and the Border itself, he never forgot how the first outstanding event in his life which led to such a mixture of events afterwards was when he left his wife in charge of the headman of the village and set out to make a better living in the *khassadárs*, the irregular tribal Levies with which we supplement our forces on the frontier. He has no history in the Levies up to the time when he got his first leave and returned to his home among the parched crags of the Khoják ; but, with that return, things begin to move with rapidity. Briefly, he seems to have found the scattered fragments of the Seventh Commandment lying thickly on his doorstep, the wife cowering in a corner, and the erring *sardár* who had heard of his imminent arrival, making a hole in the horizon.

What happened to the wife is not known, though a guess is permitted. What happened to the *sardár* transpires from what Walla told us, years after, in one of his rare moments

585

of expansion. Wallu took French leave and a "borrowed" rifle from his Levy, and hunted the delinquent. For two years, uphill and down-dale of the wide Borderland, he hunted him, and finally into India itself, his main object being to head him off from taking refuge in Afghanistan; wherein he was successful, for at last he caught him up where he was working on the new Sukkur Barrage, in Sind, and where he had risen to the position of foreman of works. As Wallu describes it, " I found his hut, sahib. I watched it for a week, and then at midnight I crept to the door, entered and stood at the foot of the *charpoy* where he slept. A small window stood at the head of the bed and gave a little light. I waited a while, and then I took him by the foot and shook him gently. He awoke and sat up. I said, ' Gul Zamán, do you know me?' He sat and blinked, and said nothing. I cut downwards, so——" and Wallu made the expressive gesture from elbow to finger-tip with straightened palm, which all Pathans make. The sleeve, falling from the raised forearm, exposed the magnificent muscles; there was no need to tell that the stroke needed no repeating—" his head fell off sideways, and he remained sitting, spouting blood. I wiped my *tulwár* on the bedclothes and walked out into the night."

So far, so good : a perfectly normal story of the Borderland.

The sequel also follows normal Border traditions. Gul Zamán had a brother, one Turabáz Khan, whom we afterwards came to know as Tor Khan, for short ; and Wallu found himself with the usual blood-feud on his hands. On Tor Khan (*vice* Gul Zamán, *obitus sine prole*) had fallen the headship of the village, and Wallu found himself in the minority of one and condemned to roam. Landless, without wife or chick, with nothing much of brains and only a great gaunt body at his command, he commenced his wanderings, his eye always skinned for the vengeance which he knew would pursue him in any place, at any time of day or night—relentless. He is rather vague about this part of his history ; he seems not to be too proud of a period of frank vagabondage, though, even from this, merry incidents emerge. To wit, what he in the end frankly admitted to be his joining a jovial gang of moss-troopers who wrecked a goods train on one of the steeper gradients of the Bolán Pass whence he brought away nothing more useful than a big bullet-hole in the right leg, the gift of the escort in the guard's van. He seems to have reverted to the Levies after that, for there is a record of a quarrel with the Jemadar, whom he dragged from his horse and pounded on the ground *after* getting that very useful sword-cut down his back, from neck to loins—and here, a little shyly, he draws his shirt over his head and shows the great ragged weal, eighteen inches long, the blood from which must have made an unholy mess of the two of them as they fought on the shingle.

Thanks, probably, to never being in any one place for too long, and to having no regular habits, he escaped the attentions of Tor Khan, who never caught him bending, though there were ample indications that the blood-feud was not going to be allowed to come to a standstill. But, whatever the reality of the danger, it seems to have been at least temporarily scotched when Wallu, blowing in from nowhere, came boldly into the battalion office, asked for the C.O., and requested the job of *chowkidár*, or armed caretaker, to the target-house on the rifle-range outside the North Fort, the same standing in what, for discretion's sake, we will call the frontier station of Baldak.

As he stood there, upstanding and dignified, speaking as man to fellow-man across the Orderly Room table, I couldn't help admiring every inch of him. Barefoot, he stood well over six feet, and a little over-broad for true proportion ; deep-chested. His arms hung from his shoulders in the loose and careless curves of the strong man. His great bony face and beaky nose, and that massive headpiece which, as I often found in later days, was a placid and unshakable rock, crowned a bull's neck hardly in keeping with hands and feet which showed that stamp of breeding to be found only in the best Pathans, whose outlines would have been a joy to Praxiteles. He answered my questions in a big level voice with a merry twitch at the end of it ; and once only his vast cheek-bones wrinkles to a grin such as is rarely seen on a fellow-man in these days of hard thinking.

Wah ! But here was a Man.

" Anybody know anything about him ? "

" Yes, sir," from the Adjutant ; " X. and Y." (two officers) " use him as *shikári* up in the hills, and say they'd trust him with anything."

Thus Wallu, armed with one of the battalion buckshot Martinis, found himself installed in the target-house on fifteen rupees a month, plus rations, and with little to do but keep the rifle-range appliances in order. This he did with the loving care which we afterwards found that he bestowed on any arm, or any appliance connected with fighting, so that even the target-paste came in for a share, and was of a smoothness and clearness unknown to the rather catchemalivo ways, in these matters, of Johnny Gurk. His realm measured a thousand yards by fifty ; it was bounded at the far end by a stop-butt, of no great height, since the wide plains of Afghanistan lay just beyond, where a flying bullet is of no more concern than the song of the short-toed lark. His headquarters, near the Fort, were the brick-built target-house, whose walls had, for the slayer of Gul Zamán, the inestimable advantage of being bullet-proof. Here he dwelt, in complete peace and brotherly concord with the little Gurkhas of the garrison, their squat Mongolian faces never failing to break into a grin when gazing up at the cherry countenance of one who narrowly escaped the fate of becoming a regimental pet.

II

SOME eighty miles north-west of one of our principal frontier headquarters, over a range of stark and craggy mountains, and out in the middle of the flat yellow desert beyond, lies the outpost, fortification or cantonment of Baldak.

It lies astride the main camel-route into Southern Afghanistan, where the grim mountain passes of the norther Border fade out into open desert, and is wedged tightly up against the line of whitewashed cairns, which, by our self-denying ordinance, spells " thus far and no farther " to the English, but not to the Afghans.

It is roughly an oblong enclosure surrounded by barbed wire, containing a fort at the northern end and another at the southern, each manned by half a battalion of Gurkhas. Between the two lie the tangled purlieus of the bazaar— an entrepôt for the camel-caravan trade from the north and beyond ; and, in close proximity to it, the open cantonment, where stand the unfortified and unprotected bungalows of the battalion's white officers. The bazaar is a perfect thieves' kitchen of cut-throats. They drift in and out, secure in the knowledge of the British " live and let live." Here men go to earth and lie hidden when a tribal feud gets too hot, or when the crudities of Afghan punitive justice are reaching out for them ; and—the law is unwritten—as long as they cause us no trouble, we do not trouble them.

Apart from the civil Kotwál and the native Political Agent, two local minor functionaries under the orders of the Political Officer at headquarters, who are supposed to be responsible for the local tribesmen—and who at this time most certainly were not—the Gurkha bazaar-guard keeps order. A strong party moving about with rifles? Not so. Reinforced by the power of the unwritten convention, the Gurkha bazaar-guard is one man, neat in close-fitting khaki, polished belt and one and a half cwt. of side. He is armed with a walking-out cane, and is lord of all he surveys for the month of his spell of duty. True, the Babel knows that we could, were we so minded, wipe the whole place out in one day and cook our dinner on the ashes; but even that hardly gives backing to what I saw once—a long thin string of a hundred trail-worn laden camels conducted by wild tribesmen; and a little Gurkha as high as a pile of sixpences and the picture of boiling fury, standing in mid-road, waving his cane and damning the tall camel-men all to heaps for taking the wrong turning into the main street. The camels wound themselves up into a confused block while the tribesmen gradually took in what was meant; whereupon the whole cortège presently unwound itself, turned wearily about and went back to the right turning. What? All right; I tell you I *saw* it happen.

So much for daylight. But after dark it is a different matter. The universal law of the Border is that, when darkness reigns, every man who owns a house gets inside it and shuts the door, *tight*; and he who has no house gets behind a rock. For then the terror that flieth by night has a nickel nose, or one of lead, or, all too frequently, one blunted at the tip and sawn so as to give those ghastly wounds which we associate with expanding bullets. Curfew? The Border makes its own curfew, and the quick shot takes the place of a challenge.

Seven miles off, on the Afgan side and astride the camel-route, stands the medievally constructed but quite useful Afghan fortress of (let us say) Kadanai. Baldak and Kadanai face each other across flat desert, and have, officially, nothing whatever to say to one another, though each is keenly conscious of the presence of its opposite number, very much as are two dogs, of equal size and fighting weight, living on opposite sides of the same street.

There you have the cantonment of Baldak; and when I add that, in addition to the mixed crowd of those whom you might style interesting characters, but whom we, on the spot,

called damned cut-throats whom we had to cherish in our
sandy bosom, the Afghan frontier stretched as an open line
of whitewashed cairns across the desert a couple of hundred
yards off—and the wire entanglement was, through lack of
funds, no obstacle at all—you begin to see that the situation
ran mainly on hope, or on a rather stiff and strained mutual
respect, whichever way you prefer.

.   .   .   .

The particular phase in the annals of Baldak with which
we have to deal occurred when the cantonment became a
gathering-place for a couple of divisions of all arms which took
the field against Afghanistan in the " war " of 1919. There
was nothing much in it, except that our entire circus went out
one morning to Kadanai, at that time the Afghan headquarters,
and, with unnecessary noise and vehement H.E., blew it to
bits. Thereafter, both sides sat down and looked at each other,
three perfectly good Afghan armies in three separate camps
across the way, ourselves in Baldak and the ruins of Kadanai,
each side unable to leave its ground, because, had it done so,
it would be advancing into an area of which its enemy held
the water supply. One incident only lightened the tedium.
A young and impressionable flying officer, scouting over
enemy headquarters, discovered at some distance in its rear
the camp of the Commander and that of the outfit of ladies
with whom he took the field. He discovered also one damsel,
bonny as a rose-leaf and conspicuously interested in the
machine and its occupant when flying low. Shortly afterwards he obtained from down-country a large two-pound
box of chocolates, and once more flew to the enemy camp,
bent on presenting his gift to the tantalising unknown.

There she was, as usual.

Now, I am no aeronaut, but I believe that in those days
our airmen went at about sixty miles an hour ; anyhow, this
fellow was travelling at a pace of knots, and the lady wasn't
travelling anything in particular. He flew low and hard
towards her, waving the box in the air with the cheery
gesture which spells " Catch ! " from China to Peru. As he
dropped the box she made a lap in which to catch it.

She caught it right enough, poor thing. . . .

Next day a flag of truce came in from old Thingummy
across the way, with an infuriated protest at our making
war on women. It nearly drove the three Afghan armies
into the movement, and now serves its purpose in driving me
back out of side-issues and into the main current of what I

am trying to tell you ; for it was just at this juncture that my bearer bolted and was seen no more.

Is there any one in this world more helpless than the sahib without a servant ?

Now, the Border was never a popular spot with servants, and they usually had to be heavily bribed to come there at all. So that when I found myself servantless I was rather up against it. No question of sharing with any one else : the Indian servant serves one man only, and him half-heartedly. The battalion being " back in billets " at Baldak for the moment, the question became acute. Its discussion at mess that evening suddenly stimulated a brain-wave.

" Wallu sometimes does for us, in a rough way, when he takes us after *gadd* in the hills. Why not try him, sir ? "

Instantly the merry notion bit. In a moment the mess orderly was doubling down to the lines. By the time the wine was on the table and the post-prandial contentment reigned, up the drive leading to where our table was laid, for coolness, in the open, came striding Wallu, his powerful figure half as large again in its outline against the glowing western sky, his treasured Martini slung over his shoulder and his hetero-geneous collection of rags swaying mightily in his long elastic strides. He came to the table and squatted on the ground beside the subalterns seated at the far end, and a hubbub of cheery chatter arose. As soon as any one could get a word in edgeways, it was " Don't sit *bukh*-ing here, Wallu. The C.O. wants you."

Up rose Wallu, and swung up to our end.

" Sthare ma she, sahib ! " said he, with a waved hand, half-salaam, half cheer-oh !

" Khwar ma she, Wali Mahomed,"[1] I answered.

He squatted once more, coughed rather self-consciously, blew his nose (quite neatly) in his fingers, laid his rifle across his knees and awaited my pleasure.

You would say at this point that we had forgotten to offer him a drink. Quite wrong. Wallu, like all the best Muslims, not only did not touch alcohol, but plainly loathed the stink of the heady stuff. Nor would he soil his great leathery hill-man's lungs with tobacco smoke. The conversation therefore proceeded directly.

" My bearer has vanished, and I can't get another. Will you take it on ? "

The question had to be repeated before the slow ripples of

[1] "May you never be tired!" answered by "May you never be poor!"

dawning comprehension grew into the wrinkles of a wide and embarrassed grin. "What, *me*? Take on *sirdár* in the Karnél Sahib's household? What do *I* know of house service?" —and the embarrassment slowly hardened to a queer hostility. For a moment the mind's eye visualised a large goshawk being asked to take on the job of cleaning out the canary's cage.

He dug his toes in. Sheer obstinacy, reinforced by a look round the table at his skinny down-country co-religionists who, flitting so quick and silent-footed about the table, drew their white coat-shirts away from contact with him as they passed, but who, in their mean souls, were deadly afraid of him.

"*Come* on, Wallu. *Be* a man. Take it on. You'll get twice the pay you're getting, and the *izzat* of being C.O.'s bearer" —thus from the subalterns at the end of the table his close friends, whom he trusted. That at last made him feel more homey. He sighed. "It's an order, I suppose. When do I begin?"

Next morning he turned up at the bungalow, where, washed and shaved and fitted out by the regimental tailor in the resplendent muslins and velvet of a Pathan of the upper classes, he slowly and reluctantly learnt the job of indoor service. From first to last he hated it all—all, that is to say, except the job of bossing the other servants and that of cleaning the shikár rifles and guns. He was never tired of the wonders of the telescopic sights and other gadgets, and loved the heartening feel of the heavy blued metal and the sharp snick of good mechanism—his long, thin aristocratic fingers busy with oil-rag and cleaning-rod, with lock and bolt and barrel, till they got that indefinable dull glow which speaks of warm steel in harmony with its owner. And when, after an hour of it, he could find nothing more to do to a rifle, sitting and nursing it across his knees he would look out with distant and contented gaze over the desert, and sing a little crooning tune to himself.

. . . . . .

The Afghan "war" of 1919 fizzled out rather than ceased. Dyer, down at Amritsar, had quelled the insurrection in the Punjab, and a mixed collection of sedentary busy-bodies was sitting in judgment on his actions. The untidy raggedness of the commissioned ranks was being sorted into something like pre-war shape by the ruthless axeing which acted as a wholesome purge to the Indian Army ; and what should have been a restful ending to a perfectly good period of five years' world-war strain, developed into a housemaid's job of broom and dustpan. Anti-climax, and a mixed time for a C.O. Kadanai had been patched together and handed back to its former owners, who installed as Governor a *persona* politically *non grata*, a minor official who had emerged rather rumpled from a palace plot in Kabul and had been exiled to this first-cousin-to-Jehannum, accompanied by a disgruntled and showy Persian wife with expensive tastes.

The year was on the turn, and the hot weather approaching. We always knew when the turn of the year was on us by the uprising of the " sand-devils," which would last steadily through the remainder of the hot weather. A sand-devil is a whirlwind which, generally on the stillest days, gets up from nowhere and travels four or five miles before dismembering and whoofing off into nothingness. It consists of a strictly localised vortex, like an inverted cone, and anything up to two hundred feet in height. It travels slowly across the desert, rotating with incredible speed on its own axis, and gathering up anything loose which may lie in its path—tents, blankets, even cooking-pots—whirling them to the top, where they spin, helpless, unable to come down till the devil has blown himself out. The devil himself is hot desert sand, and should you get in its path you must hang on tight to something firm lest you and your clothing join the mixed exhibits upstairs ; you shut your eyes and try to hold your breath as the roaring darkness envelops you ; you are then conscious of the crown-ing and quite inexplicable devilry—the overpowering and nauseating smell of almost solid human fug. Where on earth the devil picks up this last peculiarity has always defeated me, since he blows in from the untainted desert and is composed of wholesome sand ; but all the crowded tenements of all the fetid slums of Benares, packed together, could hardly equal it : the breath of the very Pit. Those devils sweep through cantonments about twenty times a day, and, as we have noted, their arrival coincides with the opening of the hot weather.

The lady of the party here saw fit to join the scheme of things. When all other right-minded memsahibs were fleeing homewards before the advancing heat, this one decided to terminate a five years' war separation, and to land in Bombay with a complete and extensive fit-out for home-making, knowing nothing and caring less about the—to say the least of it—peculiar conditions of the Frontier. Stop her ? Might as well try to stop a Bandersnatch So, flinging prudence to the winds, I made a rapid dive for Bombay to welcome

the caravan, leaving the bungalow all-standing in the capable
charge of Wallu.

We dumped the kit with the Bombay agents, and took
the first two months' leave in five strenuous years—trekking
about, deliberately shunning a permanent address lest official
business should pursue, and revelling in the historical anti-
quities of India's famous places : the sight-seeing which we,
living in the midst of these wonders, never seemed to have
previously been able to achieve. Another story altogether ;
no place for it here. At the end of the time we gathered up the
mountainous kit, wired our impending arrival to Baldak and
set out to rejoin.

The warmth of the welcome prepared, when at last we
drove in through the wire, dispelled most of the memsahib's
uneasiness, which had been steadily growing as the lush
down-country landscapes changed to scanty vegetation,
bareness, and finally, stark desert. Foremost was Wallu.
Forgetting the status of master and man—never, indeed, very
obvious between us—he shot out his great paw and gripped
mine. "Stharé ma shé, sahib ! " he shouted ; "jóriye ?
khushhálye ? mazbútye ? "—while he pump-handled my
hand in both of his, in rhythm with his greeting, laughing all
over his face and half-way down his neck like a great schoolboy. And then finally, reassured, " Shukr de ! "—*that's* all
right, then—and turned enthusiastically to the mountains of
kit.

" Hi, Wallu, come here. Come and be introduced to the
memsahib ! "

He turned about and took a pace forward ; and the great
body of a man, bunged up with wounds and healthy sin and
the gorgeous life of the open Border, stood like a self-conscious
child caught stealing jam ; his head hanging, his hands
behind his back, scratching the heel of one bare foot with
the toes of the other. For all his deep copper-colour, I'll
swear he was blushing.

The little scrap of a thing gazed up in whimsical amusement at his towering bulk—she who could have stood with
her two feet on the palm of his hand while he raised her,
erect, to shoulder height—and, friendly but properly cere-
monious, " Salaam, Wali Mahomed Khan, Achakzai,"
said she.

" Salaam aleikum," whispered the great gawk, and
scrabbled in the sand with his bare toe.

Silence.

Then, mass of confusion though he was, and hating it all, he pulled himself up as straight as a ramrod and made her just such a bow as Essex might have made to Queen Bess.

"Khush ámada éd!" said he in clear and courtly welcome.

And fled.

III

THE bare elements of furniture had been got into the bungalow against our arrival, the dry bones to which the contents of the packing-cases, arriving a week later, were to give substance and life. For carpets, there was all the store of Persia, Turkestan and Bokhara on which to draw, clean from fresh-opened camel bales down at the caravan-serai. Meanwhile would we mind pigging it for a day or so? Thus, our *locum tenens*, the Second-in-Command, who came in for ten minutes and a drink in the back office. In the first half-minute whisky was forgotten and pipes went out, while, in the fewest words which would compass the wide ramifications of a complex subject, he laid bare the sudden change in every aspect of the local Border problems which had taken place during the two months of my absence.

The subject needs a little prefacing if we are to understand how, as a matter of habit, sahibs and their families had, up to this time, been able to live openly and unprotected in cantonment bungalows at a distance from barracks or from any kind of military guard—safe in the knowledge that the rough chivalry of the clans would confine warfare to the crags and valleys of the traditional fighting grounds, and how the changing spirit of the old Border warfare had, all at once, made this habit a definite and dangerous back number.

Listen now while I attempt to set out a matter not easily described nor understood in this England of ours—a thing full of anomalies and contradictions, but the very bone of the bone to us who lived and worked in the land.

To begin with, Border warfare as we knew it best had absolutely no ill-feeling in it. It was a war of hard-trained bodies, each against the other; a war of keen eyesight and straight shooting; a war of perpetual vigilance and of quick wits, where the man in the valley knew that at no time during daylight was he free from the hidden eyes which, from the hills above, watched his every movement; and should he grow careless or slacken off, or, worst of all, indulge in any *habit* when living, moving, or fighting, then was his head a gift to his enemy. Success or disaster came with equally unexpected suddenness : a rearguard surprised and bunched together in difficult ground ; a group of tribesmen caught in a cunning trap of their own devising ; an ugly rush with knives on a camp at midnight, when the attackers went clean through wire, abattis, tents, mule-lines, and out the other side before you had grasped that they were there, leaving red ruin in their trail ; or, the same tribesmen lying out and sniping the camp in the darkness, and the scattered flashes growing inexplicably fewer till the *chapáo* party of barefoot little Gurkhas came in again through the picket-line, their kukris red with the blood of the snipers stalked and slain in silence. Through it all, the marksmanship at long range through the clear and dry desert air of the gaunt mountains, the steady hand and the clever judging of distance. And if they did cut up our dead and wounded, very rarely left out for them to cut, well, didn't we burn their villages and ring-bark their few and precious apricot and mulberry-trees— though making very sure that the village was empty before we burned it ? And if they had a rather *macabre* taste for rifling our fresh-made graves and turning the pitiful contents out to the vultures, didn't we, not seldom, bury in a grave a dummy in a blanket, containing gun-cotton slabs, not a few, and tricky contact wires, whereby the gravediggers flew to Paradise, their limbs not all together but singly and one by one ?

Each war was a war with the gloves off as long as it lasted, where brain and eye, hand and body, all worked together at the top of their form ; and, when it was all over, no rancour, no ill-feeling. Orakzai or Afridi, Mohmand or Achakzai, you could meet any of the many clansmen in Peshawar Bazaar, in Kohat, Dera Ismail Khan, or Quetta, each with a useful rifle and a bandolierful of the latest and best smokeless, and you could pass the time of day to each, openly and with a grin. Each and all would, occasion serving, gladly cut your throat, but he wouldn't be rude to you.

First and last, there were no grudges in it, and I think the core of the matter lay in the fact that we never made war on one another's noncombatants. It was good rough chivalry such as the old class of sahib loved well, carrying self-denying ordinances on both sides, which neither we nor the tribesmen ever transgressed.

Then came 1914, and the Great War. The sahibs who had

learnt the Border so long and so patiently were scattered to Flanders, to Gallipoli, Mesopotamia, East Africa—anywhere where the new war called them, and their hill troops with them. Very, very few survived, so few that never can they leaven the new generation. It is difficult to describe adequately the irreparable loss. Only we, who have lived in both periods, know the deprivation in the loss of that wonderful knight-errantry which not only made our frontier wars such a grim delight, but which, for over half a century, added definitely to the clean ideals of English youth.

In 1920, when England was settling comfortably into peace, the Borderlands blazed out into open rebellion, and all sorts were sent against them—all, that is, but those who knew the trade and its traditions. Each new brigade inevitably came to grief, and the clans armed themselves, as never had they armed themselves before, with the rifles of the slain. A crisis supervened, and the alternative lay between an irresistible uprising through the length and breadth of the Frontier, or turning against the tribes the methods of modern warfare and the new tricks learned from the Hun.

Perforce, our folk dropped explosives on them from the sky ; dropped incendiary bombs on their villages whence their women and children had not had time to escape ; set up long-range heavy howitzers and shelled their village areas with six-inch high-explosive shells, which soared over the intervening mountain ranges in their blind flight, and dropped crashing on to crop lands where men and women worked ; we machine-gunned them from aeroplanes ; every unchivalrous trick we used against them—everything except gas.

Our people succeeded—after a fashion—and, even then, incompletely. But it was a poor success that left an embittered and vindictive feeling behind it—where tales of mangled noncombatants grew no less in the telling. I am convinced that it was directly and solely due to this new and vengeful feeling that the slow-growing indignation of the clans presently blazed out into the Kohát murders and the kidnappings from cantonments, the undefended bungalows of which had till then been respected by the tribesmen. It made Peshawar, Bannu and Frontier stations farther afield no place for an Englishwoman except in the near neighbourhood of barracks. Had the Hun but known it, he, in teaching us the mechanism of unmanly destruction, dealt us a deadlier blow than ever he did by bombing and poisoning us ; for he destroyed the

old large-heartedness of the Borderland. Till now the last
of the old knight-errants are the gaunt and tatterdemalion
hillmen who, in this year of 1929, have waged such bitter and
successful war against the mongrel internationalism and
modernisation of the old Afghanistan.

We, of the old Border, hated it all, but were powerless
in the face of facts ; we, who could feel as did Chandos—
or was it Bayard, *sans peur et sans reproche* ? or du Guesclin ?
I dunno ; some splendid old fighting man, anyhow, who
hanged on sight every arquebusier he met, for the use of that
villainous saltpetre which was slowly destroying the knight-
hood of Christendom. The measure of our bitter sorrow is
the measure of our love for the old things clean and of good
report ; and now they are dead—dead and gone—and
nothing on earth can bring them to life again.

So the rankling grudge had drifted south to us of the
Achakzai territory. But the thing which had given pith
and point to the new rancour, so far as we were concerned,
and which subjected us to what eventually came to be a series
of vindictive retaliations, was, I am certain, the unfortunate
incident in which the airman and the box of chocolates
figured so prominently—and yet so innocently.

So now we understood the tale which the Second-in-
Command told, while the memsahib in another room was
sluicing off the mixed desert which had invaded her, all
over.

From the first he made no secret of the fact, that, for the
last two months, he had been up against it. Fine soldier
though he was, he yet knew nothing of the Frontier. He had
been transferred from a down-country regiment in the re-
shufflings which, at the end of 1919, filled the depleted commissioned ranks of those battalions which had made a habit
of being in the thick of it all. He had never seen rock or sand
or hawk-faced clansman before the time of his joining us ;
he differed, indeed, from the old type of Border officer who
knew how to keep his temper and never made war in driblets.
Briefly, there was something like open feud between the
garrison and the clans, and the trouble was growing; an
embittered state of affairs in which we held the undoubted
mastery by day, but the tribesmen made things almost impossible for us by night ; the reprisals growing more acute as
each side chalked up one to spot, or one to plain, in fairly
evenly-balanced sequence. It was all right for the garrisons
in the forts ; but the bungalow area, accepted hitherto as

neutral ground by the tribal code was—as it had always been—out in the blue. As I have tried to describe.

Failing conclusions with the forts, the clansmen had fixed on the bungalows. The thin end of the wedge consisted of petty thefts. Of these no notice was taken. The thefts grew greater in volume and in frequency, property being hard to safeguard in house built of unburnt brick and furnished with doors and windows from the woodwork of which, under the ravages of dry heat and white ants, all life and resistance had long departed. The Barrack Department had no money for repairs or replacements ; doors hung insecurely on stout hinges the screws of which failed to bite ; locks consisted of the usual chain and staple, anchored togethered by a heavy padlock, but easily wrenched asunder with the two-foot-long marlinspike which is the usual Border equivalent of a jemmy. This inserted point foremost in the hasp, a slow turn of the wrist is given and—pf !—chain and staple softly and suddenly vanish away, after the manner of Boojums. When to this is added the fact that Border thieves have been known to lift a sleeping sahib by the four corners of his blankets, deposit him, still sleeping, on the floor, fold up his camp-bed and go off with it ; or, more credible because more often done, lift a tent by its fly-ropes and leave the sahib to continue his sleep *en plein air* till the rising sun shines on him and wakes him ; when they have a trick with a horse which will allow of their stealing him from his stable and taking him away, treading as softly as his captors ; when all this, I say, is considered, there is credence in the reputed fact that Pathan thieves have that sixth sense which they share with cats and which allows of their doing the most incredible things in pitch darkness—a sense which surpasses and, for a time, seems to replace sight, smell, touch, or hearing.

There had been a series of these burglaries or raids ; and, in every case, the thieves had got clean away with the loot, out of cantonments, through the wire, and, by a few steps, over the border. Nobody knew, or nobody would tell, whose hand was in it, though persistent rumour had it that the Governor's expensive *khánum* in Kadanai Fort, over the way, was furnishing her quarters more in accord with her notions of good taste than her husband's pay would allow, and was gradually acquiring all our best possessions.

So much for the Second-in-Command, who confessed that he found the situation unmanageable ; and what did I propose to do ?

Sit down for a good long think? Or lose my wool and do something foolish? Not a bit. Knowledge of Pathan psychology discounted what were, after all, only pin-pricks; these small irritations, it was obvious, were only a curtain-raiser; the really important features would develop later. But, meanwhile, there was no good reason for allowing them to continue. Questioned, had there been any shooting? The sentries at the Forts had been told to fire without challenging. Had they been given buckshot Martinis and told to reserve their fire till they could shoot to kill? No; apparently not. (H'm; so the Pathans had been sticking to the time-honoured sequence of sniffing round the edge of trouble and seeing how far they could upset our tempers and our judgment before going on to the real business; the diagnosis was easy). Any sahibs done any shooting? No; in each case the mischief had only been discovered at daylight.

Next morning I sent for the Civil Kotwál, and explained that this sort of thing had got to stop, one-time.

" Fidáyat shávam ! " with a deprecating politeness; " may I be your sacrifice." Translated, it meant bide-a-wee; or, the matter is out of our hands, whichever way you like to take it.

Anyhow we turned to other things; and, whether *post hoc* or *propter hoc*, the raids ceased. Personally, I was inclined to think that the tribes were waiting to see if the returned incumbent would do anything sudden and awkward; and were marking time meanwhile. While I, thinking things over, and seeing clearly the direction which events were taking— though hand-tied both by custom and by order till the other side made the first move—blessed my stars for the day, and the brain-wave of the day, which brough Wallu, sturdiest of henchmen, within the scope of my domestic arrangements. In what was coming to us all, little time would there be for my own concerns and for those closely dependent on me; and on him, great lumbering mass of laughing courage, would devolve . . .

H'm.

Anyhow, of how we came to rely on him, and of the indispensable part he played in all that followed, let me— risking discursiveness—tell exactly as it happened. Since one thing led to another, it is difficult to know how to shorten it.

. . . .

The household kit from England arrived a few days later. In my absence at work, the lion's share of the job fell on Wallu, who was in his element, heaving bulk and weight about with a merry sweating impartiality. "Here, give a holt, you!" and a heave altogether, and in the stuff would rumble and bump—packing-cases, barrels, trunks and what not—into the verandah, which was soon knee-deep in straw, shavings and brown paper.

When once the gear was in, and things growing ship-shape, the household duties had to be brought into some sort of ordered sequence. The minor servants fell into their appointed grooves at once. But Wallu was the problem. Far from clumsy, yet absolutely untrained, it was obvious very early on that he was impossible as an indoor servant in a memsahib's ménage. His bulk alone was against him. He dwarfed everything within sight, and towered head and shoulders above the others, on whom he looked down both literally and figuratively. The memsahib had that in her eye which verged on a sentence of dismissal ; but the sahib had in his eye something more in response, which showed that the splendid old rough-diamond was going to stay at any cost, house-trained or not ; and the memsahib's tact saved the situation. We would invent a status for him, with the rank—devised for the occasion—of " major-domo." He, in all his glory of towering muslins and gold embroidery, should be taught to stand in the verandah with a silver salver, take the cards of the callers and show them in. The drill was simple, though to Wallu it was as irksome as harness to a zebra. The first day, when the Second-in-Command and the two captains called, all went well, though Wallu's hearty " Come along in ! " savoured more of the owner of the show than of its retainer. He accompanied the callers into the tiny drawing-room, where the memsahib received them, stood there, to the imminent danger of tea-tables, what nots and other flimsinesses, and prepared to take a share in the conversation till shoo'd out by the diminutive lady.

Next day the subalterns arrived. Wallu spotted them from the verandah, gave a whoop of joy and strode eagerly down the drive to meet them. An hour later they, in their glad-rags, were still sitting on the bench under the mulberry, used as a rule by the orderlies, in animated conversation with the new major-domo about some shikár ploy, past or impending, the why and the wherefore of their coming clean forgotten ; what time the *mem* waited in an empty drawing-room till the standard calling-hour had long passed, and then drifted in to lunch not a little puzzled at the absence of the expected visitors.

That was the end of the major-domo stunt. No other job seemed suitable to the wild Pathan. The lady refused to give him any job which involved tidying or handling breakables. "My dear, he'd crunch them all to bits in those great hands of his." Wherein she was wrong. I could have told her of the marvellous quickness and neatness of touch which the colossus shared with other really strong men. Anyhow, he was banished to the male end of the house, where he drifted about as before, doing some good and no harm—the good being the wholesome satisfaction which another man got when, thirsty, sand-smitten and exhausted, he came in at evening and met the great calm bulk in the dressing-room, or heaving great *ghurrahs* of tub-water about in the bathroom, or standing over the shifty syce who weighed out the ration for the horses' evening feed. He came as a breath of clean desert air whenever you met him, did Wallu ; and to no one so much as to the tired man. "Stharé ma shé "—hardly was there need for him to say it !

He avoided the memsahib. Gradually, unobtrusively and quite courteously, he refused to have anything to do with that part of the house. I think he had all a Pathan's dislike for womenkind left lying about loose ; a definite impatience, probably bred into him by generations of ancestors who, daily carrying their lives in their hands, needed a clear deck on which to mind their dangerous business, and kept their womenfolk shut safely away. He was alacrity itself when sent on a job ; but he generally managed not to be there when she wanted him. Looking back on it now, I realise that Wallu was that very rare and very lovable thing, an undiluted and wholly sincere man's man.

IV

IT was somewhere about this time that the trouble with the tribesmen of the place recommenced. One night the last-joined subaltern lost his entire fit-out of saddlery. It was Sowter's best stuff, and some kind uncle must have been generous to him : a clean sweep, right down to the hoof-pick, and even the stable-collar stripped from the horse, which, however, was not taken. He lost his temper, vowed to

pot the next man whom he saw moving at night, and had six
rounds of the best with his revolver at an indeterminate
shadow at the bottom of the compound a night afterwards.
Two nights later he woke with a sudden burning pain through
his leg and the sound of an explosion in his ears, snipèd neatly
from behind the low compound wall as he lay on his camp-
bed in the open, where each officer slept, for coolness. We
patched him up and sent him, under escort, in to headquarters to heal.

Ve-ry well, says I ; if you *must* carry it to extremes and
pot sleeping sahibs, you shall have it ! Forthwith the order
went out that any one found moving after dark, and not
carrying a lighted hurricane-lantern, would be neither
stopped nor challenged, but forthwith shot. The native
Political Agent was called up and notified ; a shrug of the
shoulders ; " Balé," and a salaam ; and off he loafed, every
inch of his insolent backview proclaiming " no business of
mine, of course ; but two can play at *that* game." I nearly
called him back, to say that the edict *included* all government
servants, of whatever ranks and of both colours. Damn the
blighter ! He knew more about the state of affairs than he
cared to tell ; I wondered whether he knew that the Sardár
of Kadanai was, at that moment, as we suspected, peacocking
round with a brand-new Sowter saddle between himself and
his scrawny mount.

Two nights went by and nothing happened. The third
night, one of unusually dense darkness, bang ! ba-ba-bang !
ba-bang ! !—rapid fire from somewhere near the North
Fort. The field-telephone answered inquiry with the information that " they'd got somebody." So they had. Daylight
revealed an old and nearly toothless man, a small boy and
a donkey-load of mixed wares, who had crept in through the
boundary pillars on a mild kind of smuggling enterprise, to
avoid the octroi post by day. Most unfortunate. It seemed
about as heartless a thing as could have been done. But there
it was ; the weakness of the position lay in the fact that in the
midst of declared inter-state peace, we were at local war ; and,
I ask you, *how* was one to notify local war regulations, however
precautionary, to scattered tribesmen on the other side of an
open frontier line ?

Anyhow, we could only hope that it would not happen
again.

Promptly came the answer. During mess, the uproar
of a rifle-shot at close quarters, a splintering of window-

glass and a scattering of plaster on the opposite wall, made a sudden and simultaneous interruption to the general conversation. Nobody hurt. But, a few hours later, as though to add insult to injury, the only pair of bullocks which drew the iron conservancy-cart—an indispensable if malodorous adjunct to all cantonments—was discovered to be missing. Their hoof-tracks led to the frontier line, and passed on into the blue.

And who, or what, was to draw our cart?

Really, you know, when I realised that the bazaar, when it heard of our loss, must have rolled in convulsions of rib-racking laughter (the full details, by the way, are omitted), I could hardly repress a giggle myself.

Here or hereabouts it was borne in on me that a lady, interposed between lamps and open windows and verandah, was almost too much of a target. In those days the Kohát murders were still to come ; but it was obvious that the old sanctions were going or gone ; that dirty work was gradually creeping in to swamp the old fair-play and that all the clean romance of Border fighting was weakening ; so that, by evening, heavy curtains had taken the place of the bonny muslins. If they must snipe, at least they should snipe blind. Furthermore, Wallu, divested of gorgeous trappings and once more back in his dingy and nondescript garments was, at his own request, on the prowl with the second-best Mauser-Rigby. It was at about this point that he threw off the depression of house-service and became his own joyous man once more This, after all, was a thing he could understand. No slinking about behind walls or round corners. He moved as silently as a cat, but with head up and chest out and that marvellous sixth sense of all Pathans tuned up till it twanged inside his soul like a harp-string. If ever the old blighter said his prayers, which I doubt, he must have stroked the barrel and butt of the Mauser, on those still and wonderful starry nights, and thanked his God for the very joy of life.

He needed, indeed, to walk warily, and to know when to shoot and when not For by this time we had begun to take measures ourselves The garrisons of the two forts were insufficient to provide standing guards—in addition to their other duties—on each and every bungalow, the mess, the dâk-bungalow, the military works godown and all the rest. Had some been guarded and others not, the unguarded ones would have been a cockshy to the prowler, and it would have been unfair. So we had to rely on moving patrols, a poor substitute, but apparently better than nothing. Theirs was the job of prowling round cantonments with buckshot Martinis in the hope of catching the lurking sniper or the silent-footed thief. Counsels, alas! of perfection. Unless he knows, by rifle flash or other sign, where to look for him, how may a man on the move hope to find a lurker, still as a mouse and indistinguishable from his background? The patrols, again, had to be only a few men. A group would have been a gift; nor could more than one patrol be on the move at any one time, lest two patrols should meet in the dark and fratricide ensue.

The situation was worrying to a degree. With cantonments turned into an open battleground from dusk to dawn, none of us could sleep outside his house. We did not sit up, teeth all a-chatter. We slept as tired men sleep; but the business of getting to sleep inside an over-heated bungalow in the infernal after-dark temperature of a desert summer shortened the temper of each of us for the next day's work, and things began to get unsatisfactory. It was about this time that somebody—not, however, myself—suggested tentatively to the lady of the station that she would be happier in the comparative safety and coolth of headquarters. The suggester didn't try it twice. In spite of the fact that if ever she hears I said it my name will be mud, I here and now register my solemn belief that, on the whole, she was rather enjoying it all!

. . . .

Real grim trouble now began to descend on us. I am never tired of saying that we were most unfairly handicapped —and with an open frontier which we were debarred from crossing, but which was treated as non-existent by the tribesmen, and a bazaar which we were unable, through Civil regulations, to sort thoroughly, were powerless to fix the guilt on anybody unless we caught him red-handed. So the score began to mount up against us. A Gurkha orderly, lying up in the long grass of his sahib's compound on the chance of getting some one, was half-blown to bits by an explosive bullet. The patrols were incessantly being sniped, and twice it was our job to bring in badly wounded men; nor was there ever a sign or glimpse of the snipers bar the sudden yellow flash of the shot, and, the spot being marked down and rushed, no trace of the sniper. Every now and again the programme would be varied by lootings. Once the entire

kitchen fit-out of the dâk-bungalow vanished ; once the
flagstaff in front of the mess, sawn almost through in the
night, descended with deadly effect on the orderly whose
job it was to run the ensign up at dawn—a piece of sheer
mischievous devilry. The regimental servants, down-country
Mohammedans of the poorer-spirited type, got restive and
threatened to bolt. My pair of one-rat-power Goanese,
imported at much expense and trouble from down-country,
came with telegrams in their hands announcing simultaneous
deaths of fathers and mothers, requiring their presence
urgently in Goa. Yet, as I say, by day you wouldn't have
known that anything whatever was wrong, and everything,
down to the single unarmed bazaar-guard, functioned
smoothly and normally.

Now, it is not easy to explain it clearly, but the fact
remains that there was no remedy except such remedies
as we ourselves could apply. It would have been useless,
nor would it have been within our dignity, to squeal to
headquarters. On the Border you are expected to run
your own show and never—if it can possibly be avoided—
run crying to mother. In the old days, with the old type
of sweaty, shirt-sleeved, pipe-sucking staff officer of the
Frontier, we could, without loss of caste, have gone up to
H.Q. and talked it over. The result would have been strictly
unofficial, but very unpleasant, pressure put upon the
Politicals, and some, probably quite guiltless, headman
of Pathans would have been held responsible, in person and
in property, that the nuisance stopped, suddenly and
definitely. But though he is, thank heaven, back with us
again at long last, in those days the old type of staff officer
had gone aloft on the wings of gas, H.E., and other sudden
departures from the normal ; and his place had been taken
by a stop-gap swarm of very junior and strictly temporary
ignoramuses, who barely knew the language of the people
with whom they dealt, and who, in the face of anything like
an emergency, were absolutely useless.

Fact is, we were the victims of circumstances ; the altered
circumstances of the Border, the altered methods of the New
Army. We were caught in the tumbled turn of the tide, where
the waters ran all ways at once and things had not settled
into any one particular direction. So we just had to makee-do,
and hang on in silence ; and, whatever else happened, neither
to panic nor show the tribes that they were worrying us. Not
for coined gold would we have admitted to a crowd of

murderous fly-by-nights that they were either interfering with our peace of mind or doing anything to take us out of our normal stride. *That*, at least, was not the way to hold the Border.

But each consecutive score-up against us made the next score easier and more probable. Once, for a while, we got a breathing space. We managed to catch one of the snipers red-handed. He put up a whirling struggle for it, but the Gurks hung on grimly and in silence, and presently we had him trussed. We had been at infinite pains to catch one of them alive and get information out of him ; so, treating him with the utmost impressiveness to be got from mystery, we marched him, bound, the five marches into headquarters, where we handed him over, *not* to the Politicals, nor to our own H.Q., by any means (they would merely have given him a lengthy trial and a term in prison), but with a strictly unofficial note to our old friend Buchanan of the Police, whose name was a terror throughout the Border where he had already put in nearly thirty years' service. The sequel was hardly anticipated, nor, thank the Lord most humbly, was it any of our devising ; for Buchanan (that, by the way, was not his name) handed the man, still stubborn and insolent, over to his native subordinates, to be kept in the cells and questioned at frequent and regular intervals. He emerged in the end, free and without a mark on him, and was turned adrift into the hills, where he wandered at will and was well cared for by the clans as one of the " afflicted of God " ; for he was raving mad. I found out afterwards that, taking it in turns, Buchanan's native constables had kept him awake by prodding him in the ribs with ramrods, and had allowed him no sleep, day or night, for a fortnight.

V

THE queer part about the whole trouble was that my bungalow escaped raiding, nor was any shot fired at or from it. Wallu, when not prowling, slept on his charpoy, fairly and frankly in the open compound, the rifle between his knees, and nothing I could say would dissuade him from what seemed like asking for it. " Lor' bless you, sahib," or the Pathan equivalent, " they won't touch *me*." And gradually I began to see that though the tribesmen were keen as mustard on getting either sahib or Gurkha, they thought twice before incurring all the infinite ramifications of a tribal feud which might ensue if they put a bullet through Wallu. True, nobody knew who his relations might be, or who would take up the quarrel. I believe, as a matter of fact, that by this time he was the only survivor of his family ; but he was a bit of a mystery, having blown in from nowhere, as it were, and nobody knew anything about him. Truly, to see the great bulk of a thing swinging freely along the roadway with a straw in his teeth and " you be damned " in his eye, any one might have believed that he had a whole clan at his back, somewhere over the skyline, and he lord of the whole push. Nor might any one guess that he himself had spent many years in uncomfortable places distant from his home, in the small matter of Gul Zamán, deceased, and was even now on the unceasing *qui vive* owing to the presumed survival of Tor Khan, the brother ; which, to my mind, make his carelessness about sleeping in the open all the more inexplicable.

For all this I neglected no precautions. At nightfall our entire fit-out of silver, glass, china, cutlery and anything else which we thought the Sardár across the way or his expensive lady, might fancy were securely padlocked into one godown at the end of the verandah near our bedroom— securely, that is to say, as far as any security might be within those worthless walls and behind those barely cat-proof doors. For the rest, I trusted to Wallu, and to our increasing immunity.

A further precaution was a form of drill, in which, on the first sound of a shot fired, the memsahib was immediately and without hesitation or question to lie flat on the floor, and stay there till told to get up, thereby freeing the fighting portion of the ménage and giving it the elbow-room and field of fire which it needed.

But Wallu was our mainstay. He swaggered about by day, lord of creation, and sometimes would absent himself for hours, knowing that the house would be perfectly safe in the daytime, though by now we had a total of five casualties to mark up, and nothing to set against them but the witless wanderer in the hills. The incident of the smuggling party went by default. The Pathans, naturally, counted it a bull's-eye to us ; but we were busy trying to forget it, and, in our secret souls, were thoroughly ashamed of it, so it lapsed from the score.

.   .   .   .

I had long ago given up asking Wallu to help by keeping his ears open and gathering information of impending raids or snipings. He was too obviously in the enemy's camp for his fellow-Pathans to let him gather the least inkling of what intentions were afoot. Apart from which, it seemed almost certain that the raids were carried out from across the frontier line, either with the connivance or at the direct instigation of the Sardár of Kadanai, who was credibly reported to have bought, at his own price, the proceeds of every raid ; while the snipings might have been anybody's work, since they rarely coincided with the lootings. But about this time I was seated on the edge of the verandah in company with Wallu, with whom I was discussing the situation ; Hamish, the Aberdeen, squatting on his hunkers up against Wallu's baggy clothing, Wallu with his arm round the dog in clear defiance of Musalman precept which holds such animals unclean.

" I got hold of a bit of a rumour yesterday, sahib. The Sardár has a new recruit, a man they say is the cleverest thief on the Border. Nobody knows his name, but they say he's from my part of the world "—nodding in the direction of the Achakzai crags, hull-down on the horizon—" and I ought to know him. Can't think who he can be. They say he's boasted he will clean out the whole cantonment, and is coming in to the bazaar before long to get the hang of the place. He's over in Kadanai now . . ." and he rumbled off into contemplative silence.

Long pause.

" You'd better potter about the bazaar a bit for the next few days and see if you can spot him. If he's from your part of the world you may be able to recognise him, and, if so, we ought to be able to round him up."

" I wonder . . ." and, with a puzzled " shaitán tamán ! " (the whole thing's the very deuce an' all !), he hove himself up on to his feet, spat contemplatively and strolled off to his quarters.

.   .   .   .

What happened two days later I pieced together from the accounts of the Gurkha bazaar-guard and from several eye-witnesses. The versions hang together in all details, so I may as well tell it just as it happened.

Wallu had gone off to the bazaar, as suggested. He was squatting in the main street in front of one of the open booths which, in the daytime, crowd the roadway in front of the shops, and was fingering over the wares while he chatted to the owner. Presently, from the direction of the South Fort, an uproar approached rapidly, and, looking up, he saw the father and mother of all sand-devils come whirling up the main street. Way and away on top of it spun a Gurkha hat and a government blanket, gathered up in passing over the Fort. The din was terrific. Strollers fled for shelter ; booth-keepers grabbed their trays and spreadeagled themselves over their wares, while the loose matting roofs of the stalls blew to pieces ; doors and shutters banged ; small boys were knocked over, and dogs yelped and scattered into side-alleys ; all who could hung on to anything solid within reach, and huddled together as the whirling breath of the Pit bore down on them with the clatter and roar of an express train coming through a dense fog. Wallu crouched low and bent his head between his knees, while for a full half-minute pandemonium raged in the thick darkness around him.

The devil went roaring on its way, pursued by yells of laughter and *décolleté* jokes as it was seen that the hat and blanket at its summit had been joined by two voluminous pairs of frill-bedecked feminine plus-fives gathered from a house-top, where they had been laid out to dry after washing. "Is it from *thy* house-top, Sher Dil?" "Nay, from *thine*, Abdul Majid?" . . . The fun grew fast and furious. But he whose Rabelaisian roars would have overtopped all— whose salty and shouted jest would have turned the sand in men's eyes to mud with the very tears of their laughter ?

Silent.

Slowly they gather round him : a tiptoe circle. Don't touch him. Don't get too near, lest men should point an accusing finger ! Each tries his best to be inconspicuous. . . . *Who did it? Who*, in the darkness of the sand-devil, did it? Whose is the axe. . . . For there lies the herculean bulk of Wallu, his fallen puggaree tangled in a heavy hatchet, his hair streaming in the foulness of the running gutter, and a great ragged hole in his head where his skull has been crushed in.

"Tora," whispers somebody ; "Tor Khan " . . . and they melt away, soft-footed.

Oh-*ho* ; so they must have known about it all the time !
. . . .

The Gurkha bazaar orderly, full of importance, bustles up. "Hallo? Man dead ? Who did it ? Here, you *janwars*, help me have a look at him. Give a hand here. Hustle ! "—

and, with his cane, he herds the reluctant onlookers forward. " Turn him over, you," to a trembling Hindu shopkeeper ; " who is he ? " He peers. Whistles softly. " Wallu ! Of the Karnél sahib's house ! Now you've been and gone and done it. *Now* you've torn it, you ——s. Here, catch a hold ! "

It takes half a dozen of them to lift him, the Gurkha nursing the shattered head tenderly. They place him on a *charpoy* and carry him to my house, whence, mercifully, the memsahib is absent. I meet the little procession on the verandah. " Wallu ! What mischief has the old devil been up to now ? " No explanations ; the shortest of inspections ; " Quick ! Off to the hospital with him " . . . and, hot-footed, I precede him.

By a mercy, Macdonald, our doctor, is there ; a man skilled in all the sudden blugginesses of the Border. He fingers the crushed and matted head carefully. " Lord," he whistles, " here's a job and a half." . . . Five minutes later, " Hope ? I dunno. These chaps are damned tough, but I think he's booked. I'll tell you more when I've had a good look at him." (Pulse ? No pulse. Cold. . . .) " Come back this evening, sir, and I'll tell you what I think. We'll do our utmost for him. Poor old Wallu," as he bends to his task, the hospital staff busy around him.

So homewards, with a heavy heart. By the Lord Harry, we'll make somebody smell hell for this !

By evening I return. There lies Wallu, cleaned, stripped of befouled clothing, lying on a ward-bed under a clean white sheet, his great head propped on a pillow and massive with swathe of white bandaging. Great blue valleys circle his sunken eyes ; his wide jaws hollow ; a grey pallor over all ; his aquiline beak points stiffly to the ceiling as the great gasps of breath come hurtling out through his chalk-coloured lips. Lying there, helpless and on the verge of death ; that magnificent specimen of lovable manhood. . . . *Dieu qui le fit de ses deux mains.* . . .

" We've had to trephine him The only chance for him. Bad case "

" Will he live ? "

" I'm afraid not. It would take the strength of three men to get over what *he's* been given. You see . . ."

Details.

Once more homewards ; two of us, since the memsahib, dainty, trim and very frail-looking against the desert back-

ground, has been waiting outside the hospital door. She slips
her arm through mine.

"You'll get even with them, won't you, Bill?"

"Please God!" says I.

VI

THERE'S nothing very much to be done. I lock up the
old chap's quarters and then stroll down to the office,
send for the Adjutant and concoct new measures. Not, indeed,
in a spirit of personal retaliation, nor in any sudden loss of
balance; but because, so far, things have followed an
awkward but definable course. Raids are raids, thoughout
the Border; also, shootings and snipings are the common
lot of Frontier mankind; but when it comes to making
personal war on the head of the show, the question of *izzat*
(what they call "face," farther East) is involved; and if we
let it slide we might as well chuck our hand in and give the
other side best man.

With many little sums in addition and subtraction, and
a close comb-out of "employed" men, we find it will just
about run to it. No more of these moving patrols, to be a
gift to the lurker and to miss the raider. A complicated
plan ensues, but one which will give a stationary escort to
every bungalow and building not within the walls of the
forts, each escort to have an absolutely free hand to use any
and every feasible measure against the common enemy.
One reservation I make, to save dwindling self-respect.
There shall be no guard on the C.O.'s bungalow. The
Adjutant stares.

"I don't think you're wise, sir."

"Never mind. I'm old enough and ugly enough to look
after myself. Besides, after what they did to Wallu, I expect
they'll avoid me like the devil. Make it so, will you?" And
the orders go forth.

So, back home to dinner and bed; an automatic under
the pillow, and a barely avoided breeze with the wife who
refuses point-blank to go and sleep in the Fort.

Poor old Wallu. . . .

    .   .   .   .   .   .

Do what we would, we could not catch up with the
situation. For now raidings and snipings synchronised.
There would be a shot at an open bungalow window, and,

while all guards in the neighbourhood turned out to hunt the sniper, a godown or a stable would be forced and the contents would vanish. Johnny Gurk is a superlative fighter, but his brains are worth about a capful of porridge ; never could we make him understand that the man on the move is a gift to the man behind cover, or that each group had to look after its own show and nobody else's. A couple of bangs, and the air would be thick with bloodthirsty Gurks, hurtling like meteorites through space from all directions, and converging on an empty but still warm patch on the ground, while half the cantonment lay deserted and unguarded. Even after we had managed to get them to keep still, losses went on in a mysterious way. The Second-in-Command lost his first and second chargers in the same night, stolen from under the very noses of the guard ; next night, in spite of redoubled precautions, his entire vine was stripped of grapes, a piece of pure mischief, since most of them were found abandoned out in the roadway next morning. Then cantonments got a bit of a rest, only to be broken by five minutes' rapid fire, down the main street of the bazaar this time ; the shopkeepers lying flat on their floors behind the heavy wooden shutters. The state of affairs was becoming chaotic, and was rapidly degenerating into a condition where Pathans with grudges against each other were beginning to pay off old scores, and saying the raiders had done it.

A mixed time altogether.

So down to the hospital for the daily visit to Wallu.

He had moved neither hand nor foot nor eyelid since the operation ; but still he lived, if living you could call it, and still Macdonald watched over him, with little spoonfuls of milk, or egg, or the pernicious brandy, which the sufferer would have spat out had he been conscious, forced between his blue lips Hypodermic injections There was nothing they would not do to keep the fluttering life within the four corners of its magnificent casket.

" Will he live ? "

" By all the rules . . ." a headshake.

Home to the wife, who asks the same question, to get the same headshake It is she about whom one frets most ; she is beginning to look peaky, though there is never anything but the cheeriest of smiles. We bar and shutter everything and take a good look round the compound, stables and servants' quarters. I slip a clip into the automatic, tuck it under the pillow and we turn in.

B'jove, thinks I, if only we could catch this one blighter, this king-pin of all our troubles, who is at the back of all this intensive work, I really think we would scotch the whole business for good. Lummy, *what* a score it would be. . . .

With uncanny persistence the raids continued, though by now the sniping in cantonments had dwindled to about a shot a night and no harm done. The Gurks had learnt the drill. But the bazaar suffered, and buzzed like an angry bee hive. Had they been able to spot the nuisance-mongers or their leader, they would have torn him to bits with their bare hands. Some one master-mind was obviously directing things, and each day brought fresh rumours of who it was that led them. Gumándar Shah, Qurbán Ali, Musa of Bostán? Names multiplied, and anybody who had a grievance against anybody in the hills or across the frontier line, whispered his name abroad as the common enemy The raiders were ubiquitous and quite undefeatable ; they came like wraiths and vanished like smoke.

Another visit to Wallu, who by now puzzled the doctor. He showed us an X-ray photograph of the head. You never saw such a mess. . . .

" Trephining relieved it ? "

" Oh, yes ; he'd have been dead a fortnight ago but for that. But the brain ; look here . . ." and he pointed.

Hope, then. There *must* be hope, even if the doctor's knowledge forbade it. Homewards, with a little of the gloom lightened, and an added relief at a clear full-moon night, in which, at least, peace might be expected. But, lord ! to think that the old virile chivalry of the Border should have degenerated into this damned bang-snatch-and-scatter game ! It was enough to make one pack up and go home to raise eggs on a poultry farm !

Same old round of the compound and, whether broad moonlight or not, testing locks and bolts. The dog to his usual corner in the dining-room near the precious godown, and ourselves to muggy slumber in the furnace heat of the bedroom.

Suddenly from unmeasured oblivion, we wake with a start, to hear Hamish barking furiously. Grab the automatic, and into the dining-room. What is it, old dog? Hamish flies to the door leading into the verandah and scratches to be let out. A quick footstep outside, and the sound of something heavy and glassy being dropped and smashed, as I shoot back the bolts and stumble over an overturned deck-chair, Hamish darting into the open godown with angry and excited yelps. Quick—after the dog—he's on to something ! Into the godown, whose outer and verandah doors hang groggily from smashed hinges, and the moonlight shows a scene of desolation. Floor, cupboards, shelves, everything ripped open and stripped bare Raiders ! Thought so ! But the dog's on to them. After him. Round the corner of the bungalow, and into the back compound. A group of three, stooping over a load to be lifted Bang ! The sickly stink of bad Pathan powder, as a chunk of mud brick is dislodged and cascades down. Pull up quick Panting I raise the automatic, and pull the trigger, *hard*. Nothing happens ; safety-catch on ! Fumble hastily with the safety-catch, just as one of the group raises his gun again. Ah-ha ; too *late*, old bird ! The automatic answers loyally to repeated trigger-pulls ; the group breaks up ; two fly for their lives across the yard and hurdle the low mud wall separating the compound from the barbed wire and the open desert, I after them. Out on to the sharp shingle ; an almighty toss and an ungainly sprawl, as one of those loose-fitting Jaegar slippers of the memsahib's providing comes off and trips me up. With breath clean knocked out of me, I make poor shooting with what remains of the clip in the automatic, and an empty pistol is all that I can point at two nimble figures skipping through the half-dismantled wire and out into the vague grey of the desert.

Bruised, dishevelled and in a towering rage, I limp back to the house. A dawning calmness brings the realisation that there were two get-aways, but three at the outset. Christmas !—there's another somewhere, and this automatic as much use as a sick headache. Must get another clip before investigating further. Dodge quickly back into the verandah and in through the open door, to find the memsahib sitting on the edge of the bed, a vision of daintiness in a silk nightie and her toes dangling, but rather white about the gills ; and Hamish—shame on you, brother Scot—cowering under the bed !—a tiger in a rough-and-tumble, but incurably gun-shy.

" Hallo, why aren't you flat on the floor ? " is our somewhat ungracious welcome to the lady.

" Never thought of it. You all right ? "

" Rather. Where are those clips ? Lie down on the floor, quick. *Flat*. That's right ; and don't move. I've got to investigate a bit more."

I grab an electric torch and dart out. By now the servants in their quarters have awoken and are beginning to hammer each on his locked door. Before starting operations the raiders have securely fastened the chains to the staples of the outside door-fastenings to prevent any interference. Let them be a moment. The fewer messing about just now, the better.

Round to the back.

M'm ; I *thought* so.

For there, in the middle of the moonlight patch, is a group composed of the big " troopship case " from the verandah, its hasp and staple wrenched off and half-open, and a grey-clad figure all muddled-up alongside, and motionless.

With automatic well to the fore, advance carefully ; no surprise, please. Closer. And now comes the subdued and whimpering cry of a man deadly hurt.

" Hwee-ee-e . . ." ; hiccup.

" Hwee-ee-e-ah . . ." ; hiccup.

" Hwee-ee. . . ."

Take no chances. With the automatic to his ear-hole, flash the torch over him. Big burly ruffian. Don't know him. Where's he hurt ? The voice rises to an agonised " Ai-ee-EE ! " as I pull gently at his clothing, and desist. Poor devil. Got it somewhere amidships apparently. A sticky mess of blood oozes from under him.

Time now to loose the servants. In strict order of personal courage they emerge. First, Jagat Bahadur, the Gurkha orderly, his kukri handy and raving at having been left out of the row. Then the syce, with a heavy stick ; then the others, tailing on to the dog-boy. The cook not at all ; but the wailings behind his door are those of a healthy man, not one who has caught a stray bullet.

Bring a *charpoy*, quick !

They come with a native bedstead. With infinite care we lift the poor blighter on to it, and set the servants to carry him off to the hospital, with a hasty note to Macdonald ; Jagat Bahadur as escort, and as full of himself as if the *shikar* were his own.

Back to the bungalow ; the memsahib, clean against orders, up and dressed, and Hamish with nose down, fussing about all over the place. A word or two ; I tumble into my clothes, and the memsahib goes off to brew a pot of tea ; or rather, to try to brew it, for in a minute back she comes again, white with rage and with unaccustomed swear-words

in her dainty mouth. " The godown and kitchen are empty—
empty, d'you hear ? They've got the lot. Not a damn thing
left ! " And the intensity of her fury banks back the tears
that should have been inevitable.

Dawn finds us piecing together in the early light the events
of the night. Everything in the godown, the *bottle-khana*, and
the kitchen, has vanished. They must have been at it for
hours—within four yards of the sleeping dog and close to
ourselves—passing each man-load out through the wire to
the rest of the gang beyond, who went off with it as fast as it
accumulated. But how they managed to handle piles of
plates, crockery, glass, lamps, tinkly knives and silver, the
whole rattlesome bag of tricks, without making more sound
than a prowling mouse, was a revelation in burglary. What
had roused the dog at the end must have been the crowning
piece of impertinence ; for the big " troopship case " which
stood in the verandah, about the same shape and size as
an oaken hall-settee here at home and which contained
nothing more important than golf-clubs and odds and ends,
this they had lifted bodily, and had managed to scrape through
the broken godown doors and so out into the back premises.
They must have made their first and slightest noise in doing
it. And all this on one of the brightest moonlight nights of
the year. 'Pon my soul, they almost *deserved* their success !

Late that afternoon we recovered one tiny survival,
close up to the boundary pillars, in the direction of Kadanai—
a handful of fragments which, when afterwards riveted
together, took the shape of a small china milk-jug (with
small pink pimpernel and forget-me-not pattern round the
edge—rather chaste), our only trophy of the night's doings.
We have it still.

The Lady of Baldak stood on the verandah edge. She,
at a range of seven miles, faced the Khánum of Kadanai ;
and, as any one could plainly see, was wishing in every
fibre of her little tiger heart that the distance had been only
that number of inches.

VII

So down to the hospital, and to Macdonald in the surgery.
" What news of Wallu ? "

" He's still alive ; it puzzles me how he manages it.
He hasn't shown sign of consciousness, to my knowledge,

since he came here ; and yet he manages to live. I can't help thinking there's something keeping that old beggar alive—some wild urge which was in his tough old mind just as he was struck down, and which keeps on now as a sort of dumb delirium—simply pushing out the thought of giving in. I've heard of it happening in other cases. Wonder what it can be. . . . But that's a bad case you sent in to me this morning, sir. Who got him ? "

" H'm—a bad case, is it ? D'you mind if I go in and have a look at him ? "

I tiptoe down the long ward. There is Wallu, as stark and immovable as he has lain these three weeks past, hardly a change in the great gaunt features. On the bed next to him, watched over by the native assistant surgeon, lies our big Pathan of the night's business. I sidle in between the beds and bend over the unfortunate. One glance ; he's booked, right enough. Questioned, the doctor-babu tells us of a ghastly and hopeless wound : the heavy automatic bullet has drilled him clean through the pelvis from hip to hip, and, lying on his back with knees drawn up, he is gasping out the last hour of his life.

Fine chap, big powerful profile ; wonder who he can be ? We study him closely. . . .

Down, Hamish ! The dog is plucking at the slack of my khaki shorts from behind. Hallo ? Can't be the dog ; left him at home. Instantly an incredible thought flashes. I turn round with a jerk. *Wallu !* The long bony hand meets my bare knee. The great sunken eyes are open. Slowly, very slowly, an inch at a time, the bandaged head turns on the pillow, towards the next bed, in a keen and penetrating stare. " Sahib," in a whisper. I bend lower. " Sahib . . ." and, with a mighty effort, " sahib . . . *Tor Khan !* "

Slowly, slowly, by perceptible inches, the corners of the deeply sunken eyes wrinkle, and the great gaunt face breaks up into a smile of the angelic beatitude ; the eyes close, and, still smiling, he sinks into the long and healthy depths of life-giving sleep.

What ? Oh, yes ; *he's* all right. Not only still alive, but as strong as ever. Following my yearly practice, I sent him ten rupees last Christmas.

THE WHIRL OF FATE

By

MAJOR a.d. FRANZ MASKE

SIBERIA! The word conjures up sad memories and dark visions of illimitable space. The friendless emptiness of grey steppes beckons to us and we instinctively think of the deadly solitude of the tundra. The curtain of prehistoric times seem to veil the mysterious darkness of great forests and vast mountain ranges. We almost see the ravening wolves pursuing the peasants' sledges over the snowy wastes, and hear the clanking of the iron chains clogging the limbs of broken men who tramp painfully along the unending path which leads to banishment.

From 1914 onwards some three thousand prisoners of war from the Austro-Hungarian, Turkish and German armies were interned in the centre of Siberia on the high bank of the Yenissei, north of the town of Krasnoyarsk. The place of internment was a stone-built barracks which had originally been erected as a depot. The camp was in the middle of the steppe, and a double line of sentries kept the prisoners from all contact with the outer world.

The prisoners were unutterably miserable, both in body and mind. They had spent dreadful weeks and months in the Russian hospitals and suffered the pangs of starvation, and when they reached the internment camp they had also known the horrors of that gruesome visitation, Asiatic typhus. Thousands of brave warriors whose warm young lives were cut short by cruel death now sleep their last sleep in the great pits, far from their beloved homeland.

One day in August, 1915, the young Danzig Hussar, Wolf von B——, and I were crawling miserably round the camp with weary limbs. We were trying to exercise our legs, which had become weak and stiff as a result of our wounds and months of inactivity in hospital. We fully realised that we must recover our physical strength. Our duty and our task was to escape, back to the homeland, back to the front.

But how? Siberia's boundless spaces, Asia's dark mystery were around and about us. No sound came from the vast steppe, and the sun was a round, violet, unearthly disc behind a vaporous, grey-blue curtain which one of the frequent forest fires was spreading over this incomprehensible land.

We stood meditating in a little hollow which led through the Russian sentry lines out into the steppe. Under cover of night a man of courage could creep out at this point and make his way out of the camp into the Asiatic immensity.

Eastwards, China beckoned ; southwards, Mongolia ; and westwards, Finland. Northwards, a boat could carry us down the Yenissei and across the Arctic Sea to the North Cape of Norway. Yet we might share the fate of so many others and lose our lives in the venture. Some one might some day stumble across our corpses rotting in the mountains or buried in some forest.

I had been learning Turkish from a captured Turkish officer. One day the Turk helped my thoughts of flight to take material shape. He had a friend in the Russian port of Baku on the Caspian—a hotel proprietor who was a good Turkish patriot. This man could direct us from Baku to Persia, which was neutral. The idea infected me like a raging fever, and I could not get it out of my head. Yet Baku was a long way away and Persia but a misty notion. But where there's a will there's a way ! My mind was soon made up. To Baku and Persia I would go ! The Turk gave me a letter of introduction to his friend in Baku. This friend would put us in touch with a certain Suleiman who would show us the way to freedom.

After weeks of thought and preparation the plan took shape. My Prussian training brought the chaos of vague hopes and imaginings down to earth and evolved three practical stages. The first comprised the escape from the internment camp to a place of hiding in the neighbouring town of Krasnoyarsk. The second meant a railway journey from Krasnoyarsk, through Siberia and Russia, to Baku. The third and final stage covered Baku and the escape from Russia into Persia.

Each of the three stages involved the most careful planning, the most meticulous preparation and luck. Much luck. Luck on the Asiatic scale ! The adventure seemed a monstrous speculation. I could not speak Russian, and would have to spend weeks in Russian trains in the company of Russian soldiers and officials. Russian Cossacks were only too fond of using their beloved knout, and Russian courts

made short work of their prisoners. But after considering
all these things the call of freedom was too strong for me.

One day chance brought me into contact with a Jewess
who came in a trap to the camp with eatables for sale. I
entered into secret negotiations with her.

The good woman seemed to me the very embodiment of
Fate, black, crafty and massive. Her little stool creaked and
groaned under the weight of all her mounds of flesh. But she
was kind and sympathetic, as fat people often are.

We talked in German Yiddish. My plan was at first a
matter of figures. She demanded three hundred roubles for
her help and an escort from Krasnoyarsk to Baku. Agreed!
Next came the scheme itself. She was to go with my little
friend Wolf, the eighteen-year-old Hussar, and then find an
escort for me in Krasnoyarsk. Wolf was very small, and
almost like a girl or small boy to look at. He was to wear
short pants and a boy's jacket and travel as " little Sasha,"
the friend of her own small offspring Volodia. Mama was
to go on a journey with Volodia and Sasha. It seemed a
fine idea.

The Jewess came back to camp several times, and at last
everything was arranged. An old Jew had agreed to
accompany me.

Our next job was to remove all traces of ourselves in the
camp. If our flight were discovered the Russians would
send Cossacks after us into the steppe and gendarmes into
the towns, while all the railway stations would be warned.
If they found us, God help us !

As all the officer prisoners were counted every day, two
German sergeants agreed to wear our uniforms. Everything
was ready and the day had been fixed for our flight. We
had arranged to meet our Jewish helpers on the main road
to the town.

A dark autumn night was descending upon the Yenissei
region when we set out. A keen wind from the steppe
searched the desolate streets of the camp. Rain pelted down
upon the roofs. Wolf and I gazed cautiously into the darkness.
All seemed clear. Somewhere far away a dog was howling.
We sped round a corner, crept along the walls of houses,
ran across open spaces, sheltered in the dark shadows of
sheds, and at length found ourselves cowering on the wet
ground hidden by a stack of timber.

Before us lay the ravine, passing through the lines of
sentries which we had watched so often and so long. The

shadows of the motionless sentries stood out against the sky. Turning up their coat collars and presenting their backs to the wind and rain they kept their silent and chilly watch.

My heart beat as if it would burst. The great moment had come. Freedom was calling and a war to which I must return. I lay flat on my stomach like a dog, and, holding my breath, crawled slowly across the puddles and through the depression which hid our movements. This stage seemed unending. The water splashed, and at every sound I froze to stone. If any sentry noticed anything he would shoot. We were at war ! I crawled on, inch by inch. At last we were through the sentries. The camp and the sentries disappeared in the darkness behind us. We were in the open.

Wolf followed me. Crouching down, we hurried over the steppe until we were at a safe distance. Then we waited and listened. There was no sound of pursuit or alarm from the camp. We shook hands fervently, as excited as schoolboys. We were free, free as the wolves in the mountains—surrounded by foes !

Our plans worked out well. On the dark road into the town we met our accomplices and went to our hiding-place in their house. The next few days were spent in transforming our appearance to something unrecognisable and more local. Wolf became a nice boy, and I a poor old man.

The day came for us to take the Siberian Railway for Russia. We had arranged to travel together, but in two groups, the Jewess with her two children and I with my old Jew.

Bending under the weight of a sack of clothes on my back I entered the waiting-room of Krasnoyarsk Station. The place was well-lit with arclights. On the platforms young men and soldiers were strolling about exchanging jokes with the girls.

My Jew whispered hoarsely into my ear, " Throw your sack down in a corner and sit on it ! " I did so. My heart beat wildly, for a large policeman was walking slowly past. At that moment the Jewess arrived with the children. " Here, Sasha ; come here, Volodia ! " she bawled out. Then she caught sight of the policeman and was petrified. She put the children down on the table. " Be good boys, and wait for me ! " Wolf produced some sweets from his pocket and crammed them into the other little fellow's mouth. When he saw me he gave me a surreptitious nod.

The train came in and every one made for the exit. We

found room in a fourth-class compartment of a corridor coach, and I simultaneously secured a berth on the third shelf. I meant to lie there as long as I could without being disturbed.

The passengers made one family from the start. Every one made himself at home, for the carriage was to be our dwelling-place for days and perhaps weeks. Talk was soon lively and general, but I lay motionless in my dark corner. Officials came to inspect the tickets. I handed them mine, but said nothing.

The first night passed, and when day came it was noticed that I did not get up. The Jew put on a sad expression and said that I was a poor devil whom he was taking to see a doctor in Moscow. There was little hope, alas ! He pointed to his throat. But a man's a man, after all, and he wasn't a tiger. What could he do.

For three days I had not visited a certain place. I suddenly had to, jumped up and rushed out. All was well. This first independent act gave me confidence, and thereafter I went frequently for a breather to the quiet spot where one can lock oneself in without exciting comment.

The passengers, peasants, soldiers, women and children, were always changing. All were full of their own interests and excited about the " journeys."

On the seventh day we reached Cheliabinsk, the frontier town between Siberia and Russia. Here the passports were checked. Would my forged passport escape detection ?

We were all bustled out of the train into a shed. Once more I sat unobtrusively on my sack in a corner. Suddenly the Jewess burst into the crowd, crying out in furious tones, " It's disgusting the way they insult ladies here. Come, children. It makes me wild ! " The gendarmes went about among the crowd, here and there picking on a passport for examination. The Jewess's turn arrived in due course. But Mama was equal to the occasion. She hunted desperately in all her pockets, her muff and her box for the passport. " Sasha, you horrid little boy, you've hidden the passport ! " Wolf shrugged his shoulders. " Volodia, stop picking your nose, you dirty little ragamuffin ! " She boxed the young imp's ears. She rummaged and swore. Volodia bellowed. She wiped her nose and then emptied her box. At length the tears poured down her cheeks. The gendarme was filled with terror of the old Jewess. He was glad to get away from her and her tears and uproar, and he hastily turned to the next victim. Saved! The Jewess knew a bit about life. Her witch's arts were too much for the strongest man.

The danger had passed me by, and we were allowed to return to the train and the journey proceeded. At Samara we had to change. The new train turned southwards through the Don region, the home of the Cossacks. I still lived on my bunk on the third shelf and tried to make myself invisible. I had become quite used to intercourse with soldiers, gendarmes and officials. Danger was ever present, and, what with lively incidents, "heart-attacks," terrors and pieces of luck, the time passed more or less quickly.

I spent fifteen days as a dumb passenger among a host of enemies in the confined space of that train. At length we found ourselves travelling eastwards through the northern Caucasus. I could already see the broad expanse of the Caspian Sea shining in the sun. A Cossack in the compartment began to sing " Volga, Volga, Mother of the Cossacks," in a loud and beautiful voice.

The train stopped at a station and we were in Baku.

So far Luck had helped us. Without Luck we could never have got so far without being found out on the road.

The next thing was to get fixed up in Baku. The Turk had given me a letter to his hotel proprietor in Baku. This man could put us in touch with a certain Suleiman, and Suleiman could arrange for us to go by road from Baku into Persia.

It was already evening when we arrived, and the old Jew and I walked into the town and found the hotel and its owner. As soon as he had read my letter of introduction he threw us out of the hotel and shouted for the police.

My Jew was smitten with fear and bolted out of the hotel. When I got out into the street again I saw him scurrying round the corner. Never again did I hear his kind, hoarse voice and rasping cough.

Mama and the children were waiting hopefully in the street. What was to be done? I sent the family back to the station waiting-room. They were to stay there till I came for them. The only hope was that I should go myself and find Suleiman. I was in a strange town, full of enemies whose language I could not speak, looking for a man of whom I knew nothing but his name. But Suleiman *must* be found.

I wandered about for some time, and then, down by the quays, I found a shelter for the night among the great stacks

of merchandise. How nice it was to be alone, away from
the noisy crowd on the trains ! It was a warm night and
the starry sky spread a mantle of velvet over my quiet bed.
I had to rise at daybreak and go back into the town. I
wandered about at random. Suddenly I found myself in
fairyland.

The Orientals had laid out all their variegated wares in
the street and were sitting cross-legged among carpets and
fruits of all kinds. Caravans, horses, camels and donkeys
were swinging their way through the crowd. The magic
of the East was awake. Suleiman must be here. Aladdin's
wonderful lamp would point him out to me.

With renewed hope, and relying on the patriotism of the
Turks living in Russian Baku, I entered an inn and asked
in Turkish for Suleiman. The owner of the place, a fat
man wearing a turban, laughed and said, " There are lots
of Turks named Suleiman." I made up my mind quickly
and handed him my letter of introduction, in which it was
written that I was a German officer and that it was the
sacred duty of every Mohammedan to help me on my way.
The Turk looked serious, shook his head and went out. A
servant brought in tea and bread. I spent the whole day
sitting quietly in the corner, and hoping to soften the fat
Turk's heart by sheer persistence, but when evening came
and the inn room was closed I was turned out.

For the second night I went back with my sack to my lair
on the quays, but when morning came I returned to the
Turkish inn.

Again I went on the third day, but apparently with no
effect. However, as I left, the Turk sent a boy after me.
The lad caught hold of my hand and, pointing to a large
public building, said, " You must come here and ask for
Suleiman to-morrow." The East is indeed full of marvels !

Early next morning I entered the building indicated, in
my Siberian costume, which was conspicuous and dangerous
here in the south. I made my way into a large room. A
portrait of the Tsar and Russian notices on the walls showed
clearly that we were in Russia. Perhaps the police, I thought,
and was afraid, remembering the brutality of the Russian
police.

I stood in front of a clerk, twisting my fur cap in my
hand, and asked in halting tones and bad Turkish for
Suleiman.

" You're no Turk," said the clerk.

F.T.S.   2 R

626 MAJOR a.d. FRANZ MASKE

" No, sir," I answered in Russian.

" You're not a Russian, either," said the clerk.

" No, sir. I'm French," I answered in French.

" That's all right," said my clerk. " I speak French too."

" Now I'm done for," thought I.

But as luck would have it the clerk's French was no better than that of a Spanish night watchman. He led me courteously to the telephone and said, " Parlez ! There's a lady there who speaks your language fluently."

All the clerks in the office stopped work and crowded round me as I talked. I used every word of French I had ever learned at school, until a woman's voice at the other end broke in with a laugh.

" You're certainly not a Frenchman, but if you'll wait a minute I'll come to you."

I waited. I was already a great expert in that department, but once more it was brought home to me that waiting is a great and difficult art, particularly when one is worried and in danger.

Two ladies arrived—mother and daughter, to judge by first impressions. They pushed me out of the room and into the corridor, chatting volubly all the time. " You're a prisoner of war," said the daughter. " German ? "

It's not easy to lie to a pair of fine eyes.

" Yes, I'm German."

The lady thrust a note into my hand and told me to take a carriage and go to the address it contained. Then they vanished.

I followed my instructions minutely until I came to a house in a back street. As soon as I knocked I was admitted, and in a few minutes I was sitting on a divan and smiling at the two ladies.

Marvels flourish in the East. For where was I ? At the house of Suleiman himself ! Frau Suleiman offered me tea, and her quiet smile inspired me with confidence and fresh hope. The young lady, who I was glad to learn had acquired her French in Switzerland, beamed on me with dark eyes— eyes as deep and dark as the bewildering marvels and fairytales of this land. Herr Suleiman, very much in the flesh, gave me local clothes and told me he would help me.

I could hardly believe my luck. Herr Suleiman arranged everything. I was to go down to the port next day and bring my friend with me.

Shortly before nightfall I hurried to the station. How

pleased Wolf would be ! I felt considerable reluctance to enter the waiting-room, with its officials and gendarmes, who were particularly active in the harbour quarters. The Jewess was sitting in the corner, brooding like a great black hen on its nest. Her Volodia was sleeping innocently in her arms. Of Wolf nothing was to be seen. I made a sign. The Jewess stood up. A head was thrust out from under Mama's warm, wide skirts. It was Wolf ! He had spent dreary days and anxious nights, and when there was danger was concealed in this way. His hard breathing showed that he was mighty glad to get a little fresh air.

We were desperately sorry to take our leave of the Jewess. How kind and courageous she had been !

.   .   .   .

When we reached the port, Wolf and myself, we found Suleiman, and with him a man called Ibrahim, who would accompany us across the Caspian to the Persian shore.

Men with deeply tanned skins and exposing half of their sweating bodies were carrying bales into a ship, while customs officers watched them and made notes. This ship was going across to Persia, and after Ibrahim had uttered some magic password we went on board.

We lay out of sight in the ship's black belly until she moved. The engines heaved and trembled. When the great paddle-wheels began to thrash the water we rushed up on deck to wave a last farewell to Russia. The shore was bright with lights and even the darkness beyond was broken here and there by the bright flames from oil-wells.

The steamer was called *Odysseus*, and the name conjured up memories of far-away schooldays and the immortal poems of Homer. Odysseus, the godlike sufferer, had much to put up with before he saw his home again.

.   .   .   .

At dawn on the second day of our voyage the ship steamed into the mouth of a river, the Kura. We had to disembark at a little town. The streets were still empty, but—oh, horror !—Russian Cossacks were watering their horses at the river. We were to wait for Ibrahim at a hut. It was several hours before he came back. On a broad, sandy road some considerable way out of the town we got into a *troika*. Ibrahim and a strange man sat in front. We took our places behind, and off we went into the blue.

The road led through peaceful cotton-fields and farms occupied by Cossacks on frontier guard. When evening came

we stopped at a farm. Before the door a black man stood
waiting ; his black eyes gleamed from under a high sheepskin
cap and he was carrying a leather belt with cartridges
across his chest and round his waist, and a rifle was slung
over his shoulder. At his feet were a number of sheep-dogs.
The stranger casually pointed to him. " That's Husein, my
servant, friend and helper. He's both the general and the
army which protects my house and my lands." I respectfully
raised my new felt hat.

Husein brought in tea and bread and laid out some dirty
blankets in a corner—our bedding for the night.

Next day the man showed us over his fields. In the
evening three Tartars arrived at the farm, and a council
of war was held over us. The Tartars were to take us across
the frontier into Persia. The farmer produced a map of the
frontier district and showed us the direction of the shortest
route, which would first take us to the frontier through
the great roadless Mugansteppe and then into a region of
high, black mountains to a lofty peak, the snow-covered
summit of which was marked on the map, " Savellan,
4813 metres." There was said to be a Persian village,
Meschgin, at its foot. The man told us that a great Persian
chief, Sergam Sultan, lived there. Once we found him he
would help us on our way.

We set off at night. The sky above the dark, brooding
land was bright with stars, and there was a slight breeze.
Husein, with his dogs and gun, came to fetch us. We said
good-bye all round and gave one more friendly glance at
this last house on the road. It seemed the last house in the
world, for at its comforting doors began the great steppe
which leads to the wild mountain region of Persia.

Husein took us far out into the steppe, where a ponderous
wagon, half-concealed in the high grass, was waiting for us.
We waved good-bye and the horses started off.

A Tartar with a grey moustache was in the driver's seat.
No one spoke as we turned to the west, where star after star
disappeared on the dark horizon. The lumbering vehicle
rolled on and little grey shadows flitted about in its wake.
The jackals from the steppe pattered behind us on our track.
Suddenly the night's calm was broken. Dogs barked, lights
appeared, cattle bellowed and men came out of the darkness,
shouting and waving sticks. The Tartar produced two pistols
from his coat and then made shrill noises like an owl. They

had a magical effect. The strange phantoms of living shadows disappeared quietly into the bushes.

Towards morning the vehicle stopped. The Tartar produced some bread and we had a meal. He told us that in the daytime the Cossack frontier guards were in the habit of riding over the steppe, so that it was essential for us to keep in hiding. When evening came we resumed our journey, and by morning reached a little village, where we halted.

There were mud huts without windows scattered over the plains, and the Tartars who lived in them were only too glad to help us. As night was falling a man came to our hut. He was a Persian soldier from the frontier guards over the border. He entered into a mysterious conversation with our driver After some time it appeared that everything was in order.

Under cover of darkness the Persian soldier led us over the grass-covered hills, and wound up by carrying us on his back across the rushing waters of the river which forms the Russo-Persian frontier at this point. We were in Persia !

The true followers of Allah the Great had helped us to cast off the chains of captivity and find safety in the Empire of the Golden Lion.

Now we were free. Russia lay behind us. Many difficulties and untoward incidents were, however, in store for us. It was just as well that we did not know that Russia had concentrated her Persian forces into an army and had already occupied all the larger towns and caravan routes of the northern provinces of Persia.

Our life for some weeks was one of continuous wandering. The Tartar Persian inhabitants passed us on from village to village. The Tartars speak a Turkish dialect, so that I was able to make myself understood to a certain extent. One day we saw a dark mountain-chain ahead of us. These were the black mountains which the farmer had shown us on the map.

At the last mud village before we reached the mountains we met a couple of strangers, ferocious fellows who were half warriors and half highwaymen, mounted and armed. They had come from the mountains to negotiate the purchase of various kinds of goods for their tribe. These two mysterious gentlemen were assigned to us as our future escort.

While it was still dark the men loaded one of their two horses with bales, mounted the other and beckoned to us to follow them. We hurried after them on foot, and the track wound on over very hilly and rough country.

At midday we halted. Tired after our weary tramp we flung ourselves on the ground for a rest. Vain hope ! While one of our honourable companions covered us with his rifle the other turned out all our pockets and helped himself to anything which took his fancy—all with a charming smile. We smiled too. Does not Allah teach us that the heart of man must not set store on earthly goods ? In any event, our escort were entitled to something for the pleasure of their company. After we had realised the fact there was an excellent understanding between us, and the journey proceeded smoothly. The mountains became higher and steeper. We toiled manfully after the little horses, which proceeded at a smart trot, but we could not afford to let the noble pair of brothers get out of sight ; still, it was hard on foot while they rode. At last night came and we slept peacefully with our bandits, under one blanket, until morning brought its fresh load of hard and painful tramping.

Shortly after setting out that day we suddenly observed lively movement on the mountainside ahead. Hundreds of sheep and goats, with a sprinkling of camels and buffaloes, were grazing in the high grass. A number of horsemen came towards us, shouting and waving their rifles. Hard eyes subjected us to a searching inspection. We looked so poverty-stricken and comical too that these savages could only laugh at us. The horsemen were from the same nomad Tartar tribe as our escort. The women of these hill-folk were having their usual evening chat at a spring, and we excited their merriment to a high degree. A shouting and laughing horde brought us through a village of tents into the presence of the Khan, the chief of the tribe. I handed him my letter of introduction with a deep bow. The Khan inspected the paper from all angles. He could not read, but the letter, though unread, made an excellent impression. We were taken into the tent, at the door of which the chief's dirty little pennant was waving in the breeze. A feast was about to begin. On a large dish was a resplendent mountain of steamed rice, crowned with a lump of mutton fat. The Khan appropriated the titbit and every one had a grab, i.e., each man thrust a greedy hand into the mountain, and crammed as much as his fist could grasp into his mouth. They invited us to take a share, and we made every effort to do our bit at this game ; but the rice ran through our fingers, while they laughed at our failures until the mountain of rice had all disappeared.

After the meal a samovar was brought in, and we squatted down, the centre of a circle of bearded ruffians who sat cross-legged on a carpet and passed a hookah from hand to hand.

"Khan, we need men and horses to take us to Meschgin," I said.

The Khan raised his hand to heaven as if he were about to pray. "Allah will give you all you need."

The words had a hopeful ring about them. Allah was going to produce horses for us. Every one went off to bed, and we turned in on the thick, gay carpet in the tent. Suddenly I felt a soft, warm body snuggling down at my side. My happy thoughts turned to the pretty little wife of the chief who had given me such an intimate and encouraging smile after the meal. Could it be possible? How nice! I delicately slipped an arm round her. Good God! A fierce, huge cur—some sort of sheep-dog—sprang up with a growl from my side and trod heavily on my stomach as it bolted from the tent. Fancy a brute like that perpetrating a silly Tartar joke in the middle of the night!

Although I had drawn my fur coat about me I was shivering with cold. It must have been freezing outside. But notwithstanding all drawbacks I went to sleep with a smile.

.   .   .   .   .

In the morning some Tartars brought three fine horses to the tent. I put on my fur coat, as I knew it would be cold in the saddle; but we were out of luck, for the Khan mounted one of the horses and two of his wives the others, and we had to continue our journey on foot behind them. I was very dissatisfied, and expressed my feelings in loud imprecations.

On the way I fell out with the Khan when discussing our next destination. I wanted to get to Meschgin, but he obstinately insisted that we must make for the tent of Sahib Khan. At length I expressed myself in vigorous terms and pointed out his error, frankly but forcibly. He took it as an insult. We spoke no more until, towards evening, he pointed out from the top of a hill a thin column of smoke rising far away in the mountains.

"That's Sahib Khan's tent," he said, turned his horse and galloped away, leaving us to fend for ourselves.

.   .   .   .   .

It was too late to go on. In Persia night falls as suddenly as a curtain, so, like prehistoric savages, we squatted on grey boulders and made short work of the bread we had

brought with us. Then for the night we crept into a crevice
in the rocks. Everything was silent, eerie, and the world
empty, and so miserable were we that we should not have
cared if the wolves had found us out.

As soon as the light began to show we got up, stretched our
weary stiff legs and made across the hills and deep valleys
to where we could see the camp-fires throwing up pennons
of smoke in the still morning air, in front of the tents of
Sahib Khan.

Ahead of us, on the broad mountain-top, lay the circle of
Sahib Khan's round tents. Shouting people and yapping
dogs ran to meet us. An old man stepped out from the
crowd and greeted us with the dignified salutation of the
Mohammedans, touching his breast, mouth and forehead
with his right hand. We did the same. He was a priest,
and after reading our letter of introduction he bade us
welcome.

. . . . .

The Khan was not in the encampment. He was away
somewhere in the mountains on an expedition against
another nomad tribe who had attacked his herds. The
priest told us that we should have to wait in the tent for the
Khan to return. He might arrive the next day or, on the
other hand, it might be three days, or possibly even three
months, so he said, but Allah would be merciful and grant
that he would not be long.

We were glad of a little rest. The people were kindly.
Our feet were very sore and cut after our long and difficult
tramp, so they brought us some oil and rags, with which
we bound them up. They liked to make us talk. The whole
encampment would crowd round us and make us talk of
Europe, of its religion and its life. They knew nothing of
the Great War except vague and distant rumours. No
stranger ever strayed into their solitudes. They lived remote
from the great world, and there was no highway to link up
life outside with their wild and desolate mountains. They
were delighted to hear all the news that we told them, and
they shook their heads and laughed like children at our
stories.

It was a pleasant life. They fed us well, gave us unending
cups of tea, and allowed us to share their public hookah
for a smoke. Now and then we sat alone outside the tent
and gazed across the hills. Behind the dark mountains the
sun's hot disc glowed and set the sky ablaze with fiery red

light. Its soft reflection painted the eternal snows on the peak of far-away Savellan a delicate pink.

They were religious and devout people also, these Tartars —Moslems, and they prayed regularly. How near indeed is God to men in the mountains ! When the priest called to prayer in the evening, the Voice of God echoed back a reply from the resounding valleys : " God is Great ; there is no other God than God."

From the valleys and the ravines the flocks and herds came thronging home. The camels stepped past with solemn, velvety tread, gaily coloured rosettes on their heads and flapping horses' tails beneath their chins. Horsemen, their rifles cocked, rode by on smart little mounts. In clouds of white dust the countless multitude of sheep and goats returned home to the safe shelter of the tents.

Glowing skies above silent mountains, a sense of isolation, peaceful life and the sound of the faithful at prayer—those are the memories which linger with me in the turmoil of the busy city, memories from those days of solitude so near to God.

Days passed, days of contemplation. We waited for the Khan. Wolf said jokingly that he was inclined to do as we were advised and choose a wife, a horse and a gun and stay with the tribe as a warrior. To be a nomad meant being a fighter. We learned this lesson one day when hostile horsemen attacked our herds. Such of the Khan's warriors as had been left behind successfully repelled the onslaught, while we sat and watched the battle.

None the less we were impatient to get on, and the priest understood our desire. I promised him my fine fur coat, with which he had fallen in love, if he would help us on our way, and he agreed ; but he considered that the first thing we must do was to have our hair cut in the local fashion, if we wished to travel in safety. With a large knife he shaved off a wide strip of hair from the back of our necks over the top of our heads down to the forehead, leaving the sides above the ears *in statu quo*. We laughed when we surveyed each other after this process, and we certainly looked hideous and anything but Europeans.

The priest then found us a man to guide us on through the mountains. When darkness fell we slipped unobserved out of the tents, leaving my beautiful fur coat behind. We met the new guide outside and followed him rapidly over great boulders and through their dark shadows.

In the silence the moon's white orb looked down on the dark world. We followed the faint shimmer of the sack containing our food supplies which our guide carried on his back. We walked for hours. The stars were already beginning to slip wearily down to the inky west. Suddenly we halted! In front, high up on the mountains to right and left of the ravine through which we were making our way, we saw fires. Watch-fires in the night. Silence everywhere. The guide whispered hoarsely, "We must get through somehow. Don't make a sound, and Allah will be merciful!"

We hurried on. Then came a report! The sound rang out sharply against the distant mountains, and its echo was thunderous. The terrors of the night awoke. We started to run. Somewhere behind us shots rang out against the dark wall.

Suddenly some one shouted to us through the darkness. Men appeared on all sides. We were surrounded and knocked down with clubs. Our guide fell on his knees, holding up our sack of food with propitiatory gestures. One man tore off my coat and another my shoes. The same thing happened to Wolf. Then the robbers vanished again.

Our guide got up, terrified, and stared at his empty hands. We had lost our precious bulging knapsack and stood there, bare-footed, in our shirts—bare-footed in the desolate mountains!

But fear drove us on. Sharp stones mercilessly pierced our bare feet. Wolf groaned that he would rather die than go on enduring such pain.

We passed the night a prey to tortures innumerable. At dawn we descended into a broad river valley. We were told by our guide that we should soon come to a village.

A village! To think that there were still villages in the world, with huts and blankets! What a consoling thought!

At last we reached our village. Exhausted, we fell in a heap on the floor of a hut. When we awoke in had been daylight for hours. We were given some coarse clothes and some dried hare-skins, which we soaked in water and wrapped round our feet to take the place of shoes. Though they were not the same as hard soles, these skins afforded good protection.

Meschgin, the next stage of our Odyssey, was still a long way off. During the day's march the inhabitants passed us on from village to village down the valley, which broadened out. We often joined caravans. Occasionally a donkey-driver gave us a ride on his little beast.

After hard going we reached Meschgin at last. Surely the tide would turn now. Sergam Sultan, the Great Persian, would help us. We hung about wearily at the door of his house.

Our hopes were dashed by a fresh blow of Fate. Sergam was away. He had gone south-west with the True Believers to join the Turks and Germans in their struggle with Russia. We were too late.

. . . . .

We sat down to consider what to do. We must go on without the help of the Great Man. Actually one seldom receives help from the great. Men always have to depend on themselves in the long run—a good thing on the whole, for suffering and struggle make stout hearts and wills of steel.

Once more we continued our pilgrimage over hill and dale, fording rivers and begging in the poverty-stricken villages. When we asked for shelter we were often shown the door, and had to spend the night in the fields outside the village.

The caravan tracks were strewn with the skeletons of camels and donkeys which, notwithstanding the lash, had collapsed beneath their burdens and lain down to die. Here and there vultures were crouching over the corpses, tearing with their strong beaks shreds of evil-smelling flesh from the bones, and gulping them down. In their greed they spread their wings and pecked savagely at each other.

The mountains stretched unendingly ahead. The strange huts were anything but inviting. Our eternal march seemed to have no prospects. Sheer determination drove us onwards —the determination to get back to Germany and fight for Germany.

At last we reached the first small Persian town, Acher. We found shelter in a caravanserai. We stayed there several days and acquired a new travelling companion, Gulam Husein Aga, a young Persian dandy who was only too eager for adventure and asked us to take him with us.

Our next goal was Tabriz—a well-known town at last. Gulam had got himself up to the nines for the journey. He was wearing his Sunday best of green cloth with brass buttons. His high black cap was set at a jaunty angle on his smooth hair. His large, hooked nose gave him a bold look, and he sang the weird melodies of his homeland in a compressed but deep bass. He strode ahead of us like some strangely bedizened giant cockatoo.

He told us that it was a six days' journey to Tabriz. The

villages were getting less scattered, and the countryside was more inhabited. More and more frequently we were asked where we had come from and where we were going. I always answered that Tabriz was our destination. " Don't go there, sir, the Russians are there," we were told one day. I was getting used to trouble. We simply *must* get through. After all, Allah always directs our steps ! So on we went.

Tabriz at last. A dusty main street, more like a village, led us a long way through the outskirts. Gulam found out from some Persians that the German consul was no longer in Tabriz. In a flash we realised the position. Tabriz was now in Russian hands ! We remembered that America had undertaken to protect Germans abroad (this was 1915), and we decided to find the American consul.

At the American consulate we inquired through a servant if the consul would see us. We waited. At last the door of the reception-room opened and in our rabbit-skin shoes we stepped across the carpets of a fine room. The consul was standing before us, but from the depths of the room came the voice of a German woman : " *Guten Tag* ! "

What magic was this ? German words !

" You needn't be afraid of talking German. I'm the wife of the German consul. My husband has had to leave Tabriz owing to the Russians coming ! "

We were bewitched.

" Sit down, gentlemen ! " she said.

Miracles never cease. There was an angel in the world who could look at our dishevelled, shaven polls, our ridiculous rabbit-skins and our torn and dirty shirts, and understand.

We sat down, stiff and sore, in comfortable arm-chairs. We told our story. Every now and then the consul's wife interrupted us with kindly words of praise, and the American called our flight from Siberia to Tabriz a very sporting effort.

These words of praise moved me so greatly that a jerk of my sleeve released a louse, which fell on the edge of the silver tray in front of us. Horribly ashamed and with downcast eyes, I looked to see whether the lady had noticed it. She had not.

" Please help yourselves ! "

I did not dare to move my arm again as the sleeve concealed several thousand more lice. Wolf chewed uninterruptedly. The louse on the tray was so surprised that it began to move, and crawled quietly along the edge of the tray on a journey round the world, but fortunately just then the servant came and cleared away.

The lady's manner became practical.

"Gentlemen," she said, "I myself am more or less a prisoner here. The Russians have occupied every place in the province. You must get away—the sooner the better," and she gave each of us a purse full of silver. We were then dismissed. In the room outside Gulam was waiting for us. He had discussed the next part of the journey and make all preparations.

However, before starting, we could now make some purchases, for we were really wealthy. Messengers went into the town to bring us all the luxuries of solid worth, above all stockings—soft stockings—and shoes with soles. We also bought a cloak each, a full brown cloak with holes for the arms and a hat like those worn locally.

We ordered a carriage, and it drew up in front of the house. It was an affair with four horses. We got in, and off we went. Some instinct must have suddenly warned us, and we slipped out of the vehicle and disappeared into the greyness of poverty and the dust of the road. My heart was thumping! It would have been great fun to fly through the countryside on wheels! It was lucky we didn't, for the main street was occupied by the Russians, and we had to take side roads to get out of the town at all.

It was nearly midnight when we reached the first post-station. At the post-house we could actually smell the stable. We drank some tea whilst they saddled horses for us to continue our journey, and then we mounted and rode on.

. . . . .

We rode through a dark landscape up the steep, rocky mountains. The air was soft and the milk-white moonlight streamed down on distant summits. Our horses snorted on through the night, and the lines of Mirza Schappy—Soul of Persia—rang out in the hoof-beats: " Earthly Paradise is being on a horse's back." Slowly and quietly we toiled up the mountainside. We crossed a finely arched bridge with a stream rushing and foaming beneath it. We went on climbing. The horses arched their backs under the strain, and stamped their hoofs hard into the ground. When we reached the steep, black wall above us, where the narrow pass was shrouded in shadow, our leader let his reins drop and relied on his horse to keep on the path. With bent head the beast sniffed its way along the narrow track between the boulders, and step by step each horse followed the leader. Suddenly a vertical wall of rock loomed ahead. Somehow or other the horses clung as best they could to the jagged rocks. One false step and all would have been over. On one side our trembling legs were dangling over a precipice, while on the other they were jammed against the rocky wall.

Gradually the pass grew wider. Once more we could see about us and breathe more freely. Shadows vanished into the greyness of the dwindling darkness. On the broad mountain there was a ghostly soundless movement. The horses cocked back their ears and strained at the reins. " Wolves," called our leader.

Dawn broke. The sky was suffused with bright light. All at once it was day. Before us stretched a wide valley. The straight lines of a farm, showing no signs of life, lay ahead of us. We rode up and were received at another post-house. Money opened the doors and unlocked the wide world to us. Fresh horses were soon produced.

So urgent was our haste that we could not rest. It was as if we were racing against time to catch up the days we had lost. We changed horses three times in the day, and were never out of the saddle. We drove our horses along the caravan tracks, and our goal loomed enticingly ahead. At night, so as not to have to stop, we took carts—clumsy plank contraptions on sturdy wheels—which rumbled laboriously along, heaving themselves over the stones. As they crawled through the darkness we were lulled to sleep by the motion of the wheels, but lying on the hard boards with limbs relaxed we were constantly awakened by painful jerks.

When mighty destinies are beckoning to them men are not deterred by such slight sufferings. We were all set for happiness. Three days and three nights we hurried, and yet we were still a long distance from freedom.

One evening we rode into a small town called Mianah. The streets were a hive of activity. Throngs of poverty-stricken people, donkeys and camels blocked the way. Suddenly the familiar flat-topped caps and green shirts worn by Russian soldiers appeared among the crowd. We pressed our knees into our horses' flanks and rode straight past them, until we came to a caravanserai. The smell of those Russian blouses had revived memories of all our misery—Russia, barbed wire, slavery, the hopeless suffering in Siberia.

Gulam went into the town to spy out the land whilst we hid in the darkness of the stable. Suddenly, as I was dozing, some one gave my leg a tug. I half leapt up, but it was only Gulam. Mianah was teeming with Russians, he said. However, there were German officers at Hamadan, about four hundred kilometres from where we were. Germans here in far-off Persia, outposts of the Turkish front ! We were filled with excitement.

Before daybreak we resumed our journey on foot. There was nothing we did not know about tramping over stones, uphill and down dale, and we hated it, but it was wiser than taking horses with the Russians all round us. At night we put up at a village. On the fourth day after leaving Mianah we turned in at a post-house. There were horses in the stable, and we could not withstand such temptation, especially as we had not seen any Russians since Mianah. We hired horses, swung up into the saddle, and set off for our destination. In three more days at the most we should be free men ! The nerve-tension became almost unbearable.

Towards evening we halted at a post-house, but the official refused to let us hire a carriage and horse for the night. What was the matter? Two strangers, armed with rifles, who were resting in the post-house adopted a hostile attitude towards Gulam. All we understood of the dispute was that we could not have any horses. Finally one of the men rode off. Where? We spent the night at the post-house, and the next morning the official let us have a carriage. He himself took the reins and the stranger also joined us.

Our horses proceeded at a smart pace, and as we went we considered whether we ought not to get out. Were we suspected? But where was Hamadan? Which direction should we take? Whilst we were still wrestling with the problem a trumpet suddenly blared from the mountains ahead, and simultaneously a number of mounted men rode towards us. We were soon surrounded. Our assailants sprang from their horses on to the carriage and pulled us out. We were knocked down and tied up with ropes. " Spies ! " some one shouted.

Dapper officers jumped lightly from their saddles. Their caps were adorned with the jaunty Russian cockade. A captain ordered his men to turn out our pockets. The Turk's letter of introduction was discovered. The captain read it and found we were German officers escaping from Siberia and trying to get back to Germany. He saluted and said in good German, " Gentlemen, I am sorry. . . . It was reported to us that you were spies ! "

Rocks crashed down from the high heavens, mountains circled about me, dark shadows flitted towards me. Everything seemed sliding and whirling about. A heavy, black curtain softly descended.

A turn in the tide of fortune ! The bright flames of action scattered at a blow.

We were placed on cavalry horses with Cossacks holding the reins. For the moment we could not even think of further flight. An escort brought us in triumph to the headquarters of the Russian troops in Persia.

A period of great misery began. Court martial, death sentence, anxious hours, then reprieve and prison. Months later we were taken back to Siberia—a six weeks' railway journey from the Caucasus to the Sea of Japan.

In the penal camp for criminal prisoners of war in distant Eastern Asia, north of Vladivostok, I had time to think out fresh plans for escape.

The spirit survives all disappointments, misery and betrayal. Will-power, immortal and inflexible, triumphs over circumstance and all the chances and changes of this world. Determination always wins !

.   .   .   .   .

Later I tried again and succeeded in escaping from the penal settlement north of Vladivostok, through the illimitable spaces of Siberia and the perils of Red Russia. In 1918 I was back in the ranks of my grey-clad comrades on the German front in France.

THE SEVERED HAND

By
CAPTAIN RAGNAR NYBERG

JACK HARVEY was my best friend for several years. He, too, was mate in the Blue Funnel Company's service, and once or twice we sailed together, he as first, and I as second mate. The last time was in a coaster which usually sailed between China and Japan, but which was occasionally sent to the South Sea Islands.

Jack was a Canadian, what you might call an educated man, and incidentally one of the pleasantest fellows I have ever come across. He was nothing much to look at—red-haired and freckled, with bright, pale-blue eyes—but his manner was exceptionally charming. He always had plenty of money, was ready to stand drinks—though this led to many a little tiff between us—and was thought to be a rich man's son who had chosen a sailor's life chiefly for love of adventure. Nevertheless he was an extremely able sailor, and valued highly by the Company.

When, after six months as second mate, I was transferred to another boat as chief mate, we promised to keep in touch with each other ; and this was not too difficult, as our boats were laid up at Shanghai at the same time. Besides, we had an interest in common. We usually met at the house of two attractive English sisters, the elder of whom was Jack's favourite, and the younger mine.

One fine day I arrived at Shanghai after a trip to the north of Japan. As usual I went straight to the shipping office and asked for my mail. I found there was a letter from Jack.

It was an extraordinary letter, and I read it through several times before I was sure that I had understood it. This is what he wrote :

> Be a sport and go at once to the Palace Hotel and ask
> for Mr. Thompson's room. It's mine, you see ! Stuff
> everything except my grey suit into the two big trunks and
> lock them. Tell them to put them into the cloakroom for

the time being. Pack the grey suit, a set of underwear and a shirt in the two suitcases. Take them with you down to the *Empress of Russia*—you know, the liner for Vancouver. Leave them with the fourth mate, and just say they are for a passenger. And by the way, please pay the hotel bill for me. You know you will get the money back. But for God's sake, don't tell a soul where I am, or where I am going. When you have finished I shall expect you at Polly's and Nelly's house. Best wishes,

JACK.

That was all ; but it gave me plenty to think about. What on earth had possessed Jack ? Travel—by the *Empress of Russia* ? Was he, then, going to leave the Company now, just when there were rumours that he was to be given the command of a boat ? Polly had probably nursed the hope of settling in Shanghai as a captain's wife. Something must have happened that forced Jack to change all his future plans helter-skelter and take flight. Yes, flight—for all this business with the luggage, and the room taken in the name of an unknown Mr. Thompson, gave the impression of being an attempt to get away without trace. But from whom, or what ?

Well, it was not much use speculating over that. I should soon hear Jack's explanation. I marched up to the hotel and succeeded, with the help of a little " handshake," in persuading the *concierge* that I was fully entitled to dispose of Mr. Thompson's luggage as I thought fit. When I had finished with the trunks and paid the bill, I drove down to the harbour with the two suitcases. The *Empress of Russia* lay in the roads, so I left them with the steward at the landing-stage for the launches, addressed to the fourth mate. Following a sudden impulse, I made a long detour, changing from car to rickshaw and back again several times. If any one was shadowing me, at any rate it was not going to be too easy to follow me to Jack's hiding-place.

Sure enough, Jack was at the girl's house, and I saw at once by his expression that something was seriously wrong.

" The game's up ! " he said, when I asked him what was the matter. " I have rubbed the Chinese up the wrong way, and if they get hold of me my life isn't worth a brass farthing."

" The Chinese ? What Chinese ? " I echoed, completely puzzled.

" The opium smugglers, of course," he said.

I stared at him. Slowly the truth dawned on me. Jack

had been in contact with Chinese opium smugglers, and for some reason or other had now fallen foul of them.

"But how about your job?" I went on. "What do you suppose they will say in the office?"

"I don't give a damn for the office," he answered. "I have collected a hundred and seventy-five thousand dollars, which I have already had transferred to a bank in Canada. I have only to go there and get the money, and then begin a new life ashore—on the other side of the world, where there aren't so many damned Chinamen."

"But what have you done?" I persisted.

"Good Lord, I never thought you were such a young innocent, that you didn't understand what went on in the old ship!" he said with a laugh. "And if it comes to that, have you never yourself found a hundred-dollar note under your pillow, without being able to account for its presence there? Has it never happened that some yellow devil of the crew has come to you, and winked and said: ' Mate nothing, see nothing hear; best so!' And afterwards there has been an extra profit of a hundred or two? Don't you pretend to be so innocent now!"

Of course I knew that sort of incident. I should think that not a single mate on the China coast escapes these temptations. But it was a fact that I had never let myself get mixed up in anything of the kind. Perhaps it was a result of my inborn Swedish horror of bribery. Besides, I had been warned. My first skipper, an old, fiery, but thoroughly honest Irishman, had several times said to me:

"Now, listen, Nyberg. There are chances to earn big money on this coast by opium-smuggling. It is a perfect scandal, the number of officers on the coastal steamers who fall for the temptation to take a hand in the game. Not that I wonder at it, though, since the Chinks pay well even for the smallest services. And you needn't do much—just go ashore with some little packets, without knowing exactly what is in them or how they got into your pocket; and you need not even know when they leave it again. But remember this, Nyberg, opium is a poison, and even if you never touch it yourself sooner or later it will get you down, one way or another! It is certain ruin both for the yellow and the white man. And the devil is in it, if he comes off with his life and job!"

I took his advice. I had even helped to get the smugglers "pinched" a couple of times. Once it concerned a consignment of opium worth some fifty thousand dollars. The day before we reached port I found a slip of paper in my pocket, on which was written : " If the honoured gentleman wants to do good and easy business, he can earn five thousand dollars by keeping his eyes shut." A little later in the day one of the crew paused in front of me and bowed deeply—but without saying anything. I pulled out the slip of paper, tore it into many pieces, and threw them over the rails. Then I shook my head, and the Chinaman crept away. He knew the answer.

When the ship was searched, I told a customs official about the matter. Nothing was found then, but during the night two sailors were caught trying to bring a chest of opium ashore.

Perhaps some of my readers will wonder that I dared to do this ; but in reality it is not nearly so odd and dangerous as it sounds. I had " clean face." In China this English expression means that a man is fair and straight. As long as he is this, he need not fear the Chinese. They are fatalists, and if it is the will of destiny that they should come up against a mate who cannot be bribed, but who warns the authorities instead, they bear him no ill-will for that.

But woe betide the man who plays a double game and " loses face " ! Should this happen, he need expect no mercy. The Chinese never forget an injury, any more than they forget a good turn, and sooner or later vengeance will overtake the guilty.

If Jack had become involved in smuggling—and I found this hard to believe, although he said so himself—what had happened, then, to make him clear out of the game so suddenly ? Had he been crazy enough to " lose face " ?

" Tell me the whole story, Jack," I said to him.

" Well, I suppose you are entitled to hear it, since I am asking you to help me," he said. " You see, for several years I have every now and then helped with big consignments of opium—and earned a packet of money over it. I know that you and many of the others thought that I had money of my own, but that isn't so. My earning from the smuggling have enabled me to spare no expenses and still to save up for a rainy day. I had meant to give up both smuggling and my life at sea as soon as I had saved up a hundred thousand dollars. About a month ago I had reached that figure.

" Of course I didn't want to leave the Company too suddenly, for fear of arousing suspicion, and I decided to wait for a good opportunity. I had told the Chinese that the smuggling was over as far as I was concerned and I knew that I had nothing to fear from them. But now, on my last trip—we went to Singapore and back here, as you know—I was asked to " keep my eyes shut." Best of all, they would have liked my help as usual. I told them they could have it—if they gave me fifty per cent. of the profit. I told them that they had underpaid me quite long enough, and now I wanted my share of the real winnings. They offered me five thousand. I said no, without a moment's hesitation, for I guessed that the net profit would be far bigger than that. I wanted fifty per cent.—and half of it in advance—or I would neither help them nor shut my eyes. And so they gave me five thousand in advance.

" I found out that the deal concerned a consignment of Persian opium—the best of all, as perhaps even you know—worth twenty thousand in Singapore and sixty thousand in Shanghai ? Do you know how opium is packed ? You don't ? Well, it is sent in little cylindrical tubes wrapped in many layers of brown paper. On board a ship it isn't difficult to find any number of good hiding-places for neat little parcels like that. I knew them all—though the Chinese didn't realise it ! It was this that gave me an idea for a really grand haul.

" I don't want to tell you where those hiding-places are —it's best for you not to know anything about it ! So I shall simply tell you that before we left Singapore I had found out where the stuff was hidden. And I made several little preparations for my stunt. I acquired several lengths of cane, and in my spare time I cut these into little pieces and dipped them in varnish. Treated like this, the pieces looked just like tubes of opium—the same size and colour and weight.

" While at sea, I fetched some opium tubes from their hiding-places every now and again, unwrapped the paper carefully, and substituted a bit of cane. I hid the opium in my boxes, and put the imitation parcels back where I found them. After a while I had all the opium in my trunks.

" Then came the most cunning part of my scheme. Of course, it would never do to let the counterfeit opium fall into the hands of the receiver in Shanghai, or of the Customs. They would examine it and soon realise that some one had tampered with it in transit. So something had to happen before we reached port. But what ?

" I had a look at the third mate, Bolton. Perhaps you

know him ? A regular greenhorn—even greener than you ! I asked him if he kept his eyes open and saw to it that none of the crew was smuggling opium. He hadn't thought of that, he said. ' Then go and have a look,' says I, and in a casual sort of way I reeled off the places where the opium was hidden —not just those, of course, but a lot of others as well, so that it shouldn't look too queer. ' Tell the captain, or me, if you come across anything,' I said.

" It was not long before he came back, his eyes simply popping out of his head, and said that he had found masses of little grey packets all over the place. I took care to be with the captain at the time, so that he should hear the report at first hand.

"The captain was furious, naturally. ' Why the devil can't one put an end to that traffic ? ' he fumed. ' But now I am going to teach them ! '

"We went up on deck together. The captain had the whole crew lined up, and under their eyes the third mate was made to bring out his findings. The skipper grew pale when he saw how much of it there was. He looked down the row of expressionless, slant-eyed faces, but not one of the Chinese so much as blinked.

" ' There is so much of this, that I daren't even take it into port,' he said to us mates. ' We might as well throw the stuff overboard ! '

" I had hoped for this; but I must admit that I sighed with relief at not having to make the suggestion myself. So we pitched the lot overboard, while the Chinamen looked on with immovable faces. The little grey packets soon disappeared in the wash of the ship.

" The skipper lectured the crew, and declared that in future he would carry out a personal search before the Customs came on board. And if any one was caught trying to smuggle, he would horsewhip him !

" Well, the rest was fairly simple. Naturally, no opium was found during the Customs' visit at Shanghai—least of all in my boxes !—and as the ship was going into dry dock for an overhaul, I moved ashore with my possessions. After a while I fetched up at the Palace Hotel as Mr. Thompson ; and then I could begin to do business.

" For any one who knows the ropes, it isn't difficult to sell opium—fine Persian opium—in Shanghai ; and it didn't take me many days to get rid of the lot. It fetched a cool seventy thousand ! So with the five thousand in advance, I had earned seventy-five thousand in one sweep. I call that good going ! "

He laughed, and told Polly to start the gramophone. While she did so, he whispered to me in a changed voice:

" But now I am done for if I can't get away as quickly as possible ! It won't be long before the opium dealers begin to wonder who this mysterious Mr. Thompson is, and where he got his Persian opium. They are, of course, expecting a large consignment just now. When they get to know that that opium is swimming around in the China Sea they will probably put two and two together !

" The *Empress of Russia* is the first boat to Vancouver, and I have already ordered my ticket. But now I daren't show myself in the town—I haven't left the house for a week— and to walk down to the landing-stage and board the *Empress's* tender would be as good as to sign my own death-warrant. You must help me ! Try to get hold of a boat, so that I can get on board without being seen ! "

I was so dumbfounded that I could hardly say a word. Jack, my best friend, a smuggler ! He had carried on his dirty work under my very nose, and in my innocence I had suspected nothing ! Now suddenly he revealed a totally different side of his nature. But in spite of everything, he was my friend. He had always been good to me, and had often helped me out of a tight corner, both at sea and ashore. And now that his life was at stake I could not let him down.

I soon thought of a plan. There was only one man in Shanghai from whom I would dare to borrow a boat for such an expedition. This was Mike O'Neal, owner of a café near the docks. He was an old deep-sea fisherman, who had lost an arm and a leg in an accident. A collection among his comrades had raised enough money for him to start a little café, which gradually brought him quite a good income ; for Mike looked after it well, and sailors liked to go there, particularly Scandinavians and—of course—Irishmen. O'Neal had a motor-boat, in which he used to cruise around on the Whang Poo river in his spare time. I was going to try to borrow it.

Mike was heart and soul a sailor, and he asked no questions when I explained that I simply must borrow his boat.

" As long as you don't go smuggling opium, you can have it," was all he said. No, I certainly had no intention of smuggling opium, and assured him of this with a clear conscience.

Next night two fairly tall and broad-shouldered young ladies left the back door of Polly's and Nelly's house. The clothes belonged to Polly and Nelly, but the two hefty young women were Jack and myself. It was not until we reached the shore that we dared to change our clothes.

We had no adventures on our way to the secluded quay where Mike O'Neal kept his motor-boat. Mike's "boy" was waiting for us here, and a little Jap to look after the engine. We rowed silently and carefully the first part of the way from the quay; not till we were a safe distance from land did we dare to start the engine.

Far out in the harbour the great *Empress of Russia* lay at anchor, glittering with lights, and it seemed an eternity to us before we reached her gangway and Jack went on board, after shaking hands with me and promising to send me the money for his hotel bill and other items as soon as he got to Vancouver and could raise some money. For safety's sake he had kept only enough ready cash for bare necessities.

I returned to Polly and Nelly and brought them Jack's farewell greetings. Then I went back to my boat, and on the way I posted a letter to the Blue Funnel Company. It contained Jack's resignation. He gave as a reason that he had been called home to Canada by a wire saying that his father had died suddenly.

Next morning the *Empress of Russia* had left the harbour, and I gave a sigh of relief.

It was six weeks before I heard from Jack. At last a letter came bearing the Vancouver postmark. He told me that he was in hospital there; when about to land from the *Empress of Russia*, he had met with an accident—a very strange accident!

Just as he was going down the gangway a large balk had fallen, and all but crushed him to death. However, he escaped with a complicated fracture of one shoulder. The balk which fell down had been roped between the davits and a lifeboat—quite a usual arrangement—to prevent the boats from crashing against the sides of the ship in rough weather. I have sailed for years, and I have talked with men who had sailed twice as long, but none of us has ever heard of a similar accident! Why should the ropes give way just as Jack passed underneath? I have often asked myself that question.

From Jack's letter I gathered that he was getting better. He was not very communicative, and did not mention his plans for the future. The tone of his letter was somehow strangely hopeless. Finally he asked me to tell Polly, as tactfully as possible, that there could be no wedding for them, at least not for a long time. There was so much else for him to attend to first, he said. He enclosed a cheque for my expenses at the hotel and elsewhere.

From that day onwards I have not heard a word from Jack Harvey. I wrote to him a few times, addressing the letters alternately to the hospital and to the bank in Vancouver where he said that he had his money. But the letters have been returned to me, marked "Address not known." I have met people who have lived in Vancouver after Jack moved there ; but no one has heard of him, no one has seen him.

Half a year, almost to the day, after the evening when I last shook hands with Jack, something happened which so far I have been unable to explain, and probably never shall succeed in explaining.

I sat in my cabin smoking and talking to the second engineer, a Norwegian. We happened to be in Singapore.

" Tell me, Raggie," said the engineer all at once, " what in heaven's name is smelling so awful in here ? "

" Well, I don't know," I answered. " I first noticed it yesterday, but I can't think what it can be."

" I'm damned if it doesn't smell like a dead body," said the Norwegian, and sniffed hard.

Right in front of us was a large, built-in mahogany cupboard, used as the cabin wardrobe. The door was ajar, and he bent forward and sniffed at the crack.

" That's where it comes from," he said. " You'll find that some wretched rat has died on you in there."

I opened the door. Almost at once I discovered the source of the smell. Just inside, on the floor, lay a brown paper parcel. I picked it up and opened it.

It contained a man's severed hand—a white man's hand. It was in an advanced state of decay, but from several signs, which I need not go into, we concluded that it had been chopped off while the victim was still alive. There were no peculiarities, except for a number of little marks and scars, such as most sailors have. It was an ordinary man's hand, rather well shaped. Jack had medium sized, quite shapely hands.

On the inner of the two brown paper wrappings was written in China ink—apparently with a Chinese brush, though the characters were European—the following words in English :

" NONE OF YOUR BUSINESS."

The Norwegian stared at me ; even his lips were white.
" The Chinks are after you," he said. " Haven't you got
' clean face,' Raggie ? "

" Yes, I think so," I replied. " This is probably more in
the way of information than a threat." And then I told him
this story, but without mentioning any names.

" Throw the damn thing overboard, as fast as you can,
Raggie," the engineer advised me when I had finished.
" Don't take it to the police. The Chinks mean what they
say. And they have their own ideas of honour."

I thought it over for a while, and finally took his advice.
And I have never heard a word about it since.

THE DEATH OF ME-TOO

By
EX-LÉGIONNAIRE 1384

The author and his American friend, McCann, have just enlisted in the Foreign Legion. They have been drafted to Sousse.

SOUSSE is a small seaport town on the North African coast, and about eighty miles from Tunis. During the first two days I thought it an ideal spot in which to be stationed. Before I had been there two months I was cursing the place as throatily as any seasoned légionnaire. By that time I had been drilled and kicked and starved and generally hammered into shape. I had known the meaning of utter blackness in a solitary confinement cell, had known what it felt like to stagger round and round the parade in the heat of a fiery sun and with a sack of sand on my back as well as my full equipment.

My next step was to report sick with dysentery. At least, Fate staged it that way. I endured the misery for weeks before I reported at the hospital. One endures a lot in the Legion rather than report sick. It's not done. Very few men who go into hospital come out again. That's a story, of course. But it happens to be a funny sort of story that is very much encouraged by the powers that be in the French Foreign Legion. Just the same, I had become so weak with the disease that I was compelled to report sick. Dysentery was rife at that time. McCann was in much the same case, but he swore he would hit the trail rather than report.

As later events proved, they had been waiting for the pair of us at the hospital. I waited two hours in the broiling heat and then went before the M.O.

" How much service now ? " he snapped.

" Three months," said I.

He turned to the corporal standing by and smiled.

" A fully trained légionnaire now," commented the corporal.

The comment did not seem to call for an answer, and I gave none. The officer and the corporal laughed together, enjoying some joke between themselves of which I was not conscious ; but I thought it strange nevertheless. An officer and a corporal of the Legion laughing and joking together ! It did not square with the rules and regulations of the Legion, which I had now come to know by heart. I thought there was something fishy in it. And I was right.

"What's your name ? "

I gave it. The two exchanged glances.

"You speak French and Arabic pretty well, don't you, Englishman ? "

"Yes, sir. I was in the Near East during the Great War."

"Very well. You will stay in hospital for six months under Corporal Du Blen. He will find you some interesting work to do, something more suited to your special talents."

And they grinned at each other. Even then it did not occur to me that a sergeant in Marseilles might have sent a report across to headquarters at Sousse regarding the mysterious death of a German boy, and the two English-speaking rookies who had witnessed that death.

"Follow me," said the corporal, in a manner quite affable.

I saluted the M.O. and marched off in the wake of the corporal, across the hospital compound and into a hut which lay snugly in a secluded corner of the grounds. Inside was a private room with a couple of cots, a table and some chairs. It was, in fact, quite nicely furnished.

"Well, Barrington, here is your home for some time, I hope."

"But what's it all about, Corporal ? Why the favours ? "

"I have been watching you for some time, Barrington. You are a very good légionnaire, yes ? The only man you have ever closely associated with is that American named McCann. *Très bien !* I will attend to him later."

"I still don't understand, corporal."

"No need to stand to attention in here, Barrington."

He indicated a chair and smiled.

"Be comfortable. I will tell you. I suppose you think it strange that a doctor should give you six months' hospital treatment ? "

I nodded, utterly mystified.

"Have you ever heard of *L'Espionage Centrale* ? "

For a moment I did not know whether to say yea or nay. By this time I was getting very wary. I seemed to be moving in circles entirely foreign to the Legion as I had known it. The incident of the German boy's death at Fort St. Jean came flashing into my mind.

"No," I said. "I have never heard of it."

The corporal's face darkened for a minute.

"And never speak of it—if you would live a long and happy life. Now, listen carefully. I am head of the Sousse branch of *L'Espionage Centrale*. Yes, I, a corporal. What do you think? That I should have the rank of colonel and the badge of secret service on my coat!"

He laughed uproariously at his little joke.

"I want to make you an agent, Barrington."

"But," I stammered, "I don't want to be an agent of any secret service."

His face darkened again.

"You have no choice, Barrington. It is that you and your friend know too much already. You had better accept with a good grace. Or . . ."

That irritating yet expressive shrug of the shoulders. I knew exactly what he meant. No one ever wept over a légionnaire. Is he not already a man who has disappeared? He is no longer a man. He is but a numbered robot. When he drops out another takes his place. It is all very simple, terribly final.

The corporal was watching me, like a hawk its prey, I fancied. I don't think I am very squeamish a sort of fellow, but I had heard enough about the infamous corps to feel the urgent necessity for keeping clear of it. Yet, as he said, I had no choice. I had better accept with as good a grace as possible.

"Very well, corporal. It is for six months, I understand? It will be a change from the squadron, anyway."

"Good! I thought I had not misjudged my man. Now let us go to the fingerprint department and arrange for your identity card, also your photograph. You will find the card a powerful weapon. Guard it as you would your life. Never display it foolishly—but only when you are in actual need."

In half an hour I was sworn—a fully fledged secret service agent. As I strolled back to the hut with Du Blen I wondered what the future held in store for me, what grim game I was to play in this infamous organisation. Certainly my status had improved, for I found an appetising meal awaiting me in the hut, together with wines and fruit, such a meal as I had dreamt about during the past few months. If this is the way we eat, thought I, it will be a very welcome change from the squadron ! I sat down with the corporal. For the next few minutes Du Blen and I were just two men—feeding. It is not extraordinary what the sight of a well-laid table will do to a man ? I was happier in those few moments than I had been for months.

"These are your quarters, Barrington. You will take your meals here with me unless duty takes you elsewhere. Your first job is not a very simple one, but it will make a good test. You appear to get along pretty well with women. The job I speak of is in the Café Malta."

I sat up and stared.

"Me-Too ! "

"Precisely, Barrington—Me-Too ! You know her pretty well, don't you ? She seems to have taken you to her heart. I have known her a very long time and I can safely say she has never paid so much attention to any légionnaire as she does to you ! "

There was much more in the same strain, which it would be unbecoming of me to recount. The fact that startled me, however, was the amazing knowledge of this fellow, Du Blen. Scarcely a night went by but I was to be found in the Café Malta, fooling around with this same Me-Too, the alluring baggage who ran the Café Malta. *But never once had I seen Du Blen in the café !* He had other spies, of course. I had been watched. The thought was hideous. No man was safe, even in his off-duty hours. This was my first inkling that *L'Espionage Centrale* actually troubled itself about the affairs of common légionnaires in cheap cafés. I believe I conveyed as much to Du Blen. He laughed in his loud and boisterous fashion.

"It is a commonplace in any espionage organisation that its spies must be spied upon."

"Meaning Me-Too ? "

"Yes. I am not at all satisfied about her work. She has been a good agent. But latterly I have had reason to believe otherwise. Even so, she is not the first woman spy to play a double game."

"What exactly do you suspect ? "

"We are trying to check this Arab gun-running along the coast."

"It's hardly a job for a girl like Me-Too ! "

"Think not ! Listen, Barrington, there is no room for sentiment in the service. It is your job to find out exactly

what Me-Too is doing. You are sufficiently intimate with her
to make your task a fairly pleasant one. You will be supplied
with ample funds, but do not throw money about as if you
had just inherited a fortune. Keep sober. Keep close to
Me-Too—as close as you please. Mix with the men of your
squadron. If they ask questions about your non-attendance
at parades and fatigues—you are on the sick list. Guard
your tongue. Be discreet. This business of Me-Too—do you
know anything of her history, her parentage ? "

" Not a thing."

" She is just a fascinating mystery to you—yes ? "

" Something like that, sir," I grinned.

" Don't sir me ! Not even in here. I am Corporal Du
Blen of the hospital. But this Me-Too. She is not the usual
half-caste to be found in the coast towns. That is merely the
part she plays. Her mother was the daughter of a Riffian
chieftain and her father a French officer. Her allegiance to
France has been without question—until recently. Her
mother died many years ago. Her father but recently—while
in action in the Tunisian Desert."

" And since then . . . ? "

" It would seem like it. Your task is to find out just
what she is doing. You are intimate with her ? "

" Yes."

" Very ? "

" Very."

" Then get into her confidence and help her in whatever
she is doing. Take the line of a disgruntled légionnaire.
You understand ? "

I nodded.

" But McCann ? " I queried.

" You will not see him to-night. He is in detention."

" Gosh ! What for ? "

" Insolence to a non-commissioned officer."

" I am not surprised. He is a sick man with a sharp
tongue."

" If he is sick, he should report to me. Now get away
to your job and don't worry about your friend. He will be
joining you in the service very soon."

I wondered. If I knew anything about McCann, he
would not join the spy service very willingly. It would
take time. He would be roped in eventually, since he had
no choice any more than I had ; but he was a stubborn
devil. He would say what he thought and damn the con-

sequences. Insolence to an N.C.O. Perhaps he had already said what he thought about such a proposition! Maybe that was what Du Blen had meant! I pondered over this phase of the matter as I made my way through the town towards the Café Malta. If this should mean a break with McCann —well, life was going to be a very miserable affair.

I entered the café and found a vacant table. Me-Too, dispensing drinks, waved her hand and flashed a smile. I felt a momentary twinge of conscience. Friendship with the lovely creature had been good fun—until now. She trusted me. I was sure of it. And now I was to start this double-dealing game. What a rotten business it all was! For the first time in my few months of life in the Legion I began to think seriously of deserting. I had money now. I had given Du Blen my thumbprint receipt for the two hundred francs in my pocket. If I could get away with the help of this cash the joke would certainly be on him. If! Desertion was something I dare not attempt now. I had not even the chances of the ordinary légionnaire. Set a spy to catch a spy! I hadn't a ghost of a chance. I must go through with it now. Six months, he had said—six months of this dirty, sneaking business. . . .

I was staring down at the table, a prey to dun-coloured thoughts, when the hand came into my line of vision, to rest on the polished table top. It was a small beautifully-moulded hand, soft, sun-kissed, a large green stone flashing on the little finger. Slowly I raised my eyes following the curve and line of the supple, honey-coloured arm, up to the softly-rounded shoulder and on to the creamy-browness of the full throat. Me-Too had the round piquant face of the French girl and the black velvet eyes of an Arab. Her red lips were pouting at the sight of my serious face, but there was laughter in the shining black eyes and a ripple of merriment in the gentle heaving movements of her high breasts. She bent low, so that her face almost touched my own and the perfume of her corsage filled my nostrils. What a swine I felt under that whiff of scent!

"But, what is it, my little one?" she crooned. "Why are you sad? Tired? Weary of that terrible Legion? Would you make Me-Too unhappy also?"

She said it all like a child, whispering softly and huskily, with the most appealing artistry. I laughed outright at her half-serious, half-mocking tenderness, caught her hands and drew her down beside me on the shabby couch. Instantly she snuggled close. She was like a child in her desire to be petted and loved. It was enormously difficult for me to think of her as a spy, and a double-dealing spy at that. Here and there through the smoke haze an Arab or a légionnaire glanced towards us, smiled, went on with his drinking and card-playing.

I never knew the girl's real name. Her adopted one had a curious history. It was given her when her mother ran this same café and she, as a mere child, made free with the soldiers who frequented the place. At that time she became very friendly with a bunch of *Britishers* who were serving in the Legion. They used to amuse themselves teaching her English, but they would never permit her to touch the wine on their table. Because of that she would sometimes pout, grow sullen, refuse to say her English piece. Then she would point to the liquor, an angry light in her spirited black eyes, and cry, " Me too ! Me too ! Me too ! "

We drank and talked. I told her I was through with the Legion, that I had made up my mind to desert. At that she stared at me with a queer look. She seemed to be debating with herself. I stared through the smoke haze and felt all sorts of a rotter. I was playing my part. I was persuading myself that I really meant what I said. Certainly the wish was there —and I compromised my conscience with that. Her hand stole into mine.

" Would you leave Me-Too ? "

" Some day I must—even if I do not go on pump."[1]

" But, why ? "

" Why ? I shall be drafted to some other garrison, sooner or later."

" *Ecoutez bien, mon cheri.* Do not be sad this night. I have much to say. I must speak with you. Jean, you must never leave Me-Too. You will come again to my room— yes ? There we can talk."

I nodded. She went off to give instruction to an Arab servant who sometimes took charge of the café for her. After a while I rose and left the café, passing a word here and there to men whom I knew, giving them the impression that I was leaving for the night. Outside I proceeded for a while in the direction of the barracks, then swung round a dark alley and made a detour back to the Café Malta, but this time to the rear of the premises. I crossed the darkened court-yard silently, felt my way along the shuttered façade, tapped

[1] To Desert.

out my signal on the door. It was opened suddenly and I stepped through, still treading cautiously in the dark. A hand closed over mine. There was a soft unmistakable laugh. I was led along the corridor to Me-Too's room.

There was nothing European about Me-Too's abode. Whatever her national or racial sentiments, she certainly loved to surround herself with Oriental luxury. Persian carpets covered the walls and floor, deadening the sounds of the outer world. A lamp burned dimly, casting weird shadows. I found the great couch and sank down among a pile of cushions. Me-Too threw a heap of cushions at my feet and sat there. That suited me. I did not want her face near mine. I did not care to gaze into her bewitching eyes any more, watch the flash of her white teeth in the dusky halo about her head. I was through with that. *Bus! Fini!* There was no room for sentiment in the espionage game, not even with one's light-o'-love.

But I need not have worried. Me-Too had much to say, and she certainly said it that night. She gave the whole show away. Her plans were all beautifully set. Since I was tired of the Legion, why should I carry on? Why not join her, go with her to the hills, to her tribe, her real home? With my knowledge of military affairs, with my experience of fighting, I should find wonderful opportunities. I would become a rich chieftain, teaching and drilling an army of my own. Other men from the Legion had gone over to the Riffs. Why not I? Soon, very soon, there was to be a great gathering of the tribes of North Africa. They were ready! They had much ammunition, many thousands of guns, equipment, horses, a hundred thousand men . . . waiting. They would drive the French to the sea!

"When do you go?" I asked, striving to keep my voice level.

I felt the sudden pressure of her hands.

"Two more nights, Jean. Not to-morrow, but the next night, a shipload of guns is to be brought ashore under the cliffs three miles beyond Sfax. We will go, you and I, Jean, to see. Then we shall travel through the desert to my people—yes?"

So it was true, this tale of Du Blen's about gun-running! As I made my way back towards the isolation hut in the hospital compound, which was now my home, my thoughts were busy indeed. As I saw it then, there was still time for me to choose. I could pretend to Du Blen that there was nothing to report, thus leaving the way open for me to accept Me-Too's offer. In which case I should accompany Me-Too a couple of nights hence, see the guns landed at Sfax, and disappear with them and her people into the desert. And afterwards ? Well, there would be all the fun and excitement I could wish for. The novelty of an adventurous life, as the natives lived, for I was thoroughly enamoured of the beauty and mystery of the East, appealed to me intensely at that time. This, of course, was the influence of Me-Too. But I happened to know that she was right when she said other Europeans had gone over to the Riffs. White men had gone native before. But was I built that way ? I began to picture myself in a *kuffieh* of white silk and gold embroidery held in place over my black hair by an *agal*, two black cords wrapped with silver and gold threads, a girdle round my black camel's-hair robe with the curved sword of a prince of Mecca stuck in it. And it was all very alluring and picturesque—as I imagined it ! There was Me-Too. And I doubted very much whether I could stand that strain !

The alternative was to report all that had happened to Du Blen and obey his orders. But stay ! Was there really any choice for me ? Set a spy to catch a spy ! And I had not the faintest doubt that my every movement had been watched. Possibly Du Blen already knew where and how I had spent the evening !

Poor Me-Too ! I resolved there and then, while trudging back to the compound, that whatever happened no harm should come to Me-Too. Even though I were compelled to play the rôle of spy, there should be limits !

When I reached the hut I found sandwiches and wine on the table. *L'Espionage Centrale* was very thoughtful of its agents ! Du Blen was nowhere around. I chose my cot and turned in. It was one of the most ghastly nights I ever experienced. I tossed about all night long, tortured by warring thoughts and the craziest dreams. Morning came and still I was undecided. If only I could have talked it over with McCann !

I would leave it to Du Blen. His manner of approach would be my cue, for even then I still hoped that I had not been watched, and that I might still make a getaway with Me-Too and her bunch. An orderly came in with breakfast. Du Blen followed him. His first words certainly gave me my cue, even though they dashed my hopes.

" Well, Barrington, I hear you enjoyed yourself last night ? "

"Yes," said I, taken aback.

"You have news, eh?"

"I think so."

"Good! I am very interested."

"You would be!" thought I.

I told him what had passed between Me-Too and myself, omitting only the endearments. I could see that he was highly pleased with my night's work. If ever one man hated another, I certainly hated that man. Also, I hated myself. I was a skunk with the fancy name of espionage agent.

"*C'est très bien fait,* Barrington. *Félicitations! Bon! Bon! Bon!* But this is excellent! It is superb! You are an agent *premièr* of France! I knew it! This Me-Too, she loves you. She thinks you are the honourable Englishman!"

And he roared with laughter. Well, I suppose I had asked for it! Just the same, I could have knifed him on the spot. I resolved that one day I should get this Du Blen, get him just where I wanted him. And then . . .

Disguised as Arabs, we rode out in the afternoon of that day to Sfax. We had no difficulty in finding the small inlet under the cliffs where the guns were to be landed. Du Blen was in great spirits as we rode back to Sousse. The thing was simplicity itself. He would arrange for a detachment to ambush the natives after they had landed the guns. . . .

"And Me-Too?" I could not refrain from asking.

His face darkened.

"Traitors of France are shot!"

"Yes," thought I, "and France will miss this shot, if I know anything about it!"

Another night of agony. Another day of torture. By the time I met Me-Too on the outskirts of Sousse on that fateful night I was in a condition bordering on hysteria—a terrible state for a man then in his middle twenties. Even then I was uncertain. If there was to be an engagement if the natives were strong enough to put up a fight, I could not say on which side I should range myself. Never was there so sullen and unwilling a spy!

I was dressed in *burnous* and *kuffieh.* My jowl was dirty and I had two days' growth of beard. Naturally dark, I made a very presentable Arab. I found Me-Too with her attendants and half a dozen mounts.

"Quickly, Jean! We must ride fast! I feared you would not get away!"

We rode at the gallop. Me-Too was a splendid horse-

Her hand clutched at mine.

woman. Not a word was spoken as we raced along. My
heart was racing with the mad beat of the hoofs. I was crazy.
I wanted to turn then and there and race into the desert,
never to come back ! I said as much to Me-Too.

" But, Jean ! They wait for us at Sfax ! We should disorganise everything ! "

On and on we galloped through the black moonless night,
and to my fanciful mind légionnaires armed to the teeth
lurked in every shadow. Supposing, should it come to a
show-down, the French troops mistook me for one of the
native gun-runners ? But, I reflected, Du Blen would have
given his orders. The woman, Me-Too, was to be taken
prisoner at all costs. No shot would be fired at her nor at the
" Arab " who accompanied her !

We halted at last. Out of the shadows several figures
approached. Me-Too greeted them in low tones. We moved
forward cautiously, descending by way of a cleft to a sheltered
patch of the coast that made a perfect landing. An Arab
dhow drew in, then another and another. Camels were lined
up. Dim figures were moving between the water's edge and
the waiting beasts. For three hours the work went forward,
swiftly, silently. Not the feeblest glimmer of a light showed
anywhere. For a while Me-Too and I sat our mounts, side
by side, and watched. I found it all immensely interesting.
There must have been a hundred and fifty men there, and
every man knew his job. There was an organising brain
behind all this. These men were practised in the tricks of
gun-running. Clearly it had been going on for some time.
Who was the man behind it ? I did not doubt Me-Too's
statement—that the whole of the Riff tribes were arming
for a big campaign against the French. There had been
whispers of it for a long time.

There came the sudden cry of a single jackal. It was the
signal ! The operations were finished. Instantly the cliffs were
alive with troops descending upon the beach at the double, and
for all the world as if they had risen out of the earth of the cliff
face. In a few brief seconds the gun-runners were surrounded.
Me-Too and I found ourselves on the outer fringe of a pitched
battle. Men were yelling vile oaths in a dozen languages,
wounded beasts were screaming. The night was suddenly
alive with the crack and splutter of Mausers. The Legion
was in action. They were driving the Riffians into the sea !
Some of the troops, apparently told off for the work, were
ignoring the fight and rounding up the camels with their

precious burden of arms and ammunition. I was conscious
of Me-Too screaming in my ear that I had betrayed her !
Her mount was dancing and rocking in the confusion. And
so was mine. Suddenly she lurched forward in the saddle.
I saw the knife. She lunged, toppled from the perilous mount,
and fell to the ground. In a moment I was down beside her.
She lay crumpled up, ominously still.

For a space I stared down at her, asking myself stupidly
whether she were dead. I felt suddenly sick, and dropping
to my knees beside her I turned her face upwards. She had
fallen on the knife, buried it to the hilt in her breast. Mechanically I drew the blade out. Her black eyes opened for an
appreciable second, seeming to my distorted mind to be blazing hate at me. She gave an awful gasp. . . .

Her hand clutched at mine, sending icy shivers down my
spine.

" Me-Too ! Me-Too ! "

" Jean ! " So feeble a moan that I could scarcely hear it.
" So you couldn't get her alive, eh ? "

I looked up into the sallow, hateful face of Du Blen. I
could have carved that hideous grin from his face in one
sweeping blow, for I still had Me-Too's knife in my hand.
That would have been the end of Du Blen. It would
also have been the end of John Barrington. The battle was
over. One or two officers, curious as to this little tableau
of a dead Arab woman and another " Arab " with knife in
hand who spoke English, had strolled over to question Du
Blen. It was a revelation to see how easily he, a corporal,
could dismiss his superior officers.

" It does not matter," he said, as we rode back. " She
had to die. She knew that. She preferred to die by her own
hand. So ! But your mission was successful, highly successful.
France is proud of you, Barrington."

Damn and blast France, said I, in the privacy of my mind.
Nothing, I felt sure, would ever erase from my mind that
picture of incredible hate which blazed from Me-Too's eyes.
It was her final votive act, her legacy to the honourable
Englishman who had betrayed her.

"THE LIONS ARE LOOSE!"

By
"LORD" GEORGE SANGER

IN 1876,[1] when I was in France, the proprietor of the Porte St. Martin Theatre in Paris sought me out at Clermont-Ferrand. He told me he was about to produce for the second time *Round the World in Eighty Days*, and as he had seen a coloured man performing with eight lions at the circus he thought they might effectively be introduced into the play in a love scene which takes place in an African forest.

Well, he engaged the lions at a salary of £320 a month, and I undertook to provide the scene for what was really a fine and exciting situation. This effective scene, representing a piece of forest, was what is professionally known as a cut cloth, reaching the full width of the stage. Instead, however, of being made of ordinary theatrical material, it was composed of gas-piping, bent in every conceivable form, and varying in thickness from three inches to half an inch. To this framing was attached the painted foliage cut from sheet iron, the whole being put close enough together to prevent the lions getting through, though they and their surroundings were all clearly visible to the spectators. It was all made from my designs by my gas engineer at the Amphitheatre in the Westminster Bridge Road, and was delayed in its transit from London to Paris till two days before the production of the piece, so that no rehearsal with the scene in position was possible.

As for the lions, I did not want to part with those that were travelling with my circus, so having another group at Margate, where I had purchased the Hall-by-the-Sea and the Kitchen Garden from the London, Chatham and Dover Railway Company, I resolved to use the latter. I therefore went to England, boxed up the lions in wooden cages, and sent them with all speed to Paris. With them I sent two men, keepers in my zoo at Margate, Walter Stratford and W. Pitcher.

The lions arrived in Paris on the Friday morning, the

[1] By this time "Lord" George Sanger was a showman of international reputation.

production being fixed for the Sunday, and as everything was behind, including the fixing of the iron forest, it was decided that there should be no rehearsal with the animals until Saturday. In the meantime the lions were lowered into a cellar under the stage.

I was very early astir on the Saturday in order to rehearse the lions before very many people were about. Directly I got in sight of the theatre, however, I was astonished to see a crowd about it. As I drew nearer I could see there were a lot of gendarmes present, and also my two men from Margate. When they caught sight of me they rushed forward with faces white as wax, Stratford wringing his hands, and crying : " Oh, Guv'nor ! Guv'nor ! The lions are loose ! "

" Loose ! " I exclaimed ; " what do you mean ? " " They are loose from their dens," he replied, " and this gentleman here," pointing to a gendarme officer, " says they must be shot in the interest of public safety."

" Oh, no," I said to the gendarme, " no shooting, please." Then, turning to my fellows, I said, " Come along ! Come along ! Let us get them into the dens ! " To my surprise they did not budge. " Come along ! " I said again ; " aren't you coming ? " But I got no response, so with a few unkindly remarks as to their want of pluck, I took the oil lamp from the watchman, who had been on duty at the theatre, and told him to unlock the stage-door.

When he had done so, I entered alone, the oil lamp in one hand and an ordinary walking-stick in the other. I rambled all over the theatre, stage, dress-circle, pit, etc., and finding no trace of the lions concluded they were still in the cellar. With the dim light I had it was difficult to find my way about, but down I went, and not seeing them in the upper cellar crossed over to descend to the lower one. As I did so a lion suddenly made a rush for the same opening, and as he came struck me with his head in the small of the back with such force as to make me turn a complete somersault.

I landed on my feet, thanks to my old circus experience, but I confess that for the moment I was unnerved. The lantern, however, was still in my hand, and still burning, so after collecting my thoughts I descended the steps to the lower cellar. Then I made for the spot on which the dens had been placed. There was a great deal of old scenery, rubbish, and cast-off properties about, so I very carefully made the round of the cellar, picking my way at every step.

All at once I saw eyes like balls of fire in the distant

darkness. " Oh, there you are, you rascals ! " I shouted, knowing that the animals would recognise my voice. Then I struck my cane on the various properties lying about, and at the same time swung the lantern to and fro. This had the effect of making the eight lions leap and bound in all directions. The rattle of the old canvas and other material that was thrown over by the heavy beasts, together with their surprise at my appearance, made them run round the cellar several times. By this time I was quite awake to the situation. I knew from experience that the beasts would make for their dens when they tired a bit. So it proved, for presently after another race round they made for the cases they had escaped from. I saw three get into one of the great boxes, and five into another, leaving two empty. Then I pushed to and blocked as well as I could the sliding doors of the cases, and hurried up to inform my men that the danger was over, and the lions were safely housed.

I got my men to come down, and while twelve gendarmes with rifles occupied the stage, we nailed up the cage doors, and made all secure for the time being. Then I went off to breakfast and to wait for the dress rehearsal.

This commenced at nine o'clock on the Saturday night, the house being filled by invited friends, pressmen, the Mayor of Paris, and a host of important personages. From the stage the theatre presented quite an imposing appearance, and after the rehearsal of each scene the manager would walk forward and ask the spectators if they could suggest any improvement. Sometimes a suggestion was made, and the scene would be rehearsed again. All this meant delay, and so the thing went on till about three in the morning.

Before the forest scene with the lions was produced there was an interval of an hour for refreshments, and after this the whole theatre was agog with excitement. The dens containing the lions had to be craned out of the cellar at the last moment owing to the space required for the early part of the play. The den with the five lions was got up, and put at the back ready for use all right, but in lifting the box with the three lions the rope slipped, with the result that the animals were thrown against the makeshift door with such force that one of them fell out.

In an instant a scene-shifter who had been helping rushed up to the proprietor, who was on the stage by me, and in an excited whisper said, " The lions are loose ! The lions are loose ! " The director for a moment was speechless, then he threw himself into a chair quivering like a jelly. Then he caught hold of my hand and cried, " The lions are loose ! My God ! Do you hear ? The lions are loose ! "

I was quite collected, and said calmly, " All right, sir ! All right ! It will be all right ! " " What ! " he said, glaring at me. " What ! All right ! Don't you see I am ruined ! " and he paced the stage like a madman. I saw that the lion had got back in his place again, and that the beasts were ready for the performance, and managed at last to bring the fact home to the director, greatly to his relief. Now came another shock. The coloured performer, the hero of the forest scene, was missing.

When he was found he was helpless. Admiring friends had been entertaining him not wisely but too well, and he could neither speak nor stand. I volunteered to pull the director out of this fresh hole, and finding my way to the dressing-rooms speedily blacked up for the part, and found a suitable wig and dress. The scene was now ready and on I went. There was only one drawback. I knew nothing whatever of the lines of the part, and as I was not a proficient French scholar could not have spoken them very well even if I had known them.

However, I " gagged " as best I could, while my fair companion in the scene spoke her part. At the proper moment came the roar of the lions, done by an ingenious instrument contrived for the purpose in case the lions did not roar when they were wanted to do so. The young actress took fright at the beasts, and I had a job to compose her in the love-making scene, after which she was led behind a small ironwork screen for safety. Then came the professional thunder and lightning, roaring and clamour, the lions being forced on to the stage at the back while with two nine-chambered revolvers I made them bound, snarl, and show their teeth, and some half-dozen men at the back kept up a rattle of revolver shots to work up the excitement.

In the finishing scene, a very thrilling one, the big lion, who was harmless as a dog, jumped when I stamped my foot, and put his fore-paws on my shoulders as he had been trained to do. Then I threw him off, and falling to the stage with him we rolled over together as if in combat, the lion at the end lying quite still as if dead, while I rose and put my foot on his body in an attitude of triumph.

How those Frenchmen yelled and screamed at this ! They seemed to go mad with excitement. The curtain was lowered and raised again five times. At the last I prevailed upon the pretty young actress to come forward with me to the centre of the stage amongst the animals before the audience. As she did so she shook to such an extent that I found it almost impossible to support her. The applause was wonderful, the curtain fell for the fifth time, and as it did so I noticed that the fair cheek of my companion had a large patch of black upon it, gained when, in her fear of the lions, she had reclined her head upon my shoulder.

There was another interval of an hour, during which the lions were cleared away, and the mayor, the pressmen, and the notabilities came upon the stage. The manager was so delighted with the success that he kissed me in the continental fashion upon both my black cheeks. All were agreed that the scene was magnificent. As it was now five in the morning, and there was another scene to be rehearsed which did not affect me, I made my exit, very tired indeed. I need only remark that with the real coloured man and my lions the piece ran sixteen months, making a fortune for the lucky and enterprising proprietor.

THE DEATH VALLEY—THE GATES OF HELL

By
DARE DU BOIS PHILLIPS

*In the story called " The Crossing of the Casitas Pass " you will
have read of the author's exploit that made him famous in America.*

MY exploit in the Casitas Mountains gave me a reputation for daring which, with the hot-headedness of
youth, I did everything to encourage. The affair itself
had been inspired more by foolhardiness and ignorance of
what I would have to face, than by any innate courage,
but the big drums of the American Press (which, then as
now, were always ready to bang deafeningly at news of an
unusual or sensational nature) made me feel that I really was
something of a hero, instead of a young man who had been
confoundedly lucky to escape with his life.

Among other results of the embarrassing publicity
following my escapade, was the establishment of my reputation as a motor-car driver. Even before, I had been known
as a useful racing driver, but the Casitas Mountains episode
sent my stock soaring, to the extent that, when it was discovered that I had entered for the famous 200 miles road race
from Bakersfield to Fresno, I was promptly made joint favourite for the event, together with a Cadillac entry—then one of
the fastest cars in America.

As I was then running the El Camino Motor Company
on State Street, Santa Barbara, and had the agency for
Haynes cars, it seemed quite natural that I should select
one of the make which had stood up so well to the Casitas
Pass, as my " mount " for California's most gruelling and
best-known annual road event.

Machado, my half-breed mechanic, and close friend
since the tough test he had passed through so manfully with
me, applied himself with terrific enthusiasm to the task of
helping me turn an ordinary 50 h.p. Haynes into a first-class
racer. Machado was the finest *peon* I have ever known.

The liking I had felt for him on our first meeting, cemented in the Casitas, kept growing, the more I saw of him.

He absorbed himself in the tuning-up of our entry to the exclusion of all else. He was like that : my fads of the moment were his passions of the moment. In addition to this quality of enthusiasm, he was possessed of amazing loyalty, steadfastness, straightness and cheerfulness. Physically, though not a tall man, he was one of the strongest I have ever encountered. He had shoulders like an ox and arms like hams ; I have seen him lifting a 50 h.p. car out of tenacious *adobe* mud by the axle, without apparent effort, while I slid planks under the two uplifted wheels.

Well, Machado was as good a mechanic as he was a good fellow, and, by the time we were finished with the tuning of that engine it was absolutely the last word in speed-mechanism.

You modern speed-fiends who read these words may smile contemptuously at our earnestness over the motor-racing of 1912 (the year of which I am writing) but let me tell you that the advance in speed during the past twenty-two years has not been so tremendous as the present generation is apt to think. When Machado and I had finished with our Haynes car, it was capable of maintaining an average of over 80 m.p.h. over long stretches of road, and could get well into the nineties on the straight.

At last we were satisfied that there was absolutely nothing more we could do to our car, and accordingly, leaving a handsome margin of time to spare for the journey, we left Santa Barbara on the long run to Bakersfield. We were in no hurry, the roads were dry and good ; and we had a pleasant ride of 110 miles over the Casitas, Calabas and Canajo Ranges to Los Angeles, where we decided to stay for a day or two.

It was in Los Angeles that I met and parted from the man who was, indirectly and unwittingly, to land me, a little later, in the worst predicament of my whole life ; an experience which, even now, makes me shudder—but of that you shall hear yourself in due course. . . .

I was in the bar of the Alexandra Hotel, having a drink with a few of my friends, when there entered an elderly little man who was so much out of place in this fashionable rendezvous, that I forgot my manners completely, and stared at him in amazement.

His entry evoked the most surprising reaction from the people around me. Breaking off their conversations in mid-sentence, they rushed off and surrounded the newcomer, patting his back and shouting out words of welcome. Then they led him in state to the bar, where he acknowledged the warmth of their greeting by buying drinks for everybody.

The newly-arrived celebrity was short and thick-set, and might have been of any age between fifty and seventy. Every motion of his tough little frame suggested physical strength and endurance in an ineffable way. He was so weather-beaten, with the skin of his face cleaving so closely to the bones, that the face, in repose, might have belonged to a little sun-dried corpse.

When he smiled, however, his face would take on an astonishing animation, which transformed it and rendered it tremendously attractive, and his blue eyes, generally half-hidden under hooded lids, twinkling as they were now, would open wide, revealing the lively humour in them.

It was his dress, though, which was particularly striking at the moment. Standing in the centre of this well-dressed crowd of admirers, he was clad, serviceably and picturesquely, in a suit of dirty blue dungarees, ragged and stained. From beneath the frayed ends of his trouser legs, high-heeled boots of the well-known cowboy pattern peeped out, and these were matched father up by a broad-brimmed Stetson hat, cocked at a rakish angle. Around his neck a glaring bandana-handkerchief was loosely knotted. Around his waist was an ammunition-belt, supporting two holsters ; I noticed, however, that the holsters were empty of firearms, and the belt of cartridges.

One of my friends who had left me, rather hastily for politeness, I thought, to greet the stranger, now wriggled out of the noisy throng and came back to my side. He was smiling broadly and impenitently.

" Who's the funny little man they're making all the fuss about ? " I grunted.

My friend stared at me in horror, as if I had committed sacrilege.

" Funny little man ! " Then he leaned forward and whispered in tone of portentous reverence : " *That* funny little man is Desert Rat Smith, himself ! "

" Really ? " I answered indifferently. " Well, what am I supposed to do now—shoot myself in mortification ? "

He smiled incredulously.

" Of course you've never heard of him ? "

" Evidently I'm supposed to, but I'm afraid I haven't."

Then it appeared to dawn on him that I was not indulging in leg-pulling, and he raised his eyes, as if silently calling upon Heaven to witness my abysmal ignorance.

"Suppose you tell me?" I suggested.

"Oh well, after all, you're a Britisher!" he said indulgently, as though that unfortunate accident covered a multitude of sins and ignorance. "As a matter of fact, Desert Rat is the most famous character in California. He's the only man who's ever prospected Death Valley. . . . But you'll be telling me next you've never heard of Death Valley!"

"Oh, I know all about *that*!" I answered triumphantly. "It's the particularly nasty section of the Mohavie Desert where people keep getting lost, isn't it?"

At that time Death Valley was much in the news, owing to talk of reclaiming it. The work of reclaiming has since been carried out, and the wilderness planted, but in these days it was, by all accounts, a grim place enough. The Mohavie Desert, of which it forms a part, was broiling hot, and sand-whirls interfered with transport through it, by clotting the engines of cars with grit. Apart from that, however, there was nothing outstandingly fearsome about the place.

But part of it known as Death Valley was a different proposition. Some accident of its configuration had made it the playground of a type of wind, peculiarly its own, which kept stirring the sand and altering the whole contour of the valley so completely and so frequently that all previous attempts to survey its shifting sandhills had been failures.

It was common knowledge that the place was gold-bearing in amply workable quantities, and it had always been a magnet for seekers for gold. But the place was nothing more than a death-trap, with its wild sandstorms and continually changing face, and few indeed were the men lucky enough to come out alive.

"Death Valley didn't get its name for fun," my friend was declaring with native eloquence. "No, *sir*, that God-forgotten spot *earned* its name. There's so many poor devils lost there, that it's only the sand blowing over their bones that keeps it from looking like a dug-up cemetery!"

"And where does Desert Rat Smith come in?" I inquired.

"He comes *out*. That's the point! He's the only man who ever brought gold out of Death Valley, alive—and sane. . . ."

I was thoroughly interested now, and pressed for more details.

F.T.S. 2 U

"Well, I don't know as much about Desert Rat as I'd like to know. I reckon nobody does ; he's such a modest sort of a guy that he just doesn't like talking about himself. The story is that he drifted into these parts about twenty years ago, looking for gold. There's not much good prospecting-ground about here, and he was running pretty low ; then he heard of Death Valley, and the gold there. . . . Here, come and sit down, and I'll tell you something. . . ."

I followed my informant to a table, and there I listened to an amazing story.

On hearing of Death Valley being gold-bearing, Desert Rat Smith had declared his intention of prospecting there. He had been warned that hundreds had failed to get gold there, of the solitary water-hole in the whole area, which could never be found, owing to the changing landmarks, of the terrible heat and the weird wind, that few ever came out alive, and that those who did were raving lunatics. . . . And, after listening patiently to all this well-meant advice, he had slipped off quietly one day, and disappeared through the pass, through which so few had come out.

Many days later he had crawled out through that pass more dead than alive. He had seen enough, however, to convince him of the mining possibilities of the area. As soon as he was fit again, he was grimly plodding back once more, having got some one to " grubstake," or finance, his second expedition.

No word was heard of him for so many days that he came to be given up for dead—another sacrifice to the evil genius of the place. Then, after many months, he came struggling back to civilisation again, thinner and more wrinkled, but fit and hard as nails. What is more, in his belt was enough virgin gold to repay his grubstake with interest, and to buy great quantities of liquor in Los Angeles.

Since then the connection of Desert Rat Smith with Death Valley had become an institution. He would disappear into that grilling Hell for varying periods, then wander out again with enough gold for a spell of hard drinking.

Always he went alone. Always he managed to find out the solitary water-hole in the shifting sand. Nothing could persuade him to take a companion, though dozens had tried. Many had even attempted to follow him, but he always shook them off, vanishing completely into the sandhills. No bribe could move his resolution to play a lone hand, though as much as $25,000 had been offered.

The idea of wringing enough gold out of the valley to let him retire in comfort did not seem to appeal to him in the slightest. He was quite content to bring back just enough to pay back his last grubstake and indulge in a drinking-bout. When that money was finished he would accept one of the many offers to finance his next trip and set off again. Truly, he was an amazing character—a typical " Desert Rat."

I determined to meet this strange man, and communicated my determination to my friend, and learned that an introduction would come best through Fred, the bartender, of whom Smith thought the world.

Fred was willing, and, when an opportunity offered, called the celebrity away from his circle of admirers.

Desert Rat's face took on still more wrinkles—a seemingly impossible feat, considering the number already creasing it ! —as he smiled at me, and shook my hand. I believe we took to one another from that first meeting. At any rate, we talked for hours.

" Have a drink ? " I suggested.

" Thanks, I'll have a large Robertson's," he answered.

" Nothing but the best Scotch for Desert Rat," Fred explained to me, as he set up the drinks.

" I reckon you want to talk to me about Death Valley ? "

" Like everybody else, I expect," I replied. " It seems to me that if you can get gold out of the place, there's no reason why I, or anybody else, shouldn't be able to do the same."

He shook his head, and drained his whisky, calling immediately for another round.

" I'm hardened to it. The others only *think* they are. And that's not all : I'm a camel, and they ain't. . . . Meaning I can *smell* out the only water-hole in the place."

" But there's surely no reason why you shouldn't take some one with you ? They'd be safe enough then," I suggested.

" Another Robertson's, Fred. . . . ! No, they wouldn't be safe. It's not only what your body's got to stand ; it's other things. The place gets on men's nerves. I couldn't take the responsibility of guiding men in there, and them going crackers on me. It's a tough spot. I guess I'm used to it, that's all—and I'm a darned camel. For anything else but a camel, it ain't so good."

" I wouldn't mind having a go at it myself," I said tentatively.

"*Yourself* is right, son; I ain't taking you along," he retorted, his hoarse voice rasping with hidden laughter. "Have another drink, and forget about the place. That's what *I'm* trying to do."

I told him that my last drink was still intact, and that I didn't need another. Grinning like a goblin, he looked up into my face.

"Don't feel sore, kid. I told you that just so as to get things straight from the start. When Death Valley comes into the talk, I'm just an oyster."

And nothing would persuade him to say another word on the subject. I was with him that night and far into the morning, during which time he must have drunk the equivalent of two full bottles of the fine whisky he insisted on. Needless to say, I did not attempt to keep up with him, and it was a pleasant time I had, for he was garrulous enough on other subjects, and the strong liquor did not appear to have the least effect on him.

He told me of his people, all long dead. His father and mother had been in the Klondyke Rush, and penetrated into the wildest and most dangerous parts of Alaska in their search for gold, and for many years the whole life of the family had been spent in the rough atmosphere of the mining-camps. His grandparents had been pioneers in the " covered-wagon " days, and his grandfather had been tortured and scalped by Indians, which incident Desert Rat would recount with great gusto and detail. It was tough stock he was sprung from !

I could spare no more than three days in Los Angeles, before going on to Bakersfield ; and most of that period was spent in Smith's company. He would visit nothing but the first-class bars, where he drank enormous quantities of choice liquors and bought enormous quantities for his clamouring acquaintances.

My interest in him was not entirely connected with what I could get him to tell me about prospecting Death Valley, though I admit my interest in seeking gold there had something to do with it. He was dryly humorous and absurdly generous, and a wonderful companion at all times.

" Come on, Desert Rat," I would say, " I mean to have a stab at that valley anyway. You might as well tell me about how to find that water-hole and save me a lot of trouble."

" You go out to Egypt and learn how to be a camel. Then come back, and I'll take you with me."

Then the little wretch's sun-baked face would furrow all over in a grin, and he would order another whisky and change the subject.

When the three days were up, I was reluctant to go. The little old prospector intrigued me as much as any man I have ever met. I could never understand how he could perform his amazing feats immediately after such drinking-bouts, nor how he could endure long spells in the desert without any liquor. But there were many things about Desert Rat Smith which were a mystery ; and nobody could understand him. Although I became as friendly with him as most, I had to leave Los Angeles with my curiosity more whetted than satisfied.

My only regret is that no words of mine can give a picture of the kind of extraordinary individual that Smith was. I think he was the greatest specialist I have ever met or heard of. I left him with a queer premonition in my heart that I had not heard the last of Death Valley. In some way the place was mystically calling me ; and I felt that, when I answered the call, it would not be of my own volition, but because I must. . . .

Arriving at Bakersfield, I made a succession of practice-runs over the course, which was utterly abominable : terrible roads, long patches of sand which sometimes silted up to the axle, wildly abrupt turns. On the very first trial our car was sand-logged, and could only be extricated by laying down a platform of sacks for her wheels to grip on.

Despite this and similar accidents, the experts seemed to like our entry and my driving, so that, although the Cadillac still remained joint-favourite with us, it was generally considered that I had the better chance of getting home first. . . . which may be the explanation of what occurred during the actual race.

The race was due to start at seven a.m., but, even at that early hour the heat was scorching.

We made an excellent start and, among billowing clouds of smoke and dust, got away among the leaders.

The car was a little unresponsive as I steered her round the first bend, but I put that down to the normal " warming-up " process because, having thoroughly examined her before locking her up the previous night, I was completely satisfied that she was in the best possible condition.

Imagine my horror, therefore, when, having gone no more than three miles, a flood of boiling water spurted from the radiator, drenching both Machado and myself in scalding jets. Blinded and in agony, I momentarily lost control; the car skidded violently, I tried to right her, only to find that the controls were utterly useless.

It was due, therefore, to pure luck and not at all to good guidance that we were both saved from certain death, for the car, being out of hand and going at well over a mile a minute at the time, was nothing less than a death-trap. Our good angel, however, contrived that the skid should jerk us off the road on to a patch of clogging sand, which effectively stopped our mad career after a few more crazy, hurtling moments.

Machado and I climbed out, badly shaken and thoroughly ill-humoured. Machado declared immediately that the mechanism of the car had been deliberately tampered with. Knowing the perfection of its condition only the night before, I was inclined to agree.

Machado's contention was borne out a few hours later, when we had succeeded in towing our entry back to Bakersfield. We set about investigating the cause of our ignominious retiral without delay. And, without delay, we discovered it.

It took the form of a piece of solid steel, about two inches long and one and a half inches thick, which Machado found slipped into the delicate and vital timing-gear. This had had the effect of completely " chewing-up " the timing-gear mechanism and, by ripping up the water-pump (which is actuated by the same gear) had contrived that we should have an unnecessary and unasked-for hot bath *en route* !

We were furious. Obviously some unscrupulous rival had inserted this deadly piece of steel while the car was in the garage overnight. Machado wanted to make violent protests and accusations, but, thinking things over, I refused to say anything. I knew perfectly well that, should I do so, I should be promptly accused of " squealing " ; and than " squealing " at a defeat nothing is more contemptible to the American sportsman.

To get a new timing-gear from the Haynes works in Indiana would mean waiting for the best part of three weeks, and I had no intention of kicking my heels in Bakersfield for such a period. Accordingly, I went to the biggest firm of metal-workers in the town and literally bullied them into cutting me a new gear. They were by no means keen on taking on such a finicky job, but in the full course of my annoyance, I was in no mood to take any refusal ; and, three days later they carried out my order. We patched up our lacerated car and set off on the return-journey to Santa Barbara.

We were a moody and downcast pair as we pulled up at our first stopping-place. This was a tiny village, consisting of one or two scattered frame shacks, a primitive garage, one general store, and a dilapidated little inn, in which we put up for the night. Altogether it was not a place calculated to uplift us out of our depression.

Having parked the car, we entered the melancholy inn. After waiting for about ten minutes, an ancient, bearded man wheezed his rheumatic way to our presence.

" Where are we ? " I asked.

The ancient answered briefly :

" Mohavie."

Mohavie. . . . ! In a flash my lethargy and gloom disappeared. I felt that my strange premonition on leaving Desert Rat Smith was fulfilled. I felt inclined to abandon myself to the queer workings of chance which had led me here. . . . For I knew that Mohavie was the name of the hamlet which was the nearest inhabited spot to Death Valley, and the jumping-off ground for all who entered there !

I was seized with a great exhilaration at the prompt consummation of my foreboding. That night, the inn was full of the local " hicks " and " hayseeds," intent on their evening tipple. I assure you they had a gala-night on that occasion. I persistently bought drinks all round, till their tongues wagged like the tails of happy dogs.

They could tell me nothing of Death Valley beyond what I had already gleaned ; but they confirmed everything Desert Rat Smith had said. They conjured up for me horrible pictures of the raving lunatics who had come back to the village from the valley. They mentioned many more who had never come back. In themselves, lust for the gold of the place had died ; they had seen too much of the effect in others. Of Desert Rat Smith, they talked in tones of awe ; he was plainly something god-like to his local hero-worshippers.

Perhaps their gloomy yarns might have turned me from the purpose I had already formed, had not I had the sensation that I had been led to the enterprise by something stronger than my common sense or my power of resistance.

I took Machado aside and said to him in casual tones, masking my intense inward excitement :

" How about having a shot at Death Valley ? "

His black eyes lit up and his white teeth flashed.

" Whenever *El Capitano* ees ready," was all he said.

" You understand what it means ? Desert Rat Smith is the only man who's ever come out alive and sane."

He shrugged. " I take da chance a' right."

I clapped him on the back.

" Good man ! " I said. " Come on. Let's go ! "

Equipment for our trip was easily purchased in that one-horse town. Indeed, it was grimly evident that the natives drove quite a flourishing trade in prospector's kit. We were alternately warned and scoffed at when we let our intention of going into Death Valley be known—but no demur was made when we asked for our equipment ! Without difficulty we got hold of a small tent, prospecting-tools, picks, shovels, three sturdy pack-mules and various tackle for surveying.

The landlord of the hotel said to us :

" I reckon the next time I see you guys coming, it'll be feet-foremost. . . ."

And, with that farewell in our ears, we went through the gap between the hills that was the gate to Death Valley, and passed into that stretch of blank desolation. The flanks of that pass had been for many, the last green things on which their living eyes had rested.

By the middle of the very first day, the genius of the place had us by the throat. The heat was like a white-hot scourge ; the arid wind blew dismal and unceasing over the sandhills, like the breath of an oven ; nothing grew there. The very atmosphere was one of overwhelming sorrow and utter desolation, so that, before you knew it, it had loaded you with an intolerable burden of nameless fear. Fear was in the hot wind, in the never-ending sandhills ; it walked beside you and jeered at you.

I wish I could describe the quality of terror aroused by the mere fact of *being* in the valley, and the living quality in that inanimate stretch of sand which aroused it. No words that I can put on paper here can do either ; and yet all others I have met who have ever seen Death Valley have agreed that the intangible sense of terror it begot was its outstanding memory for them.

We pitched camp the first night in an overwrought silence. Even Machado, generally irrepressibly cheerful, was not proof against the oppressive influence of the valley,

Exhausted after our day's march in the gruelling heat, we lay down to sleep.

But the wind rose in the night. The fretful, eerie wailing of its voice rose to a thin scream—to a howling roar. I have known the Sirocco, the Chinook, the whirlwind and the tornado, but I have never known anything like that wind of Death Valley. It swamped both of us in a crazy panic.

In no time our tent had gone. We were out in the open dunes, with the wind howling in our ears, driving sand into our eyes and sweeping it in horizontal gusts across our blinded faces. Filled with a terror such as I have never experienced, we behaved like madmen, running round dazedly in crazy circles. Thinly through the roar of the wind and the whistle of the sand came the fear-stricken whinnies of the mules.

For three hours the lunatic sandstorm raged. A maddened mule came tearing past me, almost touching me, and disappeared into the driving sand. Machado and I groped our way to one another like blind men or lost children and clutched at one another's bodies.

When the light came we were lying huddled together, face-downwards in the sand and half-buried in it.

The mules had gone. Of our tent or any of our equipment there was no sign. A good-sized hillock of sand, in whose lee we had camped, had completely disappeared, and all around us were fresh hillocks and new valleys, piled-up or scoured-out by the wind. In the night the whole face of the valley had altered.

Patient searching for any of our kit revealed nothing but a bundle of poles, intended for surveying purposes; this in spite of digging in the sand at several spots which we calculated to be the vanished site of our camp. Examination revealed that the only possessions of value left to us were my revolver, and a compass which Machado was carrying.

I swear there was an evil spirit in the valley; on that dismal dawning I could feel it clutching and gibbering at me. I knew I must fight it or go under. Affecting optimism, I said :

" Well, we've still our compass. We can find our way out."

Machado answered sullenly, quite unlike his normal tones :

" Poles no good. Heavy. We no take 'em along."

I affected not to notice his surly manner.

" Perhaps we'd better," I said. " They might come in handy. I'll carry them."

Steering by Machado's compass, we marched all that day,

our feet slipping incessantly in the loose sand. Every now and again we encountered the whitened bones of mules and humans ; grim reminders of our possible fate. The lack of food was of little moment ; but already thirst was beginning to be an agony.

Towards evening we came to a water-hole. It was alkaline and worse than useless. Beside it we found one of our mules. It was lying on its side, struggling pathetically to rise on broken forelegs. Seeing us, it whinnied in anguish and kicked out in re-doubled efforts. Drawing my revolver, I buried a couple of bullets in its brain.

Until then I had maintained my calm front without too much difficulty. Now weakness battered at my reserve, and I was taken with a terrible urge to break down in tears. I had to struggle wildly against the urge, knowing the dangers of hysteria.

When the darkening came, we threw ourselves down on the sand and dropped into a fitful doze. Each time we awoke, it was to the lost, unceasing wail of the wind. The nights were not cold, but, in contrast to the burning day, we were chilled, and shivered wretchedly in our thin clothing.

The next day the tortures of thirst were demoniacal. Our lips were cracked and tongues swollen. All night Machado had spoken no word to me, although I had addressed him several times. His behaviour was beginning to worry me.

About the middle of that flaming day, matters came to their first climax. We were limping along blankly, when I turned to Machado and suggested another reading of the compass. He regarded me with a peculiar, dull look.

" Compass—what you mean ? "

" You know perfectly well what I mean," I said shortly. " The little thing like a watch that finds our way for us."

" Oh, *dat* theeng," he said confusedly. " I t'row dat away. Eet ees too heavee. I no can walk weeth eet. Eet load me down. . . ."

" You crazy fool ! " I shouted at him in a fury of weakness and frustration. " You haven't thrown it away ! Where is it . . . ? Come on, hand it over ! "

He dazedly turned out his pockets for me to see.

" I no have eet. Too heavee. I no can walk. Eet load me down," he repeated, and went on repeating—over and over again.

I looked at him in horror. Machado was mad—or, if not actually off his head, already precious near it. Tears of weakness sprang to my eyes. Like one as mad as he, I went back over the ground we had just traversed, seeking wildly for the sun's glint on the precious compass. In places I scrabbled with my hands like a dog, where I thought our feet might have kicked sand over it.

From the first it was hopeless. At last I sank down in exhaustion. With my mind open to impressions again in that respite, I felt the atmosphere of the place clutching at me once more, panicking me. I fought it desperately. Now that Machado was patently breaking under the strain, it was all the more vital that I should keep my head.

Close beside me a human skull and vertebrae lay, half-silted-up in sand. Fixing my eyes on these grim remains, I strove to impress their image on my mind as a symbol of resistance to the power that had strewn them there in their living sheath of flesh and blood.

Machado sat some thirty yards away, watching me unwinkingly with a dour and intent stare. I shuddered at the blankness of his eyes ; it was as though they were empty shells, with no human, thinking brain behind them. My tongue kept licking dryly at my cracked lips. I continually tried to coax a drop of saliva into my parched mouth ; but the tongue was hard and swollen, too big for my mouth.

I got up and continued the agony of marching. Machado followed a score of yards in my rear, watching me unceasingly. Without turning round, I was conscious of his staring eyes on my back.

For hours we trudged in silence. Towards sundown, I came upon something that filled me with a wave of unspeakable joy. It was the tracks of human feet in the sand. Clearly, they must have been made that very day, for, otherwise, the swirling sand would have blotted them out. I called out in delight to Machado, and we followed the footprints as if endued with a new store of life and energy.

But, as we progressed, a terrible suspicion which had been blossoming in my mind forced itself more and more upon my consciousness. Then the suspicion became a horrible certainty. We came to a place all trampled down, and there I saw the human bones I had observed during that other frightful hour at noon. We had been following our own tracks. . . . We had traced a complete circle, instead of progressing. . . .

By all accounts, this experience is not a new one ; and it had been recounted many times before. But, of many awful moments I have passed through during a crowded life, that, when the discovery was made that we had been wandering in crazy revolutions instead of in a straight line, was the most catastrophic. At such a time, it is the intolerable sweeping-away of reawakened hope that gets you by the heart.

For a few seconds I stared while I made sure, then I threw myself on the ground in complete abandonment to despair, weakly sobbing. I had to struggle with the fury of desperation to get a grip on myself again.

As the sun went down, Machado sat unmoving—watching me. Added to the terror of that Valley of Hell, was the terror of the changed Machado. At any moment, the last shreds of his reason might go, and his mania turn homicidal. The phenomenal strength of the man I have mentioned. I knew that, if he took it into his head, he could break me and tear me to pieces with those great arms of his. I made up my mind, there and then, to keep my hand on the revolver-butt and to shoot him dead at the first signal of attack. I am a powerful man, but I should have been but a child in his terrible hands.

I was afraid to sleep that night, lest he should creep on me unawares. Shivering, I shifted restlessly on the sand, waiting for the light.

By the dawn I had evolved the idea of utilising the survey-poles, which I had still held on to, in a scheme to ensure that we ploughed a straight course ahead.

The poles I planted at intervals along a straight line. The idea was that we should keep going back and remove the hindmost poles, bringing them to the front, and, by leaving not less than three poles stuck in the ground at once, make sure that our direction would not waver or swing off.

To save time it was necessary that one of us should remain behind to remove the rearmost poles and bring them up, while the other went on ahead to embed the foremost. I explained the idea at great length to Machado, until at last he seemed to understand.

I stuck the poles in front of the line into the sand, and, turning, waited for him to bring me those behind. He came slowly up the line, and at each pole stopped and deliberately knocked it down. I shouted at him, and, running back, wearily explained the whole business over again.

He nodded impatiently at my words, then, immediately I had gone on again, did the same thing once more. So it went on, till I tried to do the whole thing myself; but

Machado persisted in mowing down the poles as quickly as I set them up. In the end, I had to abandon the scheme, and we continued our trek without any guide to direction whatsoever.

It was now our fourth day in the desert, and our thirst was an aching torment. My tongue was now so swollen that I could not close my mouth, whose blackened and cracked lips gaped open, exposing the lolling tongue. I would have cheerfully sold my eternal soul for one drop of moisture to cool my mouth.

At last the thought of the blood swirling through my body was too much for me. Having looked warily over my shoulder at Machado plodding in my rear, I bent and bit the flesh of my arm, and licked the drop of blood that welled up on my skin.

The fleeting relief gained in this unpleasant way was too attractive to forgo. Several times more that day I secretly bit my arm and lapped up the blood with my hard and parched tongue.

Our pace was now no more than a crawl. The physical strain of keeping walking was draining our strength. Before nightfall, I felt I could go no farther, and flopped on the ground.

Machado sat a little distance away, never taking his eyes from me. . . . Then suddenly he got up and came towards me. My heart began to pound ; my finger waited on the trigger. When about ten yards away he stopped, and said in tones of the utmost reasonableness :

" I see you, *senor*. You bite your arm—lika me. . . ." And he showed me the scars of his teeth in his forearm. " Thees a no good. We need a dreenk—my throat, eet is all dry. We open a vein in your arm . . . and dreenk."

I called upon all my reserves of will-power. By the calmness of his tone, I could see that his madness had reached a more dangerous stage. I knew that, at all costs, I must get the upper-hand of him mentally ; I did not want his life on my hands if I could help it.

I answered just as reasonably :

" That's no good, Machado, old chap. I'd simply bleed to death. You don't want that to happen, do you ? "

With patient logic, he explained, by words and gestures, that a tourniquet could be made to staunch the flow, once we had drunk ; and that the tourniquet could be loosened, whenever our thirst grew unbearable again. To those who read this by the security of their hearthsides, this calm debate on practical cannibalism may seem ludicrous ; to me, at the time, it was the very climax of horror.

I summoned an air of firmness.

" Don't be a fool, Machado. I simply won't listen to such rot. Go and lie down again. . . . If you do, I promise faithfully I'll find a water-hole for you to-morrow."

He subjected me to a slow stare.

" Go on, Machado," I repeated. " Go and lie down."

We looked into each others' eyes. I tried to focus, through my eyes, the domination of my tottering sanity over his lunacy. At last he turned and walked slowly away.

I think he slept, for I heard his heavy breathing coming regularly. I, myself, despite my watchfulness, dropped off once or twice into an unquiet delirium that passed for sleep.

He was in yet a different mood, when I went to shake him into wakefulness. He cried out in a hoarse scream :

" No, we no walk again ! I too tired. You leta me die here ! My mouth—eet ees on fire. You breeng me water ; then I walk ! "

I shook him roughly.

" Come on. Get moving, old chap. We'll likely strike a water-hole to-day."

At last I persuaded him to move. I had hardly done so, than I saw that the man was nearly at the end of his strength. He was so weak that his legs collapsed under him every now and again, and many times I had to drag him upright. I was in rather better case, though pretty well all-in ; it struck me as strange that this man, the native of a hotter land than mine and immeasurably stronger muscularly, should be the first to succumb to the mental strain and physical hardships of that nightmare.

All this time we had worn our wide-brimmed *sombreros,* the possession of which we had retained, not through fore-sight, but simply because they had been fastened round our necks by their leather thongs. Machado now began behaving in the most demented way, continually tearing off his hat, and throwing it away as fast as I retrieved it for him. In the rays of that terrible sun, I could not let him go bareheaded.

His mania grew wilder and wilder. He began tearing off his clothes. I struggled with him in a dreadfully exhausting effort to keep him from doing so. Luckily for me, he was practically dropping in his tracks at this juncture, or I should never have managed to hold him down till he became a little

calmer. He was like a man in an opium-dream. His eyes
were half-closed and blind ; his body was limp ; his blackened
tongue lay on his unshaven chin.

Presently he grew less violent ; his mania waned and
vanished into weak sobbing. I got to my feet ; and noticed,
with a sense of shock, the difficulty I had in doing so. Somehow I got Machado to his. With him leaning heavily on me,
we trudged on.

Many times he collapsed, and it was with increasing
difficulty each time that I lugged him up again. The sun rose
higher. If I had had the strength to do so, I would have
screamed aloud at the torment of my thirst. More than once
I discovered myself laughing uncontrollably ; I fought to
check the tendency, knowing that if I did not I might soon
be as mad as Machado. . . .

I began to see things. On a ridge of small sandhills to
our left, I saw a pack-train moving. I tried to tell Machado,
but my tongue was past coping with words. Making weird,
cracked grunts, I nodded my head towards the little hills.
We stumbled in that direction. But as we drew nearer, the
vision faded, and only the blank dunes greeted us.

I grew lightheaded. The rhythm of an old tune kept
beating in my mind like strokes on a gong ; I tried to rid
myself of the monotonous jangling of the melody, but it would
not cease to pound at my brain. I kicked against the rib-bones
of a mule, nearly falling my length, and found laughter
mounting inside me, for no reason.

Then I took a sharp pull on myself. I knew by a hundred
insidious signs that lunacy was not far from me. With every
hour the battle against my rising hysteria grew fiercer and
more difficult to maintain. I had not even the satisfaction
of setting my teeth together, for my too-big tongue would not
stay in my mouth.

Machado had been walking laboriously, leaning against
me, putting one foot before the other with a purely mechanical
action. He kept up an incessant flow of animal-like grunts,
fingering his throat in agony with one hand. Suddenly his
bestial mutterings rose to a higher, more urgent key. Without
warning he pushed me away, so that in my exhausted
condition I was flung to the ground, and, howling like a wolf,
began capering and gesticulating grotesquely.

It was the last ferocity of his madness ; and he was too
weak to maintain the extra effort for long. He threw up his
arms and fell backwards.

I crawled to his side and tugged at the breast of his shirt. He was like a corpse in his immobility. I knew I could never summon the strength to lift him. I tugged feebly at his shirt.

After an uncountable period of time, his bloodshot eyes half-opened. I tugged at him again imperatively ; then somehow or other struggled to my feet. I was afraid to lean over him, for fear I should topple ; I stood there, grunting at him, trying to speak.

He got to his knees. I got my arm under his, and he lurched to his feet. For a few yards we stumbled ahead ; then his weight grew too much for me, and we both fell flat on the sand.

How we struggled up again I shall never know. This time we collapsed again almost immediately. I tried feebly to get up, but my arms simply crumpled up beneath my limp body.

I lay on my face, with my head resting on my arm. This was the end. A strange lassitude stole over me, giving place, with a suddenness that shocked, to a blinding pain in my head. It was as if my brain was swelling, splitting the top of my skull. I remember wondering fleetingly, amid the black-out of that indescribable pain, if the long-threatened madness was claiming me at last, as it had claimed Machado.

.   .   .   .

One of our stampeded mules had found its way back to its stable in the village. With this evidence of a mishap to us, the natives had approached a government party of assayers, just arrived with the intention of making another of their surveys of Death Valley, and had asked the party to organise a search for us.

They found us not more than half a mile from the pass through which we had entered the valley !

As the innkeeper had foretold, we came back feet-first. But we were both alive, and that confounded his prophecies. When I was fit to be out and about again, I found myself the laughing-stock of the place, the mark for every shaft of hay-seed wit. I am afraid I was not in the state of mind to appreciate rustic humour.

I recovered—superficially at least—with surprising quickness ; but I shall not boast that what I had gone through did not leave its mark on me. Indeed, I shall admit that the very name of Death Valley afterwards was enough to make me shudder, and that I would make long detours by road to avoid passing anywhere near the accursed spot.

Poor Machado was not so lucky as I. After the worst of the physical effects of his ordeal had worn off, he had to be placed in a mental home for over two months, before he could be called normal again.

He was never the same afterwards. His former cheeriness was now replaced by a smouldering sullenness. On the flimsiest of provocation he would fly into the most uncontrollable passion. At the mention of any word which reminded him of Death Valley, such as " sand," " thirst," " tent," etc., he would become nearly demented. Instructions I gave him about the garage were completely ignored, or else he would perform the exact opposite of what I had ordered.

At last he was near to murdering a negro car-washer I had working for me, with whom he had formerly been on the best of terms, and I had to get rid of him.

It was a sordid ending to a horrible adventure ; but that is Life, and what marks the difference between real happenings and fiction. To balance the big moments of Life, it is right, no doubt, that their culminations should be drab affairs, with many loose threads left over at the end. . .

A NARROW ESCAPE FROM DEATH

By
JO HALLAM

The scene is set in Ontario in the winter of 1897. *Yoto and*
" Happy " share a log cabin with the author.

AFTER a period of stormy, snowy weather, we suddenly
entered into a period of brilliant sunshine. Yoto warned
us that this was very dangerous because of the likelihood
of getting snow-blindness. We had to wear dark glasses until
we could get used to the terrible glare. However, this weather
was much better than we had been having before, for now
we could go out and stretch our legs at last, and in consequence
our tempers as well as our appetites improved.

On the occasion of which I am speaking Yoto and
" Happy " had gone out after the " cannies," as the foxes
were called, and I was left behind in the hut. It was a rule
that Yoto had made that one of us had always to be left
behind to look after the hut. They had taken with them,
as usual, big flasks of hot coffee inside baked clay. Our
method of keeping the coffee hot sounds strange to-day when
every one has thermos flasks ; but would coffee keep hot for
long in thermos flasks with the temperature below zero?
I doubt it.

Our method was this. The coffee was boiled up and then
placed in these bottle-shaped flasks (I believe they were made
of iron ; I know they were very heavy to carry). Then the
wet clay was placed round the flasks and the whole con-
traption placed over the fire on a sort of grid to bake. When
the clay had hardened it was all ready to take out, and the
coffee would keep hot for hours.

I dawdled about for about an hour after they had gone
out, and then because the weather was so fine and because
I hate to be idle I decided to go out and chop a few logs. We
had a lot in the hut already as a matter of fact, but I thought
there was no harm in getting in a few more from our supply,
which was only about thirty yards from the hut.

I had nearly finished the job, and had carted in a lot of logs when I felt a heavy hand clap me on the shoulder. I was bending down to heave a heavy log on to my shoulder and I didn't look round, for I thought it was " Happy " back rather early. He had a habit of slapping you on the back. I remember thinking how extraordinary it was that he should have come up so silently.

Then I felt the hand upon my shoulder again.

" Oh, you're back, are you ? " I said, chopping away.

There was no answer, but I could hear to my amazement a funny heavy kind of breathing.

" Don't be a fool, ' Happy ' ! " I said, straightening my back.

Then, just as I was about to turn round *I felt to my horror something that was soft and wet and flabby gently moving backwards and forwards on the back of my head just above my fur collar.*

I stood frozen with terror. My heart seemed to stop beating, and then raced at twice its ordinary speed. I felt icy cold, then suddenly hot and clammy. . . . I dared not look round . . . a heavy thud descended on my other shoulder and I felt a tearing pain. . . . I knew it wasn't " Happy " standing behind me. . . . I knew it wasn't a man . . . those weren't hands on my shoulders . . . they were . . .

With a shriek I leapt forward a pace and flung round to face the creature. It was a bear !

I glanced at the hut. The door was still open as I had left it when I was carrying in the logs. But the bear stood directly in my path. I had no arms on me. I was helpless !

I looked back at the bear, and I noticed he was regarding me comically with his head on one side. He was curious about me ; he didn't quite know what I was. I was wearing a great bearskin coat. Perhaps he thought I was a peculiar kind of bear. I don't know. But, anyway, he didn't attack me straight away, but just stared at me curiously and panted.

I knew that Yoto and " Happy " might be back in a few minutes. On the other hand it was more likely that they wouldn't be back for nearly an hour.

I glanced at the hut door again. There was only one thing to do. I must make a dash for it. I moved slightly and the bear must have noticed, for he didn't give me a chance to move again. He lunged forward and caught me behind the neck.

I struggled frantically to get away, but he clasped his

great arms round me and practically squeezed the life out of me. It didn't seem to me that there was any hope for me at all, but he released his hold of me for a second and then tripped me up so that I fell flat into the snow. It then dawned on me for the first time that he was only playing with me !

If he had wanted to he could have killed me straight away, but he wanted to play ! It was going to be a slow agonising death !

A bear is fond of roots—he is a vegetarian—and for the job of getting these out of the ground nature has provided him with long sharp claws. These claws dug into my shoulders making me scream out with pain. He rolled me over on to my back and lay on me and licked my face. I knew then the wet clammy thing I had felt on the back of my head had been his tongue !

I gasped, and spluttered, and struggled but I couldn't move an inch. He could do just what he liked with me. His great weight was slowly crushing and suffocating me. I felt I was getting purple in the face. Then suddenly he lifted his great bulk off me, and in doing so his claws caught in my face and tore the skin away. I was almost unconscious by then and could hardly feel the pain of it, but I felt the blood trickling down the side of my face.

Suddenly I came to consciousness again and realised that the bear was not molesting me at all. Where had he gone ? I raised my face and saw him regarding me steadily. I knew that once I moved he would attack me again. So I stayed motionless. How long I stayed in that position I would not like to say, but it seemed like several hours. I think it may have been as long as ten minutes. I couldn't see the hut from that position for we had manœuvred round so that I was between the hut and the bear.

I was hoping that if I waited long enough Yoto and " Happy " would be back. But I suddenly knew that I couldn't stand not moving any longer. I decided for the second time to make a dash for it, but once again I was thwarted. I was so stiff and weak after remaining motionless in the same position for so long that I found I couldn't rise, and simply fell limply back into the snow.

In an instant the bear was on me again. I could hear myself moaning as his sharp claws tore through my coat and fur-boot and bit into my skin. I could hear myself moaning, I say, but I was so dazed and faint that I didn't realise for a moment that it was I who was moaning.

There was no struggle in me now. I lay limp and helpless. But this did not seem to please the bear. He left me almost immediately, and I lay dead still again for several minutes. Then I slowly raised my head. This time he had gone still farther off.

There was a chance, just a faint chance that if I ran for it, I might get to the open hut door before the bear caught me. I set my teeth, sprang to my feet, staggered for a second and nearly fell, then stumbled frantically towards the hut.

I heard the bear pounding after me, but I was almost in safety—only a few yards from the hut. . . . Suddenly I stopped short and groaned in my despair. *The hut door was shut !*

I knew there wasn't time to open the door for it had a complicated catch that locked automatically when the door closed. It would take some seconds to get it open. These thoughts flashed through my mind in an instant, and no sooner had I stopped than I was running on again round the hut in a last desperate effort to get away from the brute.

When I had staggered round to the back of the hut I saw to my unutterable relief Yoto and " Happy " returning. At the same moment the bear saw them too, and he paused, peering forward at them short-sightedly.

I gave one despairing cry to them, and then slumped down into the snow. I heard a shot ring out . . . a last howl from the bear . . . then voices . . . Yoto's voice, and " Happy's " voice strangely serious. . . . " Carry him in," Yoto said. . . . Then I drifted away into unconsciousness.

I suddenly became conscious again at the sound of another shot. I opened my eyes and was amazed to find I was inside the hut and that " Happy " was standing beside me with a smoking gun in his hand.

" Happy " came up wiping his forehead.

" Phew, that was a close thing," he said.

" What is it ? " I murmured.

" It's all right, Jo. You go to sleep," said Yoto.

I felt some one sponging my face, and then I drifted off again. . . .

It wasn't until the next day that I heard what had happened when Yoto and " Happy " got me back to the hut. Apparently when Yoto got the door open he was amazed to find the whole place upside down. It looked as if there had been a fight going on in there. At first, he told me, he thought

I had been fighting with the bear in there, but then he'd heard a slight movement inside the provision store-room, had tiptoed across the room, had peered in, and seen, nosing about among our provisions, another bear !

Yoto yelled a warning to " Happy " not to bring me in, but he was too late, for " Happy " was already inside and was putting me on to a bunk. The bear, startled by Yoto's yell, advanced towards him. He lifted his gun in a flash and fired, but there was only a futile click. He leapt to one side as the bear came towards him, and at that moment " Happy " fired too, and the bear reared up in the air and then fell backwards writhing. It was at that moment that I became conscious.

I told Yoto of the mysterious shutting of the door and we decided that the only possible solution was that the bear, which must have been the female of the one that had attacked me, had noticed the open door of the hut, wandered in, rummaged about, and in doing so had accidentally knocked against the door (which opened on the inside so that it could still be opened when snow had blocked up against it) and closed it, thus imprisoning itself and shutting me out. It was just as well, I thought, that the door had been closed, for if it had been open I would have rushed inside and closed it, thus finding myself with a bear in and a bear out !

THE PASSING OF ARTHUR

By
PETULENGRO

*Because of his ragged appearance the author had great difficulty
in getting accepted for a passage from the United States to England,
but at last the purser of the* Campania *agrees to take him.*

I WAS given an empty two-berth cabin in an isolated part
of the ship's bowels. I think that my benefactor, the
purser, had me put there so that, should I go mad or run
amok, I might not annoy the other passengers.

I stayed on deck till the darkness was settling round the
ship, and we were well under way, with clear water ahead.
The chill salt air was like a balm to my aching bemused head.
Across the grey waters I should find England. I felt calmer
and clearer in the mind than I had felt for weeks.

With the coming of the dark, I went down to my cheerless
little cabin. I felt more tired than I had ever felt in my life,
save perhaps on that return-trip from Australia. There was
my berth with the white sheet turned down like a great cuff
over the coverlet embroidered with the monogram of the
Cunard company. I need rack my brain no longer with
inventing tragic capers for Churchill's. I could sleep for as
long as I liked.

Why should I not sleep for the whole length of the voyage ?
I owed my system a full week's sleep, and here was my chance
to make it up. I determined to climb into my berth and not
get out of it until we were in the Mersey. I got into the bunk,
put my head on the pillow, and immediately slipped down—
down—into a deep, kindly well of sleep.

I awoke with a start. Somebody was hammering on the
door. A voice called out :

" Aren't you getting up ? "

How long had I been asleep, I wondered . . . ? Four
days—perhaps even five . . . ? I was certain it had been a
long time.

" Aren't you getting up ? " the voice repeated. " The
second call for dinner has just gone."

" What's the time ? " I called back.

" Nearly nine o'clock."

" What night ? "

There was a pause, as though of astonishment. Then :
" Sailing-night, of course."

So I had been asleep for less than an hour. I felt viciously
that I had been cheated of my right. I got up and opened the
door. With an impatient glance at me, the steward entered,
carrying a couple of suitcases. There followed him into the
apartment another man, a big-framed broad-shouldered
man, but dreadfully thin and pale. He seemed to be in the
last stages of weakness, and it seemed to take all his strength
to stumble across the floor and flop down on my berth, where
he lay panting. His wild-looking eyes, unnaturally bright
and enlarged by sickness, stared at me with a kind of intent
friendliness.

" This gentleman has come to share this cabin, sir," the
steward announced.

I felt like protesting, but did not want to hurt the sick
man's feelings. I murmured something about thinking I
should be alone, knowing as I did that there were empty
cabins all round my own.

The steward gave me a sharp look and said smartly :
" You can complain to the purser, if you like, sir."

Then stowing the newcomer's bags, he left the cabin,
snapping the door to behind him.

The man on my berth gasped out :
" Don't like that—feller—much."

" I don't either," I agreed.

We looked at one another, and the sick man smiled.
He was dressed and looked like a typical British workman,
from his new tweed cap to his thick-soled well-polished boots.
He looked about fifty years of age. Clearly he was seriously
ill, and looked all the worse for the fact that it was obviously
such a strong body that the disease had eaten up.

He gave a hasty smile.

" I'll get off your bunk, mate, an' get up on my own—in
two secs.—just as soon as I can get my breath."

" Stay where you are," I answered. " I'll take the top
berth."

He smiled at me again.

" Mean you're not movin' out o' here ? "

" No, I'm staying."

" That's good. Sometimes I get bad turns—an' it's
better if there's somebody with you. . . . . It's diabetes I've

got. . . . They had me in another cabin first, but the other
men objected to me bein' with them so they brought me here.
. . . . It's nice to be settled down."

" What about dinner ? It's ready now."

" I shan't go up to the saloon. I'll have it here."

I rang for the steward, and the sick man told him to make
the bed and bring him down some dinner. I left to seek out
the dining-saloon.

There were few passengers aboard. I sat down in the
first vacant seat I saw, which was between two couples who
each appeared to be husband and wife. They were decent
solid-looking folk with dull faces. The steward brought the
menu and I ordered my dinner. When I had done so, I saw
that the two or three seats on either side of me were vacant.
The decent folk to my right and the decent folk on my left
had each moved several places away from my contaminating
company. Perhaps they had good reason. I must have looked
a pretty wild-looking dinner-companion, and had doubtless
been glaring about me morosely. For all that, to the discredit
of my good sense, I was hurt. I have always preferred those
disingenuous people who can be unsociable gracefully to
those honest ones who despise to make any bones about it.
I thought inimically of the honest folk who had been so
admirably frank about refusing to share their cabin with my
poor diabetic friend. . . .

The chair next to mine scraped the floor. I glanced round
in surprise and saw a man wearing clericals sitting down beside
me.

" Good-evening," he said pleasantly ; then turned to the
steward to order his food.

I went on eating moodily. When he had finished ordering,
he turned to me again and made some casual remark about
the prospects of the voyage. I answered him tersely. He
went on talking charmingly and easily, and it was not long
before I, too, had thawed. It transpired that he was a Roman
Catholic priest—by name Father Cunningham—a Glasgow
man returning from conducting some mission in America.
I am sure now that he must have seen me being snubbed
by my neighbours at the dinner-table, and had sat beside me
intentionally so that I should not feel an Ishmael among my
fellows. He was that sort of man ; and there was no hint of
patronage in his kindliness. During that voyage, he was the
only soul who spoke a friendly word to me, with the exception
of the poor devil in my cabin.

. . . Not that I was not addressed by the other passengers. That same night I wandered out on deck and was staring dully over the side, when a great slack-jawed man with a Middle-West face and a Middle-West voice came and tapped me on the shoulder.

" Pardon me, but I was just wondering down there if you was a Czech ? From your looks, if you see what I mean——"

" What does it matter to you whether I'm a Czech or not ?" I demanded.

He looked hurt and indignant.

" No harm in asking, is there ? Gee, there ain't no call to bite my nose off, just because I asked you a civil question ! "

In the mood I was, I was filled with an overwhelming desire to strike him. I bitterly resented his assumption that he had the right to come and cross-examine me like this. Little did he know how near he was to being violently assaulted at that moment. As it was, I managed to control the sweet impulse to lay into him. As I walked away without a word, I heard him muttering : " Land's Sake ! Some folks sure get het up over nothin'. . . ."

I went below and sought my cabin. The sick man was undressed and lying in bed. He greeted me with a friendly nod. I think he had been lonely, and welcomed my company —such as it was in the peculiar state of mind I was in.

He nodded to my fiddle-case propped against a wall.

" What you got there—a fiddle ? "

" Yes."

" Can you play it ? "

" That's my job."

He looked at me with a kind of nervous eagerness, as if afraid he might be asking too much of me.

" Do us a favour, will you, mate——? Play ' You'll Remember Me '."

I took out my fiddle.

" I suppose you mean ' When Other Lips ' ? It goes like this. . . ." I played the opening notes, and he agreed excitedly.

While I played it, he lay back blissfully, his eyes closed. When I had finished, he smacked his lips like a chef approving a choice soup.

" Now *that's* music ! " he declared. " Real opera, eh ? None of your music-hall stuff about that. You know, I think that's the finest song ever written."

I did not tell him that I had rather different views about the song—especially arranged as a violin-solo. He talked avidly for a while, until the talking began to tire him. Then he lay still staring at the bottom of the berth above him. His eyes shone brilliantly. While he talked and after, he drank water incessantly.

I played a little to him quietly, and he went to sleep. I sat watching him for a long time. I knew all his history now. His name was Arthur something. He was a bricklayer and had been living in the States for some time, making money such as he could never have made at the same trade in England. Then he had fallen ill. The doctor had been serious, but had not, I think, told him what the end of the disease must be. Like myself, he had suddenly been seized by an overwhelming instinct to go home. He had said : " Somehow you don't feel so bad when you're at home." His only regret was that he had no relatives to go back to, save some married sister in the Midlands. Poor devil ! He was so unconscious of death flying fast behind him . . . I could have told him that he ought to be glad that he had no relatives.

My pity for him seemed to purge some of the unhealthiness from my own mind. During the period of intense mental strain I had been enduring, I had been growing more and more introspective. It was good for me now to be feeling for another human being besides myself. I knew why the steward had brought him to my cabin. I was a queer customer, certainly not fit to mix with the respectable folk aboard, and therefore the only one who might suffer the billeting of a seriously ill man on me. Clearly, they could not put him in a cabin by himself in that condition, and it must have struck them as mighty convenient to have a strange bird such as I aboard to share a roost with this other strange bird. I wonder why they didn't put him straight into the sick-bay ? I have a feeling that the cabin-steward had something to do with that . . .

I went to bed and slept long and late—a giant's feast of sleep. All day I stayed in the cabin with Arthur, leaving him only to go to the saloon at mealtimes and eat in company with Father Cunningham. Even the beginning of a normal routine of sleeping and eating and calm thinking was working its cure on me. By the evening my morbidness was almost gone, I could do something I had not done for weeks : I could laugh spontaneously at a joke. My sense of humour was reasserting itself, and that was most important of all : for it meant that my sense of proportion was coming back to me.

Three times that day I played " When Other Lips," to Arthur's great delight. To dilute the dose for my own consumption, I played a number of other things as well. Arthur, with the bogey of prospective loneliness now finally exorcised, was in fine form, and made little jokes about our " private concerts." He spoke as if they were riots of merrymaking. . . .

The next day I got a shock. I woke after another orgy of sleep and jumped down from my upper berth to find Arthur sitting up on his and struggling to pull on a pair of trousers. He waved to me gaily.

" I'm getting up," he declared. " I feel better to-day than I have for weeks."

Not without qualms, I helped him to dress.

" It's a shame to stay shut up down here," he said. " I'll get better twice as quickly if I get a sniff or two of that sea air."

We went slowly up the alleyways and up on deck. He took great breaths of the air, but began to cough. He was quiet for a little after that, gazing happily at the sunshine and the bright water.

" This is grand," he announced. " I feel fit as that fiddle o' yours below there. Do you know what I'm going to do ? I'm going to go into the smoke-room and have a bottle of Bass. It's something I've been lookin' forward to, ever since I made up my mind to take this trip. The stuff you get in the States ain't the same."

He was like a schoolboy on a stolen holiday. His eyes were shining at the thought of his own recklessness. To me it seemed that the fever in them was heightened.

We walked along to the smoke-room. He could only totter in his weakness, but he did not seem to notice it. We sat down at a table and ordered a Bass each. He took a first great gulp of the beer, then finished it in gulps. I think he had a job to drink it all. But he said how much better he felt for the drink.

" This is a celebration," he said. " I'm going to have a cigar now."

He called the wine-steward and asked for two of the best. He winked at me.

" Come on. We'll smoke these out on deck."

We left the smoke-room and wandered up and down on the deck. Arthur, in the full tide of good-fellowship, talked to every second person he passed. Most of them snubbed him (perhaps because of the company he was in!) and all of them passed on quickly. He did not seem to notice their taciturnity. Poor Arthur! He coughed painfully over his cigar, and was staggering about pitifully as we walked. He looked so frail and unsteady on his legs that I was honestly afraid that a strong gust of wind or sudden roll of the boat would knock him over. Before it was nearly half finished, he had to fling his cigar overboard.

We sat down, and Arthur inhaled the breeze exultantly—and coughed. Quite suddenly he said

" I'm tired. I think I'll go below."

We went back to the cabin. I did not want to endanger his belief in his betterment by offering to help him, but I was tempted to do so several times. When we reached the cabin he was exhausted. I helped him to undress and get into his berth.

" My, it was a treat getting out there," he declared. " What a day it's been ! "

He slept for most of the rest of the day, and I began to wonder whether his outing had indeed done him good ; but, for all that, I decided before going to bed that night that I should see the ship's surgeon the following morning and get him to see my cabin-mate.

I had barely started undressing, when he awoke.

" What a day it's been ! " he repeated. " Let's finish it off properly. Let's have ' You'll Remember Me ' ! "

I played it for him very softly. His eyes closed and he seemed to have fallen asleep again. I climbed into my berth. He could not have been asleep, however, for a little later I heard him drinking water.

We had gone to bed early. It must have been still fairly early, when I was aroused by the sound of vomiting. There was a revolting odour in the cabin—something more than the stench of the vomiting. The ugly thought was in my mind that it was like the odour of Death itself.

I jumped down out of my bunk, and asked him anxiously if I could do anything for him. He grinned weakly.

" I'm all right. But I've lost that Bass I drank. . . . I thought maybe I wouldn't keep it down."

" I'm going for the doctor," I said.

" No, wait a minute, mate. I'm all right—just bein' sick, that's all. I want company rather than a doctor. . . . Will you do us a favour ? "

" Of course. What is it ? "

" Play ' You'll Remember Me ' just once more. It seems
to buck me up, that thing. . . . Oh, I know you've played
it already to-day—but just do it again this once, an' I'll not
ask you again."

I put my violin to my chin and played. His face was gaunt
and fine-drawn as that of an El Greco saint. His eyes were
dark and brilliant. There was a tragic, utterly happy smile
on his lips.

His eyes closed. . . .

I stopped playing. His face had taken on a strange greenish
pallor which had a livid flush beneath it at the cheek-bones.
I bent over him and whispered his name. He did not answer.
I took hold of his shoulder and shook him. He made no
movement. He was in a coma.

I ran out of the cabin to find the docor. Flying along the
alleyways, I almost ran into Father Cunningham.

" Where are you off to ? " he demanded pleasantly.

" To find the doctor. There's a man dying in my cabin."

" What's the number of your cabin ? "

I told him and hurried on. When I came back to the cabin
with the doctor, we found Father Cunningham inside. He
was kneeling by Arthur's berth. Where the light struck it,
there was a sheen of oil on Arthur's brow and on his lips.
When Father Cunningham rose, I saw oil on his finger-tips.

" He is dead," said the priest. " I do not know if he was
a Catholic or not, but I have given him the Last Sacraments."

The happy smile was still on the dead man's lips. The
doctor leant over the body and covered its face with the
bedsheet.

THE MAN WHO SNATCHED
A THRONE

By
AMIR HABIBULLAH

Most people remember the visit of King Amanullah of Afghanistan to Europe, and how on his return to his own country he attempted to Westernise it, only to be turned off his throne by the brigand Bacha Saquo, who became the next King, Habibullah. The following is Bacha Saquo's account of how he brought about the fall of Amanullah. A Mullah has prophesied that he shall one day be King, but at present he is a common soldier.

IN the few years that I remained as a soldier of Amanullah, there was much to intrigue one who was looking for the sign. The Mullah must have seen the portent aright, for all over the world there were events which were gradually to produce the requisite atmosphere in which a freebooter and an opportunist might shine.

Of the unrest in India there was born the Khilafat movement. The Faithful, absorbing the general atmosphere which was exceedingly critical of everything British, came to the conclusion that the Raj was an enemy of the Faith. Thousands of Moslems, therefore, determined to shake the dust of Hindustan from their shoes. There began the Hijrat—the departure from India of some 18,000 persons, all animated by the highest degree of religious zeal. Their route lay through Afghanistan.

This human flood suddenly welled up out of the inexhaustible millions of Hindustan, and flung itself against the barren hills of my country. The first series of waves were welcomed, and Amanullah received many plaudits because of the kindly nature of his reception. But this human flood threatened to overwhelm the country. All available land was apportioned to the immigrants, but still they continued to besiege the passes, and Amanullah was forced to refuse to allow more to enter.

As a result of this edict, many hundreds of religious zealots perished, and even in Afghanistan there were many who were not slow in declaring that the monarch had been guilty of inhospitality to the Faithful in the course which he pursued.

The Hijrat gave Amanullah a definite setback in the popular esteem of his countrymen, and provided the groundwork upon which much future criticism was based. Later, when he was to introduce his reforms, the Mullahs remembered his treatment of the Khilafatists, and made much capital out of the situation.

Then came the startling series of reforms—reforms which left the Afghans stupefied, and wondering what had come over this man who was now King.

Amanullah radically altered the means of collecting taxes, and schools were opened all over the country. Primary education was made compulsory, and in some of the schools the entire teaching was in German or French. Amanullah had in mind the time when the pupils of these schools would depart for the universities of France and Germany.

This educational scheme gave grave offence to the Mullahs who ordinarily had the education of the youthful in their own hands, and many of whom were deprived of their posts and mulcted of their emoluments.

Having given affront to a most powerful class, the King turned his attention to the hakims or doctors. He gave orders that no one could practice medicine until he had passed the requisite examinations and been found efficient. This in itself was a revolutionary proceeding, and one which cut at the age-long customs of the people, and—one can do much with the Afghan, but it is advisable to leave precedent and custom alone.

Then, a new code of laws was prepared for the southern provinces. The code included the above reforms, but also another which caused the greatest misgivings and umbrage. Every eighth man was to be enlisted for compulsory military duty, and this cut across the class prejudices of very powerful families.

Out of this resentment grew the Khost rebellion in which I saw much active service as a soldier of Amanullah.

I wanted the excitement ; I wanted to see modern troops in action, and generally I was out to learn, and to keep astride of events which I was sure were pointing in one direction, and one direction only.

The Mangal tribe was the first to rise. This was early in 1924. The Mangals were soon joined by others, and soon over six thousand revolutionaries had surrounded Matun, the capital of Khost. By the middle of April, most of the south was in open revolt.

There was one incident during the course of this revolt which gave me pause, and made me realise that the ways of kings and would-be kings can sometimes be hard.

In July, 1924, the grandson of Ameer Yakub Khan, one Abdul Karim, who had long been an exile in India, crossed the border to join the revolutionaries. He hoped that the name which he bore and the memory of his grandfather would cause the country to turn to him and to proclaim him as deliverer against one who sought to impose unpopular reforms. Abdul Karim was mistaken. No one evinced very much interest in him. He was politely received. His sword was accepted as an adjunct to the rebel forces, but he never became more than an individual.

There and then I decided that a name did not necessarily mean much, and that he who would be ruler of Afghanistan must be a person of resource and action.

After the Sulaiman Khails had joined the revolutionaries and had augmented the rebel forces by several thousand men, the skirmishing and long-range shooting which had been the order of the day developed into serious fighting.

I was in an engagement at Patka which was exceedingly sanguinary, neither side asking for quarter or expecting it. It was very hot going, especially when we were called upon to retire in the face of vastly superior numbers. I could not help but notice that the recalcitrant tribesmen fought with greater verve and enthusiasm than did the regular troops.

After our reverse at Patka engagements became general nearly every day, and I had my fill of campaigning, principally because there was no real zeal behind our attacks. For the main part we were outnumbered, but there was a reluctance among those in the higher commands to take ordinary military risks. It seemed to me that reputations were in greater count than mere military expediency.

As the rebel campaign progressed, the Government forces were pushed back to within a measurable distance of Kabul. It was then that the King decided to enlist the aid of tribesmen rival to those who had revolted—Khuganis, Afridis, Mohmunds, Kunaris, Shinwaris, Wazirs, Hazaras, and the like. These men, redoubtable fighters, received good pay and modern arms from Kabul, and their incursion into the fray unloosed so many tribal jealousies that recrimination and dissension overcame the rebel ranks. In this manner was the rebellion brought to a close. First one tribe submitted, and then another, not, I am afraid, to the force of arms, but in the face of feudal acrimony and the promises held out by Amanullah that the repugnant reforms would not be enforced.

During this campaign I was able to throw off many of the irksome restrictions of the barrack square, and to indulge in soldiering as I imagine soldiering is. My methods, which to the purely military class, appeared remarkably unorthodox, earned for me something of the reputation of a dare-devil, and certainly one for bravery. Yet, both were built entirely on my ability really to shoot and my refusal to be entrammelled by parade ground methods. I did not see anything particularly brave in stalking one who was addicted to inconvenient sniping, or in meeting shock tactics with shock tactics. If, during the course of an engagement it became embarrassingly obvious that I was being singled out for attack, then I, in my turn, singled out the attacker, and the best fighter won. My comrades called it bravery. I merely regarded it as common sense. Then, too, I had my amulet, and—there was still my destiny. Perhaps I could afford to take risks.

In January of the next year (1925) I was sent to Kabul with my unit, and on February 28, when the suppression of the revolt was circulated, I had my first view of Amanullah. Also, I saw Queen Suraya for the first time, for she appeared and made a speech to the returned soldiery. She presented me, with others, with a handkerchief in which were enfolded a number of silver coins.

There followed a reversion to barrack square ways which I found particularly trying after the freedom and licence of active service. Moreover, I considered that my reputation as a fighter and a shot should have been rewarded by more rapid promotion, and consequently higher pay. I found, however, and increasing disposition on the part of the paymaster to delay those parade days when money should be disbursed, and soon I, in company with the rest of the troops in Kabul, saw my pay considerably in arrears.

In these circumstances I did not accept in too kindly a spirit the frequent chidings of my superiors, and bickerings and outspoken and definitely unmilitary language became general in my relations with others.

There was one officer, the equivalent to a major in rank,

who took a particular delight in rendering my service unpalatable, and I, for my part, took particular care that my views on his military and other qualities should be freely aired.

If he could throw down scorn upon me when I was on parade, I could see that there were those who would snigger offensively when he passed through the streets, or was in the company of boon companions.

It was not difficult to engineer circumstances when a ribald and slanderous tongue could be overheard, to his shame and acute annoyance.

We did not love one another, and gradually this mutual ill-feeling grew into enduring hate. The man could never pass me on parade without giving off some slighting and derogatory remark—a state of affairs which was remarked upon by all and which did much to break down the discipline within my unit.

There had, of course, to come the day when this officer was particularly offensive and when he transcended all the bounds of decency and decorum.

Enraged beyond endurance by my actions in public, he made a bee-line for me when on parade and gave himself over to the most objectionable commentary upon my personal and military bearing.

" These boors from the hills," he cried that all might hear. " See how they slouch. See, he carries his rifle as if it were a broom." This later, of course, was a subtle way of conveying that in his opinion I was more accustomed to the ways of a broom than a rifle—a dire insult, as the direct insinuation was that I was of the sweeper caste.

He could see the blood boiling within me, and proceeded further to taunt me, and to such a degree that I could hear around me indignant murmurs which indicated, sufficiently clearly, that if anything untoward should occur, there would be no lack of sympathisers.

Suddenly the bazaar-spawn advanced upon me, caught hold of my rifle, and shook it viciously into what he was pleased to term alignment.

I allowed it to slip back into the position it held before his interference, and again he grasped it. The man was panting with anger.

As he grasped the weapon for the second time, I released my hold, and brought up my hand to deliver a resounding smack on the side of his ugly face. Immediately, there was pandemonium. Some of the men broke ranks in their excitement, and crowded round, and the scene was more reminiscent of a bazaar fracas than a parade ground reproof.

Other officers and N.C.O.s hurried to the spot, the major meanwhile gesticulating wildly and calling down the curses of heaven upon one who had so outraged his dignity in direct defiance to all precepts of the best military discipline.

Soon I found myself under arrest, and escorted to the guardroom, charged with the crime of striking a superior officer on parade and with conduct prejudicial to good order and military discipline.

Seemingly too, this officer was somewhat of a favourite, and the outlook was not as bright as it might have been.

I knew that my punishment would be the most severe which could be meted out to me, for no attempt was made to remove my manacles after I had been put safely behind bars—a sure sign to the initiated that one is distinctly *non persona grata*.

However, I did not despair, for I still had my amulet, and Bacha Saquo had been in worse predicaments. Also, as I waited for darkness, I knew that those who had murmured in the ranks, headed by my faithful friend Jamal, would not be slow to evolve a plan which would ameliorate my lot.

It was two o'clock in the morning before I saw the cheerful features of Jamal. There had been some changing of the guard personnel, and his task had not been difficult. He had the irons from me in the space of a few seconds, and he was desperately anxious that I should immediately depart.

However, I had other views, for the guardroom adjoined the armoury, and—I had to think of the pay that was due to me. In lieu of my rupees, I selected a rifle, and purloined four bandoliers containing over five hundred rounds of ·303 ammunition which, in the circumstances I considered a worthy exchange.

Just as I was departing from the armoury verandah, my eyes lighted on a canister. Gun cotton ! I crept back. With Jamal tugging at my arm, I proceeded to the horse lines, and handing the bandoliers to my companion, advanced upon the sentry with complete effrontery.

The major sahib, I explained, required his charger. I, his orderly of the day, had orders to take it to him. Grumblingly, the man assisted me in saddling the beast, and also another required for the orderly who must accompany the major on his rounds of the posts.

I had to grin behind my hand. It was so childishly simple.

Thus armed and mounted, Jamal would have us away to the hills, but still I tarried.

"The moon is not bright," I said, "and this is the hour when all men sleep heavily. Why this haste?"

Refusing to be skurried out of Kabul, I made my way, followed by the protesting Jamal, to this major's house. It was an imposing structure and befitted one who robbed the troops of their pay and their rations, and I already knew something of its layout.

The night was hot, and there was the major lying in the open in his compound upon a gaily-coloured string charpoi. Gazing over the wall, I chuckled, for the man was attired in a single sheet-like garment, for greater comfort and for coolness. Dropping to the ground, I scouted round until I found a chicken's feather, then scaled the wall.

Approaching the sleeper with my hillman's stealth, I crouched beside his cot, and gently tickled his side.

With a sleepy movement of protest, he rolled over on his side, and he was half uncovered. Giving him a few moments' respite in order that he might sink again deeply into slumber, I applied the feather gently to the other side, and again he rolled. Carefully, and with infinite caution, I snatched his covering, and was over the wall.

From my canister I took two wads of guncotton. One I placed against the wall near the major, and another by the wall surrounding his women's quarters. Lighting some hastily manufactured fuses, I retired a short distance to watch.

The resultant explosion was satisfying and commendable. the noise in itself was enough to set all Kabul by the ears, to turn out all the guards, to wake up all the pariah dogs, and to cause hundreds to come tumbling from their repose to investigate the cause of this unwonted disturbance.

While alarm bugles brayed, dogs barked, men cursed and women screamed, I waited for the dust to settle to reveal the outcome of my handiwork. From my place of concealment it was difficult to restrain my guffaws. The walls surrounding the officers' sleeping compound had been almost entirely demolished, and that by his women's quarters sufficient to reveal the women of his household running frenziedly for safety, absolutely unveiled and quite impervious to the rude gaze of the populace.

As for the major, he sat on the side of his bed in a kind of

mental haze, gazing with horror-struck eyes at the scene of
desolation around him, and then at his bare limbs and
undraped torso.

He was so obviously torn by a desire to rush out upon
and destroy those who had invaded his privacy, and
to hide the shortcomings of his non-existent attire that I
could have screamed with suppressed joy.

He continued to sit there, wriggling painfully, doing his
feeble utmost to hide his nakedness, while the crowds surged
round, gazing their fill.

It was most satisfactory.

I had blackened more than the major's face.

And the comments he had to endure !

The crowd was angry that a man should so forget himself
as to parade his body in such circumstances.

" Who is this low-born ruffian," they asked loudly and
insistently, " who so forgets his Faith that he appears in
public unclothed ? "

" Who is this whose women show themselves unveiled ? "

It was very good. Very good.

II

AT the time of which I speak, the Bolsheviks were filling
their propaganda schools at Tashkent, and elsewhere,
with material from Hind and Afghanistan, but judging
by the efforts of Jamal, methinks they were wasting their
time.

With considerable misgivings I had decided to return at
long last to my native Kohistan. In this I was prompted both
by Jamal, and the force of circumstances. When I
reminded Jamal of the manner in which I had left my
village, he said little, beyond suggesting that the passage of
time had perhaps healed a number of the wounds. I, however,
could not be so sanguine, for there was an attack on a
woman to be considered. A theft of jewellery, came into
a far different and lesser category.

We wasted little time in shaking off the dust of the capital
from our shoes, and I must admit that the major had a
pretty taste in horseflesh. The animal upon which I was
mounted was superb in its action, and a delight to ride when
it came to the mountain paths of my home province where a
horse was required to possess the fleetness of the gazelle, the

sure-footedness of the mule, and the climbing abilities of the goat. The major's charger (now mine) possessed all these attributes, and more. I often wondered what he paid for him, or whether he, too, obtained possession by devious ways.

That ridden by Jamal was swift, but in other respects but passable. Mine was a steed on which to covort unheedingly down mountain crags, and across boulder-strewn river beds. With uncanny precision this magnificent beast would implant a dainty hoof on the one square inch of earth which would support our combined weight with safety, and would ignore with a presagement which never ceased to intrigue me, those snares and pitfalls which are the lot of less finely balanced creatures.

We had come to the hill ranges which gave on to my village, and my mind was occupied by many a dubious thought. Should I boldly descend upon the village, and announce my homecoming, or should I send Jamal forward as an ambassador to spy out the land.

As we lay up in the hills, I espied a small body of horse-men approaching from afar, and presently I recognised an Elder, now incredibly withered, but still virile and haughty, whom I had once insulted.

I decided that here was the means to test the reaction to my presence in the neighbourhood. I expected nothing but abuse and revilings from this old curmudgeon, but by the mere intensity or otherwise of his vituperations would I be able to judge of much that I wanted to know.

With a word to Jamal, we hobbled our horses, and bound their muzzles, and placed ourselves in a position where we could intercept this party bound for our village.

I allowed it to get within forty yards of us before revealing myself, and with the head which I silently protruded there was the muzzle of my wicked looking rifle.

"Tobah!" exclaimed the old peach face testily, when he saw that rifle so nochalantly aimed in his direction. "Who would have the ill-grace to hold up the Faithful within sight of their home village. Who would place this indignity upon the grey hairs of an old man?"

I watched him peering under his turban, saying not a word; then I saw him start, and a brighter look came into his eyes.

"Do I not know that face?" he exclaimed, turning to those with him—those who were cast to stone by the cold grimace of that rifle muzzle.

They forebore to answer, but the old man was not to be gainsaid. Even with the rifle pointed at him he took a step forward, the better to see, then his aged face became wreathed in an astonishing array of smiles.

"It is that vagrant, Bacha," he cried, jubilation in his voice.

"He has returned amongst us, and must needs play his pranks upon the Elders."

Peach face was quite urbane, but I was suspicious.

"O, Bacha," he cried again. "Welcome home, you profligate, and tell us how you have waxed rich with the Ferenghi.

"Welcome home," he continued, "the young man who so steadfastly upheld our tribal honour ! "

I was amazed by this display, but, carrying my rifle, I advanced to greet the ancient Elder.

He patted me on the back and gave little chirrups of joy. The old boy was manifestly pleased to see me. Out of the corner of my eye I could see Jamal grinning.

The old one went on :

"Thy companion, Jamal Gul, wrote and told us of they plight with that pestiferous Nur Khan. We know how you so bravely followed him when he robbed the Hindu money-lender and killed that man and very nearly his wife. The chowkidar, too, added his testimony, my son, for he too saw you going.

"It was a valiant deed, O Bacha, for one so young to encompass this bad one's death. Honour is yours. There shall be feasting when we reach the village ! "

Such was the manner of my homecoming.

My father, the water carrier, was well nigh dead of old age, and another sprinkled water in his stead, but that did not prevent the feasting which the old one had promised.

Round the village fires that night, the villagers gorged on mountain sheep, goats and a wild variety of pillaus, and I was fêted as the upholder of honour, and the slayer of he who had killed the moneylender.

When the first enthusiasm had worn a little thin, there were those who patiently expected more to the entertainment, and did little to hide their impatience.

"Come, O Bacha," they cried. "Display thee of thy wealth. Show us that which you have filched from the Ferenghi — thou who hast dwelt in the rich land of Hindustan."

I who had a horse, a rifle and five hundred rounds of ammunition and hardly a cowrie besides, felt uncomfortable. I attempted to laugh and to joke, but these people expected a returned traveller from Hind to be rich, and said so.

There were long faces, and not a few derisive comments when I woefully explained that I had lost of my riches in gaming in the bazaars of Jalalabad and that since my decision to fight for Amanullah, there had been few opportunities of amassing wealth.

The village wits waxed hilarious at my expense, and even went so far as to suggest that I had allowed a sleepy Ferenghi to get the better of a hillman, and that Bacha Saquo, the smart one, was not so clever after all.

But, when appraising my possessions, I had forgotten something. That which encircled my arm had slipped my memory. Suddenly the words of the Mullah came back to me, and inflamed by the taunts of the villagers, I stood upright in the glare of the fires in order that all might see, and held up my hand, commanding silence.

" You scoff at a warrior," I said harshly. " You scoff at one who has stolen rifles and horses from the Ferenghi— something which all will agree is worthy, and no easy task. You scoff at one who has fought in the late war with the men of Khost, and—you scoff because you are numbskulls. You scoff at a warrior who is learning his trade, and—who has ever known of an apprentice who was rich ? "

I made a gesture, and tossed a meagre handful of rupees into the flames.

" There," I said fiercely, " you have my regard for a few pieces of silver. Silver means nothing to Bacha Saquo. The treasures which I amassed in Hind meant nothing to me, else—why should I have sported them away ?

" You see before you," I added grandiloquently, " one who is to be the ruler of this land—one who is to occupy the throne at Kabul, and one who will be your master. Take heed, then, before you scoff, for Bacha Saquo has a long memory, and in the fullness of time you may regret your hilarity."

A great shout of laughter greeted my words, in which the Peach face joined with gusto.

" Bacha is a droll," he exclaimed through his convulsions. " He has learned to be amusing in the land of the Ferenghi."

Again I held up my hand, for I was angered.

"You laugh," I cried furiously, "but the day of which I speak will come. It has been ordained."

With what dignity I could muster, I sat down, ignoring the vapid twitterings of the delighted villagers, and rejecting with scorn further offers from the well-filled fleshpots.

Actually, I was mad with mortification that I should have been goaded into revealing my secret, for there was no denying the fact. These good people were firmly of the opinion that I was mad. I resolved that mad or not, they should have cause to remember Bacha Saquo.

There was, of course, no life for me in the village. There was no escape for one who had seen something of the world, and who saw on every hand the narrowness of outlook which was the lot of those I had previously regarded with awe, and even respect. Now I found their oft-spoken views childish and irksome, and I longed to be away upon the hillsides with my good horse under me, and with my rifle and five hundred rounds.

Also, wherever I went in the village streets, I was met with a mock deference, and ironic greetings of "Badshah," and this became too much for my proud spirit.

Soon, we were away.

And now did Fortune once more turn her face toward me, for I went abroad from where the hills were high, to those beyond, which were lower and where, lying secreted in the rough boulder country, I could watch the dust of slowly moving caravans.

Yes, the caravans. But here, they were well armed, and the merchants were well protected. What could one person do with but one rifle. True, there was Jamal, but there must be more.

Of the men of my village there were none I would take into my confidence. There I was too well known. There, men still saw the Bacha of old when they beheld me, and the Bacha who made a fool of himself on the night of the feast.

No, I must have men upon whom I could impress my personality, and the villagers were not for me.

Still, to depart into the beyond, to recruit for enterprises such as I had in mind was difficult. It was one asking for death should I fail, and one calling for cunning and for guile at the best. Once I had made a footing, the rest I knew would be easy. There are always those who will join the train of a successful freebooter ; aye—and always those ready to shoot him down in order to secure the leadership, and the greater share of the loot which goes with this position of pre-eminence.

To go forth upon the hillsides and calmly ask for recruits was impossible. There would be those who already ravaged the caravan routes, ready at once to blot out the upstart, who thought to impinge upon their preserves ; for the newcomer to the honourable trade of freebooting must needs fight not only the soldiery which accompany the merchants, but also those who are apt to display jealousy and resentment.

Many a would-be caravan robber has passed to the beyond before ever firing a shot, or getting within striking distance of his rich quarry.

Jamal, to whom I confided my thoughts, had few suggestions to offer, and none which would hold water.

I resolved, therefore, to rely entirely upon my destiny, and the protection accorded by my amulet and the goodly rifle which I treasured and caressed like a trusty friend.

" Come, Jamal," I said, when I was unable further to contain myself in the village, " prepare for further travels. Go and beg, steal or borrow food, and prepare our horses, for to-morrow, at dawn, we try a throw with Fate."

" But," Jamal expostulated, " you have a rifle—you have ammunition. I—I have not so much as a dagger."

" Who," I returned, " has the best rifle in the village ? "

" Ahmad Khan," he replied without hesitation.

" And, ammunition ? "

He nodded.

I patted him on the arm.

" Be ready, Jamal," I said confidently. " You shall be armed. Ahmad Khan shall supply the deficiency. Bacha Saquo has spoken."

That night, armed with a knife and a blanket, I went to the house of Ahmad Khan. The walls of his house were of mud, and carefully I scraped a hole near the door. With my body over the hole, I was careful to exclude all draughts from the outer air, and then inserted my hand. To unfasten the door was simple. Placing the blanket over the hole, still to exclude the wind, I crept inside. I could hear Ahmad Khan sleeping peacefully.

With great caution, I struck a match, and for about a second and a half allowed its illumination to fill the room. Ahmad Khan stirred, but did not wake, and I saw his rifle by his bedside.

Between me and my objective were two goats, one asleep,

and the other contentedly chewing. There were various
brass vessels also there to trap the unwary, and then the
light went out. Every detail of that room was clear in my
mind. But the goat which was chewing! Would it remain
content, or would it rise with awkwardness of goats and
give a bleating and all-revealing " Blah? "

It did neither. I believe it went to sleep.

I took the rifle, and also the bandolier of ammunition
which was beside it.

I made Ahmad Khan a present of the blanket. I would
not have him catch a chill from the night air, for he was
but lightly covered.

Then, there were the goats. I was certain that he would
have felt amiss had the aroma been allowed to dissipate.

Who says there is not good in Bacha Saquo?

III

THE way of the caravan robber is to waylay the merchants
as they pass through some rocky defile. Suddenly,
from the hillsides, a burst of fire will be sent over the heads
of the trailing company, and all is immediate confusion.
Should any of the armed escort show fight, they are immediately shot down. More often than not, however, the
escort disappears amidst the welter of surprised and struggling
animals, and only emerges, valiantly to throw challenges
at a departing enemy, when the richest merchants have been
despoiled and the caravan is deficient of its most richly
comparisoned camels and horses.

Caravan robbers invariably act thus, for the hillsides
lend of the element of surprise, and in such terrain it is easy
to post forward parties who will rush forward, secure the
animals to prevent a stampede, and overawe the protesting
merchants and the cringing or otherwise guards before there
has been time for scattered wits to collect themselves.

Such is the easy way, and for such enterprises a band of
stalwarts of at least twenty is required. All have to be nicely
drilled. Each man has to know his part, and there has to be
perfect co-ordination.

I, Bacha Saquo, had to seek another way, and now it was
Jamal who said I was mad.

I would ride forward beyond the hills, and take what
I wanted on the plains.

I reasoned thus : I had no men—as yet, and I had to evolve unorthodox means.

By long and bitter experience, the merchants knew what was likely to be their fate in the passes, and were prepared. No lone wolf would stand a chance there, and the armed guards would seize upon the opportunity with avidity to vindicate their valour. They would dispose of this " Army " of robbers, and demand extra pay for their martial triumph.

No, the only chance for Bacha was to engineer some scheme which would catch the prey before it arrived in the field of suspense and suspicion ; when, indeed, the guards would be no guards, but only hangers-on, and the merchants too full of their money plans and good food even to entertain the idea of danger.

That was the main theme. But the details ?

These required more than care. Inspiration was called for, for I was about to attempt something which, over the centuries, the caravan robbers had laid by as impossible and unfruitful.

We had two men, two horses and now, thanks to Ahmad Khan, two rifles. Not a large force, in all conscience, and not an overpowering armament. But, these merchants had to deal with Bacha, who was the best shot in the Afghan Army, and with a horse whose paces were supreme.

Also, Bacha had made a study of war. Even when obeying the vituperative drill officer was he thinking. And, he had seen much of the British paltans in their war exercises in the vicinity of Peshawar. Bacha was not one to go through life with his eyes shut.

This, I admit, was all vainglory. Of all this I spoke to impress Jamal, for still I had no scheme. Yet I was sure one would come.

It did.

Yet Jamal thought I was mad.

For my purpose I had to select a small caravan. A large one would have defeated my purpose, and would have rendered my task impossible. What I wanted was a convoy of less than one hundred and fifty camels, and I set out to find it.

I was out to achieve fame, to be known throughout the Kohistan country as a fighter and a bravo, but for weeks my opportunity eluded me.

We rode forth beyond the hills, and watched the caravans

with their rich spoil, for we had to be our own spies, and to provide our own intelligence. At last there came that which I required—a caravan of convenient size, not too heavily armed, yet giving fair promise of loot and gain.

All that day, hovering in the distance upon its flank, we trailed it, Jamal gazing upon me askance, and wondering when I would give the word to attack. But such was not my way.

Next morning we rode ahead, and I selected terrain which was devoid of character and which lacked anything of a formidable character behind which could lurk a possible enemy.

Here, I reasoned, where danger could not possibly be, the merchants would lay aside their cares, and the guards, more likely than not, would be riding with all thought of attack far from their minds. Their arms would be in the saddle bags, or at least, far from the ready.

Jamal and I rode on, and I selected two places each side of the caravan trail where, ordinarily, even a jackal could not hide. With our hands, and aided by my knife, we proceeded to dig—not a difficult operation in the flat, sandy terrain. I had seen the British soldiery act similarly, and—I had a plan.

We developed holes, each large enough to contain a human body when lying prone, and over the holes I distributed saddle cloths from our saddlery, and pinned them down with stones. Over the cloths I sprinkled earth and sand, and any one coming even within the distance of a yard, would have passed by unknowing. From the caravan trail these hide-outs were quite impossible to detect. I was pleased with my handiwork.

When the dust of the caravan was seen in the distance, we hied to our holes and waited.

To Jamal I had given his instructions. He was to fire like many men, but he was to take care not to hit or maim, unless the situation got beyond my control, and hitting became necessary. Following my first shots, he was to put up a barrage of musketry, and to send his bullets whistling over the ears of the merchants and their guards. Other than that, he must use his discretion, and be guided by me.

The hide-outs which I had selected were about two hundred yards each side of the trail. They were near enough for quick and accurate shooting, but not near enough to be overwhelmed by any sudden rush. Our horses we hid behind a small hillock about a mile from the road.

We lay there silently, and I watched the caravan approach.
As I surmised, there was nothing in the attitude of the men
to indicate suspicion or alarm. The merchants jogged along
on their fat ponies, laughing, grumbling, and talking ; others
were perched on their camels, and the guards, for the main
part, were walking, with their arms slung across various
beasts of burden.

Now was the crucial time approaching, with the head
of the caravan almost level, and all depended upon the first
few tense seconds. Indeed, the whole matter would be one
of seconds. If it were not, it would spell dire, abject failure.

My object, of course, was not to capture the entire
caravan. Such is beyond the scope of even the largest and
best organised band of robbers. I wanted sufficient to provide
me with temporary opulence. More than that, I wanted
proof of the fact that Bacha Saquo was not a mere braggart.

I passed the entire line under inspection, and I was
pleased. Leading were thirty or more camels, each treading
in each other's footsteps, the one behind being tethered
to the tail of the one ahead.

Following this initial party, was another of five camels,
similarly tethered, and I was pleased to note that these were
good animals and loaded in a manner which indicated that
the merchant whose goods they carried was a man of substance.
Behind came further camels in groups, all tied, and a mixed
medley of horses, pack mules, and donkeys.

I decided that the five well-laden camels would be
sufficient for my purpose.

These unsuspecting caravan men were to receive a
shock. Entirely out of the blue there came a shot. The leader
of the five camels which I had chosen as mine own, crashed
to the ground with a bullet in its brain. The other four kicked
and plunged like ships in a storm, but their tethering ropes
held. Quick as light I fired again, and this time at the second
camel in the leading string. I had noted with some satisfaction
that it was not one of those which bore a string muzzle. I
sighted carefully, for much depended upon this shot, and
the bullet went home, through the animal's tail just where it
meets the body.

With a plunge and a scream of rage and agony, the
animal swerved, and the rope tethering it to the third in
the string became taut, tweaking its maltreated member
so that the camel screamed again. It went mad ; it went
berserk. It thrust forward, insane with rage and hurt, and

buried its fearsome teeth into the haunches of the leader.

I commenced then a real fusilade, sending the bullets whining by the ears of the bewildered caravan men. Jamal chimed in with gusto, and the noise and the confusion lent the atmosphere of a sanguinary battle.

In the caravan line all was terror and confusion. The leading string was absolute pandemonium.

A guard, more perplexed or braver than the rest, rushed for his rifle, and actually had it in his hands before I detected him. I aimed a careful shot at the metal on the weapon's stock. I wanted blood, noise and terror rather than death. The result was satisfactory. The rifle was snatched from his hands as if by some invisible fiend, and parts of the stock spattered the man's face. I could see him wiping the blood from his eyes wondering from where came this strange visitation.

Then what I had counted upon happened. The shouting and the screaming and the firing was too much for the leading camels. He who had been punctured through the tail was still burying his teeth in the flanks of the leader, and that worthy decided that he had had enough. With a snort and a scream, he started off at his lolloping canter, and the rest began to follow. Soon the dust rose high, and from a canter it became a gallop and a veritable stampede. Bullets flung after the hindermost helped to lend energy to action where it promised to be lethargic, and the sight was good.

Men rode and ran alongside the frightened animals, shouting and beating in a vain effort to stop the rout. Their endeavours only urged on the terror-stricken beasts to more determined action.

Soon there was nothing left but a cloud of fast settling dust, five lone camels, one of which was dead, and a man, obviously the owner of the merchandise who stood by them, wringing his hands and crying lustily for succour and support.

A bullet nipped at the dust between his feet, and he jumped. Another bit the dust within an inch of his toe, and he backed. Another crashed into the ground just on the spot where he was about to step, and flinging up his arms, and crying shrilly, he ran up the caravan trail after those who had so expeditiously departed.

Jamal and I emerged to inspect our gains. Four camels, tied in an almost inextricable knot, were arrested to the spot by the weight of the one which was dead. And all were well laden. There were choice carpets, rich spices, wondrous silks, rough silver ingots and expensive unguents. It was a good haul.

Working with speed, Jamal and I loaded the dead camel's pack on to the backs of the protesting four, and struck out at a tangent to the road for the security of the hills.

Three days later we arrived at our village by circuitous routes. Our way was long, and specially determined, not because we expected pursuit or reprisals, but because there were many who would have been pleased to have relieved us of the results of my guile.

Our arrival was the signal for much jubilation, and for no few expressions of wonder.

When Jamal told the tale of our exploits around the evening fires, there were some who at first refused to believe, but—there were the camels, and there was the loot. What better proof could there be?

There was a new defference displayed towards Bacha Saquo when he walked abroad, for he who could fight a caravan practically single-handed was a man of note.

In the disposal of my wares, I decided to deal through one whom I knew in Peshawar, and when the time came to despatch them I bade Jamal write a letter. Only he and I knew the contents, and only he and I knew how much of the proceeds of my first freebooting gesture I was expending on the future.

Presently, sundry small and mysterious bundles arrived for me from the land of Hind, and again I was prepared to take the road.

This time Jamal and I were not to be alone, for seven men had approached me in the watches of the night and begged to be allowed to join Bacha in his raids upon the wealthy. Six of these I selected. The seventh, whom I did not trust over much, I told to present himself at some later time when I might find use for his services. Disgruntled, the man went his way, but he performed, quite unwittingly, the part which I had assigned him. The word went round that Bacha Saquo was particular and preferential, and that the ragtail and bobtail need not apply to him for employment.

Again, and not a little to the consternation of those who had thrown in their lot with me, I determined to thrust at fate on the plains rather than in the confines of the hills, but this time I wanted more than the packs of five camels. I was after an entire caravan—something which had never been attempted by any of the hill robbers through the ages. By a really bold stroke I was determined to establish myself.

Again we journeyed forth beyond the hills, and beyond even the scene of my first essay on the caravan route. Ten miles distant from there was a caravanserai where the caravans were wont to remain for rest and refreshment for the night. It was on this caravanserai that I concentrated my plans.

I found, by watching from the distance, that the caravans arrived at a late hour, usually just as dusk was merging into the night, for the trek from the previous halting place was a long one. This I regarded as a fortuitous circumstance, and one which must be bent to my will.

From my place of concealment I watched more than one caravan file in before I completed my plans, then I acted.

In the distance I could discern slowly approaching a train of some two hundred camels. These, with their heavy burdens, I resolved should be mine.

I judged, glancing at the fast disappearing sun, that this caravan would be later than usual in reaching its objective, and I made my dispositions accordingly.

With the approach of dusk my men and I closed in on the caravanserai, and when the caravan filed in to its night's resting place I had men on both sides, and at a distance of not more than fifty yards.

Distinctly we could hear the grunts and thuds of the camels, as they sank to the ground beneath their burdens, and the cursing and revilings of tired men who had to deal with animals which were churlish and obstreperous.

Then I gave the signal—my old one of the jackal, thrice repeated, and the caravanserai suddenly became illuminated in dazzling, garish light.

Verey light pistols, appropriated from the British in Peshawar and along the posts of the Khyber, gushed forth their weird streams of coloured radiance. The like had never been seen by these men before, and momentarily they were struck dead with amazement.

Then the voice of Jamal rose loudly among them.

" It is the sign," he shrieked, " the sign. The heavens are pouring their vengeance upon us. Woe ! Woe ! Fly, fly, my brothers. The heavens enact vengeance."

Streams of red, white and green light continued to shower over the affrighted men, and loud rose their voices in fear and alarm.

Exhorted by the leathern-lunged Jamal, there were those who stampeded. They rushed blindly forth to escape from this accursed spot, and their fear communicated itself to the others. In a few moments the entire company was fleeing down the road from whence it came, and one of my men followed them up to give them a further taste of these wild lights of the Powers of Darkness.

The camels, disturbed by the commotion, had for the main part rumbled and grumbled to their feet, and when we closed in upon them, there was Jamal already slashing with his knife. He was following the line of still tethered animals, and was removing the bells from the necks of the leaders. There was not much we had forgotten.

Led by Jamal, the first camels began protestingly to emerge from the caravanserai, and four other men assisted him in urging on the long line.

When all had silently departed and had been swallowed up in the darkness, I fell back upon the roadway where the firing of Verey lights led me to my man. When I reached him, his stock of ammunition was near exhausted. Him I despatched for our horses.

Lying there in the darkness I could hear an occasional grunt and gurgle in the distance as the camels were led away from the road at right angles to the trail, and I could hear also the confused murmur of voices in the distance.

Winded by their headlong flight, the fat merchants, out of reach of those awe-inspiring lights, had halted to take stock of the situation. I realised that it could not be long before the more resolute among them would be haranguing the guards, and demanding an immediate return to the camp. So it must be in the ordinary nature of things, and so it transpired.

There were wild and angry shouts in the distance as the argument persisted, and I smiled as I visualised the broadsides with which the goodly merchants would be raking their paid hirelings, the guards. I could visualise also the protestations of valour and bravery which these men would be making.

The tumult and the shouting suddenly gave over to a lower and more sustained note, and I knew that a decision had been reached, and it had been resolved to return to the caravanserai and brave the phenomenon should it reoccur. I could hear the voices coming nearer, and presently I could make out, some eighty yards away, a dense mass of men, all hugging close together for their better protection.

Sixty—fifty—forty yards I allowed them to come, and then I acted.

I had in mind a British bomb for which I had had to pay the extravagant price of three hundred and fifty rupees. But, if all went well, I would deem the money well spent.

The instructions which I had received with this strange instrument of death bade me pull forth the pin and count four. I extracted the contrivance, and counted—somewhat rapidly, I confess, then hurled it into the midst of the advancing horde.

For an interminable period I judged that my money had been misplaced and that the much vaunted Ferenghi were less clever in the arts of war than we imagined. With a blood-curdling " Whoof," however, the bomb did its work, and the air was filled with noise. There were groans and shrieks, and cries of unfettered alarm, and the whole band was in confusion, not knowing from whence had come this terrible visitation, and not knowing which way to flee.

But even yet I had not finished. I, Bacha, had still to see the result of my handiwork. From my clothes I snatched forth a powerful torch, and directed it upon the shrieking throng. I pressed my thumb, and there was an intense illumination. A dozen men were upon the ground. Some were still, and others were threshing round in a welter of blood.

For the rest, the torch meant the end. There was sent up into the evening sky one long cry of apprehension and terror, and those who could run, or walk, or crawl, made the best speed possible along the road which they had come.

It was enough. I knew that I had won. Those men, notwithstanding their fatigue, would not stop until they fell in their tracks, or until they reached the camping ground they had left that morning.

I, Bacha Saquo, was free from pursuit.

In the morn the wild land of Kohistan would ring with the tales of his dare-devilry and success. He would not lack for retainers, and he would be a power in the land.

IV

MEN flocked to the train of Bacha Saquo, and his name was known throughout the hills of Kohistan, but Bacha, still with his amulet, allowed his aspirations to soar,

Yes, I saw myself as the most successful robber of the countryside, and men on all hands bowed and did me honour, but—that was because I could distribute largesse, and could guarantee to those who accompanied me on my forays a handsome return for their endeavours.

Bacha Saquo wanted more than this. He desired the mastery, and would have it.

It is not to be supposed that my incursion into the ranks of the successful was viewed with any enthusiasm by those who regarded the looting of the caravans as a long-vested interest, and there was one in particular who displayed his umbrage.

He was Sharfuddin, who had for long regarded himself as King of the Passes, and he watched with a wry face my snatching of the loot from beneath his nose. Moreover, he made it a personal matter. He declared that Bacha Saquo was blackening his face, and was making a fool of him before the people of Kohistan.

It was not for me to argue upon or dispute this point, but the fact remained that as long as this man remained he denied me the position of pre-eminence which I desired. With Sharfuddin out of the way I should be undisputed master, and there would be none who could question my actions. As it was, I had to move with a certain circumspection which was irritating. Always had I to be certain that Sharfuddin was not on my flank, for, given the opportunity, he would destroy me.

But how to dispose of this thorn of the flesh? The man was too subtle, too full of guile to give me open combat upon the hills. His way was the ambush, and—his following was equal in numbers to mine. No, there must be some other way.

I resolved that I would attack and plunder this man's village. Dashing tactics and the unexpected had served me well in the past. I would again adopt the course farthest from the minds of men, for in the hills, although village may set upon village in the fire of feudal ire, robbers leave the villagers severely alone, mainly because the villagers would consolidate after the raid, and fall upon the robber bands from an ambush and destroy them.

But I decided when I had finished with Sharfuddin there should be no village. The hand of Bacha Saquo would fall, and the result would be there for the whole land to see. Thereafter I would be master.

My band now consisted of over one hundred men, for the

word had gone out that here was a new leader, allegiance to whom promised a rich harvest ; and day by day other men came.

To Jamal I proposed my plan of ensnaring Sharfuddin in his own lair, and he was definitely against the venture. To others, too, of my band I whispered of my plans, and they also were pessimistic. Yet I spoke of the time when I had raided a caravan practically single-handed, and of the time when I had captured one entire with but a handful of men. I boasted, and assured all of success, yet being Bacha, I did not rush straight forth into the hills, waving my sword and firing my rifle. There were other ways.

True, I went forth upon the hills, but I went alone, and in the guise of a traveller from Hind making his unpretentious way across the passes. None would have recognised Bacha in the poor, travel-stained garments which I affected.

The people of Sharfuddin's village made me welcome, for they were far from the caravan routes, and news of the outside world filtered through to them but slowly. Three days and three nights I tarried among them, telling of that I had seen, and giving these people news. In some cases it was months old, yet they had not heard, and welcomed all that I had to say.

As I slowly perambulated the village, I made good use of my eyes. I marked down the abodes of those who were Sharfuddin's principal lieutenants, for these houses gave promise of rich rewards. In the main, however, my seemingly casual eye took in the defences which, even for a village of its character, were secure and stout, and capable of maintaining a stiff resistance to the batterings of an invader.

Indeed, it was no light task that I had set myself.

The walls of the village were thick and strong and in good repair, and the watch towers were massive, and were well manned each night. At nightfall the gates were closed, and none might enter the village, and the watchmen were so vigilant that none could approach within one hundred yards of the walls without being challenged, and perchance fired upon.

Indeed, it was no light task.

I departed from the village at the expiration of three days with a clear picture of its defences upon my mind, but as yet no constructive plan.

Two nights later, when tossing miserably upon my bed,

the idea came to me, and I cursed myself for the tardiness of my brain for, indeed, it was so simple.

My principal weapon of attack must be diversion, and the more noise that was encompassed, the better for my purpose. But the matter of that diversion—that which would draw the night watch from its ceaseless vigil upon the ramparts !

Soon the village of Sharfuddin had another visitor—yet another traveller—and when he departed, for he did not tarry over long, he went when the evening shades were casting their shadows. Also, he went accompanied by a village dog, which he had enticed beyond the walls with specially prepared bits of liver such as no dog can withstand. The disappearance of the dog would, of course, be marked, but none would give over much attention to such a detail. Even the owner would merely shrug his shoulders, and murmur, " That shaitan— he roams again."

In my own village all was feverish preparation. We made rope ladders with hooks, we made pads for our horses' hoofs, and to each bridle there was looped a length of turban which would eventually bind the muzzle which might give out an all-revealing neigh.

Then on the night when there was no moon we set out, timing our riding so that we should appear in the vicinity of the village about half-way through the vigil of the second watch ; when men sleep their deepest, and watchmen yawn.

Tethered to a stake upon the hillside was the village dog. We collected him, but he did not march with us. It was a lone man who saw to his wants, and led him by the rope back in the direction of his village.

Half a mile short of our objective we dismounted, and our advance thereon was conducted with extreme caution. We went forward like snakes, and as silently, and halted within two hundred yards of the walls. We awaited the signal.

In our train we had one of our own village dogs, and he had a part to perform. Just beyond the orbit of vision of the guardsmen, and on the side of the village farthest from that which we would attack, he was introduced to the other. Carefully were they tethered, and firmly, and each had a sufficiency of movement. But when they strained their muzzles were distant an inch of each other, and the ropes held.

No self-respecting village dog will brook intrusion by

another, and no dog allowed the run of my village will fail to take up a challenge, and the result was excellent.

These dogs howled, growled and yapped, and worked themselves into a fury because they were denied the privilege of burying their fangs in each other. Moreover, because of my stratagem, the uproar was constant, and its venue did not vary. This was no running fight, and this fact and its very intensity drew all the watchmen to the farthest wall that they might peer into the darkness and discuss the strange visitation.

With this novel signal we advanced, knives at the ready, and we entered the village without opposition.

Competent hands stretched forth to deal from the rear with the unsuspecting watchmen, and others crept from house to house in the village disposing of all males who came without the category of boy.

We were well through with our pleasurable task before stealth need be abandoned, and a remnant of the village took up the fight. It was short and sharp, this encounter, and in the exchange of shots, we lost several men, yet the issue was never in doubt, for word soon went round that Sharfuddin was dead.

Indeed, the remaining villagers could not doubt the fact, for I, Bacha Saquo, had disposed of him, and I led the attack with his head perched upon a pole. It made a devastating battering ram, and its presence did much to take the fight out of those who would offer continued resistance.

With the sacking and the demolition of Sharfuddin's village and the summary slaying of the leader himself and of all his men, I became the undisputed ruler of the mountains. All men did me honour, not because of what they might receive in riches, but because they deemed it wise. And that is real power.

When the name of Bacha Saquo was mentioned in the villages, the people trembled. My star was rising.

It is not to be supposed that Kabul went in ignorance of my activities. On the contrary, there was every reason to suppose that the capital was well informed, more especially as a month after the incident of Sharfuddin's dismissal, my spies reported that a military force was on its way to seek me out and to exact vengeance for the insult placed upon the Crown.

By this time I commanded the allegiance of every able-bodied man within a radius of thirty miles, and the news left me cold. Indeed, except to enquire the position of this force, and its strength, I did nothing to combat its advance until it was within my sphere of influence.

Why should I have done otherwise? I was secure; I could bide my time; I had an adequate force, and why should I do battle away from my own doorstep? Whenever possible, I like to do these things in comfort. Besides, quite unknowingly, this government punitive force was bringing me a present. I did not want the trouble of unnecessary transport.

The government force turned out to be a company of two hundred men under two officers. Besides regulation rifles, it had an armament of two machine-guns—and I coveted those machine-guns.

In the fulness of time their capture was ridiculously easy, for these arrogant Kabulis rather disdained their task of routing out a tribal robber. They regarded the affair in the light of sport, but—they had left Kabul before the arrival there of vital information, and they were quite unaware of my strength. They were under the impression that all they had to do was to precipitate themselves upon my village, overawe it with their machine-guns, and demand my surrender.

They were mistaken.

Eleven miles from my village there is a suitable defile for the disposal of arrogant government forces, and there I repaired with but a handful of my men. To take a large force would be to show the tribesmen around me that I took this government intervention seriously. Actually, I scoffed at anything the government might attempt.

In this defile I copied the tactics which had proved so successful when I made my first descent upon the caravan routes.

Disdaining the officer I put bullets, in quick succession, through the heads of the two mules transporting the machine-guns. With these mules were twenty-one others, grouped together in threes.

Seven shots rang out with the rapidity of light, and there was not a miss. Seven mules fell, and as they fell they chained to the spot the fourteen others. On the backs of those mules were forty-two cases of .303 ammunition—approximately forty-two thousand rounds, and a welcome addition to my arsenal.

Thereafter we directed our fire upon the company, and bereft of their principal armament, they put up but a sorry resistance. Purposely, I spared the chief officer, as I wanted him to return to Kabul in disgrace. In order to save his own face he would tell a wondrous tale of the military might of Bacha.

His men dropped all around him from the fire of my men, and I, personally, gave him plenty to think about I removed his turban, smashed the hilt of his sword, and punctured his water-bottle, for now I could afford to play with ammunition, and I wanted a little amusement Besides, it was but right that the poor man should have evidence of his valour. How it would assist him when he told Kabul of the great fight he put up !

I will be kind. All I will say is that eventually the Kabuli force retired. It was wise, for we could have picked off the remnant at any moment we desired.

As it was, we took the rifles of the slain, disposed of the wounded, and returned with our machine-guns and a goodly supply of ammunition.

Kabul made one more effort to impose its authority, and then it gave me best.

The infantry having failed, it decided to pitch the air force against me, and for days two aeroplanes winged their way over the tribal lands searching for Bacha's encampment.

At that time, however, I was on a tour of my domain, and it was my custom to stop at a different village every night, so that the unfortunate pilots must have thought they were looking for a scorpion in a field of corn.

Their patience, however, was exemplary, and they deserved a better fate than that which I accorded them.

Amongst the men who flocked to my banner at this time was one whom I viewed with a certain suspicion, and in order the better to keep an eye on him, I placed him among my own bodyguard One afternoon when we had reached a village where the immediate terrain was flat—the villagers were lucky in that they had a few fields at which they could scratch—I saw this man behave strangely. He unwound his turban, and placed it on the ground in the form of an elongated cross, and—the stem of the cross pointed to the village.

It was an action which might have passed if I had not my suspicions, for the man might easily have just washed his turban, but I had spent some years in Peshawar, and I had seen British troops signal to aeroplanes by placing panels on the ground.

Later, when the two aeroplanes flew overhead, my suspicions were confirmed.

I said nothing at the time, but that night, when the time had come for rest, I said casually to one of my bodyguard :

"Abdul, bring me the red fruit of a cactus."

Wonderingly, the man rose to obey He might well be puzzled, for the cactus fruit is covered with spikes, and the interior is a mass of small hair-like pricks. It is no delicacy, and even the donkeys will disdain it.

However, I held my men in converse around the fast falling fire, and waited for Abdul to return. He did so at length, holding the fruit gingerly.

Leaning lazily against my saddle, I called two of my men close towards me, and whispered :

"The newcomer," I said. "Seize him."

Without a word the man was held and disarmed.

"Open his mouth," I ordered, and fingers pressed on to his jaw bones until he gaped.

Popping the cactus fruit into his mouth, and pressing the point of my knife against his breast, I bade him eat. His eyes alight with fury and distaste, bored into mine, but he ate.

I knew that by the morrow his tongue would be swollen to the roof of his mouth, and that his cheeks, pricked on the inside by those tiny, poisonous irritants, would be so puffed that his face would be unrecognisable.

But I had not finished.

I bade him remove his clothes, and under the menace of my knife, he did so. Then I disrobed, and I forced him to don my rather distinctive garments.

I salaamed to him ironically, and I bowed low in mock deference.

"I see before me Bacha Saquo," I said tauntingly. "Good, the great man shall have of the best. He shall rest upon Bacha's bed, for that is but right. And he shall have a bodyguard to see that evil does not befall him."

It was my well-known custom to have my charpoi well in the open, for I distrusted the shadows cast by walls, and around me the sentries of my bodyguard.

I had my charpoi carried out, and this man, attired in my clothes, was forced to lie upon it. The sentries were non-evident, but they were there all the same, and this man knew it.

I gave them orders to take up positions behind walls and

the like, and to shoot the man dead if he made any attempt to move from my bed.

Nothing happened that night, but with the dawn there came a whirring in the sky, and I laughed in my hand, for my surmise had been right. Lower and lower came the two aeroplanes, and suddenly they alighted on this heaven-sent stretch of flat ground. Figures jumped from the machines and ran with the speed of hares for the village.

They entered, and they had evidently been well primed, for they made straight for my charpoi, and threw themselves upon the prone figure there. They acted entirely without ceremony, and I grinned as I watched from a nearby hiding place while they seized this man by the hair and made play with his windpipe.

I could see his eyes entreating, and I could hear the " Blah, blah, blah," that came from his swollen mouth, and I stuffed the end of my turban in my quivering lips to stifle my laughter.

To add colour to the scene, I ordered one of our machine-guns to open out, and the aeroplanes replied, but the marksmen there were rather hampered in their work, as they could not spray the village at their pleasure. Their friends were inside, and had yet to emerge.

I saw the raiders seize upon my swollen-faced double and hoist him up. Then, with a lurching run, they carried him off, making for the aeroplanes.

As soon as the ridiculous procession was clear, the second machine, given a field of fire, started up with its machine-gun to give supporting fire, but machine-gun or not, I could not restrain the impulse.

My double, slung across a man's back, kept giving frightened glances behind him, as if he expected the worst. I was determined that he should not be disappointed. Giving a scream like a dervish, and drawing my knife, I rushed in pursuit, and that man's eyes, as he was carried on helplessly, were a picture to be remembered. They goggled fright, and his wildly uttered " blahs " to his own comrades only added to the piquancy of an intriguing situation.

Waving my knife, and prancing wildly in an absurd burlesque of an avenger, I came up to the retreating figures, and—struck.

The blow was nicely timed, and I doubt whether it even pierced this fellow's skin. It did, however, dispose of his pyjama cord, and I gave a tug. The garments were mine, anyway.

I often wondered what they said to this spy in Kabul after they landed him there. It was probably two days before he could speak coherently, and quite that time before his face became recognisable.

I was left in peace after that.

I think the pyjamas did it.

V

THE stars in their courses were shaping my destiny. My shock tactics with the merchants had made me master of the caravan routes. My manner of disposing of Sharfuddin, my principal, and therefore my only rival, made me paramount in the hills. The easy and blasé manner in which I had foiled the feeble attempts of the Kabul Government to bring me to heel, consolidated my position and placed me definitely above all others in the province of Kohistan. There, my name meant the law. If Bacha said so, then it was so, and there was none to give me even the semblance of opposition. The people flew to my bidding. Those that were sprightly received their due reward. Those who were tardy were apt to find me churlish.

Such is the way of the hills. There can be no half measures.

I was Lord of Kohistan, and ruler of the caravans, and my name was known through Afghanistan. I could, in necessity, command a fighting force of great number, for practically the entire male population of my province was conscript at my word, and—I flatter myself there was more than fear that impelled the unhesitating obedience which I could conjure. The people were glad, and proud even, to bask in the reflected glory which was shed by the name and person of Bacha Saquo.

Glory ? . . . Yes.

I was overlord—a personage of power, and—yes, of some dignity, for Bacha Saquo, though others pretended to forget, could never entirely eradicate from his mind that he was the son of the water-carrier.

And, in pretending to forget, and in doing me honour, I knew that these others did but pretend. I was not to be fooled by power and circumstance. I was no mere hillman who had jumped to an eminence from his own village fire. I had travelled, and I had seen. I had beheld the fawning, genuflecting mob that surrounded the court at Kabul, and I had seen them bending the knee, and—I had heard of their private converse. Such matters can come as a revelation, and I had no false illusions regarding the perfidy of man.

No, when persons came to accord me honour, I subconsciously stripped these praise-singers of their urbane exterior, and I sought that which was in the mind behind those smiling, unctuous eyes. Seldom did I fail to discern the cesspool of gain and jealousy, of avarice and cynicism. This analysis, to which all were secretly subjected, did much to keep me within the realm of fact and substance. Always had I both feet firmly planted on reality. Never did I allow my fancy to secure possession of my body, and to whirl me away into the fantastic spheres of improbability and vainglory.

I realised that to enhance and sustain my position I must not rest on my laurels. Moreover, I could not continue indefinitely as a mere robber of the trade routes. True, I had my amulet, but the way of the assassin's knife is sure, and there are ever those in the robber's band whose fingers tingle to perform that one, short, sharp stroke which will give them the leadership.

No, I must needs do more than that. The merchants were met when their caravans were entering the hills, and they were required to pay for safe custody. To those who demurred it was pointed out that the payment of a levy at that stage was preferable to the entire loss of one's goods in the passes. And, when it was delicately hinted that attaching to the lost goods there would be the owner's life, these merchants saw the light of day, and—paid.

When they paid they were guaranteed safe custody, and my power over the hillmen was sufficient to ensure this. Those who went awry of my will, and demonstrated a penchant for the recalcitrant, were certain of elevation.

At strategic points among the hills I had tall posts erected, and attached to these posts were wooden cages. Those who merited my displeasure were provided with free lodging in these airy confines, and were hoisted upward.

Devoid of food and drink it was amazing how long these hardy people took to die, but—the trade routes were guaranteed.

Naturally, my levying of taxes was not looked upon with any transports of pleasure by those in receipt of custom in Kabul. On arrival there the merchants would protest that they had already been heavily mulcted, and could pay no more. This was a serious matter for the Treasury, and especially for the customs officials who battened thereon, and loud were the cries of rage and anguish which went up from Kabul against the rapacious Bacha.

But Bacha saw means whereby he could further consolidate his position.

He took pity on the Kabul Government, and thereafter the levy on the merchants was increased. Bacha had a power over the caravans which the Government lacked. He could say, " Pay, or there is death in the passes." And, of course, the merchants paid.

The amount of the extra levy I transmitted to Kabul with an ironically gracious letter in which I left the court in no doubt as to the extent of my bounty. Kabul, naturally, perhaps, in the circumstances, affected to ignore me, but—it did not return the money.

Thus, in a measure, I secured recognition in the capital. Certainly, the whole countryside chuckled, and there were even those at the court who cast envious glances upon the hills in the direction of one who could afford to be magnanimous, and give the Government of his charity.

Oh, yes. It was an astute move.

This was no pandering to man's innate vanity. In adopting this course I had a greater issue at stake. Naturally, the power to be able to embarrass the arrogant Kabulis gave me pleasure, but there was a certain method in my seeming madness.

Sitting up there in the hills of Kohistan, I was in a better position to read the portents than those who were immersed in the vortex. There was much that the King was doing wrong. Gradually, he was moving to the pass where there would be a struggle of wills, and—long ago I had come to the conclusion that Amanullah Khan was both a bluffer and a blunderer. I was biding my time, and sowing the seed.

Moreover, he was one who went back on his plighted word, and—no ruler of Afghanistan can afford to do that.

When there arose the insurrection in Khost, Amanullah promised the chieftains that his ill-favoured new laws would be withdrawn. They were, but—only to be reimposed when all was at peace again.

When the time came to revert to his scheme of reformation, Amanullah committed a cardinal error in his efforts to placate the tribesmen. He informed the chiefs, with a wealth of verbiage, that they were God's children and that the only people who had resisted the reforms in the first instance were the Mullahs. He thereupon addressed himself to the task of hounding the clergy—easily the most powerful and most numerous individual class within his domain. The priests, he said, were the barriers to real progress. Therefore the priests must bend the knee, or go.

He hit at time-honoured customs and tradition, and the people began to murmur, and asked if their King had become afflicted in his mind. Not only did they hesitate to obey the Royal commands, but it was the invariable custom to refer these matters to the Mullahs. The advice tendered by the priests frequently ran counter to the Royal *firman*.

Amanullah was determined that the women of Afghanistan should forgo the veil. All women were ordered to show their faces, and his favourites were those men who ordered their womenfolk to plaster their skin with European cosmetics, and to array their bodies in the latest confections from Paris.

According to ancient custom, women only had their hair shorn if they were disgraced, but Amanullah thought that all should cut their hair, in imitation of the women of the West. Also, he decreed that the ancient tradition of regarding Friday as a holiday and a holy day, in fact, should be abandoned, and that the Moslem holiday should be on Thursdays.

His most fantastic order was that the people should desert their ancient garb and resort to European clothes. He actually gave orders that only those attired in European raiment should be admitted to certain parks and thoroughfares.

He decreed also that students should not marry, and that his army should have no relations with the Mullahs.

Also, the ancient methods of recruitment for the army were abandoned, and a system of ballot substituted.

This latter gave cause of much heartburning to another very powerful class. Under what was known as the Qomi system, every clan was required to furnish a certain number of men for the army according to its numerical strength. This was subsequently changed so that every eighth man was called up, and then Amanullah Khan conceived the idea of ballot. In some countries such a form of recruitment might work, but it could not spell anything but trouble and corruption under an administration such as then obtained in Afghanistan.

The new system was known as " Pishk." A family had

only to quarrel with one who conducted the lotteries, and the next day perhaps the only son was informed that the ballot had selected him for the army. To many of the more powerful families, service in the lower ranks, which perforce included a number of menial tasks, was highly repugnant, and for these there was a " buying-out " safety valve, the usual sum being fifteen hundred Kaldar rupees (£100). It was perhaps only in the nature of things that this buying-out process should have been fairly constant. The way of the ballot pointed to those with money with amazing regularity, and the recruiting officers were soon some of the richest in the land. Later, I made a point of seeking out Amanullah's ballot-keepers, but that is by the way.

Thus, the months passed in growing discontent. The King was squeezing all for taxes with which to pay for his new and hated reforms. In Hind, they were building a great new capital. It was even said that in far-off Australia, where men sometimes went as camel-drivers, they were doing the same. What Hind and Australia could do, Amanullah Khan could do. He commenced to spend crores of rupees upon bricks and mortar a short distance from Kabul. Amanullah also would have a great city which would bear his name, and keep his memory green in the minds of posterity.

In an atmosphere definitely antagonistic to the Throne, Amanullah decided upon his great " European pilgrimage." Had he known of the great weight of feeling against him, he would have hesitated in leaving his kingdom at such a time, but he was fully under the impression that the people welcomed his reforms, and that the only persons with whom he had to contend were the Mullahs. His courtiers told him this, and none others were allowed to approach the Royal presence. So satisfied was the King that his policy was right that his principal amusement was to hale a bearded Mullah before him and then deride him for his bearded face and his comical garments. The courtiers, in their creased trousers from London, and their faultless morning coats, would preen themselves, laugh with the King, and thus spend a pleasant hour.

Wild tales of these entertainments would make their way to the hills, and there was much reflective tugging of beards.

In order to secure funds for the King's going, the Treasury had to embark upon perilous schemes. The host of reforms which Amanullah Khan had initiated had eaten up the taxes as fast as they were garnered, and when the King asked for his fare to Europe there was much scratching of heads.

Eventually it was decided to mulct the wealthy, who were required to provide " voluntary " contributions to this great Affair of State, and for the rest, to levy three years' taxes in advance on the remainder of the population with, of course, the notable exception of Kohistan, where, if there was any tax-gathering, Bacha Saquo did it quite expeditiously.

The consternation of the people when suddenly confronted with a demand for three years' taxes can be imagined. No one is enamoured of the tax-gatherer at any time, but in such circumstances——

In some cases the tax-men were fortunate. In others, notwithstanding the machinery which was implemented to squeeze the last drop from the stone, not more than a year's taxation in advance was procurable. There comes a time when even the expert in extortion has to confess himself at a loss.

Amanullah departed, and while he was absent seeing of the wonders of the West at first hand, there was much apprehensive speculation in Afghanistan as to the outcome. But I, Bacha, sitting up in his hills like a vulture waiting for the living thing to become a corpse, could afford to display patience. A mentality such as that of Amanullah's demanded an inexhaustible supply of money. Already he had wrung the country dry. Extortion is a two-handed jade, and I could visualise the time when this spendthrift monarch would be left suspended with a poverty-stricken and hostile people on the one hand, and a series of half consummated reforms on the other.

For Amanullah there was not to be the fruit of attainment —only the dry husk of frustrated endeavour.

However, the hill vulture did make one or two preliminary flights during the King's absence, during which contact was made with Mohamed Wali, Amanullah's favourite, and to whom he had dedicated the regency.

Mohamed Wali was making the most of his opportunities as one should in such circumstances, and I was anxious to spy out the land, for in certain eventualities knowledge would mean power.

Mohamed Wali had no illusions about the future, hence his wholehearted endeavours to deplete the Treasury and when, by devious means, I met him, his reception was not that which should be accorded an enemy of the State. Rather did he appear anxious to temporise, as if he would guarantee that in the time to come there could not be brought against him any charge of obduracy. Indeed, the Vazir might even have been friendly, but in truth, he was such a poor liar that I despised him. An Afghan may admire one who can avoid the truth with grace and agility. He recognises this as one of the fine arts, but the gauche bungler merely excites his sympathy or his ire. I regarded Mohamed Wali as a time-server with but one attribute. That was an unswerving devotion to his own person. He was resolved, no matter what happened to the rest of Afghanistan, that he at least would not go hungry, and might perchance become a King himself.

On two occasions I saw this man, it being given out in Kabul that he had opened pourparlers with Bacha Saquo because the latter desired to submit to the Government. The rascal said that in order to save his face. Actually, there was no whisper of my submission, and the Vazir knew it. Mohamed Wali was looking into the distance, and was taking no chances.

That which I saw in Kabul during these visits made it evident to me that I had only to wait a favourable opportunity. I was certain that time was on my side, and events were to prove that I was not wrong in my prognostication.

Summed up, I merely had to retire to my hills and allow another to open the gates of Kabul to me.

Amanullah Khan returned from his travels, his mind aflame with what he had seen in the West, and—the train was set.

VI

IN the autumn of 1928 Amanullah Khan returned to Kabul via Persia and Herat. Throughout her travels, Queen Suraya had gone unveiled, and she was attired in the most expensive raiment of the West. At the court of the Shah, a request was made to King Amanullah that his consort should resume the veil. This in itself should have been an indication to Amanullah of the temper of his own people in respect to this ancient matter of custom. But, no. Amanullah Khan was resolved to bring his country in line with the progressives. In Egypt the veil had been largely discarded, and in Turkey, under the Ghazi, women were galloping toward emancipation. But, Turkey is Turkey, and Egypt is Egypt, and Afghanistan is a law unto itself. What changes there are must come slowly, and with the will of the people.

Between Kabul and Kohistan I had a line of trusty runners. There were those within the court circle who would do anything for money, and I, Bacha Saquo, could afford to buy my information. Also, I had means of testing its accuracy. I did not rely upon one single channel, but had several, and I was thus enabled to sift the chaff from the wheat and arrive at a mean which was near enough fact for my purpose.

Before forty-eight hours had passed after Amanullah's return, my runners were pouring astonishing tales in my ears. Some were so strange that they were difficult of acceptance, yet there was abundant proof that they were true. Were not the *dursies* of Kabul working day and night with their needles, and were not the second-hand clothes merchants of Hind pouring bale after bale of Ferenghi rubbish across the border ?

The Royal *firman* was that the face of Afghanistan must be changed. Amanullah Khan saw in our flowing pyjamas and embroidered waistcoats only that which was repugnant. He would have all, from the highest to the lowest, in European garb. He had returned from the West with the silk-hat complex, and he thought more of the correct position for a trouser crease and of the shine of his patent-leather shoes than he did of the dignity of his countrymen.

Here was his second cardinal blunder. He decreed that his countrymen should sacrifice their dignity and make themselves ridiculous—and that is something to which no true-born will submit with equanimity.

But there was the order. Every one must wear European dress, and women had to go unveiled. The net result was every peasant cursed his King, and a journey to Kabul was regarded as a penance only to be undertaken if absolutely imperative.

On the outskirts of the city there grew up a strange trade. Pedlars with European garments hired out their wares by the hour and by the day in order that those who had business in the city might appear in the hated garb and thus get by the police.

The occasion was one for ribaldry and jest, and—for curses. Stalwart peasants, who had never as much as seen a white man, were waylaid on their way to Kabul by these harpies, and informed that they could not appear on the streets unless they crowned their heads with a battered bowler, draped their arms through a bedraggled coat, and thrust their legs through misfit trousers. In some circumstances the effect might have been laughable, but there was always the reflection : there, but for the grace of Allah, go

I—and the laughter was restrained and all one heard were curses upon the monarch who would do this thing to his people.

Such stories, and more, came to me, and—with the stories a growing infiltration of men from Amanullah's army. I, Bacha Saquo, at this time had money and to spare. The levy I obtained from the caravans was not expended on exotic frivolities, and those whom I received beneath my banner could be certain of their just dues. But, there was a far different tale to tell in Kabul and in Jalalabad. For many months the army had hungered for its pay, and the twenty rupees per mensum had proved to be little more than a promise. The men who came to me were in uniform, it is true, but it was uniform which badly needed attention, and more often than not, complete renewal.

These deserters told me extraordinary tales of the disruption within the army ranks. The officers, too, were affected, for with the sepoys not receiving their pay, how were the higher ranks to exact their commissions ?

The time I now knew was rapidly approaching—the time when I must put my trust in the Mullah's prophecy.

There were murmurings among the people ; the army was disgruntled, and a rebellious clergy was stalking the land impressing upon the peasants that they were in the hands of Satan. The court was reviled ; Amanullah was likened to a madman ; tax-gatherers who still endeavoured to mulct the poor were murdered, and there was a drying-up of resources in Kabul. The King had spent all on his journeys abroad ; the country had paid its taxes long in advance, and the State coffers were running empty.

Each day, sitting up in the hills, I awaited the call which I knew must come. And I was prepared. I was sanguine of victory, too, for my star was definitely in the ascendant. The one Afghan soldier for whom I had any regard, and the one commander whom I did not despise, was in Europe, seriously ill : he was General Nadir Khan, who was away, and beyond easy recall. It required but a master stroke, and I would call Amanullah Khan's bluff.

I sat up in the hills scanning the horizon for the cloud which would mark the advent of the great storm that was brewing. As with the way of the winds, that cloud hovered somewhere else, and well to the southward. Fate decreed that the storm should break well beyond the hills, and that my path to the city of Kabul be rendered the more easy.

In times such as these, when a whole country is on the tiptoe of expectation ; when every man fears to go to bed because of what the morrow might bring, news travels quickly.

The air was electrified, and all that was required was a spark. The spark fell in unexpected territory.

A party of Koochi tribesmen were passing through the Shinwari country. It had with it merchandise of considerable value, and was apprehensive of attack. Coming upon some armed Shinwaris it mistook the locals for brigands on the pillage, and shots were exchanged. A number of Shinwari casualties spoke to the character of the engagement, and the tribesmen were furious. They rose throughout the countryside and fell upon and captured the Koochis, and hauled them before the local magistrate.

This was a small thing, and an insignificant incident in a land such as Afghanistan, and any one searching for the spark would have passed it by, and looked elsewhere.

But, such is the way of life, this magistrate had failed to receive his salary for a considerable period, and he had reached that pass when justice must needs give place to expediency.

The Koochis were men of substance. They had with them considerable wealth. What was more natural that they should disgorge and go free ? It was said that they parted with ten thousand rupees to save their necks.

Whatever the amount, and whatever went on behind the scenes, these Koochis were well on their way by morning, and the Shinwaris believed that they had been robbed of justice.

All this came to me as a whisper—as a matter of passing interest, and of no moment. Even so, it was the prelude to a revolution, and the beginning of the end of Amanullah.

The Shinwaris, already tax-burdened, already at variance with their King, already convinced that their wrongs were many, took this slight by the magistrate as the last straw, and they assembled around his house, calling loudly for him to appear that they might slay him.

Being a magistrate, he defied the mob and was able to call in the local police for protection, but the Shinwaris still wanted his blood. Village after village rose and banded together to increase the clamour, and soon thousands had joined together in armed lashkars and were looking for trouble. Amanullah sent various officers to the Shinwari country to impress upon the people the wrong they were committing in resorting to arms, and the officers were either flung into prison or so maltreated that they were glad to escape and return to Kabul with their lives.

Eventually the magistrate who was the cause of all the disturbance was taken by the Shinwaris. He was soundly thrashed in public ; other indignities were poured upon him, and he was flung into jail.

Now came the crucial moment. Having attained their immediate object, and having the magistrate at their mercy, would the Shinwaris declare themselves satisfied and disperse to their homes ?

Away up in the hills of Kohistan there was one who awaited news with the greatest anxiety. The torch of revolt had been lighted. Now, would it fizzle out ?

It seemed that it would.

A large and influential jirgah was summoned at which the Shinwari clan leaders discussed the matter.

The officer who had disgraced them had been punished and imprisoned. Was it necessary, then, to remain at arms ?

There were two views expounded. There were those, by no means in the minority, who declared that honour had been satisfied. There were those, however, who said with some truth that they had satisfied their honour, but at the expense of the King's. The standard of revolt had been raised, they explained. The King's officers had been abused and maltreated, and these men, having the ear of the King, trouble was bound to ensue.

This point was so poignant, and so easy of assimilation, that it won the jirgah. From there the scope of the discussion was enlarged, until it came to a discourse not on peace or war, but how best to maintain the Shinwaris in arms in order to obtain redress from the ruler.

Throughout the night speaker followed speaker, and it was eventually decided that Amanullah had betrayed his trust and should be thrust from the throne. It was declared also that Queen Suraya, who had bared her face to the multitude, should be expelled from the country, together with all her relations, particularly the King's father-in-law, Mahmud Tarzi, whom some held in abhorrence because of his ways and his mode of living.

The Mullahs, whom the King affected to despise, were there at the jirgah giving of their spiritual advice. It did not tend to soften the feelings of the Shinwaris toward the court at Kabul.

When that jirgah broke up, Shinwari deputations were already on their way throughout the tribal lands to induce other clans to join the revolt for the freeing of the country.

War was in the air. The vulture, sitting up on his hilltop, fluttered his wings, but did not immediately make for the killing. Bacha Saquo would allow this movement to obtain impetus and then he would strike.

I did not have to wait long. Amanullah was to play right into my hands.

First of all he sought to quell the Shinwari revolt by inciting other tribes to rise against the rebels. He poured out arms and ammunition and arrayed the Lugmanis, the Chaparharis and other tribes against the Shinwaris, but except to accept his arms and his ammunition, these tribesmen showed a distinct reluctance to fight against their neighbours. Actually, the court blundered in believing that money and arms would buy over these men at such a time. It failed utterly to realise how great was the resentment everywhere obtaining against the King and all his ways.

News was brought to me of the tribes rising everywhere in the south and in the east. The country became so disturbed that the Khyber caravan route had to be closed. Then the rebels attacked Kahi, and ransacked the armoury there and retired from the scene well armed. It was but a step from there to the capture of Jalalabad, and Amanullah poured out his troops from Kabul in an effort to confront the menace.

From Jalalabad came further and graver news. The rebels evolved twenty-one points, among them being the resignation of the King, the non-acceptance of any of his house as the future ruler, the dismissal of the Queen and her relations, the desposition of all the Ministers, and a complete reversal of all new laws.

When he received this ultimatum Amanullah despatched yet further forces to the east, and the vulture again gave a preliminary flutter of his wings.

Then came word that the rebels had decided to march on Kabul.

I, Bacha Saquo, determined to be there first.

In my province of Kohistan there was still a man who was Governor in name. Hitherto I had pretended to ignore this person's existence for he caused me no let or hindrance, and indeed was the most inoffensive of men. I will not say that he was incompetent, because I do not know how otherwise he could have countered the situation with which he was presented. Rather would I say that he was a wise man who allowed little to trouble him—not even the frequent and peremptory demands he received from Kabul to arrest and imprison that bumptious brigand, Bacha Saquo.

Now that the time had come, however, the standard of revolt had openly to be raised, and I could think of no better way of sounding the tocsin than embarrassing the man who stood for the Royal edict.

Gathering my bodyguard, I proceeded across the hills to this person's residence. Quickly the place was surrounded.

Alone, I stepped into the great one's room. He was sipping his green tea. I covered him with my revolvers, and tied him to the legs of his iron safe. It was an undignified stance for a Governor, but he had been an inoffensive man who had done me no hurt, and I did not desire his blood.

I stalked over to the telephone which gave on to a private line direct to the capital.

" Give me the palace," I cried.

" Yes—yes—the Governor speaking. . . . Quickly—the King's own personal number. . . ."

A voice such as I had heard many times came crackling over the wire. Its cadences were unmistakable. It was the King.

" I have the honour to report to Your Majesty," I said, " that I have captured the brigand, Bacha Saquo. What would Your Majesty have done with him ? "

His Majesty did not hesitate. The reply came back harshly and imperiously.

" Shoot the scoundrel like the dog that he is ! "

Amanullah hung up the telephone.

I laughed loud and long in my beard.

With all his attentions directed towards the east, the King would give no thought of a brigand chief whom he believed to be dead.

The vulture of the hills was ready to strike.

Before morning two thousand well-armed men had answered my summons.

I mustered them, and surveyed them appraisingly. Every man was a fighter, and every man had been well paid and knew that he could follow Bacha Saquo with confidence.

It was enough.

" Advance ! "

I had taken my first active step to the throne.

VII

Iknew that Amanullah Khan was a braggart; I knew that he was a bluffer, and I knew that he was a fool so utterly to give himself over to the place-seekers by whom he was surrounded. Yet, Bacha Saquo, who prided himself on his native perspicacity, was not the astute appraiser of men that he imagined himself to be. I made a profound error in my earlier calculations which might easily have cost me dear. I under-estimated the heights to which Amanullah's arrogance could carry him. I did him an injustice. I believed that in the face of profound danger he would act as would other men. That he did not I was only to learn subsequently, but the belief that the King's actions would be guided by common sense did much to circumscribe my actions when first I extended my hand for the throne.

When first the Shinwari tribesmen raised the banner of revolt, there was acute apprehension in Kabul as to what I, Bacha, the brigand chief, would do.

Through the Governor of Kohistan, certain overtures were made to me which I did not take very seriously. It was suggested to me that in return for sundry considerations I should surrender my overlordship of the caravan routes, and I replied, more in satire than anything else, that I would consent to this course if I were guaranteed personal protection, were given an adequate sum of money to meet my needs, one hundred .303 rifles, and two thousand rounds of ammunition for each weapon. I hinted that in return I would disband many of my men and send them to Kabul as recruits to the forces which would operate against the rebel Shinwaris.

When, in addition to my terms, I demanded some form of military title I did not think for one moment that the court would entertain my suggestion, but to my surprise, and no little delight, it did.

The Governor used his telephone to some purpose, the money and the rifles and ammunition arrived, and I was told that the question of military rank was only one for discussion and mutual arrangement.

I could not have been provided with a more acceptable present.

In accordance with my promise I despatched a number of men to Kabul. All were retained in my pay, and all had orders to incite the Shinwaris to further rebellion rather than

THE MAN WHO SNATCHED A THRONE 747

fight against them, and to spread the fame of the name of Bacha Saquo.

Altogether, therefore, I could muster some two hundred and fifty .303 rifles of accepted make, some fifty .303 weapons of tribal manufacture, two machine-guns and perhaps eighty thousand rounds of ammunition. For the rest my force was armed with ancient muzzle-loaders of doubtful potency— good enough for work in the hills, but lacking in precision and rapidity of action for the task I had in mind.

I, too, had to proceed warily. When actually in the foot-hills which led from my mountains to Kabul I could count on the active sympathies of the villagers. They, because of their daily intercourse with the capital, had felt the full weight of Amanullah's laws. They, more than any one else, had to participate in the senseless burlesques with European attire, and they were bitter against the King. Also, they were there *in situ* for the squeezing talons of the tax-collectors, and they sat in their villages and sighed. They looked across the ranges which divided them from Bacha Saquo, and thought of the plenty in money and victuals which was associated with his name.

There, all was well, but between the foothills and my sphere of action there was a belt of tribal land too near the capital to come under my dominance. Here there were a number of powerful Elders who had perforce to bend the knee to the dictates of Kabul. Here, there was danger.

I could not afford to descend with my entire force and initiate a battle for possession of Kabul. The place was a citadel, it was protected by many cannon, and it invariably housed an adequate garrison. If I descended in force, and there was a protracted siege, I should have a numerous and efficient enemy at my back. That could not be.

True, Amanullah believed me to be dead, but no large force could penetrate this hostile belt without news preceding it, and putting the capital on its guard.

Also, I was always a firm believer in possessing an adequate reserve—a force which a commander could throw into the breach when that moment came when a battle was to be won or lost.

I decided, therefore, that my initial descent upon the capital should be undertaken by the three hundred possessing modern rifles. The remaining seventeen hundred I would march up to the belt of hostile territory to be ready for emergencies.

I evolved a series of smoke and fire signals. This large force had to be ready to march to my aid if I so requested, to move to a flank and create a diversion if I required a corridor through the hostile tract through which I could retire with speed and without fighting, and at all times to make its presence felt by continual movement and desultory sniping. In other words, it was to prowl. It was too large to be lightly attacked. Always was it to expose a belligerent exterior. Always was it to be a menace.

It was near enough to Kabul to create uneasiness and alarm, and word had frequently to go out that I, Bacha, was in personal command.

Thus it was that I set out on my great adventure. My main body halted as I had planned and advertised its presence to some purpose. I, with my three hundred men, slipped through the hostile tract, and split up within the villages near Kabul. There, not only could I wait, but I could see.

Even as I marched, events were proceeding apace. The revolt of the Shinwaris was growing in momentum. There had been a battle of sorts at Nimla on the road to Kabul, and the Royalist troops had been routed. The way from the east to the capital was open. In the south the men of Badakshan were in arms, and were as one with the Shinwaris, and then news came that the conflagration had reached the western province of Herat.

In disguise I made several lone sorties into Kabul, and I could sense the strain in the atmosphere. I sent word to my main body to make yet more noise. They complied with gusto, and Kabul trembled lest I, who was already within its walls, should descend from the hills and sack it.

There were continuous conferences in the palace, and the courtiers went to and fro day and night. It was said in court circles that if only the King could dispose of this man, Bacha Saquo, all would still be well, and it was decided to send a force into the hills to encompass his defeat.

One Ahmed Ali Khan, who had just returned from a four years' sojourn in Berlin, was named as my executioner, and with an adequate force he set out for the hills. My men were apprised of his coming even before he knew he had been given this dubious command, for—I had my own methods of obtaining my information. Mohamed Wali, the King's Vazir, still kept his money bags open that those who cared might contribute.

Perhaps in order to show how well we understood one

another Mohamed Wali presented me with a richly chased rifle. It had automatic action and I was to prove its efficiency in battle. Also—it was a beautiful adjunct to the durbar.

This be as it may, Ahmed Ali Khan proceeded with his force to the tract which I have termed hostile to me, and there sought counsel of the Elders. He called together a large jirgah at which all the principal men were present, and for two days and two nights he reiterated one thing :

Bacha Saquo must die.

The Elders had no reason to bear me any love, and eventually Ahmed Ali Khan's words sank home. The Elders were asked to raise all their able-bodied men—they estimated that they could arm six thousand—and to dispose of the force which was creating such a clamour on their borders. Also, they were requested to despatch several hundred men to Kabul to augment its garrison and to fight the Shinwaris.

At the end of the second night Ahmed Ali Khan slightly altered his tune. He proposed three expedients.

For a reward of one lakh of rupees (less than £10,000) the Elders were to encompass my death, dispose of my men, and carry my severed head to Kabul.

For a lesser reward, the Elders were to take to arms and segregate my men from the rest of the highland peasantry and to confine me to an area from which I could not escape.

For an even lesser reward they were to induce Bacha Saquo to surrender on terms, on the Government's guarantee of security.

In the end the Elders decided that they would raise their six thousand men as an inducement to me to surrender and close with the third of the proposals, securing in the meantime from Kabul a guarantee for my personal safety.

The terms were drawn up, and as is our custom, were placed upon two Holy Qurans. On the document a space was left for the signature of Amanullah which would accord me a full pardon.

The two volumes of the Holy Book, and the document, were forwarded to Kabul, and the Elders waited.

I, of course, had not the slightest intention that this document should ever receive the King's signature, and I took steps accordingly. Bacha Saquo was not going to have it said that he received clemency from the hands of this man, and then violated that which had been rendered inviolable on the Holy Quran.

When the Holy Books were taken into the King's apartment at the palace, he from whose head the crown was even then slipping would have had a heart attack could he have seen behind the rich draperies which diffused the light from one of the great windows. That he, the King, should be harbouring in his own holy of holies the very man for whose life he was prepared to pay almost any amount of money and dignity, did not occur to him, and it was not for Bacha Saquo to enlighten him.

Then and there I could have disposed of Amanullah, notwithstanding the promise I had given Mohamed Wali, but the urge was not in me. I knew this man to be of clay, and I believed that if he were sufficiently hard pressed he would break, and—flee. Were he to die by the hand of the assassin, or were he to die gloriously in battle, there would be a halo attaching to his name, and the country would look to his son as the rightful heir. But, no Afghan will forgive a man who runs, and—I wanted Amanullah Khan to run.

Mohamed Wali entered the Royal apartment, the two Holy Books carried carefully and decorously on his open palms. He bowed low to Amanullah, who growled. For many nights the King had been without proper sleep, and he was showing the strain. There were deep lines in his olive, full-fleshed face, and as he sat he gave repeated, nervous hitches to the European trousers which encased his legs like Ferenghi drain pipes. Occasionally he would raise a hand to his tousled hair, and there was a tell-tale tremor to his fingers.

Looking upon Amanullah then I could see two great forces at variance. There was the dreaminess of the reformer hitched to a sudden obstinacy which was almost that of the schoolboy. There was the protruding under lip, drooping at the sides, which betokened sulkiness and moroseness, and a spasmodic outjutting of the chin which indicated the contumacious and the self-opinionated.

But, the tired eyes were sombre and dismal. They were heavy with dire foreboding, and they told of the fight even then being waged between the two characteristics of this King.

" Well," growled Amanullah. " Another petition ? "

The Vazir grovelled.

" Your Majesty," he replied, " it is an agreement which has been drawn up between Ahmed Ali Khan and the Elders of Kohistan. . . ."

" Yes, yes ? " Amanullah was impatient.

" It is suggested, Your Majesty, that in return for an

unconditional pardon, Bacha Saquo, the low-born brigand, will surrender."

" Oh ! " Amanullah reached forward, and picked up a pen.

" Your Majesty." Mohamed Wali spoke softly, yet tensely. " Should the King sign an agreement with a low-born who has heaped so much indignity upon the Royal house ? "

Amanullah's hand wavered, and he gazed at the document upon the Koran with distaste.

" You are right, Mohamed Wali," he muttered testily. " Ahmed Ali Khan was despatched to bring in this man's head, not his insolent demands."

" Let Ahmed Ali Khan sign it, Your Majesty ! " counselled Wali !

He flung the pen from him, and rose. He stalked angrily from the room.

With a covert glance in the direction of the window draperies the Vazir gathered up the books, and retired.

By means known only to me and Mohamed Wali I made my way from the palace, and collected my three hundred stalwarts from the nearby villages. Carefully, and moving only at night, I proceeded to the place where Ahmed Ali Khan still tarried with the Elders.

A few hours after my arrival those with the Holy Koran appeared, and made their way to the tribal fires, for it was winter and extremely cold, and all huddled there in their sheepskin coats.

The deputation's spokesman was opening his mouth when I stepped forward, a row of grinning rifle muzzles at my back, and the astonishment of Ahmed Ali Khan and of the Elders was worth that moment. Dismay mingled with perturbation in humorous extravaganza, for the flickering light of the fires illumined all, and threw all countenances into relief.

" So, Ahmed Ali Khan . . . you would give up Bacha to the King ! "

There was ridicule and insult in my words, and the commander of the Government forces moved uneasily. I had pricked his self-esteem at the first stab, and I knew that I had him at a disadvantage. As for the Elders, they sat there, silently, pulling at their beards, philosophically waiting for what Bacha should bring them.

I glanced significantly at the Koran which was borne in the hands of the deputation's leader, and shook my head scoffingly.

" There were three men in the King's room," I jeered, when the Koran was presented for signature."

I laughed loud and long at this man's discomfiture.

" The third man," I said, " has told me that the King has not signed.

My tone was caustic.

I advanced a pace nearer the fires.

" And, Ahmed Ali Khan," I continued menacingly, " this third man tells me to be careful of thee ! "

With a curse and a scramble, Ahmed Ali Khan was on his feet, and was beyond the fires and in their shadows. I withheld my riflemen, for I did not desire to slaughter the Elders of my own clan. I could not afford to antagonise them and to lose the support of my own countrymen.

But, leaving fifty of my men to warm themselves by the fires and not, as the Elders might suppose, to intimidate them, I rushed onward with the remaining two hundred and fifty and fell upon the encampment of the Royal troopers.

These parade ground men dislike the dark. They had been drilled to cope with an enemy that can be seen ; not one that emerges from the shadows and sticks a bayonet in their vitals. It was not a great or glorious fight, and we lost but one man killed and two wounded before the Kabulis took to their heels. Both Ahmed Ali Khan and his brother escaped in the darkness and the confusion, which was as well. They could return to Kabul and help to spread the terror of my name.

This small and insignificant encounter had a result which was to stand me in good stead, though I was to remain unaware of it for some days.

Ahmed Ali Khan returned to the palace to make his excuses to a highly incensed monarch. Instead of my head he had sent an insolent letter ; instead of defeating me, he had himself been routed.

In vain he pleaded that the Kohistan Elders had been in league with me. In vain he pleaded that he was confronted by an overwhelming force. In vain he pleaded to be allowed to return with more soldiers to encompass my death, or die himself in battle. He was relieved of his command and disgraced.

But the words with which he had sought to excuse himself with the King bore fruit. The hundreds of tribesmen already despatched by the Elders for the defence of Kabul were regarded with suspicion. They were not served out with arms, and eventually they drifted back to their homes. Most of them finally enrolled themselves under my banner.

VIII

THE night after the rout of Ahmed Ali Khan I was back in the villages around Kabul. I thought I knew something of the man I would dispossess, and I was determined to avoid, if possible, circumstances where Amanullah would have no other recourse but to lead his men into battle.

There would come the moment, so I believed, when the country would have to say : Who shall be King ?

Amanullah Khan must not only be dispossessed, but his name must be disgraced. Then, with no one ready to fill the breach, and with Bacha Saquo in command at Kabul, the clans would be the more likely to accept the situation.

I had no illusions. I knew that they would look askance at the son of a water-carrier, and that if any other aspirant to the throne lifted his head there would be war. But, if Amanullah could be induced to abdicate—if his nerves could be fretted to that degree when he lost his self-command, and with Nadir Khan sickly and ill in Europe, I stood to have what I could hold.

My initial move, therefore, was an attack which was not an attack. That night I ringed the city with my men, and we sniped unceasingly. There is nothing so intimidating ; nothing so demoralising as a rain of well-directed bullets from an enemy who is unseen ; whose strength is a matter for fantastic guesswork, and whose reputation is one where one instinctively thinks of rivers of blood.

The residents of Kabul had no sleep that night, even though there were several quiet interludes. During one of these I actually entered the city—no difficult task in the rain and the icy wind—and I knew that I had the place at my mercy. I could have rushed the defences that night, but there would have been bloody work in the streets, and Amanullah would have been forced to fight. I desired to nag at this man's nerves, and not to antagonise the people of Kabul. Much would shortly depend upon their reactions to certain contingencies.

I continued the sniping throughout most of the next day, and made several feints in the open against the city. None of these, however, was pressed home. Their purpose was to keep the defenders up to concert pitch, and to add weight and force to the sniping.

During the day, also, I called down a number of my men from the hills. It was necessary to increase my force now that so much was visible. In all my men numbered now over one thousand. The three hundred men with modern arms I kept at their sniping. The others I utilised for the feint attacks on the city. Their weapons produced sufficient noise for an army, and, morally, did more damage than the modern rifle.

Kabul's defences were indeed in a sorry state, for Amanullah had thrown all his men south-eastward to meet the menace of the Shinwaris. Only the men of the King's bodyguard remained, and their efforts were augmented by the students of the Military College.

News came that evening of a further defeat of the Government forces at the hands of the rebels, and I decided to bring the war home a little nearer to Amanullah.

We proceeded that night to cut every telephone and telegraph line leading out of the capital. Amanullah had lost his best means of communication, and I knew how the suspense of the unknown would further fret at his frayed nerves.

Three times that night the King despatched mounted couriers to obtain news from the Shinwari front. Three times these men were sent back disarmed.

Meanwhile we maintained a ceaseless sniping, and a maximum of noise. We would allow the firing to fade away while we snatched a few hours' sleep, then horsemen would skurry under the very walls of the citadel, shouting and screaming, and the sniping would break out anew.

The defenders spent a sorry time rushing from one end of the town to another to stave off first this attack ; then that. Gradually I was wearing down their morale.

Again that night I could have pressed home my attack, and I was sorely tempted to do so, notwithstanding the fact that the gates of the city were closed. Instead, well in the small hours, I decided to have another look at the panic-stricken capital, the more closely to view the results of my handiwork.

With the gates closed this might have presented some difficulty, but Bacha well knew how to open gates. On one of the gates of the city, well away from the main entrances, there was a small postern which was more than sufficient for my purpose. I had used it before, and I would use it again.

During one of the lulls in our sniping, five single shots

were fired in quick succession. There was a short pause, and these were followed by five more.

In the crashing of the rain and the howling of the wind I watched that small postern, and after a wait of some twenty minutes I saw movement. A shaded light shone where there was before only abysmal blackness, and I moved forward, and was within the city.

A cautious voice greeted me as I stepped low through the postern. It belonged to Mahmud Sami, a Turk who was originally imported into Afghanistan by the Ameer Habibullah Khan as a military expert, became a naturalised Afghan and the head of the Military College whose students were now taking such an active part in the defence of the capital.

" Art well muffled ? "

Mahmud Sami put the question tersely, and there was an element of apprehension in his voice, which, in the circumstances, was well understandable. The fact that one of Kabul's principal defenders should be consorting with the enemy leader might easily have been misunderstood had I been recognised.

However, Mahmud had no cause for alarm. Further to protect me from the cold and the rain, I had thrown a sheepskin over my shoulders, and this more than enveloped my ears. The end of my turban I had in my mouth, so that little more than my eyes were visible. Also, the long, loose sheepskin coat which I wore and the skin which I affected round my shoulders made recognition of bodily contours absolutely impossible.

" Caution, my friend. . . . Do not make for the lights. . . . The Vazir, Mohamed Wali, is abroad, and he has seen thee times enough."

I laughed, for Mahmud was most obviously in a state of nerves. Clearly he had obeyed my summons with the greatest reluctance, and he was chary of being seen in my company.

He was unaware that I used him as a spy upon the Vazir and that the Vazir was frequently unwittingly employed in checking up the statements of Mahmud. When one deals with men who are so open to bribery, it does not pay to take undue risks.

" Why don't you end this suspense, Bacha ? "

I remained silent.

The man pleaded, for Kabul in its present state was none to his liking.

"Bacha—I can draw away our men and leave the way open for you to-night. The defenders are few. The soldiers are disgruntled. The King, he blows hot and cold, and knows not his own mind from one hour to the other. . . ."

I moved my shoulders. "All in good time, Mahmud," I countered. "All in good time."

"Tell me," he said at length, "why have you come?"

"To see Kabul in the grip of panic," I answered lightly, and left him. In truth, I was glad to escape his presence, for his very agitation invoked suspicion. His manner was so furtive that it called loudly for investigation.

Kabul, which should have been wrapt in slumber, was a city of feverish preparation. Frightened merchants were busily engaged in transporting their goods to places of safety, and in procuring wood with which to barricade their shops. On all sides were their moans and cries of despair, for the Kabul merchant does not lightly regard the coming of trouble and danger. In many ways he is a fatalist, but where his worldly goods are concerned he sees trouble from afar, and—rather than await its coming he goes forward to meet it with furrowed brow and lachrymose mien.

Even at that hour the mosques were crowded with men who prayed that their ruler might be given guidance, and everywhere were gangs of men, working under the command of officers, busily engaged in unwinding barbed wire. Barricades were being erected in the principal thoroughfares, and round the palace itself miles and miles of barbed wire were being spun into entanglements. Kabul already bore the signs of a besieged city.

At a coffee shop, where the proprietor, more intrepid than most, still remained open for business, I halted for refreshment. The freshly made green tea would be sustaining at such a time, and forsooth, I was weary with my long activity.

Several men were within the café as I entered, and amongst them I beheld one of my runners.

He was holding forth, and there was indignation in his tones.

"Would you countenance the killing of Holy men?" he demanded.

"Do you agree that they should be placed in front of the cannon and blown to pieces?"

"Is it right that their beards should be shorn and that they should be heaped with indignities?"

"Nay," answered a man bolder than the rest, "but we

dare not say so. Walls have ears in these times, and not for all are the mouths of cannon. A solitary revolver bullet is the lot of some, and others—they are even hanged."

" This Bacha Saquo," he went on, speaking softly, and with his eyes upon the scraggy hillman who had squatted in the shadows, " would he kill the Mullahs ? "

My runner guffawed. " Kill the Mullahs ? " he echoed. " By all accounts he would have killed any one once, but since he has reached man's estate he has changed. He holds the Mullahs in veneration, and for him they are Holy. 'Tis said he met a Mullah when he was upon his travels, and that he can defy death. . . ."

" Do you think that he will take the city ? " The speaker glanced round fearfully, as if afraid of his own voice.

" Do you think Amanullah Khan could stop him ? " My man was sarcastic.

" But Kabul will have none of him. He is but the son of a Saquo. . . . Imagine such a man with a court."

" A water-carrier's son," the others growled derisively.

I rose from the shadows and made towards the hurricane lamp which gave illumination to the poor appointments of the café. I allowed the sheepskin to droop from my shoulders, and the end of my turban to fall from my mouth.

" Merely a water-carrier's son," I echoed, my eyes burning with pent-up passion.

I showed them my teeth, and grinned.

" Merely a water-carrier's son," I repeated, " but—one whose name is honoured in the hills as a warrior and a fighter. Merely a water-carrier's son who has defied the might of your King and who has laughed at the Royal soldiers who have been sent against him."

" Who is this stranger ? " one asked querulously. " Methinks he is over-bold and is in need of a lesson ! "

" Bacha Saquo, the water-carrier's son," I replied ironically, reaching for my knife. " Perhaps you would care to try for the reward which is upon his life and carry his head to the palace ? "

Astonishment and apprehension was upon these men, and they edged quietly towards the open street.

Once in the bazaar they turned and ran, crying, " Bacha . . . Bacha . . . he is upon us ! "

Reaching for my sheepskin, I followed them, crying in unison, " Bacha . . . Bacha . . . ! "

The cry was taken up. The flying group became a crowd,

and the crowd, a mob, all howling : " Bacha . . . Bacha
. . . he is upon us."

Round the palace they swarmed—hundreds and hundreds
of affrighted men and women, the latter quietly weeping,
and the men calling upon the King to give them arms.

From the palace windows there came no sign. Amanullah
Khan either failed to hear his people, or ignored them. It
mattered not which. By a fortuitous chance I had excited
them beyond measure. I had made the name of Bacha
Saquo ring through the streets of the capital as it had never
rung before.

The city was in the throes of great emotional stress.
Before many hours there would be the reaction.

People would say : " We were assailed. The enemy was
within us. We appealed to the King, and—he was silent.
Is this the man who declared that he was the servant of the
people the day after his father died ? "

Always I remained on the outskirts of this milling multitude, for it is invariably there that one sees those who, in
their turn, are there to see.

Ten paces ahead of me I discerned a form I knew. I
moved to the side, and caught a glimpse of a saturnine
countenance, and brightly gleaming eyes.

I edged up behind the figure, and whispered.

" Oh, brother," I said sardonically, " the people are in a
turmoil. They say that Bacha is upon them."

Mohamed Wali, the Vazir, turned as in a flash, and eyed
me quizzically.

Twice he opened his lips to speak before the words came,
and then he spoke haltingly.

" Bacha," he gasped. " Have . . . have you thy men
within the city ? "

I laughed behind my sheepskin, for well I knew what was
in this man's mind. He, too, would see that condition of
mind where the people would execrate the Royal name.
Then he, who was already such a power in the land, would
know how to deal with a simple son of a water-carrier, and
Mohamed Wali, who had so often knelt to the throne, would
ascend the dais and defy all to eject him.

So much had been in this man's thoughts since first the
people had reviled their King for his un-Afghan ways.

But, this was not the moment to present this man with a
crown, and to invite him to throw me to the jackals shrieking
around us in their hundreds.

The light which was in Mohamed Wali's eyes faded. He had sensed a great opportunity. For a fleeting second he believed that he had only to raise an authoritative cry. With that, Bacha Saquo would have been admitted to an undignified yet speedy death, and Mohamed Wali would have his heart's desire.

My unfeeling laugh shattered the roseate dreams which singed through his brain, and he regarded me none too pleasantly.

" More of your sport, Bacha ! " he said bitterly. " Mind that you tempt not Fate unduly."

I eyed him steadily.

" When do you attack, Bacha ? " he asked on a different note.

" To-morrow," I answered, as if the matter was of no moment. " With the dawn, there will be an assault."

" You know that the King will resist ? In the hours of light he will defend all. If you, Bacha, can enter Kabul without my knowledge, why do you not engineer a night assault ? "

" I am my own commander-in-chief," I replied austerely, and left him.

IX

IN the early hours, soon after dawn, I initiated an attack. I was true to my promise, but I had my tongue in my cheek, nevertheless. There are attacks which are pressed home, where the attackers hang on tenaciously in the face of all odds, and there are attacks which serve their purpose if the spirit displayed be such that the defenders are convinced that they must fight, or—die. My attack was of the latter order. This form of warfare can be costly to the attackers as well as the defenders, and we on our side sustained our full share of casualties, but before the day was over I considered the hours well spent. The King had seconded my efforts to the best of his ability, and had been an unwitting ally to my schemes. He thundered at me with his artillery, he filled his city with noise and smoke, he made war seem terribly near to the populace, and further harried the feelings of those pent up within the walls.

At sunrise, a large body of my men made a feint, and there was a heavy expenditure of ammunition which, however, did little material damage. Still attired in my sheepskins, and riding a mettlesome horse, I made myself conspicuous— not with the idea of inciting my men to greater effort, for that was unnecessary, and not with the object of inviting enemy attention to my person, for that would have been rank foolishness, but—to allow the people of Kabul to see that Bacha Saquo, the brigand chieftain, was really menacing their walls, and to make positive that Amanullah Khan should be under no delusions as to the character of the force which was assailing his capital.

When this feint attack was well established, and all was obscured by the rush and turmoil of the engagement, I slipped away, and with my modern-armed men made for the fortified tower which is situate not far from the walls of Kabul, and is a dominating, defensive structure. The tower is really part of the Habibia College, and gives a command of a wide field of fire into Kabul itself.

From there we raked the city with a hot fire which eventually drew the attention of Amanullah's artillery. It was a mark which the gunners could not miss, and the position soon became untenable. I had, however, achieved my object in further lowering the morale of the defenders, and I evacuated the tower and joined the rest of my men in the village of Kalola Pushtah. Later in the day I fell back upon Baghi-i-Bala.

In the evening of the second day of my attack upon Kabul, I rested for some hours, but before midnight I was again in the city. I believed, wherever possible, that it was best to check up on my intelligence service with my own eyes.

Even in the space of a few hours the face of Kabul had changed for the worse.

The people had now come to learn of the reverses of the Royalist forces at Nimla, and they knew that the trade routes were blockaded and that the rebels of the south and the east were making headway. I had cut off all means of telegraphic and telephonic communication, and I planned on the morrow to cut off the water and the electricity supplies also.

As I wandered around this city which feared to go to bed, I heard the most exaggerated stories of the strength which I had at my command and, moreover, the voice of the people was beginning to change when the name of Bacha was mentioned. Intermingling with the crowds I heard less and less of this water-carrier's son. Rather I had become the Ghazi, the defender of the Faith, and the defender of the

Holy Mullahs whom the King was still sending into eternity from the mouths of cannon.

Well muffled in my sheepskins, I joined a group of Royal troops, lounging round a fire in the vicinity of the Arg. It was easy enough to fraternise with them.

Extending my hands toward the blaze, I remarked, surlily:

" The soldiers—always the soldiers—they can find fuel for fires. They can always depend upon food, and—their twenty rupees per month. . . ."

A gasp of indignation accompanied my words, and the sepoys viewed me angrily.

" Who are you ? " one of them demanded, " that is so foolish to believe such tales."

" Twenty rupees ! " He spat his disgust.

" You are not of Kabul, stranger, if you believe in such nonsense," he went on, aggrieved.

" Where," he demanded, waving his arms in a wide gesture, " are Amanullah's soldiers ? Where is this great army which costs so much ? "

" Aye, where ? " growled another. " Nowhere, but in the pockets of the Vazir and our officers. A company which should be a hundred strong is but twenty, but the officers draw pay for the hundred."

" Ah ! " said another. " And, our twenty rupees—it has mysteriously dwindled to four. Four rupees ! " he exclaimed violently, " and three of those I have to send to my village each month."

He stood up in his tattered uniform and stamped the ground, reviling the name of the King whose presence he guarded.

I left the group, and wandered farther, where there were knots of people assembled outside the Arg palace gates. All spoke with bated breath of the events in the capital that day following the shelling of the brigand chief.

The scenes that afternoon must have struck further fear into the heart of Amanullah. The merchants had refused to open their shops, and the people had been unable to buy food. The King, secure in the Arg, and not daring to appear in the streets, sent soldiers to open the shops by force. The merchants were dragged forth from their hiding places to trade, but none could command the prices which these men demanded. There had been riots, and a number of shops had been burned, and there were not sufficient troops to quell the disturbances.

Then, the people who had been forced to acquire European

clothes approached the Hindu money-lenders, for they would
have rupees for this despised raiment. But, the money-lenders
would advance nothing on such security, and there had been
more riots. The mounted police had been helpless, and one
Hindu who had made a fortune in the disposal of Western
clothes met his death by the same agency. A mob collected
outside his house, flourishing unkempt bowlers, bedraggled
trousers, and coats which had been cast off by the waiting
menials of the West, and demanded money.

When none was forthcoming the mob piled the clothes in
the roadway, sought kerosene, and set the whole on fire. Then
they searched for the money-lender and found him, and threw
him into the furnace.

The burning of the European clothes was regarded by the
people as a gesture. It meant for them the throwing off of
an intolerable yoke.

Near me were men discussing the matter, and the fines
to which they had been subjected by the police for going
abroad in Afghan clothes.

" Aye," muttered one, still writhing under the imposition,
" I, for my sins live near the police station. The constable
there is no friend of mine, and he would wait for me when I
slipped through the bazaar to make some small purchase.
Some days I would be fined, twice, or thrice, but once, I was
caught no less than thirty times. Thirty times was I fined that
day for appearing abroad without those un-Afghan abomina-
tions."

Could the King have heard what was being said within the
shadows of his palace, he would have paused, and reflected
on the situation. But his courtiers were still with him, assuring
him that the events in Kabul were but transitory, and that
he could afford to discount anything which a hill brigand
might do. As for the Shinwari rebels—had not Royal forces
been despatched against them ?

I left Kabul for my headquarters at Bagh-i-Bala three
miles away—left it that it might contemplate another dawn.

With the coming of light I continued to menace the city,
and there was some stiff fighting at times. In Kabul itself, I
was informed, all the public offices remained closed, and the
prices of foodstuffs shot to an unheard of level. Then a runner
brought news of the gates of the Arg palace being barricaded.
Large stores of food and ammunition were being carried
within, and evidently Amanullah had determined that the
time had come to make some sort of a stand.

Also, as I could see, the King's aeroplanes were busy. They flew off carrying messages of distress to all parts of the country. Amanullah was calling up the tribal levies. In one such call which was read to me, he promised those who came to his aid almost untold wealth, and an adequate supply of arms and ammunition.

As the day wore on the first of these recruits began to trickle into the city. I did not even pretend to bar their progress. Rather did I send my men out upon the roads to welcome them with cheery cries and robust jest. The flow of humanity increased, and more and more did the streets of Kabul become choked with the tribesmen. The King threw open the magazines, and all who asked for rifles and ammunition were supplied. Not to be outdone, I disarmed several hundreds of my tribal warriors and sent them into the city. Merely for the asking, they were provided with .303 rifles and ammunition. Their ancient tribal weapons they were able to stack on one side for emergencies.

As I knew would be the case, this great influx into the city became a sore trial, for Kabul was short of food even before its arrival. I resolved to add to the confusion. I despatched Sayed Hussain, one of my lieutenants, to Jubl-us-Siraj where is situated the hydro-electric power house, and he cut off the supply. Kabul was without light and electric power.

I had by this time a number of mechanics in my force. They did most excellent work. They accomplished mysterious things in the hangars on the aerodrome, and more than one aeroplane caught fire as the propellers commenced to swing. Also, the King's armoured cars were made to do unaccountable things. Such mysteries were ever beyond my comprehension, but I know that my men drew the petrol from the reserve tanks of these vehicles, and substituted water. Thus it was that so many armoured cars issued from the city never to return.

The King's War Minister nearly went insane with rage as these various matters were reported to him. His was an unenviable task, for never did he dare to tell the King of these catastrophes.

The majority of those whom the King had armed cared not a pice for his cause, and once having secured what they wanted, either returned to their homes, roamed the city killing off rich merchants, or helped to augment my forces. A large force of Wazirs did, however, remain faithful to the King, and these men, always ready for battle, fought with spirit.

Bagh-i-Bala, where I had made my headquarters, was near the aerodrome and within a stone's throw of the British Legation, and for several days heavy encounters took place in this neighbourhood. Had the Wazirs been left to their own devices the order of the day might have been different, but they were required to fight under regular officers whose methods of waging war had been learned in the office. These ornate gentlemen would leave Kabul in their motor cars just before ten o'clock in the morning. They would take a dilatory interest in the fighting during the day, issuing orders which none could comprehend and none sought to obey, and then at four o'clock they would call for their chauffeurs to return to Kabul, there to cleanse their bodies of the grime of battle.

One morning a group of such officers, who had evidently read of the value of flank attacks from some hastily perused text-book, crept under cover of dead ground round to my right. They had with them about three hundred men. I had few men to spare at that moment, but—I had a lorry which had been " requisitioned." Also had I the quick-firing rifle which the Vazir had given me. I mounted the lorry, and had it driven right in the midst of these men, and I fired as quickly as I could renew the magazines. It was a simple matter to pick off the officers as we charged along, and the rest of the men evidently found my quick-firing tactics none to their liking. They took to their heels, leaving fourteen dead sepoys behind them and five officers.

That night I had the heads of the officers conveyed into Kabul. Next morning they were grinning at Amanullah's window from the walls of the Arg. I often wondered what were his reactions when he viewed this phenomenon.

On the fifth day of the fighting, I had my men strung out over a long line from Doukhtar to Kotal Kahir and I spent my time riding from one end of the line to the other, completely disregarding the rain of shells with which Amanullah favoured us. I knew that I was always a conspicuous figure from the walls, for it was part of my plan invariably to be in the forefront, but I think the shrapnel which caught me in the back was but a lucky accident for the gunner. True, shells had been exploding above me for some time, but I disdained them. The shrapnel caught me just below the shoulder blade, and I was rolled from my horse, in full view of the walls and all my men. The cut was a deep one, and I lost consciousness. When I recovered, there was a certain confusion. The Kabulis were lining the walls and shouting their derision. They were enthusiastic. In the ranks of my own men, however, I could discern no little alarm.

Throwing aside the hands which held me, I bade the hakim to hurry with his bandaging. Then, calling for my horse, I mounted again. I was unable to continue for more than half an hour before I had to dismount. All was going black before me, and it would have been foolishness to continue.

My injury gave the Kabulis a much-needed respite. It was during this lull that the British aeroplanes came from Peshawar and evacuated those within the British Legation. It was during this time also that Amanullah, hearted by the news of my mishap, issued forth from the Arg for the first time for several days. Again he harangued the people, yet again he had to display his extraordinary folly.

He took his place beside what is known as "The Pillar of Knowledge" which he had had erected shortly after he had come to the throne.

While the King declaimed, promising the people that the New Law would be withdrawn, and that all corrupt ministers would be dismissed, his hearers could see behind him this evidence of Amanullah's bad faith.

In the fighting which ensued after the death of his father, Amanullah had reason to declare an amnesty. Nevertheless, fifty-two leaders were arrested, court-martialled and shot, and to commemorate the event, "The Pillar of Knowledge" was erected. It bears the words : "In memory of the campaign which was in reality a battle between Knowledge and Ignorance."

Little wonder that the people openly accused him of breach of faith, and told him quite frankly that they refused to help him further.

That day Amanullah determined to have one more attempt at ousting me from my positions. I was then resting from my injury at Kafir Koh, and the King offered twenty thousand rupees for my head. The men of the bodyguard, and a large body of Wazir tribesmen issued forth, and fell upon us. Though one arm was still useless I could still fire my automatic rifle and I continued to fire until it burned hot in my hands. This encounter was one of the most sanguinary of the war, for we lost over two hundred men, and the Royalist casualties were heavier. Often the fighting was hand to hand, and when that day finished many sheepskins were matted with blood, but—not Bacha's.

We broke off the encounter toward the afternoon, and the
Royalist troops returned to the capital disgusted and disgruntled. Before evening the men of the bodyguard, declaring that they had earned at least part of the reward,
assembled outside the Arg demanding money. When this
was not forthcoming, they too revolted.

Amanullah was nearing the end.

Before darkness fell that evening every available aeroplane
was in flight. These were on their way to Kandahar. Others
had already preceded them during the days that had gone
before, and they carried the persons of the Queen and the
other ladies of the household, and—all the crown jewels and
remaining gold in the Treasury. I was not to know that
until later.

That night the runners came to me in a continuous
stream.

The King sat with his brother, Sirdar Inayatullah Khan,
in a darkened room in the Arg. He was afraid to have too
great an illumination in case a shot would come crashing
through the windows.

Finally, Amanullah signed a paper of abdication, handing
over the throne to his brother Inayatullah—he who should
have been King in Amanullah's stead.

I, Bacha Saquo, had had my way. This King had been
forced to ignominious flight. Actually, he left Kabul in his
Rolls Royce before dawn.

But, what was it that that Mullah had said? He had
mentioned many kings. More remained to be deposed before
I could wear the diadem.

When news was brought to me of Amanullah's impending
flight, I called for my horse and, with twenty troopers, I
secreted myself in the shadows on the road to Kandahar. I
wanted to be sure that this King was really running away, and
not indulging in yet another subterfuge. Also, I knew how
easily he could change his mind, and—I did not want him
creeping back with the dawn, and asking for the return of
his letters of abdication.

Oh, Amanullah was quite capable of doing this.

The snow had fallen deep on the Ghazni-Kabul road,
and Amanullah found his way almost blocked. He had to
proceed slowly, and I was able to keep up with his Rolls,
riding easily away on his flank. Never did we lose sight of
his headlights.

At Arghandi, some twelve miles from Kabul, his car

became stuck in the snow, and for two hours I had unpleasant qualms while efforts were made to dig the vehicle out.
Would Amanullah never go ?

Those with the King eventually cleared a way. They tied
runs round the rear wheels, and these at length made purchase.
The King's car slid forward.

To make certain that this leisurely departure should be a
flight in fact, I called to my men. Hulloaing and shrieking,
we made for the car. We could see Amanullah gesticulating
wildly, beseeching his driver to go quickly. Suddenly, the car
swerved. One of the rugs tied to the rear wheels had become
jammed in the mudguard, and for a moment I thought the
car would overturn in the snow.

I had hurriedly to alter my course, otherwise I would
have been upon the King. Firing our rifles, and shouting
shrilly, we circled, while a frightened chauffeur jumped from
the car and cut free the rug. Then the car once more jumped
to life, and with a swoop and a roar, we were after it.

We galloped headlong for over a mile, until indeed, the
car was but a speck in the distance.

Such was the manner of Amanullah's departure from his
capital.

Weary from my pursuit of Amanullah, and exhausted, for
my wound had not yet healed, I placed my command temporarily in the hands of my lieutenant, Syed Husain.

I felt that I could do so, for I did not take the obese
Inayatullah too seriously.

When I was informed that he had appeared on the balcony
of the Arg while the Court Chamberlain read of his accession,
I laughed, notwithstanding my fatigue.

" Go," I called to Syed Husain. " Go and prick the fat
one. And, when you skewer his belly, there you will find
three melons."

I had a letter written and despatched to this new King, in
which I told him that he must either surrender, or prepare
for battle.

Inayatullah did not immediately reply, and I signalled
to Syed to proceed. The next morning he was within the
city, and he had Inayatullah besieged in the Arg.

Shortly, the white flag was seen, and another King had
come and gone. Inayatullah signed an agreement with me
whereby he agreed to abdicate and to acknowledge me King.

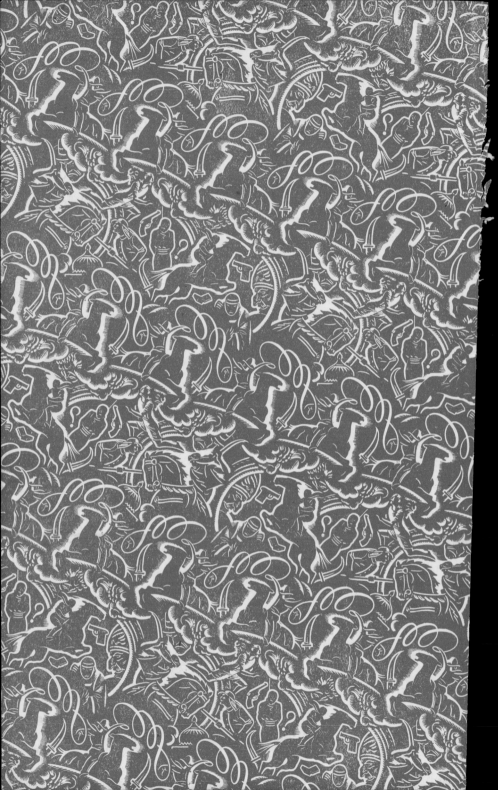